SAINT TERESA OF AVILA

TERESA
OF ÁVILA

by

MARCELLE AUCLAIR

with a Preface by
ANDRÉ MAUROIS

PANTHEON

The French original was published in 1950
under the title LA VIE DE SAINTE THÉRÈSE
D'AVILA *by Éditions du Seuil, Paris. This*
translation was made by

KATHLEEN POND

First Printing: March, 1953
Second Printing: August, 1953

NIHIL OBSTAT: CAROLVS DAVIS, S.T.L.
CENSOR DEPVTATVS
IMPRIMATVR: E. MORROGH BERNARD
VICARIVS GENERALIS
WESTMONASTERII: DIE V IVLII MCMLII

LITHOGRAPHED IN THE UNITED STATES OF AMERICA
BY THE MURRAY PRINTING COMPANY
WAKEFIELD, MASS.

PREFACE

" OUR thinking, indeed the way we work out our salvation, is by the devoted imitation of moments (in other lives) we know to be sublime. Such is, and always has been, the cult of the dead." For Ignatius of Loyola, to read the *Lives of the Saints* was a preparation for sanctity.

But a well-written life, said Carlyle, is even rarer than a well-spent one. The biographer who attempts to promote the cult of the great dead must be in a state of grace. If he did not feel the greatness of his subject how could the book he writes be great?

I was thinking about what is required for a biography—a literary genre which England justly honours—as I read Marcelle Auclair's excellent, indeed admirable book on *St. Teresa of Ávila*. Here was an occasion for meditating on the rules of the genre and on the attitude of the biographer.

Why did Marcelle Auclair choose St. Teresa for her subject? It was no casual choice that led her to write the book, nor the request of a publisher, nor the discovery of new documents. No, it was a desire conceived in her youth and accomplished in the strength of a maturing talent.

When quite a child she kept the selected works of St. Teresa at her bedside. As a girl she took as her motto this maxim of the saint's: "*Let us risk our life*—he who saves his life will lose it." At the time of the evacuation of Paris in 1940, St. Teresa's *Works* were the only books Marcelle Auclair took away with her and in the tragic circumstances of that time she made a vow to translate the *Fundaciones*.

For—and this is a second important point—by her culture and education Marcelle Auclair is as much Spanish as French. Her father, a French architect, went to work in Chile when she was a child, so that she was brought up in an atmosphere which was that of sixteenth-century Spain. To-day Chile is one of the most modern of South American countries. Then the great colonial families were still living in practically the same way as Teresa de Ahumada y Cepeda had lived in her distinguished home at Ávila.

v

In Chile, Marcelle Auclair came into personal contact with people whose daily lives were permeated with their faith; she saw the enormous crucifixes which hung even in drawing-rooms to recall the sufferings of Christ; in the evenings she attended family prayers with the whole household. That is why, when she studied the saint's youth, she did not feel she entered an alien atmosphere.

A biographer of talent can reconstruct a particular milieu: he will do this still more successfully if he finds the elements of it within himself. If neither Rastignac's ambition nor the bankruptcy of David Séchard had formed part of Balzac's personal experience, would he have been Balzac as we know him?

I am fully aware that certain biographers, Lytton Strachey among them, have maintained that the best biographies have been written by authors who were at daggers drawn with their subjects. It seems at first as if the perfect life of *Queen Victoria* from his own pen proves him right. But, as a great English historian once observed, the most remarkable thing is not that Strachey should have written the life of Queen Victoria, but that Queen Victoria should have conquered Lytton Strachey. He began the book scoffing, he finished it in admiration, and it was to this involuntary respect that he owed the perfection, beauty and poetry of his work.

Marcelle Auclair began by admiring her heroine and ended by loving her. For the charm of St. Teresa is irresistible. In the beginning that charm was merely the ardour and gracious attractiveness of a Spanish girl of good family. "She had always been the most beautiful and the one people loved most: they spoke with pride of her taste, her cleverness, her wit, her gifts as a young writer; they remarked what a graceful dancer she was, how good at chess, how bold a horsewoman. Of a piece of embroidery she made a work of art; and she made the family dinner as exciting as a firework display. In Ávila, people said: 'Teresa de Ahumada? She will marry whomsoever she pleases'."

And then this exacting person, full of the Spanish "point of honour," discovered that human love would not satisfy her. Yet "she seemed so much the less fitted for sanctity as she was very well fitted for worldly success; and in her own view was riddled with faults that were contradictory: proud, but frivolous, domineering but easily influenced; she speaks of her excessive dissimulation and of her horror of a lie, of her love of pleasing people which yet did not restrain her quick temper," and of her wretched self-love. A saint she indeed became, but by force of will.

Will—that is one of her two fundamental characteristics: the second is simplicity. "All is nothing, the world is vanity, life is short; I decided to force myself to enter the convent." Here Teresa pronounced for the first time the word she was to repeat more frequently than any other: *determinación*, decision. "I decided . . . it is tremendously important to begin with great determination. . . . The soul that begins with determination has already travelled a great part of the way. . . ." Here, philosopher and saint meet. "Happiness is by an act of will," said Descartes.

Simplicity—for me, what drew me to her heroine long before I had read Marcelle Auclair, were the wonderful things St. Teresa said about the sanctity of everyday life. "The Lord is to be found among the pots and pans." To be heroic in the face of danger is not the most difficult of achievements; then the greatness of the circumstances temporarily arouses the will. But to be perfect each day, in humble ways, to do well what one does, to treat all those with whom we work with a sense of equality, even with love, there is sanctity indeed. When she was dying, St. Teresa said it once more: "My daughters and ladies, for the love of God I ask you to keep the Rule well; if you keep it in every particular, no further miracle will be needed for your canonisation."

What is so good about this biography is that the writer has succeeded in bringing out the saint without eliminating the woman. And although her book is heavily documented, she does not overwhelm the reader with references. The author has read everything, but she has digested it all and incorporated it into the narrative. Marcelle Auclair has visited all the Carmels founded by her heroine. That, too, was necessary. A house, a countryside, make a living thing of the abstract phantom which rises from the dusty pages. How can George Sand be brought to mind if one has not seen Nohant, or Chateaubriand if we neglect Combourg, or Byron without retracing the steps of Childe Harold's pilgrimage? In the Carmels founded by the saint, life goes on as it did in the sixteenth century. A piece of linen still does duty for window-glass. The chant is the same as it was then and the young nuns gave a friendly reception to her who, like themselves, better perhaps, knew their foundress.

Finally a word must be said of the effect of this biography both on biographer and reader. One cannot live with a saint without coming closer to sanctity. Marcelle Auclair has spared us any exhortation or commentary of her own. It was not a sermon she set out to write but a work of art. Every work of art is a sign; one does not know of what, and in that lies its attraction. Just as, in a beautiful statue of Chartres cathedral each man finds his own truth, I have discovered most precious truths in looking at this portrait of a saint which has been painted by Marcelle Auclair with loving devotion. It is now for the reader to seek his truth there too.

ANDRÉ MAUROIS.

TRANSLATOR'S NOTE

IT has been said, by St. Thomas Aquinas, that the mark of a good translation is that it should faithfully represent the thought of the original, expressing it in the idiom of the language in which the translation is being made. Such has been the principle which has guided this translation of Marcelle Auclair's *La Vie de Sainte Thérèse d'Avila*, though one cannot hope to have succeeded as well as one would have wished to do, and quotations from the Spanish have therefore been re-translated from the original wherever it has been possible to trace the reference.

I should like to thank the friends who have given me advice and help, particularly the Rev. J. D. Crichton for his kindness in reading part of the manuscript and Mr. J. G. B. Gosling for assistance in reading proofs.

KATHLEEN POND.

CONTENTS

LIST OF ILLUSTRATIONS

*Grateful acknowledgement is made to Mme Yvonne Chevalier
for permission to reproduce all the illustrations in this book.*

LIST OF ABBREVIATIONS
USED IN THE NOTES

CAPITAL letters are used for the writings of St. Teresa herself. For these, I have kept the abbreviations used by P. Luis de San José in his *Concordancias* (Ed. Monte Carmelo, Burgos), an alphabetical index of persons and subjects in the saint's *Works*.

A	AVISOS (Counsels)
AB	Ana de San Bartolomé
AJ	Ana de Jesús
AT	Año Teresiano
B	Bollandists
BA	Baruzi
BG	Baltasar Gracián
BL	Bernardino de Laredo
BM	Bremond
BN	Báñez
BR	P. Bruno de Jesús María
BRE	Id., *Espagne Mystique*
BRJ	Id., *Saint Jean de la Croix*
C	CAMINO DE PERFECCIÓN (Way of Perfection)
c	chapter
CAD	CONCEPTOS DEL AMOR DE DIOS (Conceptions of the Love of God)
CC	Canticle of Canticles
CH	*Vie de la vénérable Mère Anne de Saint-Barthélémy*
CONS	CONSTITUCIONES (Constitutions)
CP	Carmelites of Paris
CTA	CARTAS (Letters)
DE	DESAFÍO ESPIRITUAL (Spiritual Challenge)
E	EXCLAMACIONES (Exclamations of the Soul to God)
EM	P. Emeterio de Jesús María, *Ensayo sobre la lírica Carmelitana*
F	FUNDACIONES (Foundations)
FR	Francisco Ribera
GJ	Fr. Gabriel de Jesús
H	Hoornaert
HC	*Historia del Carmel*
IB	Pedro Ibañez
JA	Julian de Ávila
JC	St. John of the Cross
JCC	Id., *Cántico espiritual* (Spiritual Canticle)
JCS	Id., *Subida* (Ascent of Mount Carmel)

JJ	Jerónimo de San José
JG	Jerónimo Gracián de la Madre de Dios
JGC	Id., *Crónica*
JGD	Id., *Dilucidario del verdadero espíritu*
JGM	Id., *Diálogo sobre la muerte*
JGP	Id., *Peregrinaciones de Anastasio*
L	book
LA	La Puente
LL	Fray Luis de León
LO	Llorente
LV	Leo Van Hove
M	LAS MORADAS (The Interior Castle)
MA	Gregorio Marañon
MC	Editions Monte Carmelo, Burgos
MCH	Malón de Chaide
MF	María de San Francisco
MJ	María de San José
MJE	María de San Jerónimo
MJR	Id., *Recreaciones*
MN	Muñoz, *Vida de Fray Luis de Granada*
MP	María Pinel
MVC	MODO DE VISITAR LOS CONVENTOS (Visitation of Convents)
n.	note
O	Osuna, *Abecedario*, Ed. Ribadeneira
p.	page
P	POESÍAS (Poems)
PA	San Pedro de Alcántara
PB	Process of Beatification
PC	Process of Canonization
PP	Pedro de la Purificación
PS	PENSAMIENTOS Y SENTENCIAS (Thoughts and Maxims)
PT	Anon: *Les Parents de Ste. Thérèse*
R	RELACIONES (Relations)
RD	Francisco de Santa María, *Reforma de Descalzos*
RO	F. de Ros, *Osuna*
Sb	Shorter edition of the Works of St. Teresa (P. Silverio de Santa Teresa)
XC	Schneider
SEC	Critical edition of the Works of St. Teresa (P. Silverio de Santa Teresa)
SST	P. Silverio de Santa Teresa, *Vida de Santa Teresa*
TC	Teresa de Cepeda
V	VIDA (Autobiography)
VA	Valbuena Prat

VEJ   VEJAMEN
VH   Vicente B. de Heredia
Y   Diego de Yepes

References without an author's name are quotations from St. Teresa. Footnotes (other than references) are the author's, unless they are marked Tr. (translator).

PART ONE

THE WORLD? OR GOD?

'All the things of God gave me great pleasure,
but I was held captive by those of the world.'

ST TERESA OF JESUS: *Autobiography*, c. vii

I

GLORY

ON Wednesday, the twenty-eighth day of the month of March of the year 1515, about half an hour after five o'clock in the morning, with the first glimmers of the light of day, Teresa, my daughter, was born,'[1] wrote Don Alonso Sánchez y Cepeda.

The early angelus began to ring out from the church of Santo Domingo; then all the bells of Ávila, San Juan, San Pedro, San Isidro and San Pelayo, San Gil, San Bartolomé, San Vicente, Santa Cruz, San Cebrián, San Nicolás, Santiago, San Román, Mosen Rubí, the cathedral, the convents, from the Benedictines across to the Carmelite fathers, from the Poor Clares over to the Augustinian nuns of Our Lady of Grace, from the Franciscan sisters back again to the Dominican friars of Santo Tomás, from the Cistercians, men and women, at Santa Escolástica, San Millán, Santa Ana, to the Dominican nuns of Santa Catalina, the old stones gave back the echo of the bronze voices of all the saints of the city: for in Ávila there is nothing but saints and stones, 'en Ávila, Santos y cantos.'

On the 4th April, the godfather and godmother of little Teresa asked, in her name, for 'faith and life everlasting' in the parish church of San Juan.

That very day saw the inauguration of the convent of the Incarnation, a house of Carmelite nuns of Mitigated observance: already the door of God's house into which he who was baptizing her 'in the name of the Father, and of the Son, and of the Holy Ghost' was inviting her to enter, was opening.

The child received the Christian name of her maternal grandmother, Doña Teresa de las Cuevas, who, great lady of Castile as she was, could not sign her name. The godfather, Don Francisco Núñez Vela, was a man who thought of nothing but going overseas. It was the dawn of a new era. Scarcely twenty years had passed since Christopher Columbus offered King Ferdinand and Queen Isabella the Catholic, dominion over a continent. Spain was like a caravel dancing on the open seas; Spanish hearts, looking towards the west where these promised lands blazed in splendour, swelled with a feeling of possession.

[1] SEC, vol. II, p. 91.

Don Alonso Sánchez y Cepeda was a man of tradition but also a man of progress. In his library, *Conquest beyond the Seas*, on parchment, had a place beside *The Life of Christ in Pictures*, Guzmán's *Treatise on the Mass*, Boethius' *Consolations of Philosophy*. Having a great respect for books and knowledge himself, he was resolved that his children should know how to spell from their tenderest years and to read before they were seven.

His appearance inspired respect in all who knew him, everything about him gave evidence of his noble birth and dignity of character. He was known as a man of great integrity both in morals and manners, patient and good, very devout, and so compassionate in his ways that although it was considered proper for persons of his rank to have a few slaves, he always refused to do so, and a little Moorish girl whom one of his brothers confided to his care for a certain time was treated by him like one of his own daughters. His conversation was about God, or about the wars in Flanders or in Italy; for him progress in the Indies was measured by the number of souls saved there. He went about, his sword at his side, his rosary within his hand's grasp, administered his Gotarrendura estates himself and saw to it that there was sufficient corn, meat, poultry, vegetables and fruit to provide for the needs of a vast household. Over and above this he had no ambitions and every occasion offered him of increasing his fortune he neglected.

A native of Toledo he bore two great names: Sánchez, illustrious in Castile, Aragón and Navarre; Cepeda, made glorious by Don Vasco Vásquez de Cepeda, lord of that place, who was with Alfonso XI, the Redresser of Wrongs, at the siege of Gibraltar. He was thus an important personage in Ávila, where he passed for a very rich man. On the death of his first wife, Doña Catalina del Peso y Henao, ten years or so before Teresita's birth, he was possessed of 374,000 maravedis, magnificent estates, great flocks and herds, houses and an abundance of jewels. He loved splendour, and his violet damask or crimson satin doublets, shirts embroidered in scarlet and gold, ruffs from Paris, gilt swords with black velvet scabbards and gilded belts, red and yellow saddlecloths from Rouen, the breastplates with his armorial bearings, helmets, gauntlets, steel shoes, all showed that this gentleman-at-arms was not disdainful of fine apparel.

His widowerhood after three years of marriage made him melancholy, but when in 1509—he was nearly thirty—he married Doña Beatriz de Ahumada, as beautiful as she was of high birth and perhaps younger than was altogether fitting—she was fourteen—he strove hard to please her by his display of magnificence. She belonged indeed to that branch of the Dávilas with the thirteen roundels which considered itself the finest flower of the nobility of Castile and looked down upon the other Dávilas whose escutcheon only carried six roundels. The wedding took place at Gotarrendura and with so much magnificence that years afterwards people still talked of its splendour: the bride, 'very richly attired in silk and gold,' was thought to be all the lovelier and more dazzling for her frail appearance.

The Ahumadas owed their name to a feat of arms and to a miracle. Don Fernando, fighting the Moors, had been surrounded and cut off, with his three sons, in a tower which the enemy set on fire: God willed it that the denseness of the smoke should conceal the escape and flight of the besieged. From this day forward, Fernando was named Ahumada from *humo*, smoke; and the king of Castile allowed him to crown his armorial bearings with a tower surrounded by flames.

In her new home Doña Beatriz found a boy and girl.[1] The following year her eldest son, Fernando, named after Don Fernando, was born and in 1511 Rodrigo. At the birth of Teresita this mother of twenty summers thus became responsible for five little ones, a heavy burden for one of frail constitution. Thus, despite her courage, we find her increasingly exhausted as Lorenzo is born in 1519, Antonio in 1520, Pedro in 1521, Jerónimo in 1522. According to custom, some of these children bore their father's name, whilst the others similarly honoured their mother's family. Teresa was called de Ahumada y Cepeda.

The residence of the Cepeda y Ahumada, situated in the Plazuela de Santo Domingo, opposite the church of Santo Domingo de Silos, consisted of two blocks of buildings connected by *patios* and gardens. The house, magnificent and lovely, was no whit inferior in spaciousness or convenience to those of Núñez Vela, of the Águila, of the Polentino, of the Oñate. Above the entrance door, decorated with great studs forged by a first-class craftsman, the knight's escutcheon displayed his quarterings of nobility. The furnishings were handsome without being luxurious, as befitted the rank of the Cepeda and in accordance with the fashion of the day which, without going against the tradition of patriarchal simplicity proper to the great families of Castile, imposed Italian and Burgundian taste. In Don Alonso's house there was no lack of carpets from Flanders, of cushions of rich silk; but there were also the straight-backed armchairs in wood and leather

---

[1] It used to be thought that Don Alonso's first wife had three children; in his *Vida de Santa Teresa*, the distinguished Teresian scholar's most recent work, Padre Silverio de Santa Teresa inclines to the opinion that there were only two: Juan and María. There is no positive trace of the existence of the third and writers are not even agreed on the name: some say Pedro, others Jerónimo.

known as *sillones fraileros* or monastic armchairs, crockery from
Talavera and Valencia, the copper pots and wrought-iron chandeliers
which lent distinction to the houses of all the rich folk of Ávila and
which were at the same time in daily use. The presses and wardrobes of
dark carved oak were filled almost beyond capacity with linen and
with the skeins of flax or wool which the mistress of the household
reserved for her own use for spinning and weaving, as Queen Isabella
the Catholic had done: her husband never wore a shirt which she had
not spun with her own hands.

In spite of being surrounded by numerous servants, Doña Beatriz
was by no means idle. She left to her women the care of getting the
children up and putting them to bed, as she did all duties of the kind,
but kept for herself the prerogative of a mother's tenderness and
anxious solicitude. The slightest hurt, bump or scratch could find
relief nowhere but in her arms. It was only when the overflowing
boisterousness of the boys and girls found expression in piercing
screams and wild scrambles that the noisy crowd was banished to the
most distant patio: the favourite game of the boys of Ávila has always
been to fight one another with stones.

The garden was the entire world of Juan, María, Fernando,
Rodrigo, Teresa, Lorenzo, Antonio, Pedro, and even of little Jerónimo.
There a crowd of servants, men and women, was at work on leather
or wood for the needs of this large family; here the spinning was done,
the sewing, the washing; elsewhere there was the digging, the planting,
the horses were groomed and the sheep branded with a red-hot iron.
All this meant so much talking, singing, praying, perhaps trembling
with fear, according to the news which men come from afar, galloping
by on horseback, would hastily fling in passing, or the troops of
musketeers of the Tercios,[1] on the road to the wars. And people would
repeat to each other with pride that the captains engaged the soldiers
of the City of the Knights and Liegemen on the strength of their
birthplace alone, so famous were they for their valour. To this renown
a couplet with a play on words[2] testified:

> Most skilful in war is Ávila town
> And rightly earns her great renown.

Both the accounts of combats and those of the intrigues fabricated
against Castilian liberties by the detested Flemings with whom Charles V

---

[1] *I e.* regiments (Tr.).

[2] The pun, untranslatable, is clearly seen in the Spanish:

> *Se llama Ávila en esta tierra*
> *El que más ávil es para la guerra.*

was surrounded, were handed on from mouth to mouth; the growing audacity of the Lutherans beyond the Pyrenees seemed, to all those in this city guarded by its eighty-two granite towers, a constant menace both to soul and property.

It was not the time to be afraid—what was required was to fight. 'Ávila of the Knights and Liegemen' had always been for the Cross, for the oppressed, had always fought for liberty, given asylum to kings who were minors or suffering persecution. From Ávila Alfonso VIII set out to reconquer his kingdom and, surrounded by men of Ávila, won the famous victory of Las Navas de Tolosa against the Musulman. Again it was the ramparts of this city, chivalrous as it was in no common measure, that protected Alfonso XI when an inconsiderable king of only one year's standing.

But this very city would break out into furious anger against those who wore the crown unworthily. Henry IV of Castile, for instance, whose manhood they suspected, was no sooner crowned than he was so heartily detested by Ávila folk that they accused, judged, condemned and dethroned him in effigy in the process of a ceremony wilfully grotesque.

It was better to avoid arousing the ill-humour of these knights and townsfolk who would spend the time not devoted to punitive expeditions against the Moors in fighting each other: they only gave loyalty where they met it.

The fame of these warriors, often legendary figures even during their lifetime, was sung in *romances* and *coplas*.[1] Among such personages was a woman, Jimena Blásquez. As a child Teresa never tired of hearing the story of how, in the absence of her husband the governor, and of his troops, she defended the ramparts against an attack by the Almorávides. Doña Jimena went up on the towers, leading the women who were disguised as warriors by means of false beards and large hats; there they played such a tumultuous comedy of defence that the Moors took fright and raised the siege. 'She seemed not a woman at all but a strong *caudillo*.' Were great deeds open to everyone, then? The little one dreamed that it was so.

Tales like these began with a kind of incantation:

It came to pass . . .
—Let ill depart,
—Let good draw near.
Ill for the Moors,
Good for ourselves.[2]

[1] Ballads and songs; cf. 'couplets' (Tr.).
[2] *Érase que se era —el mal que se vaya —el bien que se venga —El mal para los Moros —y el bien para nosotros* (quoted Valbuena Prat, *Hist. Lit. Esp.*, p. 179).

There were stories, too, of children being kidnapped and assassinated by the infidels who tore out their hearts to be used in witchcraft. The secret trial of the Holy Child of Guardia who was scourged, crowned with thorns and crucified at some thirty-five leagues from Ávila, had ended up, in 1491, in the marketplace amid the flames kindled by the Grand Inquisitor Torquemada.

Teresita was sorry for these pagans:

'And they'll all be damned, then? For ever?'

Those telling the story did not answer: they preferred to stress the dangers which children who leave their homes to go out alone may meet with.

'But those who die for God go to heaven, for ever?'

Her brothers were amazed that one so young should have such a passionate love for war and glory.

She was five when the *Comuneros'* revolt filled Ávila with secret and solemn deliberations, for the Holy Office met in the very cloister of the cathedral: Castile rose against the Flemish emperor, Charles V, on behalf of the Castilian queen, Doña Juana, daughter of Isabel the Catholic, though she was mentally deranged and a prisoner at Tordesillas.

The City of Saints and Stones had an imperative reason for rising: the Emperor congratulated her on not taking part in the sedition. This was all that was necessary to make Ávila the centre of it and to rally her people at the password, *Comunidad.*

The Cepeda y Ahumada children were fascinated and tremendously excited by the atmosphere of conspiracy and intrigue; the very walls seemed to whisper the names of conspirators, under the seal of secrecy details of the oath ceremony were hinted at: each one present swore on the Cross and the Gospel to defend the liberties of Castile against the abuses of imperial power. The people did not know that they were defending not their own liberties but the privileges of the nobles; not the free exercise of thought and the critical faculty, but the immutable Church. The *Comuneros* went into battle to the shout of 'Long live the Inquisition.'[1] The dean of the cathedral himself presided over the meetings, but it was a sheep-shearer, Pinillos, who, using for the purpose the end of his little switch, gave or withheld permission to address the assembly. Whoever did not side with the *Comuneros* went in dread of them. Don Alonso, often away on his estates at Gotarrendura and, when at Ávila, living increasingly in retirement, succeeded in refraining from taking sides.

[1] Dr. Marañón, in his *Antonio Pérez*, maintains this theory of the people's being the instrument of the nobility in the revolt of the *Comuneros*.

It lasted a year, until the battle of Villalar, where the popular cry of *Santiago y libertad!* was stifled by the imperialists' *Santa María y Carlos!* The leaders were beheaded and those of the youth of Castile who aspired to great things turned their eyes beyond the seas: Mexico, discovered and conquered by Cortés, was named 'New Spain.'

Towards lands beyond the seas, or towards God.

In the home of the Cepedas the stories of warlike exploits were ended: with her brother Rodrigo, four years her senior, Teresita now turned to the *Lives of the Saints.* It was no longer another Jimena Blásquez that she dreamed of becoming but St. Catherine. For it was chiefly the martyrs who excited her enthusiasm, and to her mind the blood shed by St. Andrew, St. Sebastian, St. Ursula and her companions the eleven thousand virgins, was indistinguishable from their aureole of sanctity.

On Sundays, in the parish church of San Juan, she heard preachers thunder against the heretics whose writings were beginning to infiltrate into Spain, but still more perhaps against the lukewarmness of Christians; the picture of the damned writhing in eternal flames haunted her even in her sleep. She would have liked to be able to grasp to the full the meaning and content of this word 'eternal.'

'It means for ever,' Doña Beatriz would answer in reply to her questionings.

In summer under the cool shade of the mulberry trees, in winter in the damp stables, Teresa held long discussions with her brother and both repeated over and over again till their heads reeled:

'For ever, Teresa!'

'For ever, Rodrigo!' [1]

They hid themselves in order to be able to talk about God, conscious of an interest deeper than that considered suitable to children. Teresita considered that martyrdom 'was a bargain price' [2] for the presence of God; not that she loved God overmuch but she wanted to enjoy the heavenly delights of which she had read in the *Lives of the Saints.*

The realistic pictures of religious art showed her quite clearly the tortures of martyrdom in their full horror, but that only excited her imagination the more.

. . . A St Lawrence bound, stretched on the grid, the flames envelop him, the coals seem alive, the fire is so red that just to look at it makes you afraid. . . . This noble flesh seems to be burning and roasting, the entrails are half showing, the flames curl round the breasts and round the brave heart that will never apostatise, devouring them. . . . In another altarpiece St Bartholomew, bound to a table, is being flayed alive. . . . In the next panel St Stephen is being stoned, the stones crash down one against the other and his bleeding face and cleft skull move all who see them to pray for the brutal fellows who are butchering him. . . . Finally, a crucifix, naked, streaming with blood, the body showing the weals made by the scourging, the entrails pierced. . . .[1]

Suffering which is fierce and keen, but of short duration, in exchange for eternal glory.

'All that is necessary,' she was already telling Rodrigo, 'is a little bit of determination: *una determinacioncilla*. . . .'[2]

Neither Juan, who was fifteen and already thinking of going to the army, nor María, the big sister of thirteen, nor Fernando, still less Lorenzo, were admitted to the conversations in which the children strove to find a way of anticipating eternal happiness by martyrdom. The fact of having relatives seemed to them 'the greatest drawback.'[3] Their age was no obstacle. Ávila had erected her finest basilica to three child martyrs, Vincent and his two sisters, Cristeta and Sabina, who in Roman times refused to sacrifice to false gods. Scourged, broken upon the wheel, they continued to praise Jesus Christ their Lord until someone dashed out their brains on the stones. The pagans had forbidden them burial, but a monstrous serpent, feared all around for the havoc it wrought, constituted itself the guardian of their innocent remains: it frightened away not only birds of prey, but would-be profaners and a Jew who ventured there only escaped by invoking the name of Jesus and promising the monster he would get himself baptized.

Teresita already saw in her imagination another basilica: that of the brother and sister martyrs, Rodrigo and Teresa.

That year the taking of Rhodes by the Turks threw grown-up people into consternation, but filled the mind of a little girl who knew nothing whatever of geography with a longing for sacrifice: she imagined that it would now be easy to go and get beheaded in the land of the Moors, and that by begging one's bread along the roads 'for the love of God,' one could not fail to get there. What is the judgement of a boy of ten worth when confronted by a sister, younger indeed, but already possessed of a keen power of persuasion?

They both slipped away at daybreak, as soon as the gates were

---

[1] Malón de Chaide.   [2] Sb, C, c. xvi-10.   [3] Sb, V, c. i-4.

opened, crossed the Adaja bridge, and thought that by taking the road to Salamanca they were setting out for the 'lands of the Moors.'

There it was that Don Francisco Álvarez de Cepeda, their uncle, met them: they were walking with firm step, little Teresa's long dress dragging in the dust, both carrying a few crusts of bread tied up in a napkin at the end of a long stick. Rodrigo, whose feet were already beginning to hurt, owned up quickly, whilst his sister angrily clenched her teeth in silence over her secret. They were brought back home where Doña Beatriz, surrounded by her other children in tears and by her servants who loudly accused each other of negligence, was having the well dragged in search of the little truants. When the joy of their return was over, the big brother showed less stoicism when faced with the immediate prospect of a whipping than in his desire for martyrdom.

'It was *la niña* who dragged me into it.'

And *la niña*, the little one, was punished.

The check to her escapade turned Teresa's thoughts towards the life of the cloister, but the hermitages, large enough for a person of her years, which she endeavoured to build by piling up stones in the garden quickly collapsed: would the glory of St Mary of Egypt, whose frightful penances the servants used to sing of in their songs, prove as difficult of attainment as that of St Cecilia or St Agnes? Soon odd bits of stuff lying about the house disappeared: Teresita was founding a religious order; dressed up as a little nun, she obliged her cousins to the observance of a rule drawn up by herself. Naturally she was prioress. Clapping her hands with a hollow sound, she made her sisters, who were amazed at the accuracy for detail of her imagination, kneel down, get up, prostrate themselves, arms in the form of a cross and face to the ground. The children sometimes hid themselves behind the box trees; it was to say the rosary without being disturbed.

At this time Teresa thought she would like to be a nun, but her desire for this was 'less strong than for the earlier things,' less strong than her wish to be a virgin martyr or a desert solitary: the cloistered life would not satisfy her appetite for the romantic.

The children of Don Alonso's two marriages were now, in 1522, eight boys and two girls. Doña Beatriz, still beautiful, was no longer the dazzling vision of her marriage day, attired in silk and gold: the dresses of yellow Chinese silk with their sleeve openings lined with red, the richly embroidered skirts of crimson satin which she formerly wore with a corsage of violet damask striped with black velvet, were for her henceforward merely splashes of bright colour down at the bottom of the chests which Teresita sometimes coaxed her to open.

This woman of barely twenty-seven, whose languid condition made noise and conversation an annoyance to her, chose to dress as a duenna and of set purpose lived as a recluse in her own home. She had so often pleaded her poor health as a pretext for not receiving friends who came to visit her, or even close relatives whose children seemed to her an undesirable example for her own, that the sound of the knocker at the front door seldom disturbed her peace and quiet. She shared in her husband's life of piety but there was a whole world of fantasy in which she wandered alone: that of the tales of chivalry. To say 'alone' is not quite accurate: she had all Spain with her; about the same time a young squire, Ignatius of Loyola, was in raptures over *Amadis de Gaule*.

For Don Alonso, the prevailing fashion was insufficient justification: he was already declaring what Pérez de Moya was to write before long: such tales 'are the bait which the devil dangles before the sentimental feelings of frivolous boys and girls.' [1] Doña Beatriz would not have dared to argue with him, but privately thought that this husband fifteen years her senior exaggerated considerably. Could it be said that such reading was anything more than an agreeable diversion during her long illnesses or after a day entirely devoted to looking after her household and children? Was she any the less devout for it, or less austere in her ways? Did she neglect her duties? Most assuredly not. Moreover, arguments were not lacking to show that such works of the imagination were 'very necessary to excite courage in the pursuit of arms and to stimulate manly hearts to imitate the deeds of their forefathers. Glory and virtue abound in them. . . .' [2] And so she came to encourage a liking for such tales in her children, to save them 'from coming to grief in dangerous pursuits.' [3]

This was particularly so in Teresa's case.

Since the escapade 'into the lands of the Moors,' Doña Beatriz had been watching closely this girl who was wilder than all her brothers put together. On winter evenings the child pushed open her mother's door and found her sitting on cushions flung at random over a great Flemish carpet, reading. Don Alonso had not yet returned from a visit to Gotarrendura, or from a walk with a friend as serious as himself; the boys were taking exercise with a master at arms, María was at the sermon; the house was completely still. Little Teresa would take up her seat around the brasero and throw on the glowing embers a handful of dried lavender whose scent and blue smoke she loved.

Doña Beatriz would speak to her of the love of God and of Our Lady.

[1] Quoted VA, p. 64.   [2] Idem.   [3] Sb, V, c. ii–1.

'It is she who is your real mother.'

Her continual pregnancies and increasingly painful confinements made her fear she would not live long and Teresita's inventive high spirits made her uneasy: she strove to provide a palliative by keeping both mind and hands constantly occupied: she taught her the art of fine needlework, how to embroider the designs she made with many shades of silk. But this lonely and rather too tender-hearted teacher could not refrain from talking to the child of her favourite heroes equally as much as she did of Our Lady: Oriana, Palmerín, the child Esplandián, and Amadis, the young Lord of the Sea:

King Lisuart's daughter was Oriana, the most beautiful creature men had ever seen. She was so beautiful that she was called the Peerless. The Queen gave her the Lord of the Sea to serve her and said to her:

'Darling, this is a young Lord for your service.'

'He pleases me,' replied Oriana.

This remark was so deeply engraved in the young Lord's heart that it was never more effaced. As the story relates, he was not displeased at serving her and his heart was fixed on her unceasingly. This love lasted as long as they lived, he loving her as she loved him, so that they ceased not to love one another for a single hour.

'They loved each other for ever, and for ever, and for ever?' Teresita would ask her mother.

Doña Beatriz replied:

'For ever and ever.'

'Like Glory, Love has no value, then, unless it is for ever?' This thought sometimes preoccupied Teresa as she was growing up.

The Cepeda y Ahumada spent the summer at Olmedo, at the house of their grandmother, Doña Teresa de las Cuevas, or on their estates at Gotarrendura, three leagues away from Ávila. They went there by carriage, amid a great bustle of boxes and packages, but although the twenty-six little bells which tinkled from the mules' collars had long been Teresa's delight, she now preferred to ride on horseback with her elder brothers: she liked them to admire her fearlessness and the way she bore herself.

She found at Gotarrendura what she most preferred all through her life: a country dwelling house, yet well designed, a lovely enclosed orchard, a dovecot, vineyards, fields, and, what she specially loved, a distant horizon of magnificence. It was there that she learned to love the peasants of her own Castile and to make herself loved by them. Her slender pocket money was used up in alms to tramps and the poor of the neighbourhood. Her father, whose favourite she was, loved her the more because she was both kind and merry.

But Doña Beatriz had just brought into the world a baby girl, Juana, doubtless so named in memory of Juan, Don Alonso's eldest son, who had met death in the war against Francis I. She remained so ill that that year they were unable to return to the town at the beginning of autumn. Even in what hours of warm sunshine there were, she was scarcely able to drag herself as far as the dovecots she loved so much. Though she leant on Teresa for support, the girl felt no alarm that she should be so light a burden.

On the 24th November 1528, she made her will with a calm mind: 'I bequeath my soul to Almighty God who created and redeemed it with his precious blood. I bequeath my body to the earth from which he formed it. ... .' [1]

In death her countenance remained so peaceful that her children thought her asleep.

The funeral procession set out for Ávila before dawn; peasants followed the ox-drawn hearse on foot; the servants carried lighted tapers. Teresita, nestling against her elder sister, watched the lights flicker through a mist of tears. She did not realize immediately, however, how great the misfortune was that had befallen her; she was as yet unaware of the void that death means for those who are left.

Soon her consciousness of being weak and alone was so deep that fear took possession of her: rather than put her on her guard against the mistakes of adolescence, Doña Beatriz had preserved her from them. Those who were given the entrée into the Cepeda y Ahumada home were few. But their loss brought visits from relatives and friends and it was in her black mourning dress that Teresa learned for the first time that she was beautiful and was not indifferent to the knowledge. A moment later she wept for shame.

She asked Rodrigo to go back with her along the road they had taken the day of their flight towards martyrdom, but she entered the hermitage of St Lazarus alone. There she knelt before the picture of Our Lady of Charity, the former witness of their childish vow to die in order to win heaven. In tears, her heart still naïve but now no stranger to sorrow, she besought the blessed Virgin Mary to be her mother.

[1] PT, p. 51.

II

LOVE

TERESA DE AHUMADA Y CEPEDA was now fifteen, an age at which her mother was already married; her father was usually worried and preoccupied, her sister absent-minded, while her brothers idolized her; small wonder, then, if she should find herself falling in love.

She was a beautiful girl, though the word beautiful scarcely does her justice: her charm was irresistible. According to Fray Luis de León, a writer not given to exaggeration, people said that anyone who came into close contact with her would 'have his head turned.' 'Her beauty and the care she took of her person, her polished conversation, the sweetness and refinement of her manners made her more attractive still. Saint and sinner, ascetic and worldling, old and young alike came under the influence of her charm, though this in no way detracted from her dignity. Child or growing girl, in the world or as a nun, she attracted all who came in contact with her as the magnet draws steel.' [1]

Was it to be expected that a girl who was maddeningly beautiful, endowed with an 'extraordinary' loveliness of feature, noble, wealthy and surrounded by flattery, could be persuaded that all worldly joys were worthless? A wealth of chestnut hair, naturally curly, set off her high forehead and fluffed around her laughing face which altered so much with her lively and continually changing expression that it was difficult to say if it was round or oval. The straight, round-tipped nose met the arch of the eyebrows in a single curve. It was the full red mouth closing over dazzlingly white teeth which most revealed her personality and the black, rather prominent eyes, round, well-set, as they lit up with a flash of enthusiasm or glowed softly with tenderness as occasion demanded, or again sparkled with mischief or coquettishness. Teresa's complexion was pale but there was colour in her cheeks. Three dimples near the mouth set off her smile. She was well built and of average height. People spoke of the gracefulness of her carriage and of her lovely hands. 'Perfect in every way, she had an indefinable something in addition . . .' [2]—charm, a quality which eludes analysis.

[1] LL, cited SEC, vol. II, p. 475.   [2] María de San José.

How she loved to be told she was beautiful! She simply could not believe there could be anything wrong in that.

With the desire to please came that for dress and finery, unusual in such a young girl: both hair and hands received careful attention; she used cream, rouge and perfume. She now spent more time before her mirror than she did in saying her rosary. She tried different hair styles, piled up her high tresses in imitation of the Empress Isabella, used various oils and juices of plants to make her skin more lovely, plucked her eyebrows, used musk or orange perfume, diluted carmine for her cheeks. She wore amber beads or red or white coral, threaded on ribbon, but she liked best to wear jet for it set off the dark lustre of her eyes.

Her great delight was to get Don Alonso's permission to try on Doña Beatriz's gowns; in this heavy attire she could move as lightly as gossamer and danced about on her small, well-arched feet, with their dainty soft leather slippers, embroidered with flowers worked in silver thread. Needless to say she had openwork stockings.

All this was 'without any wrong intention, for I did not want anyone to offend God through me.' [1]

At sixteen Teresa's frivolity was merely the awakening of normal womanhood. And her taste for novels was shared by most girls of her age.

She always had a passion for tales of chivalry and admits that 'she was only happy when she had new ones.' [2] She hid them from Don Alonso. The sound of her father's footsteps caused her many a heart-beat as she threw a cushion over the open book, snatched up her embroidery and forced herself to speak in a steady voice. It often happened that she had to leave her story at the crucial moment to go to the *estrado* [3] to meet elderly relatives, to play chess with her father or to pore over the household accounts with her sister María. A maddening annoyance.

It was these stirring stories that she talked about with her brother Rodrigo. She called him to listen to passages: the apotheosis of *The Quest of the Holy Grail* delighted them most. The book ended with the entering of Galahad, son of Lancelot of the Lake, into the glory of God: 'The angels attired him in vesture of gold, placed on his head a diadem of precious stones and upon his right hand a ring. It was in this way that the Holy Grail was borne up to heaven. . . .' For a moment this

---

[1] Sb, V, c. ii–2.   [2] Idem, c. ii–1.
[3] The parlour in which visitors were reccived; sometimes an alcove or balcony at one end of the great hall (Tr.).

made them long to return to the fervour of their childhood and Teresa
would have mused almost endlessly upon the golden robes, the crown,
and the ring of the heavenly nuptials if a book which she was particularly longing to read, the *Olivante de Laura*, had not come her
way.

Teresa lived these adventures as she read them and would sigh with
relief when lover met beloved again after the chapters in which he
had destroyed or triumphed over the greatest possible obstacles and
dangers.

These tales were by no means morally edifying: damsels of high
degree shared their knights' couches unlawfully and unashamedly;
the illegitimate children born of these unions were almost drowned in
tears, but none the less exposed by their mothers to almost certain
death: Palmerín de Oliva, for instance, left on a mountain in a cradle
of water-willow suspended from the branches of an olive tree, or
Amadis, placed by his mother Elisane in a skiff shaped like a coffin and
entrusted to the sea: whence his title, Young Lord of the Sea. Such
love-children miraculously escaped to become valiant if not blameless
knights in their turn. And they too were the fathers of many children.
But in those days no mystery was made of the manner of perpetuating
the human race and the gravest sins were not those of the flesh.

Such stories were calculated to arouse the spirit of chivalry. Teresa
was too sensible to believe that the fantastic exploits really happened,
but the sense of grandeur, of honour, of the love of glory, all these
were real, the very essence of the traditions of her race and lineage.
Juan, her half-brother, had died in battle and even the youngest of
Alonso de Cepeda's sons already regarded themselves as future *conquistadores*. They thrived on stories like these, of course, but they also
knew by heart the discourse pronounced by the bishop, Don Pelayo,
when he knighted Ávila's two heroes, Yague and Mingo Peláez.
They mimed the scene, one of them declaiming:

Noble Squires who are to-day to receive the honour of knight-
hood, learn what Chivalry is. Chivalry is noble behaviour, and a
noble man is one who does no wrong to any creature nor commits
any base deed. In the first place, then, you must swear to love above
all things the God who created you and redeemed you by his passion
and his blood; secondly, to live and die in his holy Law and never to
disown it. Item, to promise to serve the King your Lord loyally.
Item, to swear not to be in the pay of any other king or rich man,
be he Moor or Christian. Item, that in combat you will die rather
than flee. Item, that your tongue shall speak nothing but the truth,

for he who lies is base. Item, always to be the help and succour of the poor. Item, to be the defender of any duenna or damsel who shall summon you to her aid, fighting for her against any mighty man who has wronged her. Item, not to be proud in your speech but humble in your bearing towards all, and, speaking with courteous consideration, to honour and venerate men who are old. And never to provoke without cause any man in this world.

In the Ahumada y Cepeda children a taste for adventures ran parallel with hero-worship.

Teresa was gifted with the type of imagination which immediately transforms thought into action: her idea now was, with Rodrigo—the favourite brother comes into everything—to write a tale of chivalry herself. Wasn't it said that the author of *Palmerín de Oliva* was a woman? Frustrated in her attempt to find glory in martyrdom, she now aspired to literary fame. The two young people, born on the same day though with four years between them, were once more inseparable; after long conversations and discussions Teresa took up her pen.

On the cover of an exercise-book the title: *The Knight of Ávila* by Doña Teresa de Ahumada and Don Rodrigo de Cepeda was imposingly displayed.

Their hero, Muñoz Gil, was famous in the annals of his native city. In this lay the originality of an undertaking in which Teresa already displayed her spirit of initiative, her love of creative work and of reform. Why must the heroes always be English or French, she asked herself? Why all these imaginary great deeds when the real achievements and prowess of the heroes of Castile, and of Ávila in particular, were just as wonderful? In her taste for the marvellous the girl already showed herself a realist; it is her native surroundings she uses as the point of departure for the plunge into her dream-world. 'A fig for the fictitious blows of Amadis, for the terrible attacks of the giants, if only there were a writer in Spain to recount the mighty deeds of the Spaniards!' [1] declared Luis Zapata a little later, after describing the real prowess of a Juan Fernández Galindo, a Ramiro de Cardenas or a Jorge Manrique, who 'with a single stroke of his sword ran his enemy through, the blow passing through the saddle and even wounding his horse.' [2]

Teresa, too, had felt the want and decided to be the writer in question. For months the sheets of paper piled up. Rodrigo often preferred riding, hunting, warlike games or pretty girls to literary

---

[1] Quoted VA, pp. 60-1.   [2] Idem.

occupation, but his sister continued relentlessly and he left her the glory of the finished work. Relatives and friends said how marvellous it was; they praised the vivacity of her style, its colourfulness, the fascinating way she developed the narrative, and more than one writer of note admitted that the author showed a penetration of mind unusual in one of her years.

But winter, when it is so pleasant to write with one's chair drawn close up to the brasero, came to an end. Spring whispered that when one is fifteen, life is more exhilarating than writing, even when one is writing about the struggle between passion and honour.

Don Alonso, more austere than ever since Doña Beatriz's death, closed the emblazoned door which opened on to the *plazuela*, to visitors, but in the wall which divided his gardens from those of his brother Don Francisco, there was a private door.

Pedro, Francisco, Diego and Vincent were the names of Don Francisco Álvarez de Cepeda's sons; his daughters were Beatriz, Ana, Jerónima and Inés. There was also Doña Elvira, daughter of Ruy Sánchez y Cepeda. A fine group of young people in whom must be included Teresa's elder brothers, Fernando and Rodrigo. María was a person apart. She was twenty-four, serious like her father and engaged to a man equally serious, Don Martín de Guzmán y Barriento: their quiet affection as an officially engaged couple brought sunshine into the house.

Don Alonso had scarcely started for Gotarrendura when all this band of youngsters began to dance and sing for joy and talk sweet nothings. What more natural? Teresa loved to be loved, and one of her cousins adored her. Which one was it? Francisco or Pedro? Diego or Vincent? She mentions no one by name. When she mentions these cousins, all she says is: 'They were about my own age, a little older than I. We were always together; they were very fond of me; I used to talk to them of anything that gave them pleasure and I listened to them as they told me of their likes and dislikes and their childish nonsense, and also of certain things that were blameworthy. What was worse was that it was in this way that my soul came in contact with what was the cause of all the harm. . . .'[1] She allowed herself to be influenced because of the feeling of affection she inspired in others: 'As soon as I felt that I pleased somebody, if I found favour with him, I took such a tremendous liking to the person that I would be always thinking of him.'[2] Crystallization could not be defined in fewer words.

She mentions no one by name, keeps silence about whoever it was

[1] Sb, V, c. ii–2. [2] Sb, V, c. xxxvii–4.

that disturbed her serenity, but there was one cousin whom she would not see again as long as she lived, although she remained in contact with all the others: Pedro. Can we not deduce from this that it was Pedro she loved? What motive could she who was so loyal in the matter of family affection have had for avoiding him? One reason alone: the importance she always gave to the necessity of 'cutting off occasions of sin by the roots.'

We should not take these girlish love affairs (for which Teresa afterwards reproached herself bitterly) more seriously than is warranted by what she says herself. She accuses herself of the pleasure she found in the chatter of a cousin who idled her time away and made her share her taste for frivolities. Had this cousin the reputation of being too much of a flirt? Doña Beatriz had done her best to prevent her children from seeing her, but there was nothing sufficiently definite against her to justify her being forbidden the house. Don Alonso and the prudent elder sister frowned upon the friendship, but without result:

I had a great leaning towards everything evil [declares Teresa]. My evil inclinations were sufficient in themselves. In addition there were the servants and I found them quite ready to encourage me in anything wrong. If one of them had given me good advice I might perhaps have listened to her, but self-interest blinded them [we can see the lover slipping ducats into their hands] just as my propensity blinded me. I was not wholly bad and everything dishonourable was abhorrent to my nature, but I loved to spend my time in pleasant chatter; that does not alter the fact that the occasion of falling was there, the danger within a hand's grasp, and I was exposing my father and brothers to it. God guarded me so well that he preserved me from falling, even against my will.[1]

In a period in which all passions ran to extremes, custom authorized father and brothers to kill a girl's seducer, and it was not infrequent for a love affair to be responsible for several corpses: it is to such dramas of honour that Teresa was referring. On the other hand the guilty man might be forced to marry his victim. Examples of such laxity of morals were not wanting in the highest ranks of society: the bastards of kings, those of grandees, even those of dignitaries of the Church came in for their share of titles and benefices. The illegitimate child of a girl who could prove her *limpieza de sangre*, that is, that the blood of her ancestors

---

[1] In the attempt to identify this cousin of Teresa's, I have followed the opinion of Fr. Gabriel of Jesus which seems to me the most solidly established of all those put forward on the subject.

was clean from any Moorish or Jewish taint, was more highly esteemed than the legitimate offspring of mixed blood.

Beautiful girls longed for a lover, gallant lovers used no half measures with passion, human life was held cheap; the man or the woman in the upper classes of society who dared to defy a father or duenna in order to enjoy the other's society valued love more than prudence warranted. Honour prohibited a fall but it also forbade too much timidity.

Teresa was not afraid, but she would not have allowed the finger of scorn to be pointed at her, nor was she the kind of girl to get married because honour dictated it. If she had to defend herself from audacious overtures, she did so through a twofold instinct for purity: purity of body in the first place and then care for her reputation. It is too often forgotten that if sexual attraction is a natural instinct, virginity's defence is just as instinctive.

Teresa had an excuse for these secret love affairs: her confessor himself and many other good people of sound judgement saw no sin in her being attracted by a boy whose intention was 'a happy issue by way of marriage.' [1] It was just a love affair in embryo or perhaps a real falling in love, for despite her young years, no diminutive was possible where the sentiments of Teresa de Ahumada were in question. It was so throughout her life. Her own account of it is that one of her cousins was in love with her and that another cousin, a girl like herself, and the servants, were a party to the matter. There may have been a few secret meetings, interchange of notes, an intense uneasiness, demands, tears, repentance, jealousy, all the agitation which a first love-affair unleashes in an impetuous nature. We are not justified in reading more into the affair than Teresa tells us herself.

Yet we can perhaps imagine something of the love affair of a girl who was beautiful, elegant, a trifle coquettish, and who was at the same time closely guarded by her father and sister. An old ballad in the form of a dialogue between two sisters fits the reproaches which María addressed to Teresa so aptly that there is nothing far-fetched in supposing that their discussions would be somewhat as follows:

Miguela scolds her sister Juanilla. She speaks to her words that deeply wound:
'Only yesterday you were quite tiny and wrapped in swaddling clothes; today you bedeck yourself more than other maidens, your joys are sighs, your songs elegies, you rise at dawn and you retire to

[1] Sb, V, c. ii. 4–6, 9.

rest late. In your work I know not on what your thoughts are dwelling, for you look at your pattern and you miss the stitches. They tell
me that you are using lovers' signs: if our mother hears of it, things
will be altered. She will nail up the windows and shut fast the doors;
we shall no longer get leave to dance; she will bid our aunt accompany us to church, so that our friends may not speak to us. When she
is absent she will bid the duenna watch the expression of our eyes and
scrutinize the passer-by, to see if anyone should stop before the grating and which of us turns our head. . . .'

Juanilla replies:

'Ay! Miguela, sister! How you seek to find evil! You imagine
troubles of mine without knowing anything of them. I have a liking
for Pedro, son of Juan, who has gone to the wars. His sighs and
laments moved me. But absence has made him fickle. . . .'

Thus Teresa who thinks she knows better than persons of experience has to listen to moralizings like those of the austere Miguela
from the lips of María de Cepeda.

Your unhappiness will only increase as you grow older. If you
doubt it, listen to this proverb: 'You are still a child and think you
know what love is; what will it be, then, when you are of an age to
love?' [1]

Teresa, it is certain, clung only to that which would last 'for ever
and ever': she had not been brought up on the *Lives of the Saints* and
the tale of Amadis and Oriana for nothing.

María's marriage brought festivities in which Teresa, now in love,
was astonished to find that turning young men's heads still gave her
pleasure; but it gave her pain when she saw her lover attentive to the
guests.

The wedding took place at Villatoro, where Don Martín Guzmán
de Barrientos had distinguished relatives. It was a village half-way
between Ávila and Castellanos de la Cañada and here the young
couple were to live. The celebrations began with a merry cavalcade
and for several days it was nothing but festivities, gay and beautiful
clothes, songs, dances to the music of tambourine, flute or rebeck,
rustic games, with the whole family there and all their friends and, of
course, their first cousins, the inseparable sons and daughters of
Teresa's uncle Francisco.

While their house at Castellanos was being got ready for them,
María and her husband returned to Ávila to her father's home.

For the City of the Liegemen, 1531 was a glorious year: the Empress

[1] Anonymous ballad (quoted TI, vol. I, p. 141).

Isabella arrived there in May with little Prince Philip; it was there that the ceremonies in the course of which the future Philip II, then four years old, was to exchange his childish dress for his first princely breeches took place. The severe taste of the Portuguese princess had to give way before the official programme. Ávila glistened with gay tapestries and bright-coloured hangings that sparkled against the granite and was completely invaded by the court. Its sombre streets came to life with gay processions, in the squares tourney followed joust and there was a continual but pleasant hubbub intermingled with the sound of music and the clash of bells.

It would not do for one of the prettiest girls of rank in Ávila to be away from these festivities, and Teresa, who could always adapt herself to any set of circumstances, enjoyed them. She was elated by her success but not carried away and there were hours when the longing for Pedro or for worldly pleasure gave way to a feeling of the puzzling emptiness of it all. To one with a nature as straightforward and a character as frank as hers, the dissimulation she was practising towards her father and María could not but cause worry and agony of mind.

For two months she went from one festivity to another. On 26th July, Don Philip was to receive 'his princely liveries.' But—on the 13th Don Alonso sent Teresa to a convent. He put forward a good reason: her elder sister had just left for Castellanos de la Cañada and she could not take part in the celebrations without being chaperoned. Did he feel that the cousins in their smart attire, the velvet doublet knotted with gold tags, the full, goffered ruffles, the short cape which showed the sword beneath, were too irresistibly attractive to allow any really good father to breathe in peace? Teresa answers the question herself: 'My father loved me so much and my dissimulation was such that he did not think me capable of as much evil as was in fact the case: and so I was not sent away under a cloud. There were some slight suspicions about me but nothing definite. I had such a fear of losing my reputation that I took every possible precaution to keep everything secret.'

The goodbyes were secret too, and the servant who was a party to Teresa's love affair with her cousin kept watch while they said farewell. Teresa shed tears. Tears of despair she thought them, but then she wept again when she had to take off her necklace with its fourfold row of gold chain she was so fond of, her rings, bracelets and long earrings which she would no longer be allowed to wear. This confusion between feelings of affection and those of vainglory left her very much disconcerted.

When she was sent to the convent of the Augustinian nuns of Our Lady of Grace, Doña Teresa de Ahumada y Cepeda was sixteen and four months. At a time when there were no establishments of higher education for girls, these nuns received the wealthy daughters of distinguished families. They went there more to deepen the practice of their religion and to strive after the attainment of virtue than for learning: to be familiar with the catechism, to know how to read and write, to have some knowledge of how to keep accounts, to be a skilful embroideress, an accomplished lace-maker, a good spinner, an average musician, this was considered sufficient education: too much mention is made of women who knew Latin and Greek for them not to be the rarest of exceptions. The distinction between intelligence and wit on the one hand and much knowledge on the other was perfectly understood and the affectation of ignorance was considered better form than pedantry. Years later Teresa laughed at a nun who prided herself on her learning: 'I am not so learned as you. Who are the Assyrians? . . .'[1] She no doubt knew perfectly well, but she had too much good taste to neglect to give her daughters a lesson in simplicity.

Such lessons she herself received at Our Lady of Grace. No other convent in Ávila enjoyed such great prestige. The religious were of high birth but they were distinguished not so much for this as for their fervour and austerity. The mistress of the girls sent there for their education, Doña María de Briceño y Contreras, was with them night and day: she shared their dormitory, went with them to chapel and if one of her charges was called to the parlour she accompanied her there. Her devotion to the Blessed Sacrament had been confirmed by a miracle: one day when the celebrant had forgotten to give her Communion she could not repress a slight cry of disappointment and then people saw two hands move towards her bearing the Holy Eucharist. Quite apart from her sanctity the charm of this nun must have been very considerable, for her severity did not prevent her pupils from adoring her.

But even the vigilance of a saint could have little influence on a girl who was angry at being deprived of her liberty. 'At first I was very much upset; but I was already weary of vanity and frivolity, when I offended God I was afraid and I forced myself to confess what I had done as soon as possible. I was so troubled on this account that at the end of a week, perhaps sooner, I was much happier there than in my father's house.'[2]

[1] CTA, ccxxiii.   [2] Sb, V, c. ii–8.

Her new companions loved her, for God had given her the gift of pleasing people wherever she went.

The idea of becoming a nun however did not cross her mind, she was even 'extremely opposed' [1] to doing so, but she was delighted to be living in surroundings where goodness and piety were made attractive.

Teresa accuses the devil, and also 'those from outside,' [2] of having conspired to disturb her peace by messages: notes from the despairing lover found their way through the keyhole, through the parlour grilles or were slipped into her hand by that cousin of her own sex 'of frivolous disposition.' Perhaps there were furtive interviews: brief moments of joy to be followed by prolonged remorse. She has not given us details of the events and feelings which caused her to turn aside from human love even before she was wholly caught up in a love that was divine. But there is one incident of which she has spoken at length and if she has chosen to analyse it, if she comes back to it on more than one occasion, if she showed a particular liking for the central figure of this story, it must surely be because she found there feelings and emotions which were common to her own experience and which she therefore understood and sympathized with all the more: the person in question was Doña Casilda de Padilla, who bore one of the greatest names in Spain and was one of the wealthiest people in the country.

Doña Casilda was twelve when she was married to her uncle.

She began to enjoy the worldly finery necessitated by her rank, finery well calculated to please her girlish years. But she had hardly been married two months when God began to draw her to himself, although she did not then understand that he was doing so. When she had spent a happy day with her husband—they loved each other tenderly despite the difference in age between them, it made her dreadfully sad to find that the day had passed and nothing was left of it and to think that all other days would pass in exactly the same way. . . . [3] At that time her husband had to go away on a journey. She loved him so much that she was greatly upset at this. But soon God made her understand the cause of her suffering: her soul was really longing for that which would never end. . . . [4] As the Lord wanted her for his own, he took this earthly love away from her and gave her the desire to leave everything for him. At the time she was moved only by the desire to save her soul and to find the best means of doing so; it seemed to her that if she were deeply involved in the

[1] Idem.　　　　　　　　　　　　[2] Idem.
[3] Sb, F, c. x–14.　　　　　　　　　[4] Sb, F, c. x–15.

things of this world, she would neglect to make the effort to obtain eternity.[1]

Is not this what Teresa de Ahumada was experiencing when she was about sixteen—the passion for finery, the love so ardent that proof of its worthlessness is found in its very excess, the need of loving 'that which has no end,' 'for ever and ever,' the warm but very human love which our Lord stills before he takes possession of a heart smarting under an all too recent disappointment? We can imagine Teresa receiving one of those 'messages from outside,' and her vexation that the joy it gave her vanished so quickly.

'This soon ceased and I again found pleasure in the good I had known as a young child. . . . It seems to me that His Majesty was continually looking for a way to draw me to himself' [2]—as in Doña Casilda's case, without her knowing it.

[1] Sb, F, c. x–16.   [2] Sb, V, c. ii–8.

III

THE FIRST KNOCK [1]

THERE was no doubt that the Ahumada y Cepeda children had been badly brought up: austerity on the father's side and piety on the mother's do not necessarily go hand in hand with the art of governing eight boys and three girls, or provide a healthy outlet for their curiosity or turn their high spirits to the best account. This is shown by the fact that from the moment when Teresa, the spoilt child, the one to whom everyone gave way and to whom nothing was ever refused, found someone to take her in hand, she was a changed being.

María de Briceño was thirty-six; she had been elected by acclamation mistress of the young pupils of Our Lady of Grace, known as the *Señoras Doncellas de piso*, the 'young ladies of rank.' She proved to be extremely gifted in getting on with her pupils, making them understand what she wanted after she herself had listened to what they had to say. Her illustrious origin carried weight, she was highly intelligent, charmed people by her graciousness and radiated all around her an atmosphere of spiritual things. Perhaps her method varied according to the character of the person concerned? However that may be, far from depriving Teresa de Ahumada of the talks and conversations she so much enjoyed, she turned them to good account: 'I began to find pleasure in this nun's good and holy conversation and was delighted to hear her speak so beautifully of God.' [2]

Teresa de Ahumada had loved to exchange secrets with her rather frivolous cousin, but she found that María de Briceño was willing to take her into her confidence too: 'She told me how it was she became a nun just through reading what the Gospel says, "Many are called but few are chosen," and spoke to me of the reward which Our Lord gives to those who leave all for his sake.' [3]

Did the nun realize how impressionable Teresa was, so impulsive and ready to translate words into action that a mere spark of feeling would kindle the fire needed to bring a project to immediate realization? From early childhood her actions had always been

---

[1] MP quoted SEC, vol. II, p. 102.
[2] Sb, V, c. iii–1. [3] Sb, V, c. iii–1.

prompted by enthusiasm. María de Briceño no doubt understood this, for she turned it to good use: 'Her good companionship gradually rid me of the habits which bad company had given me and awakened in me afresh the desire for what was eternal.'[1] Teresa adds: 'My hostility towards the religious state lessened a little.' Her attitude in the matter was in fact slowly changing and her thoughts gradually turning in the direction of religious life.

But her pride suffered. Up till then everyone had obeyed the self-willed child. By artfulness or wheedling she got everything she wanted. She had always been the most beautiful and beloved of daughters. Her father and mother talked about her outbursts of temper, quoting them as instances of personality; her good taste, cleverness, wit, her gifts as a young writer were boasted of, as were her gracefulness as a dancer, her skill at chess, her daring as a rider; of a piece of embroidery she made a work of art; and she made the family dinner as exciting as a firework display. She could afford to be ambitious. It was said of her in Ávila:

'Teresa de Ahumada? She will marry whom she chooses.'

She had always beaten the cleverest at their own game. But at Our Lady of Grace she was to undergo for the first time the painful experience of realizing that there was something she lacked, a quality, a perfection that was not hers: 'If I saw one of my companions shed tears as she prayed or give proof of some other virtue, I envied her greatly; for my heart was so hard that I could have read the whole Passion through without shedding a tear: and it hurt me to be like that.'[2]

She who did not know what it was to be thwarted, thus came up against forbidden territory. The obstacle was in herself: an incapacity to understand, to feel. She was astonished that joy could be found in humiliation. In her search for adventure she had discovered a limitless world, vaster and richer than any land beyond the seas and one more difficult to conquer: her interior self.

And so it was at the convent of Our Lady of Grace that God gave 'the first knock' on the door which led to the secret recesses of Teresa de Ahumada's soul.

On the advice of María de Briceño she began to pray much aloud: she also asked others to pray for her, that God would show her clearly the state in which she would serve him best: 'I still hoped that it would not be in religious life. . . . Yet I also dreaded marriage.'[3]

In one so hard to please as Teresa, her brief experience of human love had left rather disdain than regrets: as she had known it, it had

[1] Sb, V, c. iii-1.   [2] Idem.   [3] Sb, V, c. iii-2.

nothing in common with what she had learnt from the tales of chivalry about love for its own sake. What was a married woman's life in those days? Complete submission to her husband, to his relations as well as hers, to the customs and usages of the time; in spite of strict observance of the practices of religion, the mind scarcely rose above the contingencies of material existence; confinements succeeded each other until she died of exhaustion or in childbirth. Such had been the destiny of Doña Beatriz de Ahumada and such also, in an even briefer space of time, of Doña Catalina del Peso y Henao, Don Alonso de Cepeda's first wife, three years after marriage, after having given birth to her second child.

Teresa de Ahumada later betrayed the fears of her girlhood when as a Carmelite she pointed out to her nuns 'the great grace God had given them in choosing them for himself: he has spared them the being in subjection to a man who is often the cause of their losing their life and God be thanked if he does not make them lose their soul too!' [1]

Fear of an early death would not have deterred from marriage a courageous girl who always adored children, but married life was slavery. The wife had no right to express an opinion before her lord and master, she could only have recourse to subterfuge. What became of the respect and admiration which every woman must feel before she can give submission, when the lord and master turned out to be worthy only of contempt?

Later on Teresa would blame Catalina Godínez for having considered the suitors her father proposed to her unworthy of her, but she added: 'She was not attracted by marriage, it seemed to her a dreadful thing to be in subjection to anyone, and she could not understand why she had so much pride. Our Lord, wanting to save her, knew which chord to strike to awaken her heart's response. Blessed be his mercy.' [2]

It was the same in Teresa de Ahumada's case: she knew that the love of man, love for a man, does not last 'for ever and ever.' It was for this reason she held back from marriage. She was already turning over in her mind the possibility of entering religion, but, if possible, without cutting herself off completely from the world: for instance she would never enter Our Lady of Grace where twelve nuns observed the abstinence, the silence, the practices of mortification so rigorously that the *Señora Doncella de piso* was appalled by it. There were less austere Orders. And Teresa sometimes liked to let her thoughts stray to the convent of the Carmelites of Mitigated observance—the convent

[1] Sb, F, c. xxxi–46.   [2] Sb, F, c. xxii–5.

of the Incarnation—where her great friend Juana Suárez had taken the habit. This convent was large and very pleasant, kept very much alive by its hundred and twenty-four nuns, young and old, among whom were some secular persons. These Carmelites were devout, of course, but they did not carry penance to extremes. In spite of their low ceilings and the grille separating the nuns from the visitors, the parlours of the Incarnation were among the places most frequented by the best society of Ávila.

'I looked more to the satisfaction of sensuality and vanity than to the good of my soul. These good thoughts of becoming a nun sometimes came to me, but soon left me. . . .' [1]

At Our Lady of Grace, Teresa went through a year and a half of interior struggle. 'Spiritually she was attracted to the convent, but the things of sense drew her away from it; sense struggled against spirit and made her heart a battlefield.' [2]

In all this the love of God did not enter into the matter: she weighed the chances of less suffering in this world against paradise in the other: what would be her lot, as a religious, or, on the other hand, as a married woman.

Why was she not a man! She would not have hesitated to follow Fernando, her eldest brother, who came to bid her good-bye: he was leaving for Seville and from there was setting out to join Francisco Pizarro in Peru. Don Alonso Sánchez de Cepeda's sons were crazy about going overseas. Pizarro had been imprisoned for debt almost as soon as he arrived in Spain, but what did it matter? The Emperor had named him *Adelantado* (*i.e.* governor) of the lands he was setting out to conquer, and captain-general. Over there there was so much gold and silver that it was used for the floors of houses, but the future *conquistadores* laid the emphasis on the souls to be saved rather than on the wealth to be gained. The spoils of the conquest were set out in round figures: 21,300,000 gold crowns, the treasures of Montezuma brought back by Cortés; 1,200,000 baptisms between 1524 and 1532. Some, those who said that precious stones rolled about like pebbles under the horses' hoofs, even mentioned 14,000 baptisms a day. After making due allowance for exaggeration, the conclusion was that it was a Christian duty to go off to the Indies.

Teresa was now beginning to suspect that to be baptized was not enough. If she had not had the misfortune to be born a woman, she would not have hesitated to choose the religious state, for she would then have been permitted to go and evangelize these poor people:

[1] Sb, V, c. iii–2.   [2] LL quoted SEC, vol. II, p. 477.

conquerors as well as conquered. What was still worrying her about religious life was the door that was to close 'for ever,' the anguish of feeling that the very fact of dying to self would perhaps cause her to become so bitter that she would lose heaven all the same.

The struggle made her ill, she was only seventeen. At the end of the winter she had to be sent back to her father: the conflict had been so severe, the nervous strain so continual, the alternate depression and excitement so exhausting.

The spoiled child was surprised to feel so little joy over her return home. She loved her family, of course, but she was not sufficiently mature to find pleasure in her father's serious conversation, and the pranks in which her brothers indulged drew from her no more than a tolerant but rather weary smile. Confined to bed, she spent many hours looking at a picture of Jesus and the Samaritan woman which her mother had hung in her room when she was a small child; she could not take her eyes off it and kept on repeating to herself the text beneath: *Domine da mihi aquam*. She had often wanted this living water. Had the Samaritan woman herself wanted it so very much before Jesus came to her? She was a sinner who did not know Our Lord. On the other hand she, Teresa, brought up to believe in him, could not resolve to follow him. Attentive to the heart's movement which should accompany that of the lips, she pronounced the name of Jesus, and did not succeed in awakening a spark of true love. Did not faith imply the power to love God as she loved the absent Fernando, or Rodrigo who was here, or her dead mother, or her father who was still with her? She experienced only one feeling deeply: a kind of jealousy of the Samaritan woman whose indifference Our Lord had shattered so effectively that she set the whole town of Samaria agog with her story.

Teresa's health improved only slowly, to the keen disappointment of her brothers and the crowd of cousins who were in and out and who had hoped to see her take her place again in their little band. Was this the very 'occasion' she wanted to avoid? She asked her father to let her go and join her sister María at Castellanos: the stay in the country would no doubt hasten her recovery. Don Lorenzo and Rodrigo, only too glad to hear her express a wish at all, took her there.

There were not more than ten houses in Castellanos de la Cañada and these were grouped around Don Martín's residence. Here, masters and peasants formed one big family. There was nothing but the fresh clear air, and the silence. The land round about was barren, but there was a fountain and clumps of cork-oak. To the convalescent, the distant sheep-bells as the flocks changed pasture, a sound as crystal-clear as light, seemed heavenly music.

Teresa brightened: she busied herself in the house, played with her tiny baby nephew, and took great pleasure in doing the cooking. Her sister who adored her would have liked to keep her with her always. María was a gentle creature. Her only reaction to her husband's difficult character was perfect submission; she did not rise up in protest when he started a distressing quarrel about the inheritance. Good Christian that she was, she allowed herself to be worn out by cares and worries,[1] of which the couple had many; money was scarce although María's dowry had been three thousand ducats.

If she did not find happiness in spiritual things, Teresa did not find at Castellanos any proof that she would obtain happiness in marriage. On the other hand, was she henceforward to find pleasure nowhere, to see emptiness in everything? She was a little vexed with herself for not being entirely satisfied, surrounded as she was by affection and in the heart of her beloved Castile. Already work seemed to her the only balm for a seared soul.

Work and reading. Not a day passed without her remembering with gratitude the stop they had made on their journey at the village of Hortigosa where her uncle Don Pedro Sánchez de Cepeda lived. His house was known as 'the palace' but the good and serious-minded man who lived in this lovely country residence was far removed from any suggestion of ostentatiousness. He divided his time among his books, prayer, meditation and those works of charity which one no longer dares to call good works since so many 'good' people have confused self-satisfaction with the practice of the love of their neighbour. Despite Teresa's affection for her father, his piety made little impression on her. It is nowhere apparent that he influenced her other than by continual good example and the pious habits she was taught in childhood, whereas Don Pedro's fervour created such a perceptible harmony around him that she could not help being impressed by it. In her turn she delighted her uncle by the quiet way she listened to him and her ready answers.

Don Pedro was a widower and was only waiting till his son's upbringing should be finished to become a monk. In his conversation Teresa found once more the same delight as in her discussions with Doña María de Briceño: 'His most usual subject was God and the vanities of the world.'[2] A cultured man, the only pride he had was in showing his rich library. His finger on a book which he did not take

<hr/>

[1] CTA, ii.   [2] Sb, V, c. iii–4.

down from the shelf, for the fantasies of the poets no longer held his preference, he quoted Teresa some lines from one of them.

> Where is the King, Don Juan?
> The Princes of Aragon,
>   Where are they now?
> Where are all the courtiers,
> Where are all the pastimes
>   Which they devised?
> The jousts and tournaments,
> Caparisons and trappings,
>   And helmets plumed?
> Were they nought else but dreams?
> Were they nought else but chaff
>   On threshing floor?
> Where are now the ladies?
> Their kerchiefs and their gowns,
>   Their perfumes rich?
> Where are they now, the flames
> Of passion's fire enkindled
>   By lovers young?

At this time when Spain, enriched by the new world, was moving towards the zenith of her earthly power, her most highly esteemed poet was still old Jorge Manrique, and among all his works the most appreciated were these *coplas* which sang of the transitoriness of things.

> Our lives are the rivers
> Which flow into the sea,
>   The sea of death.

Teresa's lovers, her finery, her pleasures, were fading away into nothingness. The boy who had loved her and whom she herself had loved, what more was he to her now than Palmerín or Amadis? Scarcely a memory. With this difference: that that particular memory was tarnished with a sense of shame; a proud girl like Teresa would never forgive herself. No earthly joy could last for ever, then; the only thing which seemed to be unending was the remorse at having been mistaken.

Touched by the attention his niece showed him, Don Pedro made bold to take down his biggest volumes from the shelves: he asked Teresa to read aloud to him:

'I wasn't very keen to do so, but I made him believe I found pleasure in it. For I was extremely anxious to please people, even if it meant doing things I disliked; but what would have been virtue in someone else was a great fault in me, for I often went beyond the bounds of discretion.' [1]

Don Pedro chose the letters of St. Jerome. 'God,' Teresa says, 'forced me to do violence to myself. I only remained with my uncle a short time, but the words of God, both those I read and those I heard, and his good influence made such a deep impression on me that I understood the truth which I had but dimly sensed as a child: ALL THINGS ARE NOTHING.' [2]

And so at Castellanos, while she was smoothing little Juan's curls or stooping to pluck a sprig of rosemary, or thinking of Rodrigo who was soon coming to fetch her, she repeated to herself again and again: 'All things are nothing.'

For a long time she watched the water from a tiny spring gush forth among the rocks, spurt upwards and bubble, and she was surprised to see that 'the sand once disturbed never ceased to rise.' Perhaps in the same way the love of God would one day cause the slime of which she was made to rise upwards too?

She pondered over the joy of the thirsty earth when watered and this made her alarmed at the aridity of her soul, but she remembered that Christ is 'a good gardener.' [3]

---

[1] Sb, V, c. iii–4.   [2] Sb, V, c. iii–5.   [3] Cf. Sb, V, c. xvii–1.

IV

REASON, NOT LOVE

ALL things are nothing, the world is vanity, life is short: I began to be afraid that if I died I should go to hell, and although I was not yet prepared to become a nun, I saw that it was the best and safest state of life: and so gradually I determined to force myself to enter religion.' [1]

Teresa here pronounces for the first time the word she was to repeat most frequently, the key-word of her spiritual life as it was of her life of action: *determinación*, determination, decision. 'I decided . . .' 'I am deciding . . .' 'It is tremendously important to begin with great determination . . .' 'She who begins with determination . . . has already travelled a great part of the way . . .,'[2] '. . . almost nothing, the smallest of decisions . . .'

When she came back from Castellanos de la Cañada and Hortigosa she was eighteen. At an age when those who are enthusiastic and gifted want to have everything, to find an outlet for all their powers, and when they allow the wild branches to grow side by side in their soul with those that bear fruit, she took the pruning shears and *determined* to cut down those which were weakening the tree and which might prove harmful to the development of perfect fruit.

She had already gradually brought under review the workings of the mind, of her passions, that of the influences to which she was subjected and the movement of the will, all-powerful when we *determine* to rule our conduct, and even tendencies which seem uncontrollable, by it. The astonishing change which had taken place in her since her arrival at Our Lady of Grace was the result of a discipline first imposed from without and then understood and accepted: she had tried out the effects of discipline on herself. She knew for the future that feelings, desires, wishes, attitudes, that which can form our character and yet is nothing but a collection of tendencies which practice and habit can overcome or develop, are under the control of the will. God created man free to choose perfection. 'This act of the will (*determinación*) is what he wants.' [3] He wants nothing more than our willed choice

[1] Sb, V, c. iii–5.   [2] Sb, V, c. xi–13.   [3] Sb, V, c. xi–5.

(determinación): then he does the rest himself.' ¹ 'The Lord helps
those who are determined to serve him for his glory.' ²

In the sphere of action it could be said of her: 'She thought out
thoroughly what she had to do and gave the matter consideration;
and after she had made up her mind about it she displayed great firmness and constancy in the execution and fulfilment of her design.' ³
Even when speaking of the highest spirituality she declares: 'All is
already as good as done when a soul *determines* to practise mental
prayer.' In a short chapter of the *Autobiography* the word *determinación*
occurs ten times and is associated with the idea of liberty: 'It is very
important to begin with this liberty and this determination. . . .'
'Those who have this determination have nothing to fear. . . .' 'She
must be determined not to allow Christ to fall with the Cross even
though this dryness should last all her life.' ⁴

In 1533 she had not yet found love, but she knew she would not
find it in the world; she was *determined* to go in pursuit of it, like the
youths of Ávila who were far from possessing the gold they hoped to
win, when they took ship for overseas.

The decision to force herself was taken but the interior struggle
went on all the same: the end of the journey was decided but the
horses were restive and reared up in protest. Teresa argued with
herself thus:—

> *For*: The efforts and sufferings which life in the convent would
> demand of me would not be worse than purgatory, whereas I had
> truly deserved hell; to live the years I had to live as if in purgatory
> was only a small thing, since afterwards I should go straight to
> heaven as I wished.⁵
>
> *Against*: The devil whispered to me that accustomed to comfort
> as I was, I could not stand the restrictions of life in a religious Order.⁶
>
> *For*: Against this I put forward the sufferings of Christ: it was a
> small thing to bear a few painful things for him; he would help me
> to bear them.⁷
>
> *For and against*: I was much tempted during that time. . . . It was
> servile fear far more than love which urged me to embrace this
> state.⁸

Temptation was often disguised under the appearance of good.
Her father and brothers were glad to welcome her back. She ran the
house competently, for her it was a labour of love and they all wondered

¹ Sb, F, c. xxviii–19.   ² SEC, R, iv, p. 28.
³ FR.   ⁴ Sb, V, c. x–6. Idem, 15–12–10.
⁵ Sb, V, c. iii–6.   ⁶ Idem.   ⁷ Idem.   ⁸ Idem.

how they had been able to live two years without her. Her talent for organization, her extreme love of order and cleanliness, her intuitive knowledge of character, her need of affection—at that time her need of being loved was greater than her need to love—made of her a woman as attractive as she was accomplished: while she put practical things first, she also gave her attention to what gave people pleasure. Don Alonso had never been so full of joy nor his children better understood or looked after. They crowded around their big sister, so eager for her company that she sometimes had a scruple over it: was not her duty to act as a mother to the two youngest, Agustín whose wildness made her anxious, and the baby Juanilla? As for the others, Jerónimo at eleven was a dare-devil, Pedro, who was twelve, complained of being ragged, Antonio was all submission, Lorenzo at fourteen was already attentive to girls and pious in church; Rodrigo, the eldest of all, busied himself with his love affairs and made his preparations for departure overseas. Teresa was the link that held them to each other and to the old home.

Once more she felt very close to her father, although she did not tell him of the pain it caused her to do violence to herself until she had definitely and irrevocably chosen religious life as her state: she would struggle and suffer alone, now as always. Her worst sufferings she never remembered confiding to anyone; she said one day: 'In that, I am not a woman: I have a hard heart.' [1] Household cares now left her little time for reading, but she was by no means unhappy on this account; she had now come to distrust the tales of chivalry and preferred the *Letters* of St. Jerome. She did not read Erasmus, who in the eyes of such a sober-minded and orthodox person as Don Alonso was a stirrer up of muddy waters, but she could not avoid hearing him spoken about. Spain was then divided into Erasmites and anti-Erasmites, to the extent that the students in Salamanca and Alcalá fought for or against him at the sword's point. Erasmus attacked the vices and abuses of the clergy; all those who allowed no criticism of the Church's representatives, even in the name of the Gospel, rose up so violently against him that his loyal partisan, Manrique, had to take up his defence at the Junta of Valladolid in 1527. The thought and writings of this cosmopolitan—for Rotterdam, Paris, Oxford, Cambridge, Louvain, Basel, Bologna, Padua, Florence, Turin, Venice, Rome were then the entire intellectual world—combined to restore to Spain the traditional sense of austerity which she seemed to have lost in the first twenty years of the reign of Charles V owing to the influence of the

[1] SEC, R, iii, p. 18.

emperor's Burgundian entourage. Erasmus's *Enchiridion*, the manual of
the Christian knight, seemed to have been written expressly for devout
caballeros. It set out to 'lead to salvation a man destined to live in the
world. . . . The end of all our works, prayers and devotions must be
Jesus Christ alone.'

A wave of mysticism was passing over Spain. To such an extent
that the *Alumbrados*, whose name at first had no unsatisfactory associations, went much too far for the liking of the orthodox in the way they
handled Scripture; they depended on illumination alone for their
interpretation and thus fell under the ban of the Inquisition: the
Church sifted to the bottom everything which smacked of Lutheranism
however remotely. If prayer alone was sufficient for salvation, what
became of the Church's claim to guide and control the faithful? The
air of this passion for liberty that was abroad seemed to have something
of schism about it.

Teresa was completely untouched by such seductive heresies: she
longed for the paradise she had glimpsed in childhood, that of the
Lives of the Saints, the most orthodox of heavens, and would have
been most uncertain of getting there by the devious paths which the
Alumbrados and *Dejados* [1] used.

She was not one for half measures; she would not have been contented like the *beatas* [2] to save her soul in the world, setting herself up
as a living reproach to the frivolous, talking nothing but piety, and
dressed with challenging austerity. Except for the reticence with which
she now met her cousins' overtures of friendliness, she was in no way
outwardly different from the girls of her age whose sole thought in
life was to find a husband.

In the spring of 1534 Charles V came to Ávila. Doña Teresa de
Ahumada took part in the celebrations. She was there when the
youthful Charles, mounted on a black horse and with the imperial
crown set on his fair hair, was met at the gates of Ávila by the Marquis
of Las Navas, who begged him to swear, before entering the city, that
he would respect its privileges, exemptions and liberties, for the knights
would set aside nothing of their rights even in the presence of their

---

[1] *Alumbrados* and *Dejados*. Both these terms, and also *iluminados*, were used
to describe an heretical sect active in Spain in the sixteenth and early seventeenth
centuries. Among other false doctrines, they held that in ecstasy one could not
sin, even venially. Seventy-six of their propositions were condemned by Cardinal
Pacheco in 1623 (Tr.).

[2] *Beata* is the term used for a woman wearing religious habit, but living in
her own house, practising prayer and works of virtue. But the term is applied
loosely in Spain to devout ladies given over to prayer and good works of all
kinds (Tr.).

sovereign. Charles V took the oath and the Marquis presented him with the keys on a silver paten. He gave them back immediately. Amid the noise of salvoes, acclamations, the cantering of one hundred and fifty of the finest flower of the youth of Ávila's nobility mounted on chestnut steeds, Charles entered Ávila, the city that was always loyal but never in servitude. And Teresa held her proud head high under her curls, as she would do later when she had to hold her own against the great and mighty of this world.

The reception was enthusiastic, but by the royal wish no extraordinary expense was incurred: austerity in spending was the fashion.

The heroic deeds of Ávila's past were recalled and Charles declared: 'This city is the model which all other cities of our realms must imitate,' and Teresa's love of mighty deeds, *hazañas*, which was now moving to the spiritual sphere, grew more ardent in her generous soul: [1] to force herself to follow the only master worthy of her ambitions, self-renunciation, the snapping of the threads of sensible attachment to passing things and to those she loved—that was, she judged, a *hazaña* worthy of the City of the Knights and Liegemen.

She began stern struggles against herself and her health suffered; her fever came back and her frequent fainting attacks frightened her father and her numerous brothers. Rodrigo, although there was so much affection between them, no longer understood her: both the Cepeda and the Ahumada came from fighting stock, they served God by dispatching the greatest possible number of his enemies and Rodrigo was preparing to follow their example in setting out for foreign conquests. The house in which Teresa was fighting her interior battle single-handed re-echoed with Rodrigo's projects. His outfit and equipment cost Don Alonso many ducats and Teresa a great deal of work. But Pedro de Mendoza's expedition to which he was to be attached was the most splendid that ever set sail. Juan Osorio, the master of the camp, was from Ávila and thirty-two noble families of Spain gave him their eldest sons for the war on the Rio de la Plata, whose name of Silver River was given to it because men made their fortunes there. The hopes of the future *conquistador* were so confident that he renounced his inheritance in favour of Teresa, so that a large dowry should help her to make a good match.

For her his departure was one more confirmation of the bitterness of human joys and even of human tenderness, but the irrevocable step was difficult to take; she was resolved, but she must now put her resolution into practice. She often went to seek fresh courage from

[1] Cf. Sb, C, c. vi-4.

María de Briceño or from the Dominicans at the monastery of St
Thomas, but her most frequent objective in her walks was the Incarnation, the convent of Carmelites where Juana Suárez seemed to have
found happiness. Such visits passed unnoticed by Don Alonso: no
well-born girl went out except to Mass and Vespers, to hear a sermon
or for some other devotional purpose. The less devout met their lovers
in church. And so when Teresa went from one end of Ávila to the
other, with her velvet basquine [1] fastened round her waist, swinging
her wide skirt of orange taffetas with its crossbands of black velvet on
which everyone complimented her, and covered in jewels, dignified
but laughing, who would have thought she had made up her mind to
enter a convent?

Finally she grew weary of her own hesitations and *determined* to
bring matters to a head: she would inform her father of her decision
to be a religious: 'This for me was tantamount to taking the habit, for
I so honoured my word that I knew I should not draw back for anything on earth once I had spoken to him.' [2] Thus the *pundonor*, the
point of honour, that form of pride which she, in common with all
Spain, had learnt the meaning of in the tales of chivalry, gave Teresa
de Ahumada the strength which she had not yet found in the love
of God.

The declaration was dramatic: nothing could have led Don Alonso
to foresee that a daughter of whom his only complaint was her excessive love for the world and its pleasures might want to leave him to be
a nun. 'My father lóved me so much that I could not obtain his consent; the most he would concede was that I could do as I wished after
his death.' [3]

She called in friends and relatives to intervene, but no one, not
even Don Pedro de Cepeda, could make Don Alonso give way. He had
been willing enough to enter into a contract to give bushels of wheat to
the poor every year but he persisted in refusing God the daughter he
loved so much; his spirituality did not go as far as complete renuncia-
tion, his generosity only sacrificed what he did not need. Would
Teresa be able to wait and to maintain her inflexible resolve? She
admitted, but to no one but herself, 'I am afraid of myself, of my own
weakness.' [1]

For the world she wanted to flee from still attracted her strongly
at times; she still sought to please people, she still caught herself trusting to the warmth of someone's look and telling herself all of a sudden

---

[1] A sort of outer petticoat—Tr. [2] Sb, V, c. iii–7.
[3] Idem. [4] Idem.

that perhaps that particular person would understand loving 'for ever.' But what about heaven? And hell? To turn to God she sometimes had to wrench her attention away from other things as if she were twisting it with her hand. She knew now, after her experience at Our Lady of Grace, that once at the convent she would have no regrets; protected from 'temptations' she would carry out methodically and to the letter, with all the patience the task demanded, the slow work of transformation. Once there, nothing would come to turn her mind away from God. She was simply longing to begin and exaggerated the risks she was running. Her disposition was not one that could brook delay: 'When I want something, I want it for all I'm worth.' [1]

After Rodrigo had gone, she chose the gentlest of her brothers, Antonio, who was only fifteen, as her confidant. She was always talking to him about what she did not yet experience except at intervals, and the more she was tempted by the illusory things of earth, the more ardently and persuasively did she speak to him of eternal life: it was really to herself she was speaking and herself she was persuading. She read St Jerome to him aloud, especially the terrible *Letter to Heliodorus*.

Your widowed sister will come and hold out her arms to you, the servants will come and the nurse who reared you and her husband who are like a second father and mother to you, and barring your route they will say to you amid their tears: 'Master, to whom are you entrusting our old age? Who will help us to die? Who will bury us?' More than this, your mother, aged and venerable, her forehead worn by wrinkles, her breasts shrunken and drooping, she too barring your way, will give vent to her grief, going over your past life from the day she brought you into the world until now. . . .

Don Alonso, moreover, had recalled Teresa's childhood; he departure, too, would cause both relatives and servants grief. She read on: 'On you alone depends this house now about to totter. . . .' It was true that her father's house depended entirely on her. . . . She turned the page: 'What are you doing beneath your father's roof, weak and cowardly soldier? Even if your mother with dishevelled hair and torn garments, even if your father himself lies across the threshold, step over your father's body. . . . Here filial piety shows itself only by having no pity.'

Antonio was caught up in his sister's fervour and just as *la niña* had persuaded Rodrigo to set out with her in search of martyrdom, so now she persuaded this younger brother of hers to leave their father's house at the same time as she did and to enter with the

[1] SEC, R, iii, p. 18.

Dominicans while she went to join her friend Juana Suárez at the Convent of the Incarnation.

This convent had originally been a community of fourteen *beatas*, fourteen as an act of homage to 'Jesus Christ, our sovereign Good, and his most holy Mother, in the company of the Twelve Apostles.' In short, a group of pious Carmelite women tertiaries, joined together to practise prayer in their own chapel: this particular chapel was a former synagogue which the bishop had set aside for their use. They only took simple vows, but in 1512 their prioress, Doña Beatriz de Higuera, induced them to strive to reach a higher degree of perfection by adopting monastic life and the Rule of the Order of Our Lady of Mount Carmel; this Rule, which was less austere than the primitive one handed down by the prophet Elias and the Fathers of the Desert, was known as the 'Mitigated' rule.

Doña Beatriz began by instituting a lawsuit against her father to obtain possession of her property, and she erected a vast building, outside the walls of Ávila, on the site of a former Jewish cemetery. It was considered a poor place when compared with the carved granite of the palaces of the nobility, but the convent had plenty of fresh air, built as it was in rural style, with arched cloisters opening on to a green patio; the cells were small but well arranged, and some of them formed a small apartment—two rooms and a kitchen with a stove in it. There was a large central staircase and the whole building got the full benefit of the sun. There was a fine view over the city ramparts and a wide background of hills and an abundance of water enabled them to have an extensive orchard. The man-made materials might be poor, but the monastery was rich in natural beauty, the handiwork of the Creator. Teresa liked this contrast and she saw a sign from heaven in the fact that the new convent was inaugurated on the very day of her baptism.

One morning towards the very end of October 1536, when as yet the tops of the trees in the garden were scarcely visible in the grey light of dawn, she came out of her room without allowing herself to give so much as one backward glance, walking on tiptoe and holding her breath as she passed the rooms where her father, her brothers and her young sister Juana were still sleeping. Antonio helped her to move the locks of the heavy entrance door silently, to pull it open and then hold it so that it should shut to noiselessly on all those they were leaving. Teresa recalled her flight with Rodrigo thirteen years before: then she had felt no grief, the fact that she had parents had only been a 'major obstacle' for her and the thought of their grief did not make her suffer. Was she more affectionate now? Or weaker? Had her struggles with herself, the first effects of the awakening of the love of Christ in her soul, softened her hard heart?

On the threshold she hesitated, but Antonio was there, unfaltering because of his very unconsciousness of what was involved. Teresa's code of honour did not allow her to show weakness before one so young. And just as on a former occasion, in the uncertain light of dawn, two thin silhouettes could be distinguished against the grey façade and were soon lost in the crowd of merchants, servants, worshippers who were crossing the Plaza Santo Domingo to go to market or to church. But this time, it was for ever, Teresa knew it by the anguish which she felt.

I do not believe that I shall suffer more when I come to die than when I left my father's house: it seemed to me that each one of my bones was being torn apart from the others: and as I did not feel anything of that love of God which makes one forget the love of father and relatives, I had to make so great an effort to do it, that if Our Lord had not helped me, my reason would not have sufficed to make me go forward. He gave me courage against myself.[1]

It was in this way that Doña Teresa de Ahumada y Cepeda entered into a bond with her heavenly Bridegroom, but guided by reason, not by love.

[1] Sb, V, c. iv–1.

V

LOVE AND GLORY

TERESA DE AHUMADA was determined to turn her marriage of convenience into a love match. If she had foreseen, as she made her way towards the convent in the coldness of the October dawn, that for twenty years she would be torn between the world and God, she still would not have hesitated in the slightest: she had made Ávila's motto her own, *Antes quebrar que doblar*, to break oneself rather than to yield, to die rather than give up.

She was perfectly well aware that what she would chiefly have to fight was herself. It seemed to her that she was the less fitted for sanctity because she had all the gifts that made for worldly success, and she regarded herself as riddled with faults and inconsistencies: she was proud, but frivolous: domineering, but easily influenced; she talks of herself as being 'terribly given to subterfuge' [1] and yet mentions her horror of lies, or again of her liking to please people which does not, however, bridle a quick temper liable to break out into 'terrible' rages. Then there was the point of honour, this 'wicked self-esteem,' self-esteem regarded from entirely the wrong point of view, which she calls a chain on which no file can make an impression. [2]

Teresa did become a saint by sheer force of willing it and with the grace of God. It is this process of achieving sanctity, the slow and costly transformation, that make her life an unparalleled example for us.

When she had passed the ramparts and crossed the gully which divides the Incarnation from the town, she felt there was now a whole abyss between her and the past. In saying goodbye to Antonio outside the convent, she detached herself from her earthly family; when the enclosure door opened with much screeching of locks and bolts and closed behind her again, convinced now that all things were nothing, she resolutely accepted the fact that God was everything.

Juana Suárez was waiting for her, in the midst of a crowd of young nuns who forthwith proceeded to treat the newcomer both with sisterly love and curiosity. Teresa unbent, smiled and immediately won all hearts. Would it not be easy to tread the path to heaven with companions like these? They had not lost their spontaneity through keep-

[1] Sb, V, c. xxxi–23. [2] Idem, 20.

ing their Rule. Their Constitutions were severe in principle but in practice very accommodating. She had put on her plainest dress but the nuns thought the material lovely. In her eagerness to be at once on the same footing as the others, she begged the prioress, 'the most Reverend and Magnificent Señora Doña Francisca del Águila,' to whom she was related, to give her the Carmelite habit at once. But Doña Francisca had already summoned Don Alonso: nothing would be done without his authorization.

The poor man was at his wits' end: the Dominicans had likewise come to tell him of Antonio's decision to become a Friar Preacher. It meant a hard and bitter struggle between God's service and a father's love. Strongly suspecting that once more it was *la niña* who was responsible for everything, and that if he got her back the boy would follow, he rushed to the Incarnation trembling at the thought that he was really confronting not only his daughter, but God.

With the very first words she spoke in her eager voice, Teresa put his responsibilities so clearly before him that, good Christian as he was, he did not dare to resort either to entreaties or authority, although on his way to the convent he had rehearsed in turn both phrases of tenderness and orders which should brook no refusal. He knew now that even if she were to give way, he could not in the future enjoy the company of the daughter he loved so much without remorse. So he gave way, and all arrangements were made for the dowry and the clothing.

On 31st October 1536, he gave an undertaking before a notary to make over to the convent of the Incarnation every year, twenty-five measures of grain, one half being wheat and one half barley, or, in their default, two hundred gold ducats. Teresa renounced all claims on the family inheritance and made over Rodrigo's eventual legacy to her sister Juana.

Her father also gave the novice a bed, blankets and quilts, six linen sheets, six pillows, two mattresses, two cushions, a carpet, as well as the clothing she would need during the noviciate and after profession: 'the habits, one of fine black cloth and the other of thicker material; three underskirts, one of red wool, another white and the third of fine serge; a sheepskin cloak, her veils, undergarments and shoes; and finally the books which it is customary for nuns to be given.'

Teresa was to take the habit on 2nd November. On the night before, her night of vigil, she did not sleep: all the bells both far and near which had pealed when she was born now tolled to remind her that to-morrow was All Souls' Day. A solemn knell, a discordant clash

of bronze which brought no peace to the soul but rather shook it to
the depths of its self-satisfaction, forcing it to contemplate the effects of
God's anger. Teresa wept; not for the world, but for her sins; not for
what she was leaving behind her, but for what she could not escape
without making expiation: the fear of purgatory and that of hell. A
whole lifetime spent in penance seemed too short. She deserved
damnation. 'For ever and ever, Rodrigo. . . ?' 'Teresa, for ever and
ever. . . '

The idea she formed of purgatory still resembled the pictures of
which she was so much afraid as a child, pictures which she remembered as patches of vivid red at the back of some dark church, in which
men and women thrust bare arms upwards out of a sea of flame: Our
Lady, the angels leaned down towards them and saved a few. How
many nights had she not aroused the whole house by her screaming as
she awoke from a nightmare in which she had dreamt she was in hell!
When she was quite tiny, she made sacrifices, gave alms, said the
rosary for the *ánimas*, the souls in purgatory. And on her night of vigil
when the bells seemed to be tolling 'for ever' she only found peace in
sacrifice, begging Our Lady of Mount Carmel to accept her as a
hostage that the souls who were most forsaken might be taken out of
the abyss. This practical sympathy for the souls in purgatory was to
remain with her all her life.

When the time for the ceremony came, instead of being pale from
insomnia, the postulant's face was shining with the joy of the first of
her 'heroic acts.' [1]

Teresa kept her name as a novice and thus was still Doña Teresa
de Ahumada to her sisters in religion, but her gift of adaptation made
her immediately conform to nunnish ways: after a few days no one
would have recognized in the young nun who walked with measured
tread and downcast eyes, her hands under her scapular, the girl whose
yellow dress and careless demeanour had caused so much talk. She
seemed to find a kind of pleasure in exercising control over the
expression of her face, and she who never spoke without using 'many
words' [2] to express herself, now gave the briefest replies and forced
herself to silence. Perhaps she realized now to what an extent comport-
ment influences one's interior dispositions. Or was it a sign of the
deep change wrought in her by the taking of the habit? She admitted
that from the very beginning she felt so much joy at having chosen
the religious state, that it lasted all her life through. 'God changed my
soul's aridity into immense tenderness. Everything to do with the

[1] SEC, vol. II, p. 244.   [2] Sb, V, xiii–17.

Order was a delight to me; true, I was sometimes busy sweeping at times when I should formerly have been giving myself up to pleasure and finery, but when I realized every now and then that for the future I was free of all that, fresh joy came over me, so intense that I was astonished and could not understand where it came from.' [1]

She did not realize that it was partly the relief and comfort of having carried out a decision and so of making the step irrevocable; though only twenty the girl had brought so much penetration to her understanding of the world, both as regards people and things, that it was not surprising that she now rejoiced to be free of it all.

In her first contact with religious life, then, Teresa realized the efficaciousness of what she calls 'the heroic act': 'When I remember all that, nothing I have to face seems so difficult as to make me hesitate to undertake it. Experience has shown me that if in the beginning I force myself to the determination to carry out, for God's sake, something that seems to me terribly hard, the sweetness of the reward will be in proportion to the greatness of my dread of it.' [2]

More fervent now and already experiencing some small beginnings of the fire of divine love, she began to exact more from herself. For a few weeks she perhaps thought she had done everything in leaving the world and her family, and for the future had no more battles to wage; then she discovered that the peace she was enjoying was that of a woman who settles down peacefully in her bed after having bolted her doors against robbers, but leaves the robbers in the house all the time: 'There are no worse robbers than those we carry within ourselves.' [3] Everything was effort and humiliation to her:

I knew few prayers, and nothing about what had to be done in choir, I was so careless and taken up with vanity; other novices could have shown me what to do, but I committed the fault of not asking them so that they shouldn't see how little I knew. My singing was bad. . . . Through self-esteem I was troubled about this and so I did even less well than I could have done. . . . Finally I forced myself to say so when I didn't know how something went. This cost me a good deal at the beginning but afterwards I found pleasure in it. [4]

It was bitter pleasure to a proud nature like hers. She resented annoyances, rebelled when accused without sufficient reason, and in spite of her decision to accept everything and love everything in religious life she experienced discouragement, particularly when she

[1] Sb, V, c. iv–2.   [2] Idem.
[3] Sb, C, c. x–1.   [4] Sb V, c. xxxi–23.

compared herself to some nuns at the Incarnation who were leading lives of penance all the more admirable because they were rare. There was one who rolled herself in nettles like St Benedict, fasted all the year round and did not speak except to God; another was so holy that she worked a miracle while still alive: the candles she lighted on Our Lady's altar burned without being consumed; and there was Doña Teresa de Quezada who, despite her illustrious birth, refused to have a cell to herself and slept in the common dormitory of those who could not afford more.

Teresa had chosen a relative poverty; she liked the two comfortable and well-arranged rooms assigned to her; she gave herself the discipline, using nettles, but did not seem to feel the inequality which in this overcrowded monastery created two standards, one for nuns who were wealthy and another for those who were poor. The perfection of some pricked her self-esteem, but the poverty of the majority seemed to escape her notice. Her distractions in choir and her aridity grieved her, and she was exasperated at not understanding good nuns who talked to each other in her presence of the delights of prayer. Her soul was all disorder and confusion.

Who, then, was it who gave her to understand that there is no progress in the spiritual life so long as we are not loving our neighbour more than ourselves? When they suddenly found her weeping for her sins they made the mistake of supposing that her tears were for the world she had left. This vexed her. Was she thinking only of herself then? She soon put an end to self-centredness.

There was one nun suffering from a disease so loathsome that it was impossible to look after her without shuddering with horror; to do violence to heaven Teresa constituted herself her nurse and when she had to dress the ulcerous stomach which discharged pus, blood and excrement at the same time, her repugnance was changed to compassion. The stench was so appalling that it made her feel sick and she had to rush away quickly, to vomit. But she would come back again, smiling.

The long hours of attendance upon this sick nun, especially at night, coupled with penances so severe that the prioress had to forbid them, undermined what little health she had left; at Office, in the chapel where rain, wind and snow came in through the roof tiles which were not properly laid, she shivered with cold. In the grip of fever and in considerable pain, she asked God for the grace to bear her sufferings for his sake and by them to obtain the mastery over her body which the more fragile it was the more it seemed to require. She repeated to herself again and again: 'We come here to die for Christ and not to coddle ourselves for Christ.' [1] To go on living now seemed to her so hard that she found herself repeating over and over again the argument of her childhood: martyrdom is certainly the cheapest way of winning heaven. Wouldn't it be better to die of some fatal and painful disease as quickly as possible? After her profession, would Our Lord help her even more?

The ceremony took place a year and a day after her clothing, on 3rd November 1537. During the year she had measured the extent of the effort she still had to make. Her face was now just as pale as it had been radiant with colour when she was clothed.

In the chapel, amid the blaze of the candles offered by Don Alonso, the *caballeros* and their lovely ladies, magnificently attired, chattered busily as they were wont to do at weddings, or wept as at a funeral, according to their mood; the present ceremony was, indeed, both wedding and funeral.

Teresa moved forward between two rows of nuns singing the *Veni Creator Spiritus*. She was dressed in the habit only. This was fastened on the chest with a loose knot in order to be able to take the discipline more easily. She carried, neatly folded, her scapular, veil, girdle and a paper on which the *Pater noster* was written, symbol of a life which was henceforward to be vowed to prayer.

She prostrated before the grille, now open on to the sanctuary, touching the ground with her forehead.

The prioress was heard to put the traditional questions:

'What do you ask?'

'I ask God's mercy and the company of my sisters in perpetual enclosure.'

She pronounced her vows in a firm voice after she had listened to the reading of the Constitutions with their severe regulations. And, conscious of her weakness, it was with her whole heart that she identified herself with the prayer: 'May the Lord our God who gives us the desire grant us also to carry it out, *per Christum Dominum nostrum.*

The nuns answered: 'Amen.' [2]

Two sisters conducted her to the parlour. Behind the grille she saw her friends and relatives as in a dream. She had no regrets and was even exultant with a joy shot through with pain. Years afterwards, one day when she was searching for a term of comparison by which to describe a particular suffering, she said: '. . . I do not think that anything in my life hurt so much, not even my profession day. . . .'

[1] Sb, C, c. x–5.   [2] Cited SEC, vol. IX, pp. 494–495.

There were festivities at the convent, a collation and dinner offered by Don Alonso who also gave each religious a fine linen coif. There was singing and dancing to the accompaniment of flute and tambourine. Doña Teresa de Ahumada displayed all her charm and high spirits. She who took so much pleasure in pleasing others charmed those present by her gaiety just as she touched them by her devotion. They knew nothing of her interior struggles. People were amazed at her many gifts.

'Doña Teresa de Ahumada is like silk of a golden colour which matches every other shade, for to win us all she suits herself to the character of each. . . .' [1]

All of a sudden there was quite a sensation: an old nun remembered that a *zahorí*, a diviner seeking for gold, who had come to the convent many years ago, had said that one day the Incarnation would have a Teresa who would be a saint. At that time there was no saint of the name and anyone called Teresa kept her feastday on the feast of St. Dorothy.

The newly professed nun hid her feelings under laughter, but she exclaimed:

'God grant it may be I!'

'God grant it may be *I*!' echoed Doña Teresa de Quezada.[2]

From the moment of taking the veil, she redoubled the demands she made on herself, and tightened the grip on her will. When she was tempted to give way a little to softness, telling herself: 'I am no angel ... I am no saint,' [3] she upbraided herself; she told herself that by continuing to struggle she would doubtless become so. God helps the brave. A moment later she accused herself of vanity.

The fight against vainglory was such hard work for her that, over-excited by the excessive and spectacular penances of certain of her companions, she forgot her sense of proportion and horror of all exaggeration and, trying to crush even ordinary common-sense, she one day came into the refectory walking on all fours, a mule's pack-saddle loaded with stones on her back, dragged along like a beast by a sister who was pulling at the halter which Teresa had put round her neck.

Extravagances of this sort ended in further fainting attacks, in 'pains at the heart' [4] so acute that all who saw her suffer were scared, and in other sufferings too. She frightened the other nuns even more by her refusal of the care that was absolutely necessary than she did

[1] Cited SST, vol. I, p. 296.   [2] FR, L. I, c. vi.
[3] Cf. Sb. C, c. xvi-12.   [4] Sb, V, c. iv-5.

by her pallor. Scarcely able to walk, she turned up again in choir, pale and tottering. To those who implored her to take care of herself she said:

'What does dying matter? If we don't make up our minds to swallow both ill-health and death at one draught, we shall never do anything. It is more important to take this decision than we realize. In this way we shall gradually conquer this body of ours.' [1]

She endured so much pain that the nuns whispered: 'God must be dwelling in her. . . .'

When Don Alonso came to see her, she dragged herself painfully to the grille, except on the occasions when she had to be carried there. She did not complain, but her father was increasingly dismayed by the deathly pallor of her face in which the eyes, formerly only slightly protruding, now seemed to be starting out of their sockets. He sent round to the Incarnation the best doctors in Ávila and the neighbouring towns. Matters however grew worse: increasingly frequent and prolonged fainting fits were often responsible for a rumour of consternation in the convent:

'Doña Teresa de Ahumada is dead!'

Medical skill failed. The nuns' prayers seemed of no effect. Was Christ listening only to those of the patient, who begged him to allow her to share his sufferings and agony?

In the last resort Don Alonso decided to take Teresa away to Becedas, a small village where a woman healer famous throughout Castile was accomplishing wonderful cures. In the Carmelite Rule of Mitigated observance, enclosure was not of strict obligation; Teresa was therefore allowed to leave the Incarnation, accompanied by Juana Suárez, in search of the cure she did not want.

[1] Sb, C, c. xi–45.

VI

NOT QUITE SO MUCH! [1]

THE doctors could not understand the illness of Don Alonso's daughter at all. They hastened to agree with his own explanation of the matter: the different kind of life and different food were at the root of her complex symptoms; their verdict, given in their pedantic jargon, was that if she returned to the family circle where she would have a more abundant and more discriminating diet, it would not take long for this fine young woman of barely twenty-three to regain her health. They saw, of course, no more than she was willing to let them see—a suffering body; the real key to the problem she hid from them. What this was she tells us later when she writes: 'I spent my first year at the Incarnation in very bad health, *although I don't think I offended God much at that time.*'[2] Thus she attributed her illness to a non-physical cause and she was right. She regarded illness as a trial, or else a punishment, and whereas she had not deserved the punishment, she had begged God to give her trials. Because she envied the endurance of the nun whose nauseating wounds she tended, she besought His Majesty to teach *her* patience, too, and to this end to send her 'whatever illness might be necessary.' Soon she was in such a condition that 'although my disease was not the same as hers, I think what I suffered for three whole years was no less painful and hard to bear.'[3]

The violent constraint which Teresa de Ahumada put upon herself to enter the convent had brought on the first crisis; now that she actually was at the Incarnation, all she could see in herself were failures and weakness; certain of her fellow-nuns had attained to the prayer of contemplation—she tried to imitate them and did not even succeed in meditating without distractions; her mind was unable to concentrate on one subject for any length of time; she forced herself, at the cost of extreme nervous tension and although she felt that her 'persistence was injuring her health.'[4] Her fierce anger against herself, her self-imposed penances, her stern persistence in self-conquest, the fits of depression during which 'quite small things caused her intense

[1] Sb, CAD, c. vi-2.   [2] Sb, V, c. iv-5.
[3] Sb, V, c. v-2.   [4] Sb, V, c. iv-8.

suffering,'[1] indiscreet fasting and vigils and finally her earnest prayer for expiatory suffering, precipitated the second crisis: those who really want to suffer seldom fail to get their wish. Teresa was relentless in wearing down her rebellious body, which was too earthly for her soul's flight and brought her spirit to earth with it.

Her tormented mind should have been treated in the same way as we treat hypochondriacs to-day when merely by brooding over their nervous fears they produce in themselves the symptoms of every possible disease. Instead, she was given injections, poultices, was bled, given pills which had to be taken in ones, threes, fives or some other odd number—this gave her devotion because the number of pills reminded her of the seven Gifts of the Holy Ghost or the Five Wounds of Jesus—she was rubbed with scorpion oil, considered to have soothing and stimulating properties and to be good for opening the pores of the skin—or with brick oil refined again and again after a whole process of boiling and grinding of specially chosen bricks, which must be very old and very red in colour. This was supposed to cure diseases of the nerves and joints or those of the bladder and kidneys if the complaint was due to cold. All these were remedies liable to kill a person in good health. Dismayed at the results obtained by such methods, Don Alonso put all his hopes on the *curandera*, the medicine-woman at Becedas. She used simples, a treatment doubtless less brutal than official medical practice.

As the treatment was not to be begun before the spring, it was decided that Teresa and her companion should spend the intervening month of April at Castellanos de la Cañada, with María: Becedas was quite near. The handsome litter which had formerly served frail Doña Beatriz for her journeys was done up for Teresa's use: it had good webbing supports and cost a thousand maravedis at a time when the Cepeda y Ahumada denied themselves nothing. Don Alonso, still in mourning for his wife, as he always would be, and so in black from head to foot and riding a horse with black saddle and breast-strap, accompanied Teresa, as did Juana, her Carmelite friend, who travelled on mule-back, and two or three servants.

The party made a halt at Hortigosa, at Don Pedro de Cepeda's 'palace.' The worthy man was deeply moved at seeing once more the niece whom he regarded as in some degree his spiritual daughter. He had her brought into the library until the meal should be ready. He was solicitous for her comfort and strove not to show the grief he felt at seeing her emaciated condition. Behind the window-panes the

---

[1] Sb, V, c. v–i.

snow was falling steadily. Warming those lovely hands of hers, almost worn to a shadow now, at the *brasero*, Teresa talked with her uncle and told him the secrets of her interior life, a matter on which she had been reluctant to speak to anyone: was it not he who had opened heaven for her by showing her 'good books' and St. Jerome? What a long way she had travelled since those years!

She told him frankly of her struggles, her hopes, her discouragement, the lukewarmness into which she habitually fell back after transports of love and devotion.

He shook his head.

'It is essential to pray, and to pray much.'

'I do pray.'

'How do you pray?'

She explained that she recited her prayers aloud: some sort of vocal prayer was her only means of keeping her attention fixed. And even then she found herself giving way to distractions during her many *Pater nosters*. But her heart was no longer dry and unresponsive before the crucifix: God had given her 'the gift of tears.'

'The only thing that counts is prayer, by which I mean mental prayer, recollection.'

Mental prayer! Her attempts at it ended in failure. She did not even know how to practise recollection.

Don Pedro went over to the shelves and took down a book which he placed in Teresa's lap. She read: *Tercera parte del libro llamado Abecedario espiritual. Compuesto por el Padre Fray Francisco de Osuna.*[1]

'There's a treatise on recollection for you: the *Third Spiritual Alphabet.*'

Teresa opened the book at random.

. . . Vocal prayer, as thou hast seen, is a petition we make to God to ask him for what is necessary for us.

. . . The second form of prayer, that is without pronouncing the words with the lips, leaves us free so that our heart alone speaks to Our Lord. . . .

. . . The third, which may be termed mental or spiritual, is that in which the highest point of the soul, sustained by love, soars upward to God in the purest and most loving way possible on the wings of desire. . . .[2]

---

[1] Part III of the book known as the *Spiritual Alphabet*, written by Father Francisco de Osuna. [An English translation of this work, now unfortunately out of print, was published by Burns Oates in 1931—Tr.]

[2] O, pp. 464–7.

That was what she wanted! Why had she not come across this expert in prayer before! And what she liked was that he supported his definition by concrete examples: 'In short, the first is a letter we send our friend. In the second way we send him a person whom we love as our ambassador. By the third method we go ourselves. . . . Or, if you prefer, in the first we kiss his feet, in the second we kiss his hands. In the third we give him a kiss on the lips.'

Recollection consisted primarily in refusing admittance to one's heart to all created things; the writer epitomized his thought in one line:

> *Desembaraza el corazón y vacía todo lo criado.*

'Unburden your heart by emptying it of everything created,' and, he added: 'From everything, extract love.' Love everything, but in God and for God.

Teresa scarcely listened to what Don Pedro was telling her about the author, who had taken part in the battle of Tripoli, became a Franciscan friar and published the *Third Spiritual Alphabet*, his first work, in Toledo in 1527. She dipped into the volume, browsed here and there, fascinated by what she found she could understand of its theory and also by the methodical common sense of the practical applications. One passage arrested her attention:

> Look well to the time after Matins, for that sleep is meant rather for the soul than for the body. Do not retire to bed drowsily but rather be fully wakeful in your desire for Our Lord; and like the bride, at night time, seek for God when you retire to rest. . . . Happy are those who give themselves to prayer before they slumber and who promptly return to prayer on waking. Such people, like Elias, feed, sleep, feed again and remain nestled in God's arms as children sleep on their mother's breasts after having drunk her milk, then wake again, feed once more and again fall asleep. With such glorious intervals the time of sleep can be considered more as prayer than sleep. . . . And then, even if they have slept, on waking again they know full well that their soul has slumbered in the arms of the Beloved.[1]

This was Teresa's first experience of that tenderness and intimacy so characteristic of Franciscan ways of talking about divine love. And she discovered that she had, after all, been practising mental prayer without knowing it; it was her habit to fall asleep in the presence of God, as she strove to live in his presence. Perhaps she was not as slow

[1] O, p. 471.

as she feared in climbing the uphill path? She never forgot this abandonment of the babe on his mother's breast and later often used the comparison herself.

When it was time to go, and the litter was ready and the horses saddled, she could not tear herself away from the book; with her ready pen she copied down sentences from it. Her uncle watched her with a kindly smile, but they came to fetch her. She closed the *Third Spiritual Alphabet* regretfully.

'Take it,' said Don Pedro, 'it is yours.'

It was in this way that Teresa began her initiation into recollection and mental prayer: through a book.

Don Alonso left Teresa in María's hands and returned to Ávila. In the spring the three women set out for Becedas. They stayed in a comfortably furnished house there, belonging to the Guzmán y Barrientos. In those days Becedas was a small village with winding streets; the stream which encircled it left but little room for the low houses which were huddled against the church. To the sound of the rippling of water, the rustle of the breeze through the great walnut-trees, rose the fragrant smoke from the fires kindled with vine-shoots at the hour when the garlic soup was cooking on every hearth in Castile. When night fell, the patient closed her book and prayed in the gathering darkness.

At first the treatment was not too painful; the medicine-woman kept her patient under observation and merely prescribed a few simples culled from among the 'holy remedies.' But, since her brief stay at Hortigosa, Teresa's principal preoccupation was the study and application of Osuna's teaching. Already progress in the spiritual life seemed to her a matter of laborious detail involving the utmost carefulness; it meant all the difficulty of progressive abandonment, the rebellion of her human nature, the slow awakening of a slumbering soul which little by little begins to make the necessary adjustments and then puts on the armour of light.

From this time onwards His Majesty showered graces upon her: 'The Lord began to load me with favours to such an extent that I received the grace of the prayer of quiet; sometimes I even had the prayer of union, although I did not know what either was. . . . It is true that it lasted only a very short time, I'm not sure if it was as long as an *Ave Maria*, but the effects were so tremendous that although I was barely twenty, I felt as if I had the world under my feet. . . .' [1] Union

[1] Sb, V, c. iv–7.

is the prelude to ecstasy: and Teresa, although only for brief and occasional moments, was already detaching herself from the senses, from images, from the use of the understanding and was being raised to the sphere where God alone is perceived. And she was forcing herself to live in the continual presence of Christ.

For her prayer, however, she needed a book and was afraid to try and recollect herself without its help, 'just as afraid as if I had to fight with many people.' [1] Reading stirred up her ardour for spiritual things and helped her to gather together her scattered thoughts. In this way she managed her soul 'as it were by coaxing.'

The words 'struggle,' 'combat,' 'effort,' 'trouble' recur constantly in her account of her life at this time. Not only was she ill, undergoing severe treatment and suffering acute pain, but at the same time she was fighting for the conquest of the kingdom of the Spirit.

For the *curandera* was now using remedies of a more positive kind, too positive for Teresa's fragile body and frayed nerves.

The young Carmelite let her have her way; she was indifferent to it all. Had she not the universe 'under her feet'? Not that she did not need help. Her keen desire was to find a sure guide who would help her to scale the heights whose steep summits Osuna had shown her. 'And it was there that the demon began to trouble my soul. . . .' [2]

A man. A young man. A priest. But a young priest who was living in sin. He was appointed to the parish of Becedas and had 'great qualities, he was intelligent, he had some education though not too much. . . .' [3] Teresa made him her confessor.

She is frank about it: 'This man I am speaking of grew very fond of me, for I had very little to confess. . . . This affection was not bad, but, because of its very excess it was not a good thing. He understood that I was determined not to offend God gravely for anything in the world, he assured me that it was the same with him and our conversations went on interminably.' [4]

At that time she thought that only mortal sin mattered; when she read in Osuna that it is just as essential to preserve oneself from venial faults, she did not take it in, vigilance to this extent seeming to her impossible. She was not yet aware that in love no offence is trifling.

Thus in the beginning she did not worry about the slight uneasiness she experienced in the presence of this priest—a priest who never forgot he was a man as well. As to his reactions—hitherto women had only inspired him with sinful, physical desires—in the presence of

[1] Sb, V, c. iv–9.
[2] Sb, V, c. v–3.
[3] Idem.
[4] Sb, V, c. v–4.

this girl, beautiful under her Carmelite veil and so pure that when they met he felt ashamed to be deceiving her as he was, although he had not the courage to refuse to go on seeing her, he felt new feelings arising in him. 'I was then so absorbed in God that all my conversation was about him. And as I was such a child, it made the priest ashamed to see this. . . .'[1]

She spoke of God when the priest would have liked to talk with her of themselves. Sitting with his back to the light that he might the better conceal the fact that he was scarcely listening to what she was saying, he looked into her deeply expressive eyes, shining with sincerity and with a love not of this world.

To attract this angelic being, to capture her interest, to hold her down to earth!

Accordingly one evening, the confessor told his penitent that he was living in sin. Perhaps he hoped that the sinfulness would be contagious: 'For seven years he had been in an extremely dangerous state on account of his relations with a woman in the village whom he loved, and yet all the time he had continued to say Mass. The matter was so public that he had lost both honour and reputation, but no one dared to take him to task about it. That made me terribly sad, for I was very fond of him.'[2]

Teresa did not break under the strain; her friendship became deeper. True, she was very fond of him.

What she said about his affection for her was: ' I never saw any harm in the great affection he bore me; yet it might have been purer; there were, too, occasions when we might have sinned gravely if we had not had a lively remembrance of God's presence.'[3]

How did it happen that María, who could not plead the excuse of inexperience of life, or Juana Suárez, who was older than Teresa and to whose care the prioress of the Incarnation had entrusted her, allowed such an intimacy to form between a girl and a priest whose conduct was the talk of Becedas? It clearly goes to prove that a woman's only protector is herself, and also that at that time people shut their eyes to the faults of the clergy.

Teresa thus went through this sad 'adventure' of sympathy and affection alone. When, more mature, she saw the danger of it she was indignant for a second: 'Oh the blindness of the world. . . . The madness of the world dismays me! . . . Cursed be the law that goes against the law of God!'[4]

[1] Sb, V, c. v–4.   [2] Idem.
[3] Idem, 6.   [4] Idem, 4.

But at the time she saw only the peril in which the priest who put himself into her hands stood. He had hardly gone when she called María and Juana and begged them to find out all about it, she wanted to know everything 'about the persons with whom he was living.' [1] They told her then about her confessor's mistress, describing her appearance and her ways; she even caught a glimpse of her through the window. Teresa now fathomed the depths of her friend's fall and refrained from judging him: 'The poor man was not so much to blame.' Such deep understanding and mercifulness can only come from unsullied purity.

So she continued to receive 'the poor man' with the same smile and an affection which was now more openly manifest because it was sisterly and full of compassion. Day by day he told her everything:

> The unhappy woman [Teresa does not reproach her either] had put charms in a little brass idol which she begged him to wear round the neck for love of her, and no one had succeeded in persuading him to part with it. Not that I believe in these charms. . . . As soon as I knew all that, I began to show him still more affection. My intention was good, but my conduct bad; for however great the good, one may never do anything wrong however small, to bring it about. I habitually spoke to him of God, but in fact he loved me so much that it was that which counted most with him. [2]

He loved Teresa so much and he had to watch her gradually becoming worse. The cure was turning out to be ruthless indeed. She suffered to such an extent that she sometimes cried out complaining that sharp teeth were lacerating her heart. Fears were entertained for her sanity. She no longer took food, could only swallow liquids and those with repugnance. Was the man who loved her so much going to add to her torments the grief of knowing 'that he was lost for ever'?

One evening he knelt by her, loosened a long cord from his neck and threw at her feet the little brass idol. He wept. So did she. Gently motioning him to go away, she called María who came in immediately; without turning her head, Teresa asked her to go at once and throw the amulet into the nearby stream.

From this moment Teresa watched the priest awake as it were from a heavy torpor; she listened to him as he recounted the story of his years of perdition which he now spoke of with detestation. Finally he told her he had broken off relations with his mistress and could not thank God enough for having opened his eyes. After this the two were

[1] Idem, 5.   [2] Sb, V, c. v–5, 6.

united in a friendship that was completely blameless: it was not sin that had proved contagious but white-hot chastity.

Teresa, however, was dying 'of an over-application of medical treatment,' [1] the famous healer had used purges too freely—one a day —her inside felt as if on fire, the fever never left her, she was a martyr to nervous twitching, she was suffering unbearable pain 'and a very deep sadness.' [2]

At the end of July, in this condition, she said goodbye to the 'poor man' whom she had saved and who despaired of ever seeing her alive again. In actual fact it was he who died a year to the very day after entering the house at Becedas for the first time, as confessor to the young Carmelite of whom everyone said in the village: 'She is so ill. She is so beautiful. And she's a saint. . . .'

Don Alonso hastened to bring his daughter back to Ávila where a bevy of doctors again visited her bedside. This time they got out of their predicament by condemning her without hope of reprieve: to their already numerous mistakes they added that of diagnosing tuberculosis.

Teresa was now back in the room which had been hers as a child, near the one in which Doña Beatriz had brought her into the world and had suffered so many years from slow decline. For three months longer she was in such a state that it seemed impossible that anyone could endure such great and manifold sufferings and live: from head to foot there was no part of her that was not in pain. She kept up her courage by saying over to herself the words of St Gregory's version of Job: 'We have received good things from the hands of the Lord: why not evil?' But her poor body could not keep up its resistance.

On 15th August she asked for the last sacraments. Her father dissuaded her, thinking to reassure her.

'You can go to confession later when you are better: for you know you are going to get better!'

That very night she fell into a syncope. The priest who was called to administer Extreme Unction judged her to be dead, not dying. Don Alonso, in despair because he had not allowed her to make her Communion, let his prayers and groans be heard all over the house.

The first day Teresa gave no sign of life.

On the second day her breath did not dull the mirror they held to her lips and the hot wax of the candle which her father held over her

[1] Idem, 7.   [2] Idem.

to look at her more closely fell on her eyelids without awakening her to consciousness.

The third day they dug her grave at the Incarnation. She was washed and wrapped in her shroud. Her brother Lorenzo kept vigil during the night. He fell asleep; a candlestick overturned, the bed-curtains caught fire and the seemingly lifeless body was very nearly burnt.

On the fourth day the nuns of the Incarnation came to fetch away the dead body of their sister that it might be buried within the precincts of Carmel. Don Alonso refused to allow her to be taken away, and when he kept on repeating, 'The time is not come for my daughter to be put under the ground,' [1] it was thought he had gone crazy with grief. He claimed to be able to hear the beatings of her pulse and his fingers never left Teresa's wrist.

The nuns stayed on, kneeling upright in prayer around the bed—a couch as tragic on account of the demented father as it was on that of the dead girl.

Suddenly Teresa painfully raised her eyelids which were weighted down by the now cold wax of the funeral tapers. She saw the *capilla ardiente* and other tokens of death around her, with her sisters waiting to carry away the corpse, and she gropingly fingered the shroud.

Her first words were to ask once again for the sacraments. Then she continued speaking: her faint voice seemed to be coming from a long way off; she was alive, but she had not yet completely returned to earth. She said: 'Why did you call me back?' She declared she would have much to do in this world, they had told her so where she had been—in heaven. But she had seen hell, too. In her confused sentences interrupted by sobs—her pillow was wet with tears—they made out the words: 'convents . . . foundations . . . to save souls. . . .' [2] Finally she said:

'Don't think me dead until you see my body covered with cloth of gold. . . .'

The return of her sufferings, now more acute than ever, brought her out of her trance.

Now that his daughter was won back from heaven, or from hell, Don Alonso wanted to clasp her in his arms, but she cried out with pain: the slightest touch caused such agony 'that only Our Lord can know how unbearable these sufferings were.' [3] When the bed had to be made, two persons had to lift her in a sheet. She felt as if she were being torn to pieces, she was delirious. It was impossible for her to lie

[1] FR, L. I, c: vii.   [2] Idem.   [3] Sb, V, c. vi–1.

full length and she lay curled up, her muscles contracted, her knees up to her chin.

The silence and expressions of dismay of those about her frightened her. She wanted to convince them—and herself—that she was not paralysed, but she was unable to move 'either arm, foot, hand or head.' [1] All she could move was one finger of her right hand and with this one more or less normal finger she stroked the sheets. Her throat was contracted, her tongue so parched and swollen with her having bitten it that it felt as if torn into a thousand pieces, and she choked as soon as they tried to pour a drop of water between her lips.

'That went on till Easter Sunday,' [2] nearly nine months; she was shaken to the point of exhaustion with ague, and severe depression impeded her recovery. She now considered herself fortunate, however, for the pain subsided when they left her alone. Each day, on every possible occasion, she begged her father to take her back to the Incarnation. In absolute despair he had her taken there.

Her sisters came forward to receive the body they had been prepared to bury; the soul was still there, but the body itself was worse than dead, reduced to mere bones covered with skin, and frightfully weak.

For three years Doña Teresa de Ahumada remained in the infirmary completely paralysed; it was now her turn to be the great invalid whom her sisters, all eager for an occasion of exercising charity, vied with each other for the honour of looking after.

Her patient endurance amazed the convent and even when she complained, her expressions were those of praise and love:

'Lord, I did not want as much as this!' [3]

And she affirmed that she would not exchange her sufferings for any treasure they could offer her.

At last she recorded a slight improvement in words that are truly terrible: 'When I began to walk on all fours, I thanked God.' [4]

Had she been able to rid herself of her feeling of guilt? Did she now feel pardoned, redeemed? She was conscious of having won a victory, of having the right to receive 'the hidden manna,' 'the white garments,' 'the morning star.'[5] She had never been so free as she was on her wretched pallet. Tried like gold in the fire by the sufferings she had undergone, she had taken her own measure and now that she knew how slight her strength really was, admitted that she had been crushed by the demands of her hard heart—hard not for others but against herself.

[1] Idem.   [2] Idem.   [3] Sb, CAD, c. vi–2.
[4] Sb, V, c. vi–2.   [5] Apocalypse ii–17; iii–5; xxii–17.

One morning when the rising signal went and she heard the nuns go to chapel for Prime, a burning desire to follow them came over her and she wished she could be cured: this was tantamount to granting herself absolution for the past. She also wanted to get back to her cell again, for she found it difficult to be recollected in the infirmary where she had other people round her.

She wanted to live to serve God better. In her case, to desire a thing meant to will it.

But earthly doctors had declared her incurable. So she decided to appeal to heavenly ones, and by a refinement of logic she chose St Joseph. 'This glorious saint helps us in every need; Our Lord shows us that he obeys St Joseph in heaven, just as on earth he was under him and called him Father. . . .' [1]

In asking for the cure, she made it emphatically clear that by so doing she was not putting herself into the category of those, 'particularly women, who follow strange devotions which made not the slightest appeal to me, and which have been clearly proved to be nothing but superstition.' [2]

No doubt when in the infirmary she already had the *Subida del Monte Sion* of Bernardino of Laredo to read—the Ascent of Mount Sion—for the book had recently been published. In the appendix were included some exquisite pages on devotion to St Joseph. How Teresa, who clung to life so tenaciously, must have loved the portrait there given of him: 'A youngish man in the prime of life . . . extremely handsome . . . for how could we imagine that our God would have given the Mother of his Son for her companion, to be the one who served them, was with them for twenty years supporting them by the work of his hands—a decrepit old man such as fools described him. It's laughable. . . .'

The 'young' St Joseph 'showed clearly who he was'. One day when Teresa was dragging herself about on all fours, she suddenly felt she could stand erect. She leant her weight on the soles of her feet, found her balance, drew herself up to her full height and walked with as much ease as if she had never been ill. What she called her sins were forgiven her.

The nuns around her declared it was a miracle.

[1] Sb, V, c. vi–6.　　　　　　[2] Idem.

VII

DOÑA TERESA DE AHUMADA

'DOÑA TERESA DE AHUMADA is wanted in the parlour!' With a step whose regained vivacity she owes to the 'young' St Joseph, the *miraculée* goes to the parlour assigned to her to see her friends. She appears behind the grille, more beautiful and charming than ever; the habit and scapular of fine cloth, the white muslin wimple tastefully folded, the black veil lined with white become her to perfection and she has too much good taste to attempt to trim up the religious habit, as many of her sisters do.

The parlours of the Incarnation had always been made use of as meeting places for worldly society and were frequented with predilection by its most brilliant members—gentlemen as well as noble señoras. Doña Teresa now became the principal attraction: her cure brought her to the front and 'many people of every station in life came to see her on account of her kindness and graciousness.' [1]

At first she contented herself with answering their questions, with her eyes cast down, embarrassed at attracting attention, her only thought to get back to her solitude and her prayers. But the cell from which one is frequently absent ends by becoming less desirable and the fusion of Christian charity with the desire to please others cannot be effected without unfortunate consequences. Was she to let her visitors go away again without warm words of greeting, and to show no interest in the news they had come to tell her? Teresa had so grateful a heart that she was later to declare: 'I can be bribed with a sardine.' [2] All her life she understood the art of making even the smallest gift she received seem precious by the way she thanked people; she knew how to give, to congratulate, to sympathize, to give pleasure. Soon all Ávila was aware of the charms of the young Carmelite's conversation.

People thought it wonderful that a religious of twenty-six should have retained the charm of the pretty girl whom the world had fêted so much and that she should have in addition 'something solid' [3] acquired in the course of her years of solitude due to her illness and also the fruit of her extensive reading, her meditations and her trials. Her

---

[1] BN and PB, art. 2.   [2] CTA, ccxlviii.
[3] MJ quoted SST, vol. I, p. 244

ÁVILA

The Fortifications

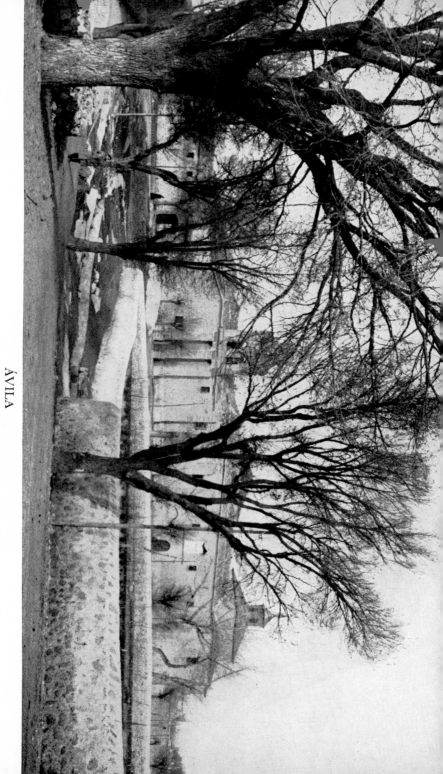

ÁVILA
The Convent of the Incarnation

soundness of judgement and openness of mind charmed people all the more because at a time when so many good-looking women prided themselves on their Latin and Greek, she laughingly excused herself for not being erudite. This gift of attracting and holding people lasted throughout her lifetime; Don Antonio Aguiar, a licentiate who knew her in later life, at Burgos, said that he spent

all day long with her without noticing the time, and all night long in the hope of seeing her again next day, for her way of speaking was delightful—and the word *gracioso* in Spanish adds a touch of wit to the delightfulness, and her conversation pleasant and at the same time serious, simple, full of good sense and absolutely sincere: she was so much on fire with the love of God! The warmth radiating from her words was so gently persuasive that it melted the hearts of all who came in contact with her without causing them pain; for among her qualities she possessed *gratia sermonis*, graciousness of speech, and drew to her, as she wanted them and for whatever purpose she wanted them, all who heard her. . . . It might have been said that she held in her hand the helm that steers all hearts. . . .

At the Incarnation Teresa, whom Aguiar himself was to call 'the world's magnet',[1] was already creating a sphere of influence about her.

At the time it was considered very good form to talk of matters of high devotion, more especially in a convent parlour. Could a nun withdraw herself from discussions on mental prayer in which the methods of Osuna were compared with those of Laredo, or in which the merits of the Society recently founded by Ignatius of Loyola were extolled? The way in which Doña Teresa de Ahumada spoke of God was wonderful, but she was listened to all the more readily because she never tired of hearing others speak of him. Any pious nobleman who, during his travels, had had the good fortune to hear Padre Juan de Ávila or Fray Luis de Granada preach was sure to find an appreciative audience at the Incarnation.

'Doña Teresa de Ahumada, in the parlour!'

A circle was formed, Doña Teresa drew up close to the grille—already the visitor was pleased with himself and therefore with her.

'It was on Good Friday. The church was full as could be. Fray Luis got into the pulpit and spoke of the single word "Passion" with so much force, so burning an eloquence and so much feeling that the entire congregation fell to weeping. People sobbed so loudly that the preacher was obliged to interrupt his sermon. . . .'[2]

---

[1] Quoted SST, vol. I, p. 294. [2] MN, L. I, c. xvi.

Teresa praised the speaker and, from sacred matters, the conversation dropped easily into worldly ones. The frigates which sailed overseas from Seville and returned laden with gold and exotic fruits were always an exciting subject. People brought Teresa news of Fernando, of Rodrigo whom Lorenzo and Pedro had gone to join in 1540. Or perhaps the subject of discussion might be a remedy against fever, one of those recipes of which herbs formed the basis, about which the young nun was curious; or, better still, a well-turned sonnet, or again a battle which had been well and hardly won. To know where and in what manner they were fighting for God and the emperor against Turk, Frenchmen or Indians was to know the fate of the sons and brothers of the well-born families of Ávila.

Everything interested and fascinated Doña Teresa, and there was nothing she said which did not interest, amuse and fascinate her devoted clientèle.

When Don Alonso came to see her now, more and more frequently he found himself interrupting such gatherings. She received him with affectionate deference, but when her friends got up to go she kept them back by vigorously steering the conversation round to general subjects. The poor man was crestfallen and went away broken-hearted. What had become of the time when his Teresa had talked with him at length, just he and she together, with such irresistible eloquence that it was to her he owed his initiation into the art of mental prayer. His daughter had so much persuasive force that she had accomplished one of the most difficult of feats: to raise to the heights of the mystical life one who was merely an everyday Catholic. Could it really be the same Teresa whom he now found laughing and chattering, inattentive to her father and, it seemed, inattentive to God?

One day when he happened to find her alone he reproached her with this. She did not attempt to deny it: she admitted that she no longer practised mental prayer and pleaded ill-health as an excuse. 'For me going to choir is a very considerable effort.'[1]

Don Alonso had now attained the heights of contemplation; he judged his visits to the Incarnation to be 'time wasted' and spaced them out so well that the *habitués* no longer had any need to fear the few minutes of embarrassment which the arrival of the old man dressed in black and with the gentle, sad and penetrating look had caused. 'I was caught up in so many vanities,' said Teresa, 'that I didn't trouble about it.'[2] She had not the courage to tell her father she could no longer recollect herself 'without enclosing within me a multitude of vanities.'[3]

[1] Sb, V, c. vii-12.   [2] Idem, 13.   [3] Idem, 17.

When she recovered from her long and serious illness, or rather from the long crisis, for she remained more or less ill all her life, she very naturally found pleasure in renewed vitality. The delight which friendships and conversation gave her, the distractions which occurred during her spiritual exercises and her long periods of dryness, the fact that she sometimes found herself waiting impatiently for the bell that announced the end of the Office, all these things formed such an utter contrast with her ideal of fervour that she believed herself to be lost, so much so that she no longer dared look God in the face; and she gave up everything the *Third Spiritual Alphabet* had taught her. Disappointed in herself, this 'regal soul' punished herself by mediocrity. What! She had aimed at sanctity? Had dreamed of heroic acts? She had almost died through such pretentiousness and God himself had laughed at her presumption. Is it not possible to save one's soul without extravagant austerities? The convent of the Incarnation seemed expressly created for such a *via media*. Was not that why she had chosen it? How foolish the ambition that had urged her to want to make herself singular by piety and mortifications more severe and intense than those of her sisters! 'The common law seemed to me the best for I was vile and worse than any; to say the prayers of obligation, vocally, would be better than to practise mental prayer and the presence of God for one who merited the company of devils and who was deceiving people; for externally I appeared to be good. . . .' [1]

In choir as in the parlour or at recreation, Doña Teresa de Ahumada had the gift of putting herself at each one's disposal, and, as far as her companions were concerned, made herself 'all things to all, as much by what she was as by what she did, with such a perfection and gift of adaptation that we sometimes even laughed at it',[2] Ana de Jesús wrote afterwards. She imagined she was deceiving those about her, for the standard by which she measured her progress was that of the highest ideals she had set herself; in reality she was living in conformity with the use and custom established in a convent where a multitude of compromises with the Constitutions were 'lawful,' although it was not one of the most relaxed among Spanish convents.

Anything served as pretext, excuse or good reason: tolerance seemed the essential point about the Rule, except for the novices who followed its obligations to the letter; it was on this account that they were only allowed visitors very occasionally. The professed nuns, on the other hand, wore jewellery, chattered unscrupulously during silence time, paid visits in each other's cells and at recreation time

[1] Idem, I.   [2] Cited SST, vol. I, p. 295.

regaled themselves with worldly music. Did not their devotees bring them the latest songs? And did they not munch, at all hours of the day, the sweetmeats they slipped into their hands through the parlour grilles? One religious, chosen from among the most prudent in the convent, always formed the third party when visitors came to the parlour, but hunger was not the prerogative of the frivolous-minded and even the prudent were not proof against a *pâtisserie*. The convent was poor and overcrowded, and the starvation diet to which the nuns were subjected was due more to their extreme poverty than to observance of the rule of abstinence as practised by the Fathers of the Desert who were the Order's founders; accordingly when a nun found a good pretext for going back to take meals at home for a time or with devout people who were only too anxious to have a Carmelite in the house, the prioress was not slow in giving permission, on condition that the nun took one of her sisters with her as companion: two mouths less to feed. This was the reason Teresa herself was often absent; the great families of Ávila quarrelled as to who should have her with them.

How could unremitting fervour be expected of one hundred and eighty young women who kept one foot in the world like this, many of whom had only become nuns in despair of finding a husband? Since the discovery of what were called the Indies, young men preferred their visions overseas, even if these should prove to be illusory, to the sparkling eyes of a Spanish fiancée: in the Cepeda y Ahumada family alone, the whole seven went off, seven fine young men, any one of whom would have made a good match, leaving seven girls free 'to dress the saints,' that is to join the confraternities of pious women who held sway over the collection of robes used to dress the statues of Christ or that of the velvet and gold brocade vestments for Our Lady.

With the exception of a few devout nuns, the convent of the Incarnation seemed more like a guest-house for single ladies where each one, in the measure of her fortune, rank and personal tastes, arranged for herself a more or less pleasant existence, practising the virtues considered indispensable if one wished to acquire, without too much trouble, a moderately exalted position in the next world.

In the next world: for in this 'it is impossible to succeed in achieving anything good when there are more than forty women together: things are nothing but noisy confusion and chaos: they upset each other.' [1] Teresa found many friends to help her to sink to the lowest level among the one hundred and eighty nuns of the Incarnation, but when she wanted to rise above this standard she stood alone.

[1] CTA, xlvi.

It was 'Doña Teresa!' here, 'Doña Teresa de Ahumada' there: there was always a sister to come and distract her when she was trying to practise recollection. They loved her only too well, desirous as she was that people should love her; her gaiety delighted people, her loyalty reassured them; with her you were sure she would not talk about you disparagingly once your back was turned. Those who were of an effusive nature coaxed her; 'My life! My soul! My treasure!' [1] But they soon learnt that the feminine craze for terms of endearment was no more to her taste than tittle-tattle, quarrelling and 'Have you heard . . .' They admired her exquisite thoughtfulness and charity: sometimes when they came to choir for Office in the early hours of the morning, her sisters would be astonished to find their old worn-out cloaks darned: Doña Teresa, feeling that she did not show enough love towards her sisters, had got up in the night to mend them.

Who would have thought, then, of blaming her for the hours she spent in the parlour? She kept within the letter of the law. It would not have occurred to any man of good family, young, handsome, elegant, that a nun of equivalent social standing could dream of refusing to chat with him in the parlour. He was known as her 'devotee,' she was considered to be helping him to save his soul, and if the good-looking nuns were more sought after for such work than the plain ones, this occasioned no surprise. Teresa had too much pride to follow the example of those who continued their apostolate when parlour hours were over 'through the cracks, over the walls, or during the night. . . .' [2]

When Doña Teresa blamed herself for acting as her sisters did, she showed towards herself the severity of the athlete who curses himself when a glass of alcohol endangers his form, whereas those who have already attained the world record drink their bottle without remorse. The nuns of the Incarnation did not know from what heights Teresa had sunk to the level of their routine religion. They sometimes saw her go out of her way to be alone, refrain from speaking evil, abstain from disobedience. They noticed she was punctual and exact at Office, recollected at prayer time. They heard her speak of God with exceptional eloquence. Doña Teresa de Ahumada was always ready to give money to have holy pictures painted on the convent walls, she decorated her own oratory, caused edifying ceremonies to be performed in honour of her favourite saints—particularly St Joseph; at the Incarnation less than this was necessary to pass for a model nun. Her conduct was 'legitimate' for her companions, her superiors, her confessor.

[1] Sb, C, c. vii–8.　　　　[2] Sb, V, c. vii–2.

To her, that was not the point. What had become of the heroic acts? Of her aspirations to sanctity?

Oh, what a terrible thing it is when religious . . . do not observe their rule. . . . Their youth and the attraction of things of sense draw them towards the world. . . . The monk or the nun who wants to follow God must fear those of his or her own family more than all the powers of hell. He or she is forced to use more prudence and dissimulation in order to obtain the liberty to live in God's friendship than is required for the particular friendships which the devil brings about in monasteries. . . . If parents took my advice, since they don't seem to think of putting their daughters where they can best save their souls, but rather where there is more danger than there would be in the world, they would look at the matter from the point of view of honour; and they would then prefer to marry them off beneath their station rather than put them in such convents . . . or would keep them at home.[1]

Teresa saw the danger, allowed it to brush past her lightly and escaped it in time thanks to her impregnable sense of honour, but she made no effort to avoid it.

This was not, however, for want of warning.

Among the gentlemen who were devoted to her there was one for whom she declared she had *mucha afición*, which we can translate as 'to whom she was very much attached'—using the expression in the right sense. It appears that this person was Don Francisco de Guzmán; he was young, well endowed with worldly goods and belonged to one of the noblest families of Castile. Was he more dangerous for Teresa than the cousin she had formerly thought of marrying or the 'poor wretched man' of Becedas? God took a hand in the matter—the devil too: 'I had only known him a very short time when Our Lord made me understand that such friendships were not for me. Christ appeared to me with a most severe countenance and showed me clearly that this was not pleasing to him. I was alarmed and troubled and I did not want to see the man again.'[2] But the devil made her believe that this vision was only the effect of her imagination, the visitor persisted, the sisters around her affirmed that the company of so worthy an *hidalgo* not only did no harm to Doña Teresa de Ahumada's reputation, but actually enhanced it: thus it was that she returned to this 'pestilential recreation.'[3] During Office, the thought of this friend became a constant distraction. One day when she was in the parlour 'with the person in question,' an enormous toad appeared to her. Several persons present

[1] Sb, V, c. vii–5, 4.   [2] Sb, V, c. vii–6.   [3] Idem, 7.

saw it 'walk much more quickly than such creatures usually do.'[1] Teresa was very much afraid, but this second warning, too, was neglected.

And when an old religious who was also a relative of hers thought fit to put her on her guard, her only reply was to shrug her shoulders: 'You take scandal over nothing!'[2] and she sulked over it.

The young generation which was contemporaneous with the new world then being born found their elders unprogressive and hidebound with ridiculous prejudices.

All the same: when Doña Teresa was called to the parlour now, her dainty arched feet in the elegant shoes on which 'he' never tired of complimenting her no longer ran there so eagerly. The Bridegroom was keeping watch. His vengeance on such a butterfly bride was to inundate her soul with spiritual delights. He knew her so well; for her it was 'a kind of terrible torture,'[3] to receive graces of which she knew she was unworthy. She pulled herself together but knew all the time that she would fall again.

'From one pastime to another, from vanity to vanity, from temptation to temptation. . . .'[4] 'O Lord of my soul, how shall I ever be able to express my gratitude for your mercies during these years?'[5]

The solicitude with which not only God but the devil surrounded her was truly astonishing. God willed to make her his own, the devil to snatch her away from God. For the thought of spiritual joys weakened the pleasure she found in her eager friendships, and yet when she withdrew to her cell to be alone with God, the memory of such friendships would not leave her.

Thus seven years after she came to the convent 'this soul who has so often worked her own ruin,'[6] was still torn in two directions.

Teresa was to find help at the bedside of her dying father. The year 1543 was drawing to a close. The Carmelite had returned to the house in the Plazuela Santo Domingo to nurse Don Alonso. '. . . There was more sickness in my soul than in his body, taken up as I was by a multitude of vanities, although I do not think I committed mortal sin at this time—a period more wasted than I can say. . . .'[7]

Under her father's roof and surrounded with objects that were familiar to her, she was able to measure the ground covered since the day she had suffered so much at leaving it all and abandoning the old

---

[1] Idem, 8.   [2] Idem, 9.   [3] Idem, 19.
[4] Idem, 1.   [5] Idem, 19.   [6] CTA, ccclxxxviii.
[7] Sb, V, c, vii–14.

man who now turned his gaze in her direction with eyes already dim. Her departure had meant for him cruel suffering and perhaps financial ruin as well: he was not the sort of man to look after his own interests. Doña Beatriz and then María and Teresa had been the necessary stewards. Left alone, he had become impoverished through his generosity to his sons whose equipment for the army had been on a lavish scale, to María—always in difficulties—to the poor. Don Alonso was considerably in debt, but he was rich in the love of Our Lord.

Teresa, though she thought herself so far away from God, brought deep peace to her dying father. Acute pain in the kidneys was causing him much suffering:

'Father, you have a devotion to Christ carrying his cross. Why don't you imagine that His Majesty is giving you a share of his sufferings while he was carrying it uphill?' [1]

This thought gave him so much consolation that he no longer moaned in his pain. He died fully conscious, reciting the *Credo* and reminding all those of his children who were present that they must remember that everything has an end. 'When dead, he looked like an angel.' [2]

Teresa went to confession to P. Vincent Barrón, who assisted the dying man. He was a man of calm disposition, but exacting and with an eye for detail. She gave him a full account of the state of trouble and confusion in which she was, declaring that for a long time past she had deemed herself unworthy to practise mental prayer.

The Dominican's directives read rather like a doctor's prescription, leaving no room for scruples or hesitations:

(1) Receive Holy Communion every fortnight.

(2) Take up mental prayer again. That cannot but do great good in any circumstances.

With his calm penetration and insight, P. Vincent Barrón gave Doña Teresa de Ahumada the help she needed to become Doña Teresa de Jesús: he charged the patient not to deprive herself of the remedy for her ills any longer, no matter what might happen.

Teresa has summarized the effects of this consultation:

'I returned to prayer without, however, avoiding the occasions of sin; but I never gave up prayer again.' [3]

'My life was full of suffering, for in prayer I saw my faults more clearly.'

This of course was what the experienced director had foreseen.

'On the one hand I felt the call of God; on the other, I continued to

[1] Idem, 16.   [2] Idem.   [3] Sb, V, c. vii–17.

follow the world. All the things of God gave me great pleasure, but I was held captive by those of the world. I might have been said to be trying to reconcile these two extremes, to bring contraries together: the spiritual life on the one hand and worldly satisfactions, pleasures and pastimes on the other.' [1]

'I spent many years in this way. . . .'

To be precise, ten years, dating from her meeting with P. Barrón. But for the future she had 'the strong pillar of mental prayer as her support.' [2]

From God's first insistent call at Our Lady of Grace until the shattering experience of 1553, Teresa de Ahumada continued to live for just over twenty years with her heart divided between the world and God.

[1] Idem.   [2] Sb, V, c. viii–1.

PART TWO

THE ROYAL ROAD

'Lord, he who loves you truly travels in security along a wide and royal road.'

Autobiography, c. xxv

THE WOUNDED CHRIST

ONE day in 1553,[1] as she was passing through the oratory, Doña Teresa de Ahumada noticed a bust, an *Ecce Homo*, which someone had left there until some other place could be found for it. 'It represented, and that in a way so well calculated to arouse devotion that from the very first glance I was moved at the thought of his sufferings for us, Christ covered with wounds. My heart was shattered with remorse when I thought of those wounds and my ingratitude. I threw myself on my knees before him, in tears, and begged him to strengthen me once for always, that I might not offend him for the future.' [2]

After Communion she often imagined herself like Mary Magdalene, at the feet of Our Lord, and wept, but such impulsive movements of repentance were soon forgotten: 'Doubtless what was wrong was that I failed to put my whole trust in His Majesty and did not divest myself of my self-confidence.' [3] This *Ecce Homo* with the pallid, death-like flesh showing the wounds, some red and gaping, some congealed, the face streaming with the blood that spurted from beneath the crown of thorns, the heart-rending expression of the glazed eyes, made her understand what she really was: she saw she would find help nowhere but in God, she would not get right again until he answered her heart's appeal.

Such was the first shattering experience. It was Christ penetrating into 'the hard heart' after knocking so often in vain. She was to discover that his love 'is above all the joys of earth, bliss surpassing all other.' [4]

From this day forward she was able to record progress: she avoided the parlour, redoubled both constancy and fervour in the matter of mental prayer and her charity became humbler and more patient. The change did not pass unnoticed among her sisters: they often surprised her at prayer, so absorbed in God that she saw no one, any more than

---

[1] P. Silverio de Santa Teresa assigns to her second conversion the date of 1553. He bases this assumption on the date (1554) of the arrival of St. Francis Borgia in Ávila (SST, vol. I, p. 331).

[2] Sb, V, c. ix-1.   [3] Sb, V, c. viii-12   [4] Sb, M, V, c. i-6.

she read what was in the book open in front of her. For she still needed help to become recollected: 'I find a book useful . . . the country, water, flowers, helped me too. . . .'[1]

At the beginning of 1554 she was given St Augustine's *Confessions*, the Spanish translation of which had just been published. Teresa de Ahumada thought she recognized herself in this man who had loved the world so much and struggled so hard to be detached from it, the reader of worldly books, the sinner for so long impenitent: 'When I got to his conversion, to the point where he hears the voice in the orchard, the feelings I experienced were so intense that it might have been myself Our Lord was calling. For a long time tears streamed down my face.'[2]

This second experience finally delivered Teresa 'out of so mortal a death.'[3] After going the round of temptations and dangers, this was a return to the point of departure, to her early childhood. For in the child Teresa her future development already existed in embryo.

'Teresa is not like herself,' said her companions at the Incarnation, whereas in reality she was at long last like herself, like the child who wanted to be born again in the glory of God 'for ever, and ever, and ever,' even if the price was martyrdom.

'From now onwards a fresh page has been turned for me, I tell you it is a new life.'

'Up till now it has been *my* life. Now God lives in me.'

'God be praised for having delivered me from myself.'[4]

Our Lord was only waiting for Teresa's decision to shower spiritual graces upon her. 'Hardly had I turned my gaze away from the occasions of sin when His Majesty already began to show his love for me again. . . . It seemed to me that I had only just made up my mind to serve him when His Majesty began to spoil me once more. . . .'[5] She was given 'very frequently the prayer of quiet and often that of union which lasted a long time. But at that particular time there had been many women who were the victims of illusion and of the deceits of the devil: so great were the delights and sweetness which I experienced in spite of my resistance, that I was scared.'[6]

To whom did she speak of these fears and favours? The confessors at the Incarnation had never understood her. She dared not speak about them even to the most serious-minded among her sisters. Already, when the first moment of astonishment was over, the change in her

[1] Sb, V, c. ix–5.   [2] Sb, V, c. ix–8   [3] Idem.
[4] Sb, V, c. xxiii–9.   [5] Sb, V, c. ix–9   [6] Sb, V, c. xxiii–2.

caused a certain uneasiness around her: the wise virgins did not yet consider her one of themselves and the foolish virgins were exasperated to find that the very person whose 'frivolities' justified their own was now repenting—such repentance was tantamount to an accusation of them all. When they saw her they began to whisper together; soon many of them pointed the finger of scorn at her, and eventually the whole convent was seething with sarcasm or pity:

'Doña Teresa de Ahumada thinks herself a saint!'

'Doña Teresa thinks she's invented something new!' [1]

The first of her meritorious efforts was the humble willingness to be less acceptable to others; but this was not enough to calm her distress. One day, during the Hours, she heard Our Lord speak for the first time: 'Serve me, and do not concern yourself about all that.' [2] She was more frightened than consoled by the divine words, 'my soul was frightened and upset,' [3] for want of an experienced director.

Fortunately the Cepeda and Ahumada connections were almost unending. The good uncle Don Pedro was connected through his wife Doña Catalina del Águila, with Don Francisco de Salcedo, whom Teresa later termed *el caballero santo*, 'the holy gentleman,' so deep was his piety. And it was enlightened piety: for twenty years he had studied theology at the Dominican college of Santo Tomás and Fray Pedro de Alcántara considered him 'the best bonnet in Ávila'—the most worthy to wear the doctor's cap. Of the many men who practised virtue in the City of Stones and Saints, there was no one equal to him. Best of all: he was kind.

It was to him that Teresa de Ahumada turned. Yet she did not tell him either of her graces or her fears: she merely spoke of the difficulty she had in overcoming self, of her efforts to do better which always ended in disappointment but which she always began again: she was accused of making too many demands upon herself, whereas she reproached herself for her excessive weakness. She needed a director to help her to see clearly and to impose upon her what she had not the courage to impose upon herself: in her own eyes she was not mortified.

Don Francisco brought to her P. Gaspar Daza. All Ávila admired the apostolic zeal of this preacher who did not confine the privileges of hearing the Gospel preached merely to city-dwellers. At a time when the ignorance of country folk was such that in isolated spots the good people did not even know the *Our Father*, he went preaching in remote hamlets, summer and winter alike. Teresa hoped to profit much by his virtue and spirit of refusal to compromise. But Don Gaspar had much

[1] Sb, V, c. xix–8.   [2] Sb, V, c. xix–9.   [3] Sb, V, c. xiii–4.

to do in the Lord's service: he felt he had no time to waste on a nun who was not satisfied with the confessors provided by her Order.

He did not even trouble to put her at her ease.

'I was extremely uncomfortable in the presence of such a holy man. I acquainted him with the state of my soul and my manner of mental prayer. He didn't want to hear my confession, saying he was extremely busy.' [1]

Teresa noticed that he regarded what she said to him 'as something which has to be finished with once and for all. . . .' [2] His judgement of her was based on the degree of mental prayer she had attained. He thought her a strong character and ruthlessly cut across her remaining attachments. But she knew how weak she was in spite of the graces Our Lord was showering upon her, still a mere child as far as the practice of the virtues and mortification was concerned and she judged herself incapable of doing what he ordered. 'This was enough to make one lose heart and give up everything,' [3]

Francisco de Salcedo, with somewhat more kindness, came to see her frequently, her confidence in him increased, and one day she told him of the delights of her supernatural prayer: 'That is my expression for what is obtainable neither by skill nor diligence, however much one forces oneself and prepares oneself for it.' [4] She told him about the feeling of the presence of God which took hold of her in so intense a way that she could not but doubt that God was within her and she incorporated [5] in him. She told him, too, of the continual feelings of tenderness, the joy she experienced, 'neither entirely of the senses nor entirely spiritual,' [6] 'sweetness, delight defying all comparison, agony the joys of which surpass all one can say.' [7] 'It is a hard but blissful martyrdom' [8] to 'die to all the pleasures of the world and find one's joy in God.' [9] She admitted to Don Francisco that she was 'as it were beside herself, drunk with this love' [10]: 'pain full of delight,' 'glorious aberration, heavenly folly. . . .' [11]

The good gentleman was completely nonplussed. He summoned Gaspar Daza with all urgency. The latter left all his preaching and came. This nun whom they both thought so imperfect spoke with accents of shattering sincerity of unheard of graces with which Our Lord was favouring her.

'Such things don't go together,' said the one.

[1] Sb, V, c. xxxii-8.   [2] Idem.   [3] Idem, 9.
[4] SEC, R, v, p. 31.   [5] Sb, V, c. x-1.   [6] Idem, 2.
[7] Sb, V, c. xvi-1.   [8] Idem.   [9] Idem, 1.
[10] Idem, 3.   [11] Idem, 1.

'Spiritual graces are only found in those who are very well exercised in virtue and greatly mortified,' said the other still more conclusively.[1]

And their mutual conclusion was:

'Be careful . . . certain factors indicate the work of the devil. . . .'

'They had no sooner spoken,' said Teresa, 'than I was greatly upset and in tears, for I was frightened enough before this.'

And Doña Teresa de Ahumada, the brilliant conversationalist of the Incarnation's parlour, nearly forty and in full possession of her faculties, her genius about to flower to its full perfection, was so much intimidated by these theologians, so terrified at the idea that what she experienced might be a diabolical illusion, that she could not find words with which to give a satisfactory account of the graces God was giving her.

The 'sleep of the faculties' had seemed particularly worrying to these worthy gentlemen. Like a child in desperation at being unable to express itself, she sought in Bernardino de Laredo's *Ascent of Mount Sion* for the phrases which seemed to her to describe what she was experiencing, without stopping to think that the choice of a Franciscan writer was not a particularly happy one: the sons of Ignatius of Loyola, and both Salcedo and Daza were under their influence, accused the Franciscans of too much sentimentality.

In the place where union with God is spoken of, I found all the signs which I had in myself with regard to the impossibility of reflecting and the 'thinking of nothing' mentioned.[2] I underlined certain passages. . . . 'Let him who has ears to hear, hear, and learn that in this absence of thought is comprised a vast world, which includes perfect contemplation and contains all that is, so much so that when this is present, the rest is nothing: and if it is nothing, one has not to think about it. For truly in the presence of Our Lord and God, all created things are nothing. . . . Of the soul, then, which through the union of love in quiet contemplation is busied with God, one can in truth say that she should think of nothing, for in this absence of thought, she has what is the essence of all thought.'[3]

The two 'holy servants of God,' then, were going to study Teresa de Ahumada's 'case,' documents in hand. Submissively she waited for their decision: 'I was prepared to abandon mental prayer if they considered this necessary. What was the use of running such risks if, after

---

[1] Sb, V, c. xxiii-11.
[2] Sb, V, c. xxiii-12.
[3] BL, c. xxvii.

twenty years of the practice of recollection, I had gained nothing but to be deceived by the devil? It would be better to give it up. . . .' [1]

For the second time Teresa found P. Gaspar Daza's attitude discouraging; not that she minded being crushed, she had a nature which preferred that to yielding. He was one of those 'people who are only half-learned and easily frightened,' [2] of whom she says that they cost her very dear.

She passed the time of waiting in suffering and prayer.

At length, these half-lettered men, who even taken together were not equal to a single person of ordinary common sense, pronounced their verdict:

'The devil!'

Don Francisco de Salcedo did not desert Teresa. In his opinion the only one who could extricate her from such perilous straits was a Jesuit. He was on excellent terms with the Order, for his brother-in-law had been the principal agent in the erection of their latest house, the hospice of San Gil. The apostolate was what they were founded for, and their methods of spirituality and the austerity of their personal life did not prevent them from understanding human weaknesses. The merits of the Jesuits had often formed the subject of conversation in the Incarnation parlours. It was decided that Teresa should write out a general confession and put it into the hands of whichever of the Fathers might prove willing to deal with her case.

But what a lot of fuss to arrange the visit! And the tittle-tattle that would probably arise from it! Teresa begged the portress not to tell anyone that a Father 'of the Society,' one of those holy men, was coming to see the 'vilest' of the nuns of the Incarnation. As ill-luck would have it, a nun who happened to be about when P. Cetina arrived was one of the gossips. The whole convent talked about it and soon it was all over Ávila.

P. Diego de Cetina was not a great Jesuit. 'Poor health . . . not very intelligent . . . has a liking for the Divine Office and for mental prayer. Likes sermons, Masses and to talk of God.' A confidential report adds: 'Preaches indifferently. Hears confessions. No use for anything else.' [3]

At the time he was twenty-three.

His verdict was:

'God!'

[1] Sb, V, c. xxiii–12.   [2] Sb. M, V, c. i-8.
[3] SST, vol. I, p. 339.

As the Dominican, P. Barrón, had done ten years earlier, P. Cetina, her Jesuit adviser, ordered Teresa not to give up mental prayer on any account. In strict compliance with what Ignatius of Loyola laid down, he asked her to focus her meditation each day on one of the Stations of the Cross, and to think of Christ only in his human person. He found her little inclined for penances—her bad health was to some extent the reason for this—and imposed on her mortifications which she found 'little to her taste,' [1] but to which she submitted.

Finally he charged her to resist as far as possible whatever pleasure of the senses she might experience.

'He directed me so well that it seems to me I am no longer the same. What a great thing it is to understand souls!' [2] For twenty years she had been looking for a confessor who would understand her. The 'not very intelligent' P. Cetina was proving his ability for other things besides mediocre preaching: he devoted himself to the exceptional soul who had been confided to his care. When he whom Teresa speaks of as 'the Father Francis who was Duke of Gandia,' *i.e.* Francis Borgia, came to Ávila in the spring of 1544, Diego de Cetina spoke to him about the Carmelite and persuaded him to go and see her.

P. Francisco was famous for having renounced one of the greatest names in Spain for God's sake. The story of his conversion had for long supplied the people of Ávila with a subject of conversation of the sort they loved, grandiose and sinister at the same time.

The event took place in 1539; the Empress Isabella had just died, and her son, Prince Philip II, who was only twelve, was leading the funeral cortège on horseback, as the queen's remains were conveyed across a grief-stricken Spain to her last resting-place in Granada. To Francis Borgia, Marquis of Lombay, son of the Duke of Gandia and of Juana of Aragón and one of the dead empress's favourite servitors, fell the honour of being chosen to identify the corpse.

When the coffin was opened in the mortuary chapel of the Catholic sovereigns, a nauseating stench caused the escort of nobles to draw back. These lords, however, swore—their hands on the hilts of their swords—that this was indeed 'the royal corpse of Doña Isabel de Portugal, empress of Germany, spouse of the magnificent, mighty and Catholic king, Charles our lord.'

The silence of Don Francisco de Borja astonished the archbishop.

'You are not going to swear?'

He looked at the putrefied flesh amid the still glittering gold of the royal robes.

[1] Sb, V, c. xxiv–2.   Sb, V. c xxiii–17.

'I can say only one thing; I have seen to it that the body of our noble Lady was under strict guard throughout the voyage from Toledo to Granada. But that I, who ever admired her great beauty, should swear that it is really she—I dare not.'

The archbishop insisted:

'Do you recognize your Lady and your Queen, or not?'

Francis placed his right hand upon his knight's cross of the order of Santiago, a patch of purple on the voluminous white cloak, whilst his left hand let the funeral veils fall back on the royal corpse.

'Yes. But I also swear never more to serve master who is mortal.'

On the death of his wife a short time afterwards the duke renounced honours, fortune and titles and entered the Society of Jesus.

The news came out in 1550 'like a thunderbolt.' There was one man who envied him: the emperor, Charles V, who had already sent emissaries 'to report on the residence, the site, the climate and the general arrangement of the monastery of Yuste.'

In the year 1554, then, P. Francisco came to Ávila from Tordesillas, where he had been staying for a time to be near the queen, Joan the Mad. His sermons drew such vast crowds to the great cathedral that the triumph might have gone to the head of anyone else except this perfect adept of the virtue of humility; in this, as in everything else, he saw only a reason for humbling himself.

Was he perhaps humbler than Prebendary Gaspar Daza—the prelate who had witnessed the dissolution of the spouse of the mightiest of monarchs? P. Francisco did not intimidate Doña Teresa de Ahumada when she had to set out the secrets of her inner life before him. He knew by experience the delights which Christ showers upon those who leave all for his sake.

He confirmed P. Cetina's diagnosis:

'It is truly the spirit of God.'

He added that it would not be right to resist.

'Allow yourself to be delighted by His Majesty, rejoice in him since he wants to give you joy. . . .'

The interview was not without its lighter side: when she was trying to describe the kind of dull stupidity in which she sometimes found herself, though completely absorbed in God, Teresa said:

'It seems to me that my soul is like a little donkey busy grazing. . . .'

Thus Francisco de Salcedo and Gaspar Daza were reassured, the busy tongues of Ávila silenced by the assurances of a Jesuit father 'who was a duke' and Teresa de Ahumada fully justified and encouraged.

But her troubles were not ended.

II

DOÑA GUIOMAR DE ULLOA

DOÑA GUIOMAR DE ULLOA was just over twenty-five. She was the widow of Don Francisco Dávila, lord of Villatoro. In her mourning she was more beautiful than ever and her piety had not yet led her to see the necessity of renouncing a life of luxury and refinement when she made the acquaintance of Doña Teresa de Ahumada, through the Fathers of the Society of Jesus at the church of San Gil. Teresa was charmed by her sympathetic face. Doña Guiomar quickly made friends with her: she soon grasped the fact that Teresa was not getting the solitude and opportunity for recollection she needed at the Incarnation which was indeed a perfect Babylon.

When the Carmelite visited her and Doña Guiomar, with a gracious gesture of welcome, showed her the vast apartments and beautiful patios of her palace, saying: 'My home is yours, too,' she understood that in this instance the usual formula of politeness was meant in all sincerity. And often when her sisters' lack of discretion made life too difficult and prevented her from devoting herself to the task of unremitting vigilance over self which gradual progress in the spiritual life demands—at all events in its initial stages—she took refuge with Doña Guiomar. She was able to give the prioress a sufficient reason: she was escorting one of the young widow's daughters who was a 'secular' at the Incarnation.

Doña Guiomar introduced Teresa to her own confessor when the departure of P. Diego de Cetina for Salamanca left her stranded once more. P. Juan de Prádanos, a young Jesuit who was understanding but severe, added to what his predecessor had required by imposing on his penitent a strict ascetical discipline: God was overwhelming her with his graces and the Jesuit's directive was that henceforward she must no longer neglect even the smallest thing that would please him. Much 'diplomacy and gentle persuasion'[1] were necessary to persuade her to sacrifice what cost her most: 'a few friendships which did not offend God;'[2] such purely human contacts deprived her of silence and solitude and were harmful to the regular life which was so necessary for her.

[1] Sb, V, c. xxiv-5.   [2] Idem.

A nature as affectionate and strong-willed as Doña Teresa de Ahumada's contrived to find good excuses: deep affections like these were in no way sinful: was it necessary to be ungrateful to please Our Lord?

P. Prádanos advised her to leave everything to God and to say the *Veni Creator* frequently. One day when she was saying over the words of the hymn, she was suddenly rapt in ecstasy for the first time and heard Our Lord's voice: 'Henceforward it is my will that you no longer converse with men but with angels.' [1]

Teresa was much afraid. When she returned to her normal senses again and saw her astonished sisters all round her, she was still more afraid. All speaking and shouting at once, they deafened her:

'You were like somebody dead!'

'Your limbs were stiff and your body icy cold!'

'Your pulse was scarcely beating at all. . . .'

She hoped they would think it was a fainting fit.

'We've seen you faint more than once. Your face was not ecstatic as it was this time.'

In spite of her efforts she could not yet find the strength to move: her soul seemed to have taken all her strength with it. For two or three days she seemed to have lost the use of her faculties, to be beside herself, bereft of her senses as it were, lost in God.[2]

She confided to Doña Guiomar:

The poor soul does not realize what is going to happen to it. . . . The being rapt in ecstasy takes the form of a sudden call on the part of His Majesty in the very depths of one's soul, it rushes upon one so swiftly that it seems to raise the soul to its very apex so that it almost leaves the body. Great courage is then necessary to abandon oneself into Our Lord's arms and to allow oneself to be rapt until the moment when His Majesty sets you down in peace, where he wanted to lead you to communicate the highest revelations to you. Certainly when such things first begin to happen, it is essential to have the determination to die for God. Any attempt to resist seemed to me impossible. . . .[3]

When she had eventually recovered the use of her faculties and the turmoil at the Incarnation over the 'novelty' had died down a little, she experienced great joy and felt herself so much strengthened that she broke her worldly attachments without regret. Her only friends now were those who loved God.

Doña Guiomar and Don Francisco de Salcedo were naturally of the number. And P. Prádanos, of course. She loved them tenderly. When

[1] Idem.   [2] Sb, V, c. xx–21.   [3] SEC, R, v, pp. 33–4.

P. Prádanos was seriously ill with heart disease his two penitents took him away to the village of El Palo, where Doña Guiomar had large estates, and there constituted themselves his nurses and servants.[1] Teresa was an expert in cooking and preparing delicacies. The Father was somewhat embarrassed at so much attention and Teresa laughed to herself about it:

'I have always had much affection for those who look after my soul; for me they are God's representatives and I treat them as such. It has happened in the case of some of my confessors that they were afraid I was too much attached to them—although in a holy way—and so I incurred their displeasure. I laughed to myself at their mistake. . . .'[2]

She did not fall under P. Prádanos' displeasure, he was her confessor and director until 1558.

As to Doña Guiomar, she was a different person: one was not the friend of Teresa de Ahumada for nothing; it was impossible to hear her speak of God, of heaven, to hear her affirm in her thrilling voice, 'All is nothing' without a deep and radical change of heart and conduct. It was not that she saw her for long at a time even when she lived with her: just for a few brief moments after meals which the Carmelite took alone, contenting herself with a few herbs when she was not fasting,[3] but her presence permeated the whole house. She was so careful to avoid anything detrimental to progress in perfection, took so many disciplines and such lengthy ones, wore so penitential a hair shirt, that the young widow was soon ashamed to continue to revel in her life of luxury. Her taste for magnificence had been criticized in Ávila, people had even accused her of being so luxurious and extravagant that her thirty thousand *reales* of revenue were insufficient: she was eating into her capital: the evil tongues now took on another tone:

'Doña Guiomar has made a sort of convent of her palace!'

'She no longer deigns to receive anyone except monks, nuns, *beatas* and other servants of God!'

'Have you seen her dressed as a poor person?'

'Have you seen her go to church without attendants, carrying the cushion she uses when she spends hours on her knees, herself?'

All the pride of the *hidalgos* might be discerned in a final reproach:

' She shows as much politeness to all and sundry as if she were a servant instead of a noble lady!'[4]

The widow of the lord of Villatoro! To consider it an honour to lodge in her house Maridíaz, a saint if you like, the greatest saint that

[1] SST, vol. I, p. 407. [2] Sb, V, c. xxxvii–5.
[3] FR, L. IV, c. xviii. [4] SST, vol. I, pp. 401–9.

Ávila then boasted of, but the daughter of nobody, that is, of poor folk. Doña Guiomar's servants did say she had no chemise.

'They say that the servants, tired of having to serve riff-raff like that, take it out of her by giving her nothing to eat. The fool does not dare complain lest she should be the cause of their dismissal!'[1]

One pious woman assumed a superior air and confided to her listeners:

'That's charity. Maridíaz has given everything to God. She had only one cloak left, she's given that too. God has drawn her to himself from her youth upwards. Before Doña Guiomar arranged a room as a cell for her, she used to spend whole days and nights in a gallery of the church of San Emiliano. She prays unceasingly. She's a real saint.'

Another who claimed acquaintance with the very highest stages of spirituality but said she had returned to lower levels because all that sort of thing smacked of illuminism and smelt of heresy a mile off, wagged her sententious head:

'Mysticism's in the fashion. I've examined it from every angle and I don't trust it. Look at Maridíaz: she's a saint, it's true. But I've none the less heard her complain of the trials which the Lord does not spare her as a recompense for the penances she performs for him: the greater part of the time she lives in a state of terrible aridity.'

'She complains?'

'In a pious way! She says: "Lord, after taking everything in the world away from me, are you leaving me like this?"[2] Isn't it better to confine oneself to honest, every-day prayers, to virtues which put no one in the shade, rather than to make as much commotion as Doña Guiomar's other friend, Teresa de Ahumada?'

One of the duennas assumed her most intelligent air:

'That person isn't a saint. She couldn't be compared with Maridíaz. I knew her as a child. She always liked to attract attention. Poor Doña Beatriz de Ahumada—God rest her soul—didn't know what to do to master her. Didn't she take the idea into her head, when she was five or six years old, to run away from home, taking her elder brother, Rodrigo, with her, to go to the land of the Turks?'

There on the balcony they drew their faces close together when somebody whispered:

'What about her ecstasies?'

For some time past the name of Teresa de Ahumada had been sufficient to cause the speakers to lower their voices in the large, sombre

[1] Idem.   [2] CTA, cdiii.

apartments where the ladies of this very aristocratic town liked to congregate to munch sweets and speak ill of their neighbours. For when the fires of the Inquisition were burning in Valladolid and Toledo the rumours that were bandied about concerning the Carmelite were enough to make one tremble.

'She says that God speaks to her.'

'She has visions!'

A well-informed person added:

'I've seen the friend in whom she confides, Don Francisco de Salcedo. He pretends to be discretion itself, but it's obvious that nobody in the world is more uneasy than he. As to Padre Daza, he can no longer sleep for the business. Both are convinced that it doesn't come from God, but from the . . .'

The *señoras* crossed themselves on forehead, lips and breast and then made one final sweeping sign.

Thus the graces Teresa received were the talk of the worthy town. This time, too, as in the case of the bodily suffering she had asked for, she might have exclaimed: 'Lord, I didn't want so much!' At this time any supernatural manifestation was an object of much suspicion in Spain. The trial of the Poor Clare of Córdoba, Magdalena de la Cruz, had been a great shock to public faith in such matters. As a prophetess she had foretold the battle of Pavia and the captivity of Francis I; her credit was so great that they would have liked to canonize her in her lifetime, had it been possible. Empress Isabella had given her her portrait, that she might be continually in her thoughts and prayers and was granted the very special favour that the nun would make the first robe worn by Prince Philip with her own holy hands. Feminine superstition ? Even a serious man like the Inquisitor General, Don Alonso Manrique, went to Seville purposely to recommend himself to the miracle worker. But on 1st January 1544, Magdalena de la Cruz, suddenly seized with remorse, publicly confessed that her holiness was simulated, her ecstasies feigned and her wonder-working the result of a pact with the devil. The Holy Office took up the matter and the story profoundly shocked the whole of Spain.

For there was much confusion throughout Spain—people mistook the marvellous for true religion: extravagant behaviour was found side by side with sincere faith. It was the reading of Osuna which first suggested to Teresa that it was desirable to restrain external signs of devotion. In the *Third Spiritual Alphabet* he collects from his own experience facts which it seemed to him ought to be mistrusted:

. . . A woman who was seized with trembling and convulsions whenever she approached the Holy Table sighed and cried aloud. The priest, having seen other instances of the kind, waited patiently holding the Host until this crazy servant of God had become calm again and could communicate. . . .

. . . A monk confessed his sins in public.

. . . Servants of God ran about in the fields imploring Our Lord with great cries to teach them to do his holy will, or singing hymns of thanksgiving. . . .

. . . Haloes of light surround the forehead of men at prayer. More rarely, they hear a mysterious song within their breast. . . .[1]

In the churches the faithful prayed with arms outstretched in the form of a cross, kissed the ground, dragged themselves to the altar on their knees, struck their breasts violently, cried out loud to Our Lord. For the congregation to be in tears during a sermon was a common occurrence. People were seen in ecstasy before their favourite saint. The humble were not exempt from such hysterical manifestations: 'One morning a day labourer was seized with a rapture and was seen to fall to the ground as if paralysed. When he recovered consciousness and they tried to help him to his feet, he exclaimed: "Leave me alone! You are hurting me by holding me back, just as if you were crushing the wings of a bird ready to fly away!" '[2]

Genuinely pious people, false claimants for the stigmata, sham ecstasies, sincere recollection, orthodox faith, short cuts towards heresy, all this was so interwoven and mixed up together that, after a long period of confusion in which the airs and graces of the *Beata* de Piedra-hita as she made way to allow the Blessed Virgin, who, she said, never left her side, to pass, 'edified' all and sundry, the wind suddenly changed and, with the help of the Inquisition, every effect of the love of God perceptible to the senses became suspect: where people thought they had seen Our Lord, they now saw the devil.

If there was a danger of external manifestations being judged as mere pretence, the abandonment of them entirely was no less danger-ous: such abstention might be taken as evidence that you were an *Alumbrado*, an *illuminé*. To remain kneeling during the Gospel, to fix one's eyes on the ground during the elevation of the Host, not to fast or mortify oneself to outward eyes, to affect not to amass indulgences, was to invite the Inquisition to concern itself with your affairs; such interventions were all the more dangerous because positions were not

[1] RO, pp. 72-101. [2] Idem.

defined: no case was clear. Francisca Hernández, a Franciscan tertiary, 'who exercises an inexplicable influence, a kind of dictatorship over various associations of spirituality,' venerated by the Friars Minor who regarded a medal touched by her as a pledge of heavenly graces, was treated by some as 'Medusa' whilst others considered her 'a very holy woman.' [1] She cast such a spell over a brilliant young priest and lector in philosophy, P. Ortiz, that some time after Francisca's arrest by the Inquisition, he went into the pulpit at Toledo and exclaimed in the course of an official inquiry, in the presence of the Chapter and all the civic and religious notabilities: '. . . the reason for the present drought is to punish an immense injustice: the imprisonment of a servant of God in this town!' There was no need for him to continue: a three years' stay in prison persuaded him to submit 'unconditionally' to the judgement of the Church.

A word, a gesture, were enough to arouse suspicion and get one arrested; but to clear oneself thousands of arguments in the course of a trial which lasted for years were necessary. Unless the worst happened and the terrible silence of a secret dungeon closed upon the accused.

Since the opening of the Council of Trent the position had been clearer: the Holy Office was less concerned with subtle distinctions between *Alumbrados*, *Dejados*, followers of Erasmus, reformers and other shades of heretical doctrine, but on the other hand it was no longer satisfied with mild penalties: whoever was suspected of deviating from orthodoxy was accused of Lutheranism. Any work of spirituality written in Spanish was placed on the index, with a very few exceptions, such as the works of Laredo and Osuna. Even the writings of Fray Luis of Granada and John of Ávila did not escape.

To be taxed with Lutheranism meant a request by the Inquisition to clear oneself before its tribunals: those in error were invited to correct their convictions. The obstinate were burned with much ceremony. Those who loved excitement travelled days on end to enjoy the spectacle.

On 21st May and 8th October 1559, the year in which Doña Teresa de Ahumada's visions caused most stir, two typical autos-da-fé were held at Valladolid. Princess Juana, widow of the King of Portugal, sister of the King of Spain and regent of the kingdom, represented the absent Philip II. Thirty heretics on the one occasion, eighty on the second, dressed in the Sambenito, the ignominious yellow tunic, their heads covered with mitres of all sorts on which were painted devils

RO, p. 84.

and flames, and a green candle in their hands, made their way in procession towards the stake or the prisons.

In Ávila there was much talk of such edifying manifestations, particularly at the Incarnation. People spoke of the Princess Regent, in mourning, with black head-dress and gloves and playing with her black and gold fan, of the Prince Don Carlos, the long ranks of monks and penitents carrying lighted torches, followed by the standard of the Holy Inquisition on which the black and white escutcheon of the Order of St Dominic was juxtaposed on crimson damask with the royal arms embroidered in gold. People quoted the sermon of the famous Melchor Cano, the final admonitions to the condemned on the part of the clergy, admonitions which 200,000 spectators gathered from north, south, east and west echoed with their litanies and their groans.

Neither great name nor exalted reputation stayed the arm of the Church. The daughter of the Marquis of Alcañicez, Ana Enríquez, was only restored to her parents on account of her tender years. But Doctor Agustín Cazalla, canon of Salamanca and preacher to the Emperor Charles V? To the stake! Don Cristóbal de Ocampo, Knight of the Order of St John? To the stake! Doña Mencia de Figueroa, maid of honour to the Queen? Condemned! Even the dead did not escape punishment: Doña Leonor de Vibero, who had died before her trial, had been disinterred, her corpse dragged along in the procession, and then she was burned in effigy.

After that people knew what to expect and Teresa had good reason to feel some alarm. Her best friends did not conceal the fact that they were uneasy about her; as to her greatest enemies, one of them voiced the sentiments of all:

'I hope to live long enough to see this nun end up as she deserves, at the stake set up by the Inquisition.' [1]

Unknown persons took the trouble to put her on her guard, or to frighten her.

One day she was asked for in the parlour of the Incarnation. Behind the grille she saw a very distinguished nobleman, richly dressed, in whom she thought she recognized Don Alonso de Quiñones, one of the noblest lords of Ávila. Was it that he wanted to see for himself the nun who was so much talked about in order to form his own opinion of her? When he had greeted her in his grave manner, he stood there in silence. Finally he said:

'Do not forget Magdalena de la Cruz. Spain thought she was a

[1] GJ, vol. III, p. 148.

saint whereas she was the slave of the devil.' [1] Teresa turned pale, bowed her head and answered in the humblest tones: 'I never remember her without trembling.'

Don Alonso was thoughtful as he left the Incarnation and from that day was one of Doña Teresa's defenders. He reasoned: 'So much humility is never found in a tool of Satan.'

[1] FR, L. I, c. ix.

III

HEAVEN AND HELL

A S Teresa was at prayer on St. Peter's day, she felt Christ near her. She saw him neither with the eyes of the body nor with those of the soul but was none the less certain that he was there and was speaking to her. 'Knowing nothing about this kind of vision, I was very much afraid at first and did nothing but weep. A few words from him sufficed to reassure me, and then I was at peace, happy, free from all fear.' [1]

From then onwards she felt Our Lord near her always; instead of being 'full of distractions' she was constantly aware of his presence at her right hand.

One night, coming back from Matins, she said to María de Cepeda, her niece:

'Oh, Sister! If you only knew who our escort was, how delighted you would be!' [2]

Doña Teresa was prouder than Oriana escorted by Amadis, for *her* knight was Our Lord Jesus Christ carrying his cross.

But the enjoyment of such a privilege brought its own difficulties: Teresa had to tell her confessor about it. When she knelt down in the confessional, she was more afraid than if she had had a mortal sin to confess. She managed to get out the stupendous words:

'Father,' she said in a choking voice, 'Our Lord is with me continually, by my side.'

There was silence. She wept. P. Baltasar Alvarez heard the sobs. He was extremely puzzled: yesterday it was divine words she thought she heard, ecstasies—now it was visions. No, she was not lying but, like so many others, she might be the victim of illusion or perhaps trapped in the devil's snares. Unless His Majesty really had manifested himself to this Carmelite. . . .

He questioned her calmly, as if it were a quite ordinary matter:

'How do you see him?'

'Father, I don't see him.'

The priest gave a start:

'Then how do you know it is Christ?'

[1] Sb, V, c. xxvii-2.   [2] MP, quoted SEC, vol. II, p. 113.

'I don't know how I know, Father. But I know it's he.' [1]

She strove to make him understand what must seem unintelligible, sought for comparisons, found none in the world of tangible things and groped hesitatingly for words that would express the divine.

'Perhaps if I put it that he's there in the same way as in the darkness we know that a person is by our side. It's something like that. But not altogether. It's more like a piece of news which is communicated to the soul, an announcement which is clearer than the light of the sun. Not that you see the sun or any brightness, yet a light enlightens the understanding without one realizing it is a light and disposes the soul to the enjoyment of this great good.' [2]

P. Baltasar followed what his penitent said with the utmost difficulty. He grew impatient:

'A light which is not a light? . . .'

'No, for its brightness does not dazzle. It is a soft white glow, so different from earthly light that the sun seems dim in comparison.' [3]

'You say now that it dazzles without dazzling. . . .' The priest's voice became almost curt: 'Who told you that it was Jesus Christ?'

'He tells me so himself. But before he tells me so, my understanding knows it already.' [4]

Teresa who now lived uninterruptedly in Our Lord's presence did not hear the priest say, 'Go in peace,' but 'Watch. . . . Fear. . . . Be on your guard. . . .' Her certainty about the matter was in no way lessened by such admonitions to caution. She was now in a state in which her prayer never ceased, even during sleep. [5]

One day Christ showed her his hands, 'so wondrously beautiful that one couldn't describe them.' [6] This time, too, she was very much afraid; in the beginning, each fresh grace terrified her, but was not this the case with the disciples? The Gospel is full of their fears and terrors.

A little while afterwards she had a vision of Our Lord's countenance and finally, on the feast of St Paul, Christ showed himself to her in his sacred humanity, 'as the risen Christ is depicted in all his beauty and majesty.' [7]

Such gradual advances on the part of the heavenly Bridegroom so completely dissipated her fears that like Psyche she was eager for more: 'I wanted so much to see the colour of his eyes or his stature, in order

---

[1] Sb, V, c. xxvii–3.   [2] Sb, V, c. xxvii–3.   [3] Sb, V, c. xxviii–5.
[4] Sb, V, c. xxvii–5.   [5] See O, p. 114 (Tr.).
[6] Sb, V, c. xxvii–1.   [7] Sb, V, c. xxviii–3.

to be able to speak of them, but this was altogether beyond my deserts and each time I strove to look more closely he vanished altogether. . . .'[1]

Vision followed vision and at the same time the love of God increased in her, burning so intensely that she felt that henceforward she would find life only in death. 'I felt this love with such intensity that I no longer knew what was happening to me, nothing satisfied me any longer, I felt as if I was being swept off my feet, as if my soul was being torn out of me. Oh, what clever tactics Our Lord used! . . . The force of his love crushed me with a dying so sweet that the soul would have wished never to return to life again.'[2]

The final grace was transverberation, which she received many times, both at the convent of the Incarnation and when staying with Doña Guiomar.

One evening Ana Gutiérrez, one of the nuns in the convent, rushed downstairs on hearing cries and groans coming from Doña Teresa de Ahumada's cell. 'How you frightened me!' she exclaimed when she found Teresa quite well. But her countenance was aflame with the glow and radiance of ecstasy; slowly she returned to consciousness of the world around her:

I frightened you? Daughter, I wish you could have seen what I've seen![3]

. . . I saw an angel close to me, on my left, in bodily shape, a thing granted to me but rarely. He was not large, but small, very beautiful, his face radiant. . . . No doubt he was one of those they call cherubim. He did not tell me his name but I see clearly that there is such a difference between one angel in heaven and another, that I could not express it. He held a long golden lance in his hand and I thought its tip was all flames. He seemed to plunge it several times into my heart, right to the very depths of me. When he drew it out, he seemed to pluck my heart out with it, leaving me all on fire with an immense love of God. The pain was so sharp that I moaned but the delight of this tremendous pain is so overwhelming that one cannot wish it to leave one, nor is the soul any longer satisfied with anything less than God. It is a spiritual, not a bodily pain, although the body has some part, even a considerable part, in it. It is an exchange of courtesies between the soul and God . . . so sweet that I beg God to let whoever thinks I'm not telling the truth taste it. . . .[4]

As the love of the creature met the Creator's love a divine spark leaped forth.

[1] Sb, V, c. xxix–2.   [2] Idem, 8.
[3] GJ, vol. III, p. 324.   [4] Sb, V, c. xxix–13.

ÁVILA

The Gallery round the Cloister of the Convent
of St. Joseph

When she had been thus transpierced and consumed by divine love, she remained 'as it were, stupefied,' 'no longer wishing either to see or to speak, but to be alone with my pain, which was greater glory than any created thing. . . .' [1]

She complained of feeling great heat and asked Ana Gutiérrez to cut her hair, to give her some small relief. Ana was so astonished at the hair's sweet perfume, 'the perfume of heaven,' [2] that she hid a lock of it. Teresa read her thoughts:

'I order you not to think foolish things and to throw that away with the rubbish!'

Henceforward it was impossible for Teresa to resist the super-natural visitations which occurred 'even in public.' [3] 'As a giant lifts a straw,' [4] so the force of ecstasy raised her from the ground and held her suspended in the air. One day after Communion, the congregation who filled the convent chapel saw her raised two or three palms' height above the ground.[5] She strove to prevent this happening, 'with immense fatigue, like someone who is struggling with a strong giant, she held on with both hands to the communion grille, or lay down on the ground.' [6] Nothing was of the slightest use. She felt the force under her feet and it raised her from the ground 'with an impetus so swift and strong that you see and feel the cloud rise—or perhaps I should say this mighty eagle, and he sweeps you upwards with his wings.' [7]

Those who witnessed such divine manifestations gossiped and chattered about them, whereas Teresa was for days in a state of deep intense sadness and her great need was solitude.[8]

Solitude, when one is the laughing-stock of a small town? Peace, when Ávila knew full well that the fires of the Inquisition were blazing for the benefit of lunatics of her sort at Valladolid, Toledo and Seville?

Never had the families of the one hundred and eighty nuns of the Incarnation, their friends or their devotees shown themselves so eager for visits to the parlour. They hastened there 'for news.' Even before she was asked, one sister volunteered breathlessly:

'To-night when she came to Matins, as pale as if she were dying, she began to call out to Our Lord with great cries like someone calling for help, she seemed to be suffering greatly and the contrast between

---

[1] Sb. V, c. xxix-14.
[2] GJ, vol. III, p. 324.
[3] Sb, V, c. xxix-14.
[4] Sb, V, c. xii-13.
[5] FR, L. IV, c. xii.
[6] Sb, V, c. xx-14.
[7] Idem.
[8] Cf. Sb, V, c. xx-10.

her suffering face and the radiance of her countenance when she presently fell into ecstasy was tremendous!' [1]

There was no need to name the one they were speaking of: 'she' was Doña Teresa de Ahumada, whom some called 'the saint of the Incarnation' but whom the majority of people suspected of imposture or pretended to pity, saying she was possessed.

Things came to such a pass that she would have preferred 'to be buried alive' [2] rather than show herself in public: she thought of escaping to some convent where as a simple lay-sister employed in the most menial tasks she would be forgotten. Her confessor, P. Baltasar Álvarez, would not consent.

P. Álvarez, a Jesuit like PP. Cetina and Prádanos, had been directing her since 1558. He had the open mind of a young man but also youth's lack of experience and timidity allied with a certain intransigence, and he had not yet succeeded in overcoming his natural harshness although he strove to do so by the practice of mortification. When he arrived at San Gil, he chose a cell so small that he could hardly move in it. There was no table: just a plank covered with big books. No chair: a stool. When at Doña Guiomar's, he refused the armchair she respectfully offered him, sitting stiffly and uncomfortably on a seat without a back:

'To suffer in a thousand ways when one has not deserved it is like a mouthful of tender meat in which there are no bones.' [3]

The young father talked of penances as if they were his chief delight. In the choice of the mortifications he imposed on Teresa, he introduced a certain refinement of cruelty:

'You will make your general confession at the College of San Gil (the Jesuit college)—with unveiled face. . . .' [4]

To force Teresa, for whom a general confession was always the most painful of sufferings, for the thought of having offended God was so bitter to her—to make an exhibition of her sins in this way was more than severity: it showed a want of all fine feeling. However she obeyed without a murmur.

He deprived her of Communion for days together: she did not complain.

He ordered her to avoid solitude instead of seeking it: she gave up her own judgement in the matter.

With him there was nothing but 'questions at one time and at another reproaches' [5]; he subjected her to question and criticism as he

---

[1] Cf. SEC, R, i, p. 4.   [2] Sb, V, c. xxxi–12.   [3] LA, c. x.
[4] SST, vol. I, p. 456, n. 1.   [5] Sb, V, c. xxvi–3.

pleased, alleging that she needed all these trials and rebukes because her will was not yet conquered. But, inflexible master though he was, touched by her sweetness he confided to his friends:

'She obeys like a little child. . . .'[1]

The Rector of the Jesuits, P. Dionisio Álvarez, who was choleric in disposition and harsh in character, had given him his instructions: he was never to relax his severity. The pious coterie under Salcedo-Daza leadership wanted to go a step further: Teresa must be crushed and broken to find out what there was at the bottom of the woman. Instead of complaining the victim was moved to pity for them: 'Timid souls, but good ones, those who treated me most harshly were those who loved me most. . . .'[2]

For now more than ever, at the Incarnation, among the clergy and throughout the whole of Ávila, there was only one cry:

'Teresa de Ahumada's visions are diabolical!'

P. Baltasar kept a cool head. He stood by his penitent in his own fashion—which was somewhat grim. When the panic of all those round her was too much for her, she would complain in the confessional:

'Father, I am afraid of deceiving you and deceiving myself at the same time.'

He replied with a tinge of self-conceit but not unkindly:

'Child, don't be afraid. I've got a good enough brain not to allow myself to be duped. . . .'[3]

He gave her some comfort all the same, this terrible man. He went to an infinite amount of trouble over her, his tiny cell was littered up with everything that saintly theologians, including St Thomas, had written on the mystical life and its manifestations, until he ended by declaring despondently:

'I've got to read all these books to understand Doña Teresa de Ahumada.'[4]

He himself had no experience of supernatural graces, but he was convinced of the Carmelite's good faith, and was often awed by the account of her visions. If his treatment of her was harsh it was so that her soul might be strengthened by self-discipline and that she might find resources within herself which would enable her to guide and control her nature. We might accuse him of want of courage, of not having firmly stood out against those who were crying out: 'All that is devilry!' But important people in the city, of whom the Society of

[1] SEC, vol. II, pp. 506–7.   [2] Sb, V, c. xxx–6.
[3] Sb, V, c. xxx–13.   [4] FR, L. I, c. xi.

Jesus, which was still classed as a new Order, had in its own interests to take account, and other zealous and pious souls, were advising him not to trust the visionary.[1] Perhaps she was possessed? There were many who thought they were being charitable when they suggested that she should be exorcised.[2]

Teresa's outlook on all this was calm and sane. If it is true that she was momentarily tempted to take a less severe confessor—'I am,' she said, 'a person who cannot do my best when led by force' [3]—she did not give way to this transitory weakness and soon admitted that so far she had made more progress under P. Baltasar than under anyone else, even though he constantly mortified her and tried her as much as he could. To him she said, breaking out into her delightful laugh:

'I'm very fond of a certain Father I know, in spite of his bad character. . . .'[4]

The problem was still as perplexing as ever: was it the devil or God?

Teresa sometimes had to master a gesture of impatience: how *could* she mistake one for the other? Who except Our Lord could have brought to her soul so much light, such fulfilment of love and development of new strength in the exercise of every virtue? She argued: '. . . One single word of those I am privileged to hear, one vision, one moment of recollection which does not last as long as an *Ave*, and soul and body are in such peace, the understanding is so enlightened that I am amazed. . . . I know what I was before, on the way to losing my soul, and I no longer recognize myself, I do not understand how I come by these virtues: they are given me, I don't work to win them. . . . God has taken this means not only to win me to his service but to save me from hell. . .' [5]

She knew perfectly well that the devil used no disguise when he wanted 'to play at ball with her soul'; [6] she saw close to her 'a most vile little black creature,'[7] or perhaps a tiny imp sat on her missal making faces at her. She had seen the place allotted to her in hell and declared when she returned to consciousness again: 'There one burns in such a manner that to be burnt here on earth is a trifle in comparison.' [8]

And the 'holy gentleman' with all his pious clique was attempting to identify the God of love, him whom 'one cannot look at any more

[1] Cf. Sb, V, c. xxv–15.   [2] FR, L. I, c. x.
[3] Sb, V, c. xxxii.   [4] FR, L. I, c. xi.
[5] SEC, R, i, p. 4.   [6] Sb, V, c. xxx–11.
[7] Sb, V, c. xxxi–3.   [8] Sb, V, c. xxxii–3.

than one can look at the sun' without falling into ecstasy, with the hellish vermin she was determined to ignore!

For such was her attitude. A daughter of Ávila, the City of the Knights, was not going to allow herself to be intimidated by devils even if they were legion!

'I snap my fingers at devils! [1] They frighten me no more than flies! [2] It is they who are afraid of me! I don't understand why people are afraid of them. Why should we say: "Devil! Devil!" when we can say "God ! God!" and make them tremble? Come on, all you devils! I am God's servant and I am curious to see what you can do to me!' [3]

She added, referring to her pious persecutors:—'I fear those who are afraid of the devil more than the devil himself. . . .'[4]

She was too exceptional not to puzzle and disturb the small minds which she was not yet of sufficient stature to dominate. And so good, but ordinary, folk entertained doubts for Doña Teresa de Ahumada's sanity. Dangerous and cowardly as they were, they even went so far as to impose on her the most cruel suffering she had yet undergone. The idea was Gonzalo de Aranda's—a fine fellow of a priest who had joined the vigilance committee formed by Salcedo, Daza and their associates. They hurried to the Incarnation:

'Doña Teresa de Ahumada is wanted in the parlour!'

They imparted their idea to her in all its crudeness, gave her their order quite baldly:

'When you see what you think is Our Lord, hold out the cross and make horns at him with your fingers . . .(*las higas*). It's the devil and you'll catch him like that!' [5]

Teresa was completely taken aback. For *them* to talk of making horns at God! She knew something of the gentleness of Christ, but also had experience of his 'terrifying' majesty. 'I say terrifying, for although this presence is more beautiful and delightful than one can imagine . . . his majesty is so great that one is filled with awe.' [6]

There was nothing for it but to submit. The Lord made this trial the occasion of fresh graces when, with humble apologies, she made 'horns' at him:

'Daughter, you do right to obey.' [7]

She offered him the cross as one would offer it to Satan in person. He changed the cross into a jewel sparkling with the precious stones of paradise.

---

[1] Sb, V, c. xxv–22.   [2] Idem, 20.   [3] Idem, 19–20–22.
[4] Idem, 22.   [5] Sb, V, c. xxix–5.
[6] Sb, M, VI, c. ix–5.   [7] Sb, V, c. xxix–6.

But when her mentors enjoined upon her not to practise mental prayer any more, Christ was angry:

'Tell them from me that that is tyranny.' [1]

God—or the devil? God—or the devil?

'It was enough to send one out of one's mind.' [2]

She did not go out of her mind. Imperturbable common sense together with her fondness for household tasks fortunately provided her strong nature with an outlet which had a soothing effect upon her 'interior troubles.' When her sisters maliciously endeavoured to catch the saint—or the possessed nun—by surprise, they found her busy arranging flowers or decorating an altar; even more often, broom in hand, they found her making war on the dust in every nook and cranny.

And the woman who spends her time cleaning and polishing keeps her wits about her.

[1] Idem.   [2] Sb, V, c. xxviii–18.

IV

FRAY PEDRO DE ALCÁNTARA

THE sun beats fiercely down in Castile in August and at siesta time every road is deserted: not a man, not even a dog. I am wrong, however. In the distance a dark blob shows up against the light which is so brilliant that every speck of dust is separately visible. A friar. A pilgrim perhaps? His brown habit which is all in rags sweeps the dust, the Franciscan hood is well down over his eyes. Not that he is afraid of being blinded by the dazzling light—the brilliance of his interior vision is more intense than any sunlight—but he despises the world which he treads beneath his bare feet. Vagabond that he is, he has never consented to travel otherwise than as the very poor do, begging his bread; he has been all over Spain and Italy with his regular, measured tread. Moreover, he asks for alms but seldom: with a hunch of bread every three days, he has as much as he wants. 'It's a matter of habit,' he says. Witnesses affirm that he has sometimes remained a whole week forgetting to take any earthly nourishment.

He goes on his way towards Ávila, his eyes cast down all the time, and does not see the battlements and bell-towers silhouetted in the distance. But the sun has been travelling too, sleepers yawn, life seems to reawaken from its torpor, its resurrection being immediately expressed by the cheerful trot of a donkey, or a song interspersed with words of encouragement addressed by the donkey-boy, a bright lad who is not content to be quiet for long, to his beast. He calls out to the friar as he passes:

'Hey now, friar! You're on foot but I have a donkey to ride!'

The friar trudges on his way without raising his eyes, his 'peace be with thee' is uttered from under his hood. His cheeks are hollow, his beard white. And the swarthy, wrinkled body hidden under his Franciscan rags is twisted and knurled like the roots of trees.[1]

'Fray Pedro!'

The friar does not so much as move an eyelid. His silence betrays his identity and the lad spurs on the donkey with his bare feet, forcing it to trot more quickly, and hurries off to the town where he cries out to all and sundry:

[1] SB, V, c. xxvii-18.

'Fray Pedro's along the road! He's coming to Ávila! Fray Pedro de Alcántara! The saintly Fray Pedro!'

The saint: the man who imposed on himself the severest of penances, and spent all his time standing or kneeling in order to conquer sleep. For forty years he allowed himself only one hour of sleep in the twenty-four and that in a sitting posture 'his head resting against a block of wood.' [1] Moreover it was impossible for him to lie down in his cell, which was only four and a half feet long. He never wore any other garment but his drab-coloured habit and had no cloak, however bitter the cold or drenching the rain. Even in the snow he never went otherwise than barefoot.

All Ávila knew his story: he was born in wild Estremadura of a distinguished family connected with Hernán Cortés, the famous conqueror of Mexico. He became a Franciscan at nineteen and, with the habit, acquired something which was of greater value, St Francis' burning love of God, his love for his brethren and for 'Lady Poverty.' Even in those days he had dreams of reforming the Order, of bringing it back to its original Gospel severity, but he decided to begin by reforming himself. It was known that when quite a young man he remained three years in one monastery without distinguishing his brethren otherwise than by the sound of their voices, for he had imposed on himself the mortification never to raise his eyes; 'and so he didn't know the way to the place of necessity, but merely followed the friars.' [2] For years he had not so much as looked at any woman. Now, it was indifferent to him whether he saw one or not. As he walked people would try and catch the sound of the chinking of his penance—made out of pieces of tin. [3]

'Fray Pedro de Alcántara!'

All the pious folk flocked to meet him. 'The blessed man' had many friends in Ávila and often went there. Juan Velázquez de Ávila, lord of Loriana, offered him his house which was not far from Doña Guiomar's palace.

'It's God who has sent him to us.'

And Doña Guiomar ran off to the Incarnation to drag permission out of the prioress to keep Doña Teresa with her for a week: she *must* have the opportunity of seeing Fray Pedro de Alcántara. At last! A saint would study her 'case' and the authority of Fray Pedro was such that his verdict would certainly be the accepted one. For Doña Guiomar had never had any doubt: her friend's visions 'were from God.'

---

[1] Sb, V, c. xxvii–17, 18.   [2] Idem.
[3] Sb, V, c. xxx–2.

Soon all Ávila was aware that Fray Pedro was treating the Carmelite with marked kindness, nay, even more: that he found joy in her visits.

'He says that her presence is a comfort to him, his greatest consolation being to meet those on whom God lavishes great graces. . . .'[1]

The tribe of loud-voiced critics lowered its tones when he declared publicly that he was very sorry for her because she had suffered the most severe trial possible: that of opposition from good people. . . . He added that no one in Ávila was capable of understanding her.[2]

He understood her, not through theology or because he had studied mysticism, but from personal experience: he knew all about this invisible presence of God, the mind taking flight, the complete overthrow of the senses which occurred in adoration, the divine words, their effects, the joy they gave the soul.

'Don't be troubled any longer, child; thank God and rest assured that all this is *his* spirit. There is nothing more certain, nothing in which you can more safely believe, except the truths of faith themselves. . . .'[3]

He offered to speak to P. Baltasar Álvarez, to the Daza-Aranda following, and the 'holy gentleman' heard someone who was holier than he solemnly affirm: 'After the Holy Scriptures and all the Church orders us to believe, there is nothing more certain than the divine origin of what this woman sees. . . .'[4]

All were convinced except poor Salcedo: he did not dare to protest, but all the same he secretly retained a certain amount of misgiving. It could well have been argued against him:

'If Teresa were not holy, she would not put up with such an obstinate blockhead as you. The very fact of her never having said a bitter word against you, of having shown so much affection for you, of being entirely without spite, the delightful letters she has written you. . . . "Don't say so much about your being old, for to think of it makes my head hurt all over . . ." [5]—that alone deserves a halo. . .'

In Fray Pedro de Alcántara Teresa had won a lifelong friend, more than lifelong even, for he appeared to her more than once after his death, 'in very great glory.'

Not only did this good man extricate her from a difficult position, but she found him charming. What a contrast between his gracious kindness and the hard rigidity of the 'learned' and pious! 'With all his sanctity he was very courteous and easy of approach; a man of few words, except to answer the questions put to him, but what he said

---

[1] Sb, V, c. xxx-5.   [2] Idem, 6.   [3] Idem, 5.
[4] PA, quoted SEC, vol. II, p. 307.   [5] CTA, x.

was very much to the point and showed that he had a sense of humour.' [1]

Teresa breathed again and came to life, now she had every joy, even that of intelligent and delightful conversation. 'God preserve us from gloomy saints!'

Teresa and Fray Pedro did not part without promising to correspond and to recommend each other to God. 'His humility was so great that he set some store by the prayers of this wretched creature, to my great embarrassment. He left me greatly strengthened, reassured and happy. . . .' [2]

Francis Borgia's approval had protected Teresa only for a short time. Would that of Peter of Alcántara prove more effective? In the end Teresa succeeded in winning Ávila to her side, but this was due more to her own humility and obedience than to the influence of distinguished 'servants of God.' Like her first master, Osuna, she never failed to recognize that 'weak women' may be the victims of illusion and so she left herself entirely in the hands of the learned Doctors. But one does not cease to be a human being because one is an expert in theology, and such pious persons, conceited as they were in their own fashion, finally ceased to doubt the genuineness of the graces received by a woman who treated them with all the submission and veneration they considered their due.

It had become a sort of habit with them to insist upon her 'giving an account of her soul' to experts of their choice: after P. Francis Borgia, Fray Pedro de Alcántara, after Fray Pedro de Alcántara, P. de Salazar, after P. de Salazar, Master Juan de Ávila, after Master Juan de Ávila, P. Pedro de Ibáñez, not to mention all those for whom she had been asked to write out a general confession. They all approved her; P. Ibáñez even wrote: ' I cannot do otherwise than consider her a saint.' [3]

Although the fact did not occur to them, these frequent accounts of her spiritual life and mystical experiences were actually a remarkable intellectual training and a valuable exercise in literary expression. Forced as she was to analyse her feelings, examine her conscience, deepen her self-knowledge, and constrained to comprehend what she would have been content to feel, to define the indefinable, to describe the indescribable, her reasoning faculty became more developed and acute, while her spirit cleaved to God. Salcedo, Daza, Aranda, with

---

[1] Sb, V, c. xxvii–18.					[2] Sb, V, c. xxx–7.
[3] IB quoted SEC, vol. II, p. 149.

their punctilious demands, were thus partly responsible for building up in Teresa a realist mind so clear and virile, and for her forming a style so precise, persuasive and expressive. The memory of these various worthies survives only because she recorded their names.

The first of these *Relations* is dated 1560. It is addressed to P. Pedro Ibáñez, a learned Dominican whom Teresa often went to consult at the monastery of Santo Tomás. It introduces us to a woman of forty-five who is emerging from her trials and the flood of graces she has received unscathed and unspoiled—a woman with a wonderfully clear mind and so well balanced that she seems able henceforward to stand up against anything. The progress since the time when she gave herself over to spectacular penances is evident. The desire for perfection can be seen manifesting itself in small things—which, after all, are the most important—forgetfulness of self, detachment, obedience, poverty, kindness, the determination never to offend God again, even by venial sin. This admirable ascending curve shows only one deviation: the conviction that 'all is nothing' is over-emphasized to the extent that the beautiful things she has loved so much, 'water, the country, perfumes, music,' seem to her as nothing 'but rubbish.' [1] But the time will come when she will learn to praise the Creator in his creatures.

Fears, tears even, still persist but from a fresh and different cause: 'The desire of serving God which comes to me is so intense that I should like to shout out and tell everybody how important it is not to be satisfied with giving only a little. . . . This desire is so keen that the very notion of my weakness crushes me interiorly. This body of mine fetters me. If it were not for that I should do great things. My helplessness in serving God causes me unbearable grief. . . .' [2]

This was the first manifestation of Doña Teresa de Ahumada's great need to express herself in activity although she had only just won the right to live in peace.

Daughter of Don Alonso and Doña Beatriz, sister of seven young men gone off overseas, would she be able to remain quietly in her convent? She had a fighting nature, certainly, but at the same time she was practised in every form of self-discipline and *ascesis*: without this discipline her impetuous nature would doubtless have only stirred up turbulence and disorder. But in her prayer she 'gathers up' her forces, binding them into a bundle of which her will to serve is the cord.

Doña Teresa was to prove to the world that contemplation is the most powerful lever for action.

[1] Cf. SEC, R, p. 4. [2] Cf. Idem.

V

THE TROUBLES OF THE KINGDOM OF FRANCE

TERESA DE AHUMADA'S desire was to plunge into action the moment she was ready to do so: she would never be found letting opportunity slip by until it was too late. In her, joy was uppermost, for love is joy and Teresa was now wholly possessed by love. What one does through love, with love, never hurts.

The gateway which leads to God for her was not a narrow one; on two occasions, in almost identical terms, she for whom Our Lord 'is not a dead man, but the living Christ,'[1] and who owned her preference for the risen Christ 'without suffering and full of glory,'[2] affirmed: 'Lord, I do not see in what way the road which leads to you is narrow: it is not a footpath but a royal highway.'[3] And again, 'Lord, he who truly loves you moves in security along a wide and royal highway.'[4]

The characteristics of the woman of action could be clearly discerned in her: 'God endowed her with an amazing courage. She who was formerly so timid now put the devils to flight. She knew nothing of the affected ways and foibles peculiar to women. Scrupulosity was foreign to her nature; she was extremely frank and straightforward. The clarity of her mind, her understanding of spiritual things, were remarkable.'[5]

Teresa had regained her equilibrium. Or, to put it more correctly, they at last allowed her to show that she had never lost it: if the worthy folk by whom she was surrounded had not driven her nearly distracted with all their talk and fuss about the devil, she would doubtless have quickly overcome her initial fears, and from earthly things would have turned to move in the sphere of heavenly ones with perfect ease, radiating heaven upon earth.

Obliged as she was at this period of her life to give some care to temporal matters, she acquitted herself well. Through her father's death and the absence abroad of her elder brothers, she had now become

[1] Sb, V, c. xxviii–8.
[2] Cf. Sb, V, c. xxii–6.
[3] Sb, V, c. xxxv–13.
[4] Idem, 14.
[5] Cf. IB quoted SEC, vol. II, p. 132.

the head of the family. There was the business of getting the damages reduced in a lawsuit instigated by a crochety heir, Martín Guzmán, María's husband. She had to face it alone, as she did the departure for overseas in their turn of Antonio, Pedro and Agustín, who removed the furniture and belongings from the family home, let it out at 30 ducats and left her with the responsibility of bringing up her young sister, Juana. Teresa brought her to the Incarnation where she shared her own cell, and in 1553 married her to Don Juan de Ovalle, a distinguished gentleman of Ávila. Amid her visions and all they involved, she had to see to it that the father-in-law, 'Juan de Ovalle the elder,' gave the young couple a sufficient allowance.

At the end of the year 1560, in spite of wretched health to which she paid no attention, Teresa was at the height of her powers; in addition, she also had the precious advantage of tried and henceforth unshakable friendships. All of them, Francisco de Salcedo, Gaspar Daza, Gonzalo de Aranda, P. Pedro Ibáñez, were now not only convinced, but completely won over to her: even should she ask them to go through the eye of a needle, she would not lose their friendship. The veneration of the 'holy gentleman' for her would soon be as remarkable as his doubts had been:

'If they were to tell me that St John the Baptist was at the gates of Avila and Mother Teresa in some other part of the town, I would throw away the opportunity of seeing St John the Baptist to cast myself at Mother Teresa's feet and ask her blessing.'

Fray Pedro de Alcántara was her friend, P. Francisco de Borja sang her praises, 'those in the Society' respected her, the Dominicans revered her, the Franciscans loved her; and Doña Guiomar de Ulloa, who never ceased to stand up for her, was always there.

At the Incarnation hostility died down, the sceptical apologized; more than forty nuns followed her example in the ways of prayer and imitated her virtues. Her virtues and not her ecstasies: she strove to persuade her sisters that heaven was more easily to be won by obedience and forgetfulness of self than by the desire for supernatural graces: raptures and ecstasies proved God's loving kindness; they were no guarantee of perfection.

In this convent Teresa could gently pursue her progress heavenward. Along a royal highway? The convent was more like a main street or a fair in the market-place. The number of nuns, to which must be added that of the secular persons in the convent, was always excessive and those who troubled to observe the Constitutions in the minority. The noise and bustle of the world penetrated everywhere and Doña Teresa de Ahumada was called to the parlour too frequently for her liking.

All these conversations were a waste of time, a source of distractions in prayer leading to coldness in divine love. Henceforward for Teresa relatives and friends were merely the enemies of the interior life: she had proved by experience the dissipating effect of useless talk, the corrosive action of criticism which it was not always easy to put down.

On the other hand, solitude would mean silence; silence, concentration; and concentration, strength. Strength for love. Strength for happiness. Not in her own interests, but for the world. The awakening in her of the need for action manifested itself under the form of desire for the apostolate.

Teresa, being a Castilian, was a realist. In her obedience to the divine law she found such joys, so concrete an increase of happiness, that human ways seemed to her only 'rubbish'; she was seized with compassion for those who persisted in not understanding this.

> *Come to me, all ye that labour and are heavily burdened, and I will re-*
> *fresh you.* . . . What more do we want, Lord? What are we asking
> for? What are men running after if not rest and refreshment? Help
> us, my God, help us! What does this mean, Lord? What a pity it
> is, what blindness to be seeking where it is impossible to find!
> Have pity on your creatures, O Creator. Consider that we do not
> understand ourselves, that we do not know what we desire and
> have no idea what we are asking for. Give us light, O Lord
> . . . . What a hard thing I am asking of you, my true God: to
> love one who loves you not, to open to one who doesn't knock, to
> give health to one who enjoys being ill and looks for diseases! . . .[1]
> Have pity on those who have no pity on themselves! [2]

Teresa was well aware that God had created man for happiness in the accomplishment of successive resurrections in him [3]; in the Gospels he taught the art of living happily. By breaking the divine law, man made his own unhappiness, just as anyone who infringed the natural law by refusing to breathe would cause his own death. But this was what the creature persisted in refusing to see: 'God wills that we seek truth and we choose a lie; he wants us to seek what is eternal and we love passing things; he wants us to aspire to great and high things, but we love what is dust, and earthy; he would wish us to love only

---

[1] Sb, E, c. xviii-2, 3.   [2] Sb, E, c. ix-1.
[3] *I.e.* in the spiritual life, every degree of surrender to God brings its own 'resurrection' or new and deeper life in him (Tr.).

certainty, but all we love here on earth are things that are uncertain. . . .' [1]

Teresa now experienced a new feeling: that of compassion for mankind and in particular for the kingdom of France. At that time France was Spain's most formidable enemy, but Teresa's love goes beyond the concept of patriotism. 'At that time I understood the calamities and miseries of France and the harm the Lutherans had done there. That hurt me, and, knowing that this was the only way I could do something to help, I wept before Our Lord and begged him to remedy the condition of affairs. I would have given my life a thousand times over to save a single one of the souls that were being lost there. . . .' [2]

The passing moment in which she spoke in this way was one whose influence would endure unto eternity. The combat which she was ready to wage was not a war of hatred: Teresa was against no one, all she wanted was the unrestricted penetration of love. She did not judge, she loved; she did not condemn, she did not castigate, she only wanted to give and to give herself. 'The world is burning!' [3]

Like Loyola's legionaries, she had the gift of infusing love wherever it was necessary. But the human voice is not so far-reaching in its influence as a soul grafted in God by prayer; silence which is gathered up in him is more powerful than vociferations.

From the negative conception of unity expressed in the phrase 'all is nothing,' Teresa passed to that of constructive and positive unity: 'God is all.' She was fully aware of the strength of two or three gathered in his name. She pondered over what Our Lady's Order had been like before Pope Eugenius IV, on account of the extreme wretchedness of the times, mitigated the rigours of the primitive Rule, thus turning Carmels which were formerly strongholds of penance and prayer into sanctimonious houses of refuge for lonely bachelors and spinsters.

Such thoughts worried Teresa. At this time they formed her principal subject of conversation.

Doña Teresa de Ahumada's cell was attractive; it was detached from the main convent and consisted of two rooms built one above the other. On the ground floor was an oratory, very well kept, and having a recess adorned with pictures; above them was a Latin inscription: *Enter not into judgement with thy servant, O Lord.* She slept on the first floor and this she also used during the day; here she had a room

[1] Sb, C, c. xlii–4.   [2] Sb, C, c. i–2.   [3] Sb, C, c. i–5.

whose windows looked on to the garden. Here also she received many visitors, for visits from cell to cell were one of the pleasures of life at the Incarnation.

One day Doña Teresa de Ahumada, sitting on a cushion on the floor, as was quite usual since so many Moorish customs had crept into daily life, was working at her embroidery; her closest friends were there with her: Ana and Inés de Tapia, her cousins, and the faithful Juana Suárez. Leonora and María de Ocampo, her special favourites, loved to hear her talk, for their aunt Teresa spoke of Our Lord with such charm and eagerness that they never tired of hearing her. As she narrated them, the lives of the holy Fathers of the Desert in the far-off times when the Order of Carmel first began were so full of colour that they reminded one of an illuminated manuscript. Not that one could really hope to be fed by an angel like the holy prophet Elias any more than plaited palm would now be a suitable material for nuns' habits— but what grandeur there was in their silence and what strength in their solitude!

'The Eternal was not in the strong and mighty wind, he was not in the earthquake, he was not in the fire, but he was in the still, small voice, and he spoke to Elias. . . .'

From the patio used for recreation rose the sound of flutes and tambourines through which could be heard someone singing one of the latest *romances*.[1]

'Who indeed among us here would be able to hear the still, small voice? Life in this convent is difficult, there are too many of us. . . .'

'Superiors themselves make a complete withdrawal from the world impossible.'

Did they not frequently oblige Teresa to go and make a long stay in the house of some noble family of Ávila 'who enjoyed her company?'—People so important that they dare not refuse them. . . .

And the parlours . . .

It was María de Ocampo who spoke first:

'Let's go away then, all of us here! And let's organize a solitary life for ourselves "like the hermits did." ' [2]

Teresa gave her young niece a searching glance and lowered her eyes again over her embroidery. She thought to herself: 'At last!' and thanked God.

María was seventeen. She was a lay boarder at the Incarnation as her aunt had been thirty years before at Our Lady of Grace. When Teresa saw the grandchild of her uncle Francisco for the first time at

---

[1] *I.e.* ballads (Tr.).   [2] FR, L. I, c. xiii.

La Puebla de Montalbán, on the occasion of a pilgrimage to Our Lady of Guadalupe, she was so taken with the child's bright face that she asked to have her with her: she would bring her up in her cell instead and in the place of her sister Juana. She loved children so much.

María de Ocampo, however, did not come until ten years later and even then put off her arrival: she could not come without renewing her wardrobe, for 'she was then very grand and elegant and to keep up this appearance she had to display much ingenuity and use extraordinary contrivances.' [1] She took so much pleasure in these contrivances that the idea of becoming a nun which she had entertained for a short time was completely stifled. Teresa did not receive her young guest any the less affectionately for that. Nor did she reproach her for thinking of marriage:

'Juana lived here for ten years, she left to marry Juan de Ovalle.'

She did not blame her for liking tales of chivalry and never thought of forbidding her to read them:

'You get a taste for reading that way. I used to like them, too. You'll perhaps come one day, as I did, to want more serious reading. . . .'

That was why this sudden desire for the solitary life made her both smile and give thanks to God.

The idea was launched, 'in jest.' But those who were present found it so attractive that 'one word led to another and the evening was spent in devising ways and means of setting up a small convent and in discussing what it would cost. . . .' For earthly wealth is necessary to found a miniature paradise.

What of it! María was determined to have her hermitage and appealed to her aunt:

'Found one! Like the one we've been talking of! I'll help you with my fortune!' [2]—her share, that was, of the family inheritance.

Such enthusiasm amused Teresa very much. The next day, still laughing about it, she said to Doña Guiomar:

'These young people were in high spirits yesterday. They amused themselves with working out a plan for us to found a small convent after the style of the Discalced Franciscans.'

Doña Guiomar did not treat the project as a joke.

A great movement for the reform of the religious Orders, the lax condition of which was openly admitted, was sweeping over Spain. New Orders were founded, the Rule of old ones put into force again where necessary. The Society of Jesus was a new Order: the reform of the Order of St Dominic, intensified in Spain by Hurtado and his

---

[1] Idem.   [2] Idem.

followers, represented a return to primitive austerity. In short, in a Europe rent asunder with the struggles between Catholics and Lutherans—to use Teresa's terms, for she did not so much as mention the name of Calvin—Philip II was going to make the maintenance of religious unity in his realms his primary aim.

The girl who thus suggested the idea of reforming Carmel 'in fun' was impregnated with the thoughts and dreams of the woman with whom she lived; it also happened that she was thinking along the same lines as her sovereign who was then preparing to build the Escorial, the place where kings would crumble to dust, that he might dwell there amid the continual vision of the hollowness of this world.

That was why Doña Guiomar treated the matter with all seriousness. She said to Teresa:

'Found. I will help you.'

This was to respond to the Carmelite's secret wish by a call for immediate action. But she alone had considered the project deeply enough to realize the difficulties of carrying it out; she alone, because she had experience of such things, knew how sharp the uprooting would be. She alone knew, moreover, that from the moment when she 'decided' no amount of opposition would make her draw back.

We admire Teresa de Ahumada for many things, but we love her for having told us her very feminine reason for a momentary hesitation: 'I liked being in the house where I was very much, for I had my cell arranged exactly to my taste. . . .' [1]

She gave a quick look round; she felt regret leaving such pleasant surroundings.

But it was not for her to choose: 'We decided quite firmly to leave all that in God's hands.' [2]

---

[1] Sb, V, c. xxxii–10.   [2] Idem.

VI

THE PLOT OVER ST. JOSEPH'S

TERESA DE AHUMADA received from God the command to do her utmost to found the new convent.

From that moment, 'shoulder to the wheel,' her life became active as well as contemplative and henceforward she was no longer her own mistress. He whom she called 'His Majesty' was an insistent director of operations. His orders were clear from the start: she was first to lay the plan before her confessor, telling him not to oppose it.

Her feminine instincts made her recoil for a moment: she wanted to gain time, owned that she had loved to dream 'of a poor house where she would live with a few sisters of the same mind as herself, and where they would all give themselves solely to prayer, with no parlours and no grilles, detached from all earthly things, their hearts consecrated to the Bridegroom alone,' [1] without really believing that she would one day be obliged to turn the dream into reality. So many obvious difficulties could be foreseen that she might have complained once more: 'Lord, not quite so much!'

His Majesty insisted. Teresa argued:

'Lord, are there not others, particularly theologians, men who, if you spoke to them, would do what you ask much better than a worthless person like myself can?' [2]

Our Lord replied 'in a tone which showed his heart's pain':

'It is because men and theologians will not listen to me that, despised by them, I come like a beggar to talk of what I want with poor, humble women, and to find rest in their company. . . .'

The divine compassion sought to win her by appealing to her imagination:

'This convent will be dedicated to St Joseph. He will guard one door, Our Lady the other. . . .' [3] He reasoned with her: 'What would become of the world if it were not for religious?'

Her Master had spoken. She was beside herself with joy, but so scared at the idea of conveying the message to P. Baltasar Álvarez that

[1] Y, L. I, c. i.   Cf. IB quoted SEC, vol. II, p. 150.
[3] Sb, V, c. xxxii-11

she could not make up her mind to do so by word of mouth; her skill as a letter-writer was already so persuasive that the formidable man, although he did present objections 'in conformity with right reason,' advised her to put her request before the Carmelite Provincial, P. Gregorio Fernández.

Doña Guiomar undertook to transmit the request: a rich widow was more likely to obtain a favourable hearing than an obscure unknown nun. The Father Provincial seemed very pleased, entered into the details of the plan, declared himself glad to learn there would not be more than thirteen nuns and promised his authorization.

The news so far was good, too good: it exploded on Ávila as if it were a bomb. Doña Teresa de Ahumada was beginning to get herself talked about again! This Carmelite, so much the subject of discussion and hesitation that it had taken the evidence of several holy men to get the genuineness of her visions attested, was now presuming to want to revolutionize her Order and to found a convent where mere weak women would be setting themselves up as rivals in austerity with the Desert Fathers! Some ridiculed the idea, others were indignant, all said:

'She's mad!'

The most charitable found it difficult to defend her.

'Why doesn't she try to let people forget her and stay quietly at the Incarnation?' [1]

Doña Guiomar was not spared :

'If she wants an outlet for her zeal, she has one ready to hand: it's time she looked after her children!'

Ávila was in an uproar and took sides for or against. And every man or woman thought he or she had the right to throw ridicule on the plan for this convent.

At the Incarnation itself matters were much worse: as might be expected, convents where the laxity permitted by the Mitigation was enjoyed took a poor view of a return to the primitive Rule. The calmest were sentimental about it:

'We thought Doña Teresa loved us. But not only does she show she has no love for the house in which she's been living for more than twenty years, she's trying to found another. If she's in a position to get hold of money and revenues, why doesn't she give them to us, her sisters, for we haven't the money to buy enough to eat?' [2]

Those who even in the service of God did not divest themselves of their pride felt themselves injured:

[1] SST, vol. II, p. 22.   [2] Cf. Sb, V, c. xxxiii–2.

'Her pretensions are against all reason, they're an insult to us! Haven't holier people than she adapted themselves to the Mitigated Rule?' [1]

And those who were most incensed over the matter:

'The prison cell's for rebels of her sort!'

Teresa was unperturbed. The time had gone by when 'the opposition of good people' was pain to her. 'She cared nothing for what people said, for honour or dishonour, for the exhausting labours she would have to undergo, for the money—though it was so necessary and she had nothing. She went forward in the boldness of the Holy Spirit, for her courage exceeded that of ordinary men and women.' [2]

She did, however, put up some pretence of being sensitive to the general feeling of anger 'in order not to seem to be showing contempt for what was said to her' [3] . . . A truly angelic ruse; unless you love men and forgive the injuries they have done you, you will not resist the pleasure of showing them that you do not feel what they do to you. Only on one occasion did she burst out laughing in her opponents' faces: when certain well-intentioned persons who had heard a rumour that she was going to launch out upon 'this venture' because of a revelation, tried to frighten her with the threat of the Inquisition. In the parlour she had found some very terrified people who said to her in hushed tones:

'Beware! Times are terrible! They're talking of denouncing you to the Inquisition!'

Teresa could not prevent her laugh from breaking out:

'You amuse me! I've never been afraid of it. For all matters of faith, for the very least of the Church's ceremonies, for any truth of Holy Scripture you like to name, I would die a thousand deaths. Reassure yourselves: my soul would be in a very bad way if there were anything in all that to make me fear the Inquisitors. If I really thought there was any reason, I would go straight to them myself; but if anyone does delate me falsely, Our Lord will save me, and it will be of great benefit to me.' [4]

The clergy, however, and other religious Orders attacked her violently: every priest and friar felt himself threatened for his daily bread, in these times of famine and growing poverty. Were there not too many convents already in Ávila to share the insufficient alms? In the church of Santo Tomás a preacher even took her to task in the course of a sermon, thundering against 'religious who go away from their

---

[1] Cf. Idem.
[2] JA, L. II, c. i.
[3] Sb, V, c. xxxvi-13.
[4] Cf. Sb, V, c. xxxiii-5.

monasteries; under the pretext of founding new Orders they only seek their own liberty—with other references so pointed that her sister Juana who was with her blushed at the insult and wanted to make her escape.' [1] Teresa, calm and smiling, did not seem to understand that it was levelled at her. Out of the corner of her eye she glanced at her Book of Hours opened at a series of short ejaculations of peaceful self-conquest which she had composed and liked to repeat:

> Let nothing disturb thee,
> Nothing affright thee.
> All things are passing,
> God never changeth.
> Patience gains all things.
> Who hath God wanteth nothing.
> Alone God sufficeth.[2]

The campaign against the poor little convent of St. Joseph's proved efficacious, for it was well organized.

Influenced by people of rank and importance and upset by so much scandal, the Provincial withdrew his authorization.

At the instigation of his rector, P. Dionisio Vázquez, P. Baltasar Álvarez ordered Teresa to give up having anything to do with the foundation. 'One day you will come to see that all this was only a dream,'[3] he wrote to her.

To crown everything, on Christmas night a priest refused Doña Guiomar absolution unless she stopped aiding and abetting the scandal.

Our Lord, who was Director of operations, ordered Teresa to obey her confessor and keep quiet for the moment.

'. . . And we had just bought the house, small but well situated! I wasn't upset over it: Our Lord had told me to do my best and that I should see what His Majesty would do. I *have seen!*'[4]

Teresa had one very powerful ally: P. Pedro Ibáñez. From the very beginning Doña Guiomar laid the project before him. He had asked the two women for concrete details as to their aims and the means they had to achieve them, the house, María de Ocampo's promises, what the young widow was able to offer; and all this was explained to him with a clearness which augured well for the future Foundress's gifts of organization. Teresa had said nothing about visions, she had given 'human reasons.'

[1] TC quoted SEC, vol. II, p. 333.

[2] *Nada te turbe —nada te espante —Todo se pasa —Dios no se muda —La paciencia —todo lo alcanza —quien a Dios tiene —nada le falta —Sólo Dios basta.*

[3] Sb, V, c. xxxiii–3.   [4] Sb, V, c. xxxii–18.

He asked for a week to think the matter over. They were already taking their departure and crossing the courtyard in front of the convent of Santo Tomás when he called them back:

'Are you quite determined to follow my advice?'[1]

The assent was unanimous. A week later he sent them his reply:

'Get on with this foundation with all possible speed. You have very little money? Then you must put yourselves into God's hands. . . . If anyone raises difficulties let him come and talk to me.'

The result of this unqualified approval was to win Teresa the whole-hearted adhesion and collaboration of P. Daza, Salcedo and a few other worthy men.

They were not going to be deterred on account of a prohibition. Our Lord inspired them with the wits to defeat their opponents. Teresa could not disobey her confessor. What of that! Urged on by P. Ibáñez, Doña Guiomar, in her own name and in the greatest possible secrecy, asked Rome for authorization to found a convent in accordance with the primitive Rule of Carmel. It would be under the jurisdiction of the Bishop of Ávila instead of depending on the Provincial of the Order, and would be none the worse for that.

There was a change for the better: the Jesuit rector who was so hostile was replaced by P. Gaspar de Salazar, who had only to meet Teresa to be instantly won over both to her and her project. He authorized Baltasar Álvarez to allow his penitent to go on 'courageously' with her plans as Foundress. There was only one condition: to act with the greatest secrecy.

But to go and found a convent in Ávila without people knowing about it!

Teresa complained: 'Lord, why do you command me to do impossible things? If I were only free, it would not matter so much being a woman! But I am bound on every side, without a farthing, and, what's more, without the means of getting any money, without the brief, without anything, what can I do, Lord?'[2]

In her convent she was closely watched and in the town enmeshed in the net of espionage formed by all the other Orders and their friends. To go to the site where the new convent was to be, she had to cross the whole town, or else take the route right round the walls. To allay suspicion she used to make as if she were going to the convent of Santo Tomás which was not far away from the future foundation. It was really essential to find a solution.

In August 1561 it transpired that Doña Teresa de Ahumada's

[1] Cf. Sb, V, c. xxxii–16, 17.   [2] Sb, V, c. xxxiii–11.

sister and her husband Don Juan de Ovalle were leaving Alba de Tormes and coming back to live in their native town. What could be better? The prioress of the Incarnation did not dream of refusing to allow her subject to spend some time with her beloved Juana, to help her to settle in.

The ruse succeeded. The little house purchased in the name of Teresa's brother-in-law was to become the cornerstone in the reform of the Order of Carmel, the glorious convent of St Joseph of Ávila.

The Ovalle house was adapted as follows. On the ground floor was the future chapel and on the first floor thirteen cells and the necessary offices. All this was built round a patio and looked out on to a tiny cloister: Teresa wondered—though she still had not a farthing—if it would not be better to buy something bigger.

The Director of operations was displeased:

'Did I not tell you to begin as you could? Oh, the greed of the human race, always afraid that the earth will not be large enough for it! How many times did I not sleep in the open, amid the night dew, for want of a place to lay my head?' [1]

And so Teresa was satisfied with her small house. Situated in the northern part of Ávila, in the populous district of San Roque, had it not indeed what she loved best in the world, 'a most beautiful horizon and the country'?

Teresa stayed some months with the Ovalles who obligingly played up to the pretence of setting up house. 'Doña Juana is an honest woman, courageous, and with the soul of an angel.' [2] Don Juan's character was far from easy and Teresa often pitied her sister: her distinguished husband was both suspicious and fickle, jealous to the extent of being hurt over his sister-in-law's friendship for Doña Guiomar, but completely devoted to the foundation.

The work progressed slowly as St Joseph's 'conspirators' managed to find a few maravedis. María de Ocampo was not yet free to dispose of her inheritance. Doña Guiomar took what she could from her revenues, ready, when she had no more money at her disposal, to sell a scarlet quilt or a cross embroidered in silk.

Teresa made her plans, gave orders to the workmen, provided for a double grille between the chapel and the choir, made of bars extremely close together, so that the nuns could follow the Offices without being seen. The walls would not even be rough-cast and everything would be very poor, but very clean. Teresa had such good taste that all the proportions were harmonious.

[1] Sb, V, c. xxxiii–12. [2] CTA, ii.

The difficulties were so great that the courage of some of the little group faltered, but that of the Foundress never failed; she was 'determined' to go through with it. She had already become the woman who 'will not hesitate to undertake great and extraordinary things and will make it her delight and pleasure to go through with them to the end, for things that were easy gave her no satisfaction.' [1]

A wall collapsed when in process of construction. Doña Guiomar, in spite of all the persistence she had shown, lost her head:

'It's the devils who've knocked it down! God isn't pleased with this convent.'

Teresa could no longer be frightened with the prospect of the devil's tricks, she was unperturbed.

'The wall is down? Let them put it up again then!' [2] and her authority overcame all reluctance.

The brief asked for from Rome was late in arriving. Once more, Doña Guiomar got anxious. Teresa's only reply was to ask her to get missals and a bell for the future convent. The Foundress gave herself to prayer and then acted. She wrote late into the night.

In obedience to P. Pedro Ibáñez, she began the account of her life and of the graces Our Lord had given her. Was this writing a pleasure to her? Her only allusion to the work thus imposed on her was that it was an additional burden, added to all her other labours. But one cannot be gifted with such liveliness of expression, describe people's characters with so colourful a pen, exercise the gift of the balanced phrase, of the striking realistic image, one is not a born writer as she was, without finding some pleasure in writing. With an expansive nature like Teresa's, constrained as she was to keep silence about her activities for the time being, it was a relief to let herself go and say all there was to be said about the past. Her only regret was that her confessors had forbidden her to speak 'in detail and clearly' about what she called 'my great sins and vileness'; were not the wonders God wrought in her so much the more marvellous in proportion to her unworthiness? She asked her readers not to forget that she had been 'so vile,' [3] that she had not been able to find a single example as bad as herself among those saints who had returned to Our Lord after having been sinners. 'After the call of God they did not offend him any more, whereas not only did I become worse than before, but it could have been said of me with truth that I set my mind to resisting the graces His Majesty favoured me with. . . . May he be blessed for ever, he who waited for me so long. . . .'

[1] FR, L. XVI, c. i.   [2] SEC, vol. II, p. 320.   [3] Sb, V, JHS-1.

She called this autobiography 'my great book,' 'the book of the mercies of God,' and when she sent it to Doña Luisa de la Cerda, it was with the words: 'It is my soul I am entrusting you with.'[1]

It was an account of her life, certainly, but also the clearest and most accurate route-map ever drawn up for men and women who want to use the path of mental prayer, to mount step by step from earthly illusion to spiritual reality.

Teresa de Ahumada's first analysis of the greatest experiences which it is given to a human being to undergo, was made when she was beginning her life of activity. The uninterrupted presence of God was the connecting-link between these two poles.

One day P. Pedro Ibáñez asked her:

'How do you spend your time?'

'I thought,' he said, 'that she devoted some hours to mental prayer and the remainder to other exercises.'

He saw Teresa's beautiful face light up with love:

'Imagine a person so much taken up with another that she cannot spend a moment out of the presence of the one she loves. . . .'[2]

'That was the way,' the Dominican added, 'that she lived with Our Lord, speaking only of him or with him . . . all her actions for him alone, writing only of his marvels.'

Wherever she was, she brought God with her. She diffused divine love in her sister's home. The effects of such love were wonderful, but its demands were such as to make one afraid.

Teresa seemed to have power over life and death. The Ovalles had only just arrived at Ávila when Juan 'one day found his son, little Don Gonzalo, lying across the doorway giving no signs of life and quite stiff. He took him in his arms and called him, but the child did not answer.' Was he dead? They did not know. Juan de Ovalle carried him to Teresa.

Doña Juana was in the other room, heard the noise and was up-set; Doña Guiomar calmed her, pretending that everything was all right, for it was the ninth month of Juana's pregnancy. All the same she came out in great anguish to see what it was and called loudly for her son. Teresa was silent, as they all were; they waited in suspense to see what would happen. Teresa lowered her veil; they saw her crouch down with her face close to the child, but inwardly she was calling on God. She remained like this for a good space of time, until the child showed signs of life again, putting his hands on her face as

[1] CTA, viii.   [2] IB, quoted SEC, vol. II, p. 148.

if to caress her and play with her; and as if nothing out of the ordinary had occurred, as if he were merely awaking from an ordinary sleep, she gave him back to his mother saying:

'Oh, dear Lord! What a state she was in about her son! Take him. . . .'

The child at first showed some weakness and could not stand; afterwards he ran about in the room, coming back to his aunt and kissing her from time to time.[1]

When later Doña Teresa was asked how she had given back life to little Gonzalo she was displeased and asked them not to say foolish things.[2]

But there was an occasion when she brought death.

The child whom Juana was carrying was born in September; she called him Joseph after the protector of the future monastery of the reform. He was given her dearest friends as god-parents: Doña Guiomar de Ulloa and Don Francisco de Salcedo. There was a feast for the baptism and Gonzalo, the child whom Teresa had raised to life, was there round the cradle.

Teresa loved the fine, healthy babe—but her affection had no trace of earthly feeling in it. Doña Juana was frightened when she saw her press the infant in her arms as she murmured a strange lullaby: 'If you are not to grow up a good man, I pray God, my son, to take you as you are, you little angel, before you offend him. . . .'

Three weeks later the babe was dying. Teresa took him on her knees, covered him with her veil—the sign of her consecration to Our Lord and separation from the world—and, her face aflame, fell into ecstasy. A very long silence ensued. Doña Juana durst not move and yet she felt sure the child was dead. When Teresa came out of her rapture she got up, slowly, without saying a word, and bearing the tiny body in her arms, went out of the room.

'Where are you going?' called Juana. 'Why don't you tell me my child is dead?'

Teresa turned towards her with a countenance of joy and wonder

'Let us go and thank God together. For we should praise him when we've seen the soul of one of these little ones go up to heaven, and the host of angels come to fetch it. . . .'[3]

It was never told whether Doña Juana would not have preferred to keep her son, not very good, perhaps, but alive.

At that time Teresa made long stays at Doña Guiomar's 'in order to

---

[1] FR, L. I, c. xv.   [2] SEC, vol. II, p. 507.
[3] TC quoted SEC, vol. II, pp. 339-40.

be quieter.' The Ovalles themselves were perhaps 'quieter' in their daily routine.

The building progressed as money came in. Certain things were of urgent necessity, but Teresa durst not order them to be done for want of funds. The good master carpenter St Joseph appeared to her and ordered her to get in the workmen *sin ninguna blanca*, without having even a farthing: the Lord would provide for it.

And on 23rd December, she wrote to her brother, Lorenzo de Cepeda, the *conquistador* of the family who had been most successful and who had made a rich marriage in Quito:

Señor,

It is, I think, by an inspiration of God that you have sent me so much money. For, for a nun like myself who considers it an honour, thanks be to God, to wear a darned habit, I've had all I needed up to now.

But for reasons which I could not gainsay, for they came from God, certain holy and learned persons will have it that I must not be slothful, but must do all I can to found a convent of thirteen nuns living in very strict enclosure in that they will never go out, and never go to the parlour without covering the face with a veil, the life being based on prayer and mortification.

. . . I didn't know how to construct certain things. Relying on God alone, I sent for the workmen. This seemed sheer madness, but His Majesty has intervened and inspired you to provide for it. What amazes me most is the 40 piastres which you have added and of which I was in most urgent need. . . .[1]

All was well.

Was all well?

On Christmas night a messenger from the prioress of the Incarnation came to Doña Guiomar's to warn Teresa de Ahumada; she was to be ready to start for Toledo, where the daughter of the Duke of Medinaceli, Doña Luisa de la Cerda, was demanding her presence at the earliest possible moment.

This was indeed the sort of enforced distraction which she hoped that absolute enclosure would set her free from in the future. What was she to do when she was with these grand people? Would her absence be long? It was impossible to say. Several months, no doubt.

> Let nothing disturb thee,
> Let nothing affright thee,
> Alone God sufficeth. . . .

[1] CTA, ii.

VII

DOÑA LUISA DE LA CERDA

DON ARIAS PARDO DE SAAVEDRA, Marshal of Castile and one of the richest men in Spain, had died a year before, but the grief of his widow, Doña Luisa de la Cerda, daughter of the second Duke of Medinaceli, grew more intense instead of diminishing; it amounted almost to delirium and those about her feared for her reason. That was why Doña Teresa de Ahumada was asked to come to her. Obsessed as she was with grief, only a saint could turn her thoughts away from herself and give new meaning to the words: 'I believe in the resurrection of the body,' which although she had lost hope she kept on repeating. But it had to be a saint possessed of the necessary tact for dealing with a great lady who took it ill that God should have taken away from her what she loved.

Up to that time no one had succeeded in consoling her, neither her seven children nor the princes of the Church, nor the princes of this world: this woman who had so much, took their attentions for granted. Only the God of the humble could perhaps save her through the intermediary of one of his servants who, in the poor convent of the Incarnation, was dreaming of still greater poverty and the most austere penances.

Doña Luisa heard a good deal of talk about Teresa on the balcony of the Moorish apartment where the portrait of her uncle, Cardinal Tavera, held the place of honour. The widow spent all her days there, lying on cushions embroidered with her coat of arms and surrounded by her maids who chattered over their sewing. She did not want to forget, but she was so worn out with her sleepless nights and her tears that she began to hope for some consolation.

And so she listened to those who sang the praises of a Carmelite of Ávila, Doña Teresa de Ahumada. One of her close friends, P. García de Toledo, son of the Count of Oropesa and a near relative of the Duke of Alba, had a very high opinion of Teresa who had occasionally been his penitent at Santo Tomás; he praised not only her spirituality but her intelligence, the wit with which she seasoned her conversation, and her lovable character; she would be a helpful and pleasant companion for any disconsolate woman.

The youngest of her attendants, María de Salazar, so pretty at fourteen that it almost made one overlook her wit, yet so witty that it would not have mattered had she been plain, never tired of hearing this nun spoken of. When her mistress was beside herself with grief, she would say to her with childlike faith:

'Your Ladyship will see . . . when the saint from Ávila comes. . . .'

Was Teresa's reputation, then, so great outside her native city? The Carmelite Provincial, a great friend of Doña Luisa, was partly responsible; he was by no means displeased that there should be this opportunity to take his subject's thoughts away, by a change of scene, from her tiresome idea of reforming the Order. It looked as though she was not thinking about it any more? Sly tongues affirmed the contrary: it had very naturally been impossible to go on with the work at St Joseph's without a certain amount of help, discreet or otherwise.

The idea that people should think her a person of great merit caused Teresa an 'interior upset' which could only be calmed by His Majesty.

' . . . I who am so vile! . . .'[1]

'Go there,' Our Lord said to her. 'As to the convent, it is essential that you should be elsewhere until the brief comes. Fear nothing, I will help you there.'

In the beginning of January 1562, the journey across the Castilian plains under the icy breath from the Guadarrama, so faint that it would not put out a candle, though it would cause a man's death, was long, uncomfortable and bitterly cold. Teresa was escorted by her brother-in-law, Juan de Ovalle, and Juana Suárez. Juana Suárez had been her constant companion for years; little is known of her except that she was constant in her loyalties, that is, opposed to any change, for she would not leave the Incarnation for any of the new foundations. Thus accompanied, Teresa at last entered Toledo by the Bisagra gate.

It was the first time she had seen such a large city, its streets always noisy with much traffic, with the merchants and their business or the pageantry of some great noble passing by with his retinue. Ávila was only like that on high days and holidays. There was the continual click of the thousands of looms on which thousands of weavers wove for the whole of Europe velvet, satin, taffeta, cloth and brocade. At Toledo shoes were made, wax candles, iron was forged, the steel of the famous Toledan swords was tempered in the waters of the Tagus, there was smelting, engraving, niello-work, and the songs learned from the Moors mingled with the sound of men's voices, with the clang of hammer on anvil, with the rumble of carriages and the neighing of horses.

[1] Sb, V, c. xxxiv–2.

Philip II had just made Madrid the capital of the realm, but Toledo kept her title of crowned imperial city. The nobility had not yet deserted this ancient stronghold of Castile against enemies from the east—in a still more distant age the bastion of the Moor towards the west—the promontory on which the flashing blades of two civilizations and two religions had been shattered in turn. The Moorish style of art had infused itself into the decoration of church and palace; this mozarabic style which she scarcely knew astonished Teresa, and in the heart of the narrow streets, behind austere Castilian façades, the half-open doors provided glimpses of patios adorned with the arabesques of Islam. Her slightly protruding eyes, keen and accustomed to take in every detail, scrutinized this new world. Her gaze passed from people's faces to the wrought iron gates, from the paving stones to carved doorways, from the belfries to the sky, silvered by a light clearer than any other in the world.

Toledo, the very cradle of the Sánchez y Cepeda: at Ávila Don Alonso had been surnamed 'the Toledan.' Teresa always loved the city with a special love: 'I feel better there than I do elsewhere.' [1] She never referred to these ancestral ties, but her gaiety sparkled the more brilliantly for being set in a framework of Toledan charm—that 'school of polished conversation,' and perhaps she owed the sharpness of her wit to the race which had given its name to the steel of which the finest blades in the world were made.

The travellers dismounted in front of the Master of Calatrava's palace: there it was that Arias Pardo's widow was living in royal state, dying of grief.

At the entrance, squires, valets, footmen, pages, duennas, maids, a gaily-coloured, motley, bustling, curious, yet solemn crowd, welcomed Our Lord's delegate with every mark of deep respect. The staff of ceremony of the major-domos resounded on the steps of the great staircase of marble with its agate banister which led to the apartments where Doña Luisa was waiting for them.

With lowered gaze, her eyes looking down on the rose pattern of a great Flanders carpet, the Carmelite passed through an archway elaborately adorned with foliage arabesques. The huge, rock-crystal lustres, gleaming with lighted candles, lit up her darned habit and her faded veil almost yellow with age. And the richest woman in Castile stepped down from the *estrado* to clasp in her arms the nun for whom God alone sufficed.

Doña Luisa had prepared a sumptuous apartment for Teresa and

[1] CTA, xii.

her companion—everything in this palace was sumptuous. Here she had to practise a new form of mortification: that of accepting, through politeness, the comfortable, wealthy surroundings which to her were irksome. Along with the bundle of which her entire luggage consisted she had brought, her discipline, and certain fixed ideas about the great and wealthy, inspired by tales of chivalry in which these exalted personages are of superhuman calibre; she was considerably surprised to find that the higher the rank the more cares they had: ceremonial 'does not allow them so much as to breathe'[1]; the nun was sorry for the woman who was the daughter of dukes. To restore this woman whose nerves were overstrained to sound health of mind and body, some change in and simplification of her diet would have been advisable, whereas she was forced 'to eat at irregular hours dishes considered appropriate to her rank, but which suited neither her temperament nor her taste. . . .'[2] No relaxation, never the smallest degree of liberty: Doña Luisa had to watch her every word, restrain any expression of enthusiasm, for the quarrels over precedence between duennas and attendants were such 'that one could not be spoken to more than another, under pain of causing the rest to turn their back on whoever appeared to be favoured.'[3] Teresa herself had to suffer on account of these jealousies and was accused of 'mercenary and selfish pretensions.'[4] It gave her the opportunity of discovering 'that from then onwards backbiting did not hurt her any more than it would if she were someone deprived of reason.'[5]

Poor Doña Luisa! 'For persons of her condition everything is bondage and one of the world's great lies is to call lords those who are merely the slaves of a thousand and one things. . . . I derived great benefit from observing all this and I told her so.'[6]

Teresa had the art—or perhaps it was kindliness—of persuading Doña Luisa that she had not come either to teach or to preach, but that she too had a lot to learn and if she discovered that the great lady 'was a woman and subject to weakness and passion like herself,'[7] the great lady learned from Teresa that nuns had their passions and weaknesses too. This exchange of confidences formed a lasting bond between them. Doña Luisa showed Teresa every possible delicate consideration: as, for instance, the day she tried to cure her of an attack of fever by showing her the sparkle of the only substance in the world in which fire and water are mingled: her diamonds[8]; Teresa even ventured

---

[1] SB, V, c. xxxiv-4.   [2] Idem.   [3] Idem.
[4] Idem.   [5] SEC, R, ii, p. 14.   [6] Sb, V, c. xxxiv-4.
[7] Idem.   [8] Sb, V, c. xxxviii-4.

to offer the wealthy woman tiny gifts: 'A mere trifle gives her pleasure.'[1]

Doña Luisa de la Cerda had a distinguished face, she carried her head like one accustomed to the weight of jewels, and in her mourning attire she was truly majestic; for all this, she was none the less humble of heart, a true Christian, a devoted friend and as simple as the solemnity of her rank allowed. She could not bear, now, to be far away from Teresa de Ahumada who spent long hours in her room, at prayer, or writing her autobiography, and she clutched at any excuse to bring her out on to the *estrado*, where Doña Luisa spent her time when there was no sermon at San Ramón, no procession at San Clemente or benediction at Santo Domingo el Antiguo: for at Toledo one seemed to be 'in a perpetual Holy Week.'

Doña Luisa worked at her embroidery while she listened to one of her attendants reading a few pages from the *Lives of the Saints* in which new beauties were discovered: Doña Teresa made the reading more interesting by comments which were all the more delightful for the gracious tones in which they were uttered, without the smallest display of learning. Soon all the wits of the town flocked to the palace: they all wanted to meet this nun who was said to speak of God more eloquently than the Doctors and to have saved the widow of the Marshal of Castile from despair.

Yet Toledo was the most exacting town in Spain in the matter of fine talk: 'The Toledans are distinguished for cleverness not of the hands, as in other places, but of speech.' [2] Teresa soon learned to adapt her way of speaking to court circles without departing from her extremely tactful reserve. Here, it was her business to please people and if she attracted them without meaning to do so, when she did try to please she enraptured her listeners. She was in need of friends for God, for her reform, and she made friends, and influential ones: the Duchess of Escalona, the Duchess of Maqueda, the Marchioness of Villena, Princess Juana, the Duchess of Medinaceli, the Duchess of Alba, and they helped her all her life.

It was there, too, that she made a less fortunate acquaintance in the person of Doña Luisa's niece, Ana de la Cerda, Princess of Éboli, who had not yet begun to be talked about, but who, at twenty-one, was already famous for her piquant beauty and her no less sharp character. Ana was by no means willing to pass unnoticed, and to attract the attention of this Carmelite who seemed to be in the fashion, by turns made witty sallies and affected devotion. A close friend of Queen

[1] CTA, xii.   [2] BG.

Isabel of Valois, the gentle French princess whose marriage with Philip II awakened so many hopes that she was called 'Isabel of Peace,' she flattered herself on being able to obtain whatever she wanted from Teresa and to give her just what she chose. To such offers, which were accompanied by a great jingling of bracelets in the cool breeze of her fluttering fan, the Carmelite replied:

'I thank your Highness, but a daughter of God needs nothing other than God,' for it did not take her long to sum anyone up.

She learned, too, how to distinguish those who should be called Your Highness from those whom it was sufficient to address as Your Grace, and was no longer obliged to conceal her ignorance of etiquette under a peal of laughter.

Nothing of all this troubled her interior recollection: that was firmly established now and Teresa de Ahumada would not let herself be caught up again in the entanglement of worldly vanities. From Toledo she wrote to P. Pedro Ibáñez, anticipating Calderón de la Barca: 'I go forward as in a dream, and I know that when I wake up it will all be nothing. . . .' [1] As often as possible, when the conversation in the drawing-room veered round towards the theatre, of which Toledans are passionately fond, or towards games of one sort or another, bullfights or running at the ring, slipping quietly from the room and through one gallery after another, she made her escape from the visitors. Sometimes at the rustle of a silk skirt her face betrayed her secret feelings: Doña María de Salazar, the child already mentioned, was still there watching her, drawing back the tapestry hangings quickly or hiding behind a door which seemed to open of its own accord. María endeavoured to convince the saint, both in prose and in verse, of her desire to enter religion. One day she slipped a poem into her hand in which she made a great parade of her love of God:

> . . . If aught of good you owe to me,
> Mine eyes, you'll not refuse a tear.
> For tears alone can solace be.
> Much more than grief, I pleasure fear. . . .

> . . . How should I seek mine own content—
> To set my soul from bondage free,
> My King from sufferings dire is spent
> And scourging cruel—and all for me. [2]

Teresa took in at a single glance the exquisite profile, the be-ribboned hair, the gay silk dress stiff with its silver embroidery.

[1] SEC, R, ii, p. 14. [2] MJ, quoted EM, pp. 41–2.

'Child, you're preparing for convent life by many frivolities!'—
and avoiding such naïve demonstrations as she avoided the rest, she
took refuge in prayer.

She did not suspect that the women of the household took turns
at the keyhole of her door. A rapture which had come upon her 'in
public' [1] had caused a lot of talk, and nobody believed what she said
about heart attacks and fainting: they were on the watch for her to
have an ecstasy. The fiery radiance of her countenance seemed to
penetrate the very walls, the breath of God breathed over the palace:
'All made progress in the service of the Lord.' [2] She converted Ham-
mete, the Turk, which caused a great sensation, and P. García de
Toledo, whom she now met again, was so much impressed by the
earnestness with which she begged him, good though he was, to
become still holier, that he gave himself up entirely to a life of prayer.

She was adored by the servants below stairs as much as she was
admired by the court above, and it is said that when after communing
with God she again turned her attention to earthly things, she liked to
talk with the maids.

It was during this stay with the rich and mighty that Teresa's 'hard
heart' melted with compassion. Perhaps it was the contrast, the
inequality of circumstances, so much luxury for some, so much
wretchedness for others. In bending over sordid rags to dress a dis-
charging wound, she now felt more tenderness than repugnance. Doña
Luisa had 'her poor'—which gave her an excuse for not bothering
about the verminous, half-starved, repugnant rabble that swarmed in
this city of eighty thousand inhabitants. In Ávila charity called the
poor each by his own name; in Toledo this seething, nameless wretchedness appalled and sickened Teresa. It was on one of the tables of
precious wood in the Master of Calatrava's palace that she wrote: 'It
seems to me that I have more compassion for the poor than formerly,
I pity them greatly, my desire to help them is such that if I let my
heart speak I should give them the habit off my back. I feel no repugnance at all even though I am close to them and touch them: I see
that this, too, is the gift of God, for I used to give alms for the love
of him without feeling any natural pity.' [3]

The footmen were accustomed to strange tatterdemalions coming
to ask for Teresa. One day they came to call her: a woman in the habit
of a Carmelite *beata* but in rags, the pilgrim's staff in her hand, wanted
to see her. Teresa hastened to her, kissed her, and, a few minutes later,
in her forceful way of expressing herself, she explained to Doña Luisa

[1] SEC, R, ii, p. 13.   [2] Sb, V, c. xxxiv-5.   [3] SEC, R, ii, p. 14.

that this woman, María de Jesús, had tramped sixty leagues on foot to come and talk over with her a project for the reform of Carmel: she too wanted to found a convent where the primitive Rule would be observed: and she had the brief of authorization!

The great lady gave orders that the visitor was to be shown into a room where a canopied bed was prepared for her.

María de Jesús' energy was prodigious. Born at Granada and left a widow when she was still very young, she had consecrated herself to God in a Carmel of Mitigated observance. She left before being professed: Our Lord had commanded her in the same month and on the same day as Teresa, to found a convent which should conform to the primitive tradition of enclosure, austerity and penance. Unlike Teresa, María de Jesús was free. She sold her possessions and, dressed in sackcloth, with a little money sewn in a tight-fitting bodice padded and secured, she set out, barefooted, for Rome.

Pius IV saw coming slowly towards him an emaciated creature, worn out by her journey, and whose every step left a trace of blood. But what valour in her countenance! He listened paternally to what she had to say:

'Courageous woman! Let all she asks for be done!'

The papacy encouraged the reform of the religious Orders on the lines laid down by the Counter-Reformation. María was allowed to enter the enclosure of the Carmel of Mantua, where the primitive austerities were so rigidly observed that the religious were known as 'the immured.' María de Jesús was able to investigate all that was still observed of the ancient traditions as regards clothing, manner of life, the arrangement of the Rules and Constitutions. And Doña Leonor de Mascarenhas, the king's former governess, gave her a house at Alcalá de Henares to found the monastery of La Imagen there.[1]

For a fortnight María de Jesús talked and Teresa de Ahumada made notes. The *beata*, who was gifted with the excellent memory of those who cannot read, could remember the Rule by heart; Teresa reconstructed it. This penitent was so austere in her ways that the palace began to take *her* for a true saint: Teresa herself felt unworthy in her presence: 'She is so much more fervent than I am in the Lord's service!'[2] María de Jesús also had a good head: she initiated Teresa into the details of Vatican procedure with all its red tape through which she had threaded her way admirably.

When they parted the opinion of both on an essential point disputed up till then was strengthened by each other's support: in the

[1] SST, vol. II, pp. 93–4.   [2] Sb, V, c. xxxv–2.

reformed convents the nuns were to live by the work of their hands
and to have no revenues. On that point it was essential not to yield
either to bishops, the city 'juntas' or to anyone at all: the primitive
Rule was explicit. Teresa had not known this, but the discovery was
an 'immense joy' for her.[1]

She was none the less anxious about it for she knew that those who
were supporting her most effectively would consider such complete
dependence on Providence madness. From this moment she never
ceased to 'argue with theologians.' She wrote to P. Ibáñez on the
subject and he countered her idea with two pages of theological arguments. Confessors and doctors of divinity hurled such a multiplicity
of arguments at her that she knew not which way to turn. For she
was the last person ever to think it possible to dispense with advice:
throughout her life, one of her most absorbing occupations was to win
round divergent opinions to her own way of thinking after having
listened to everyone, for win them round she did.

In the spring of 1562 the matter had still got no further than lively
discussion when that supreme arbiter, Fray Pedro de Alcántara,
arrived in Toledo. Doña Luisa, who was enthusiastic over the idea of
thirteen women living together in absolute poverty for the love of
Our Lord, had invited the holy man.

This grand old man, wasted away by austerities, spoke of renuncia-
tion beneath the panelled ceilings, with their immense stars, of the
Master of Calatrava's palace; there he was, treading on marble with
those feet which had grown hard from contact with the stones by the
wayside; there he was, seated on a chair of Córdoba leather, his emaciated hand resting on a table of ebony inlaid with silver and mother of
pearl; his ascetic profile showed up against the background of the new
tapestries from Flanders.

It was in this luxurious setting that he discussed with Teresa de
Ahumada the bases of the Rule of absolute poverty in her convents.

She showed him the letter she had received from P. Ibáñez. Fray
Pedro smiled and with a good-humoured air threw a few stones into
the doctor's garden:

I am surprised that Your Reverence should submit to theologians
points which they are incapable of understanding. . . . It is only
those who are living the perfect life who can speak of it. Can it even
be questioned whether it is essential to follow the evangelical counsels or not? . . . If Your Reverence wishes to follow Christ along
the perfect road of poverty, you should know that it is open to

[1] Sb, V. c. xxxv–2.

women just as much as to men. . . . But if you want to take the advice of theologians destitute of spirituality, look for great revenues, and see if all that is worth more to you than renouncement in obedience to the words of Jesus.[1]

Teresa admitted that His Majesty had given her the grace to desire poverty:

As to myself, there are days when I could wish to possess nothing, not even a roof over my head, and to beg my bread for the love of God. But I'm afraid that those who are not yet ready to go so far as that may be dissatisfied and that our penury may be a cause of distractions to them. . . . I know poor convents where there is little or no recollection.[2]

Teresa was thinking of the convent of the Incarnation. Fray Pedro insisted:

Because such religious are poor against their will, and not out of obedience to the will of Christ. I am not extolling wretchedness: I am praising poverty patiently borne for the love of Christ Our Lord, and, still more, poverty which is desired and embraced through love. I shouldn't consider myself a man of sure faith if I felt otherwise. In this as in all things I trust Our Lord; I believe firmly that his counsels are very good, I believe that he who follows them is much more perfect than he would otherwise be. As His Majesty promised us, I consider the poor in spirit, those who do not seek their own will, blessed. I trust God more than my own experience, but all the same I can say that I have always seen those who are poor through the love of that condition live a happy life, by God's grace, a life such as those who love God, abandon themselves to him and hope in him have here below.

Don't for a single instant believe those who affirm the contrary, because they haven't tasted how sweet the Lord is to those who renounce all goods which do not help to increase their love.[3]

After this interview Teresa replied to P. Ibáñez that she had decided to keep the vow of poverty faithfully; she would follow the counsels of Christ in their perfection without taking advantage of the opportunity theology offered her of dispensing with their observation. . . .[4] At the same time she informed him that she had finished writing her autobiography.

The convents of the reformed Order of Our Lady of Carmel were then to live in the same way as St. Joseph's was founded: *sin blanca*.

This was the reason His Majesty had sent Doña Teresa de Ahumada to Toledo. The stay need not be prolonged now. It had lasted six months.

[1] PA quoted SEC, vol. II, p. 125.　　　[2] Sb, V, c. xxxv–2.
[3] PA quoted SEC, vol. II, p. 125.　　　[4] Sb, V, c. xxxv–4.

VIII

24TH AUGUST 1562

DOÑA LUISA'S patio was an oasis of flowers and greenery. Teresa was happy for she was surrounded by good friends. When her Provincial, P. Ángel de Salazar, left her the choice of returning to Ávila for the election of the new prioress or of remaining in Toledo, she decided to remain where she was: 'Very glad not to be arriving there in the midst of all the bustle,' [1] she said in her letter to the convent of the Incarnation, as she begged her sisters not to vote for her as they wished to do.

When she had recovered her equilibrium a little, her gift of adaptability came to the fore again; at Doña Luisa's, she found 'quiet and consolation, and was free to give long hours to prayer.' [2]

But there was to be no rest for her. The Master of the work gave orders for departure.

'You wanted the cross: I have an excellent one in readiness for you.' [3]

Had she so far forgotten the little convent of St Joseph's that she thought for a moment that the cross would be that she would be elected prioress at the Incarnation? She wept at first, but after a few tears immediately accepted the idea of the journey: 'I saw clearly that I was about to fling myself into the midst of a fire, for Our Lord had told me so . . . and yet, in spite of all this, I was even then so full of joy that I couldn't contain my impatience to begin the fight. . . .' [4]

Her confessor was afraid of the journey for her in the great heat and imposed a delay: but she entreated him: 'If I am to die through this, I must die!' [5] and he allowed her to go.

Her belongings were quickly packed, she tore herself from the arms of her friends who wept as they bade her goodbye, and pushed away María de Salazar who clung to her habit; all this affection touched her, she felt she ought to have shared their grief, but in her joy was uppermost: 'I am blessed with so grateful a nature that at any other time all this would have been enough to upset me very much, but at this moment I found it impossible to feel any grief. . . .' [6]

---

[1] Sb, V, c. xxxv-8. [2] Idem, 10. [3] Cf. Idem, 8.
[4] Idem, 10. [5] Idem, 8. [6] Sb, V, c. xxxv-11.

After a brief moment of weakness, she was once more wholly resolute and ready for action.

The courtiers who watched her as she gradually disappeared from sight were of opinion that the Carmelite would have made a fine Amazon. They did not realize how correct their judgement was.

She arrived at Ávila in good time. 'It was so imperative for the business of this blessed house of St Joseph's that I shouldn't be away one day more, that I don't know how matters could have been brought to a conclusion if I had not returned then. Oh, how great God is! I often marvel when I consider how His Majesty helped me to found this little hidden house of God.' [1]

The brief, so long desired, which authorized Doña Guiomar de Ulloa to found a convent of reformed Carmelites under the jurisdiction of the Bishop of Ávila, arrived that very day.

Doña Juana and her husband, weary of waiting so long, had left for Alba de Tormes. One might wonder how the building of the convent could be carried on with the requisite discretion, but 'God's help effects more than rising betimes. . . .' [2] By a decree of Providence, Juan de Ovalle, who had come over to Ávila on business, as he got off his horse was seized with 'terrible' fits of shivering, followed by a severe attack of double tertian fever. Nobody pitied the poor man for never was an illness better timed: there he was, back in the house he had left, and his sister-in-law installed there to look after him, while she speeded up the building operations. The conspirators of St Joseph's had no need to do any more scheming for a long time. 'Truth suffers but does not perish.' Teresa liked to embellish her conversation with proverbs.

They still had to obtain the Bishop's permission for the convent to be founded 'without revenues.' Don Álvaro de Mendoza, son of Don Juan Hurtado de Mendoza, brother-in-law of secretary Cobos, one of the most mighty personages in the kingdom, was a great lord indeed. Poverty? This was an aspect of life according to the Gospel that seemed to him out of date: did not the sons of St Francis and St Dominic possess rich convents, were they not now rich Orders, well provided with everything? It was true that not one of these friars possessed anything of his own, everything was common to all. To refuse revenues was just like a woman who was said to have visions. . . . This convent would either have revenues or not be founded!

The timely intervention of Fray Pedro de Alcántara saved the situation. Prevented by illness from visiting his Illustrious Lordship, he

[1] Idem, 12.   [2] CTA, xxviii.

wrote to him begging his consent that the convent 'should be most fervent and in every respect perfect, conformable in all things to the primitive Rule of the Order of Our Lady of Mount Carmel.' He also mentioned the Foundress: 'I think the spirit of Our Lord is in her.' [1]

His Illustrious Lordship left for his country house without replying to one of the most revered men in Spain. Was this a tacit refusal, or displeasure, or perhaps annoyance?

With no more thought for his dignity than he had for his old bones, Fray Pedro had a mule saddled and covered twelve leagues in order to take Don Álvaro by surprise in his retreat at El Tiemblo. The only thing he minded was that he was obliged to travel in such great state, for he always went on foot.

The Bishop was impressed with the importance which the great Franciscan attached to this insignificant convent of thirteen women devoted to penance, but all the same he let him go away again with a refusal: it took more than this to make a Mendoza yield. He repeated, obstinately:

'I won't have poor nuns!'

Perhaps when he was alone he suddenly realized how strange his persistent repetition of this prejudice sounded upon the lips of a representative of Jesus Christ on earth. Perhaps the eulogies of Lady Poverty, expounded so lovingly by Fray Pedro despite his weary voice, found the way, beneath the purple, to a Christian heart. However this may be, that very evening the Bishop sent the Franciscan a double message:

(1) The convent of St Joseph might be in conformity with the law of evangelical poverty; (2) Doña Teresa de Ahumada was to prepare to receive a visit from him: he was returning to Ávila on purpose to make her acquaintance. The very next day, his Illustrious Lordship, Don Álvaro de Mendoza, asked for her in the parlour.

It was all very well for Teresa to say that in future it did not matter to her 'that people were fond of her' [2]; she did more than persuade the Bishop; he was completely won over, charmed, all resistance gone. It was the end of the good man's whims and caprices: whether he knew what he wanted or not, he would always know quite definitely what Teresa wanted and he would always be entreated, with all the graciousness in the world, to do his very utmost on behalf of the reformed Carmels. Teresa was to find in him her most constant and efficacious support and she gave him her affection till he died, as she alone knew how to give it—an affection that was the most reverent, most tender and most exacting in the world.

[1] PA quoted SEC, vol. II, p. 127.   [2] SEC, R, iii, p. 17.

The game was won. Fray Pedro could go back again. Their farewells cast a cloud over Teresa's joy: both knew they would never see
each other again on earth. She begged him, if he had any affection for
her, to come and take his last meal in Ávila in one of the Incarnation
parlours, and, like the fine cook she was, she devised exquisite dishes
for this poor friar who was accustomed to eat only bread. A snow-
white tablecloth, simple crockery spotlessly clean, Teresa, who stood
behind Fray Pedro, serving with lowered eyes, a few prying sisters
who must poke their noses round the door: but they saw Christ himself feed the friar with his own hands and the whole town knew that
the meal had been 'an angels' banquet.' [1] Great friendship, like great
love, is written in heaven.

Pedro de Alcántara left with Teresa one of his spiritual daughters,
Antonia de Henao. At St Joseph's she took the name of Antonia del
Espíritu Santo and was one of the 'four poor orphans' [2] who were to
become the cornerstone of the Reform.

Gaspar Daza gave Teresa Úrsula de Revilla y Álvarez—Úrsula de
los Santos. Doña Guiomar's gift to Carmel was her favourite attendant,
María de la Paz, who became María de la Cruz, while the future
chaplain, Julian de Ávila, made a Carmelite of his own sister, María de
Ávila—María de San José.

Julian de Ávila was an excellent priest and a charming man. He had
a good heart and a ready tongue and he amused Teresa with his keen
and ingenious wit. His courage was all the more meritorious since it
meant the overcoming of a natural cowardice, at which he laughed
himself. This brother and sister came of good stock. Their father, a
humble weaver, left, in what is one of the most delightful documents
of the time, a testimony to his love of God:

I, Cristóbal de Ávila, this day, the feast of St. Mary Magdalene in
the year 1536, have decided to reform my life in order to serve God
and his holy Mother, Saint Mary, better, if the Holy Spirit consents
to give me his grace, his help and the necessary fervour for this
service.

Of the twenty-four hours of the day and night, I will take six
to sleep; one to hear Mass, another to read in the book of the Gospels
the Gospel of the day, or the *Lives of the Saints*; another for my
prayers, another for walking. I shall have fourteen hours left in
which to work and earn my living.

May all be for the greatest service of God and of his blessed
Mother, Saint Mary, and may she graciously be with me in all
things. [3]

[1] SST, vol. II, p. 131.   [2] Cf. Sb, V, c. xxxvi-6.   [3] SST, vol. I, p. 317.

The first Discalced Carmelite nuns were evidently the fine flower of the race of Castile.

Essentials were now ready and the final preparations for the opening of the convent moved very quickly. Teresa found it difficult to hide her joy. Happiness brought out all her charm and made her so gay, so humanly beautiful that a gentleman could not refrain from complimenting her on the dainty foot peeping out from beneath her nun's habit. She burst out laughing.

'Look at it well, for soon you won't see it any more!' [1]

She was in a hurry to get behind walls and grilles where she would be alone with her sisters in poverty; not to prevent herself from going back to the world but to erect an obstacle between the world's importunities and a solitude filled to overflowing with God. With her faithful friends, working night and day, she herself cut out and sewed the habits of frieze, hemmed the back veils, cut out the coifs in the rough crash. She wanted these last to be close-fitting, to hide the roots of the hair, in order that the nuns might save time over doing their hair, a solicitude which in no way implied negligence, for she saw to it that the coif was always carefully adjusted. She found a delightful expression with which to reprove someone whose coif was put on awry:

'A nun badly coifed is like a woman badly married. . . .' [2]

The convent's protectors were installed, one on each side of the chapel doors—a gilt wood statue of Mary bearing 'her precious Son' in her arms, and a statue of St Joseph, their patron, sumptuously attired in a tunic embroidered by Teresa herself and a silk mantle; he held his lily in one hand and a hat in the other. . . .

The church was so tiny that there were not more than ten paces between the entrance porch and the choir. The bell which summoned the people around to Mass and the sisters to work or prayer weighed scarcely three pounds.

There was much noise of saw and hammer, things were hung in place here or hooked to the wall there. It was Teresa's heart's delight to polish, to wash and iron the altar cloths or to decorate the chapel with flowers or sweep out a corner. It seemed difficult to believe that such a woman had ever been so ill that they thought her dead. Yet even now she vomited every morning, suffered from continual headache and frequently from fever, but her vitality was such that, despite the cost to herself, she displayed as much energy as those in perfect health.

At long last it was dawn on the 24th August 1562: for Don Alonso's

[1] Quoted H, p. 55.   [2] SST, vol. II, p. 588.

daughter, all the great events of her life began, as that life itself had begun, 'at the first streak of dawn.'

That morning the district of San Roque awakened to the tinkling of a bell, cracked, for it had been bought second-hand. Sleepy, but curious, the people of the neighbourhood were at their doors, the sound of the bell guided them to a chapel which seemed to have sprung up in the night,[1] the first ever dedicated to the great St Joseph. It was poor like the stable in Bethlehem, but 'the very walls sufficed to touch people's hearts,'[2] and the atmosphere of prayer was so palpable that they held their breath.

Master Gaspar Daza said Mass on an altar which was spotlessly clean: this was the only sign of luxury. A nun from the convent of the Incarnation, Doña Teresa de Ahumada, very much beloved by the humble folk of the district, gave the habit to four girls whom nobody knew. It was a habit that was strange to people, of stuff so rough that it reminded them of the camel hair in pictures of hermits.

There were three other Carmelites there: Doña Juana Suárez, Doña Inés de Tapia and her sister Ana; also Don Juan de Ovalle and his wife Doña Juana, as well as some people who were often known to stay with them : Don Francisco de Salcedo, whom everybody called the 'holy gentleman,' Don Gonzalo de Aranda, Julian de Ávila, who always had a witty remark to make as he passed you, and the rich widow who was dressed like a poor person, Doña Guiomar de Ulloa.

The people round about St Joseph's asked about the convent and thought it all wonderful. They commented:

'They're going to live enclosed. . . . The fast. . . . The discipline. . . . To pray for you and me. Saints in our part of the town— what a grace from God!'

Everyone tried to get out more quickly than her neighbour to spread the amazing news.

At long last Doña Teresa was to know the glorious achievement of a work which had been one of long preparation and waiting, a work she had so much desired. 'It was like heaven for me to see the Blessed Sacrament exposed, to know that four poor orphans . . . great servants of God, were now safe and free to serve him. My happiness . . . at having accomplished what Our Lord had commanded me . . . was so great that I was as it were beside myself and deep prayer came upon me.'[3]

[1] SST, vol. II, p. 148, n. 1.   [2] TC quoted SEC, vol. II, p. 321.
[3] Sb, V, c. xxxvi-6.

IX
GRAVÍSIMA CULPA

THE news of the foundation of the new convent soon spread all round the town. The joy which broke out was so vociferous in its acclamations that one was forcibly reminded of the entry of Jesus of Nazareth into Jerusalem; it only needed the crowd assembled in front of St Joseph's to cry out: 'Blessed is he that cometh in the name of the Lord!' [1] for the resemblance to be complete.

But on that fine Sunday, the Passion was not far off: God, whose ways are hidden, allowed a change to come over the opinion of the notables of Ávila. They took offence; in less than two hours enthusiasm gave way to fear, and, consequently, to hostile opposition. Anyone would have thought that this poor humble house was a danger to the city.

'Down, down with the convent! Let's save our children's bread!'

The principal argument was that the town could not feed these few nuns who, moreover, asked for nothing.

Stones were thrown, people hammered on the door, there was a threat to break in and destroy everything. It was a veritable riot and merchants shut their shops to join the band of brawlers. Fire, or the French at the city gates, could not have produced a greater mob of people, more feverish activity or swifter decisions.

The hubbub brought Teresa out of her ecstasy.

At the convent of the Incarnation the fury was no less. Every one of the 'Calced' Carmelites felt herself insulted by this return to the strict observance of the primitive Rule, the essential points of which were absolute enclosure, silence, fasting, bare feet, penance, and they were all seized with panic: might it not be that one day someone would take it into his head to 'reform' them too and to force them to practise these austerities? On this 24th August 1562, Doña Teresa de Ahumada had no longer any friends among the Mitigated Carmelites.

They sneered:

'She's never been capable of following even our Rule, which she says is lax, in every detail. How then will she set about observing the Rule a Pope found too severe?'

---

[1] JA quoted SEC, vol. II, p. 191.

'Through her pride she's made trouble in the community,' ran their accusations.

Already the most senior among them, those who knew the Constitutions, were predicting the punishment that would fall upon her. They weighed up facts, gauged the circumstances, and worked them out in the ratio of 'grave fault' (*culpa grave*), 'graver fault' (*culpa más grave*), 'very grave fault' (*gravísima culpa*), the last implying life imprisonment and sometimes even the refusal of Christian burial.

They wrangled over it in the Lord's name.

'She lied: and so there's *culpa grave*. She'll be given the discipline twice in chapter and put on bread and water for two days. . . .'

An old nun threw up her arms and interrupted this verdict with indignant exclamations:

'What! *Culpa grave!* Are you thinking what you're saying, sister? Hasn't she sown discord here? Hasn't she fabricated intrigues with secular persons, stirred up scandal, thrown discredit on the Order? Isn't she rebellious and contumacious? It's *culpa más grave* we must call it! And even *gravísima culpa!* Since Father Provincial refused his authorization, she's clung to her error obstinately. *Gravísima culpa!* Life imprisonment! Ah, she wants austerities, does she? Fasting and abstinence all her life long, here, at the Incarnation, in the name of the Mitigated Rule!'

The punishment seemed adequate, but by no means spectacular. More than one hoped that Teresa, guilty of having by her attitude brought the convent and its prioress into ill repute, would do public penance in the refectory, wearing a habit on which tongues had been sewn 'in order that the great wickedness of her tongue might be punished.' [1] She would eat her hunch of bread on the floor and would finally be taken away to the prison cell.

While the fate of those they looked on as her accomplices—the two Tapia sisters, Juana Suárez, María de Ocampo—was being decided, they treated them as if they had the plague.

The whole convent was up in arms: yet thirty of these same nuns were later to follow her whom they would call 'Mother Teresa of Jesus,' 'the Mother Foundress,' 'the Holy Mother,' and were to be pioneers of her Reform.

These poor nuns of the Incarnation were blinded and driven on to fury by the devil; he attacked Teresa herself and plunged her into the midst of a great 'spiritual conflict.' [2]

[1] SEC, CONS, pp. 20-5.   [2] Sb, V, c. xxxvi-7.

After the ceremony of inauguration, when she heard the noise of this great surging mob of people all ready to attack the poor little convent, she went to seek for strength before the altar: what she experienced there was fear in every shape and form.

Fear of having failed in the obedience due to the Provincial, although she had not acted without the consent of her confessor; fear of being unable to feed those who joined her, since she had no revenues; fear of being unable to stand so much austerity herself, with her ill-nesses. Fear, too, that she might regret the great dismantled, but spacious and delightful convent of the Incarnation and of not finding the same friendly understanding with her new companions. Kneeling there, within the space of a few moments she went through 'the pains of the agony of death.' [1]

'Our Lord's commands, the approval expressed, the unceasing prayers, I had forgotten all this. . . . Faith and every other virtue seemed temporarily in suspense. . . .' [2] 'This was one of the severest trials I've ever suffered in this life.' [3]

But she then felt the presence of Christ who reasoned with her as if she were a small child.

What was she afraid of, he asked? Why should her strength fail in his service? 'The more difficulties one has to overcome, the greater the reward.' [4] Remember, Teresa: 'Thou art mine, I am thine. . . .' [5]

He flooded her soul with light and she was comforted, 'although very weary after this battle with the devil; I came out of it laughing at him, for I saw clearly that it was all his work.'

It was time for the mid-day meal and for a siesta: she had worked all through the night and the past few days had been exhausting.

At last! The table in the little refectory, the five places laid, the frugal meal, seasoned with the joy of this solitude in God which was theirs at last. The noise in the street had died down, all Ávila was taking its siesta, it might have been thought that all Ávila had grown calm again.

It was at that very moment that a messenger from the prioress of the Incarnation, Doña María Cimbrón, arrived to intimate to Doña Teresa de Ahumada that she must return to the convent which she was not authorized to leave.

She met this occurrence as she met all great disappointments, calmly, joyfully, determined not to give way. Her grief at leaving the four girls who had just been clothed, her fear of seeing what she had

---

[1] Idem, 8.   [2] Idem, 7.   [3] Idem, 8.
[4] Cf. Idem, 9.   [5] Sb, V, c. xxxix-21.

built up destroyed, can well be imagined. But God so strengthened her that in spite of the many reasons she had for distress and despondency, she was completely happy: the convent had been founded, and was she not now being offered a precious opportunity of suffering for Christ? She was already prepared to be thrown into the prison cell: that would be welcome when it came, at last she would have some sleep and innumerable hours for prayer; she felt 'battered all over for having been among so many people.' [1]

After committing the new Carmelites to the care of their father, St. Joseph, she gave them Ursula de los Santos as prioress, and set off to confront Doña María Cimbrón.

Julian de Ávila offered to accompany her:

'I will be your squire and your chaplain. I mean it, if you will have me.'[2]

Doña María was expecting to find a rebellious nun: she saw a humble subject come into the choir, abjectly prostrating before her and fully conscious of her faults.[3]

Teresa could now no longer hide anything, so she freely spoke of Our Lord's command to found the convent of St Joseph and of her confessor's approval in consultation with the rector of the Jesuits; she mentioned the encouragement of P. Pedro Ibáñez and finally, besides the brief from Rome and the authorization of His Lordship the Bishop of Ávila, she produced the letters of Fray Pedro de Alcántara who had so constantly counselled, encouraged and upheld her during this year of struggle.

The prioress's anger died down so considerably that those who were awaiting the result of the investigation learnt to their amazement that Doña Teresa de Ahumada was not being sent to prison: she was merely enjoined to keep her cell; she was not made to fast on bread and water: they even brought her the wherewithal 'to make a very good dinner.' [4]

From then onwards a few courageous nuns took her part against the over-excited who accused the prioress of partiality.

'Doña María Cimbrón is related to the Ahumada. But Doña Teresa's got to go before the Provincial. *He* won't be weak!'

Ángel de Salazar. Excellent Father Provincial. To suppose him capable of resisting Teresa was to expect a good deal of his powers of indignation; for she was not fighting alone; her humility and her con-

---

[1] Sb, V, c. xxxvi–11.   [2] JA quoted SEC, vol. II, p. 192.
[3] Sb, V, c. xxxvi–12.   [4] Quoted SEC, vol. I, p. 309, n. 2.

After this, how could she be otherwise than 'as calm as if the whole world had been negotiating on her side'? [1]

Only one person, but a distinguished one, rose to speak for the defence; P. Domingo Báñez, one of the most renowned and revered theologians of the Dominican Order. He was opposed to the immediate suppression of the convent which all present were unanimous in demanding, with the exception of Brizuela, the Vicar-General.

The Dominican was enthusiastic for a return to traditional practices, as well as for the twofold ideal of a life which should be both contemplative and active, such as Hurtado and his followers had introduced into the Order of Preachers in Spain. The Vicar-General spoke on behalf of the Bishop. [2] Their combined efforts resulted in a decision to go to law: it was so much time gained.

'The commotion lasted for the half of a year.' [3] The matter was brought before the Royal Council, Don Álvaro de Mendoza did not yield, Gonzalo de Aranda went to court to defend the convent at his own expense, powerful friends whom Teresa had made at Doña Luisa de la Cerda's used their influence, and whilst all this 'busy-ness' was going on the people of Ávila found other subjects of conversation. Not only did Ávila grow calm, Ávila forgot.

The moment had come to remind the Provincial of his promise. Teresa begged him to allow her to go back and join her abandoned 'lambs' at St Joseph's. He still hesitated but she had the courage to insist:

'Father, have you considered that we're resisting the Holy Spirit?'

Her tone was such that he saw clearly that she was speaking under the impulse of the Spirit, and he was won over. [4]

At the beginning of the spring of 1563, Doña Teresa de Ahumada was authorized to leave the Incarnation and even to take four nuns who wanted to go with her to St Joseph's: Ana de los Ángeles, María Isabel, her cousin Isabel de San Pablo and the Marchioness of Velada's daughter, Ana de San Juan.

She bade her companions a tender farewell, as she did the house in which she had lived twenty-seven years, suffered greatly and experienced joys unknown to mortals.

Along the road which was to take her to perpetual enclosure, her heart was as light as the small package consisting of a few items of

---

[1] Idem, 17. [2] VH.
[3] Sb, V, c. xxxvi–18.
[4] HC quoted SEC, vol. I, p. 515, n. 3.

immediate necessity which she borrowed from the prioress and gave a written undertaking to return:

> One straw mat.
> One penance, of metal links.
> One discipline.
> One old habit, very much darned.[1]

As she passed the basilica of San Vicente, she went in, going down into the crypt and taking off her shoes before the Virgin of the Soterraña: Doña Teresa de Ahumada was henceforth dead to the world. From her ashes Teresa de Jesús was born.

[1] Idem.

X

THE WAY OF PERFECTION

IN the convent of St Joseph's the few nuns and their prioress were, so to speak, gathered up by Our Lady of Carmel in her great white mantle. Teresa of Jesus installed herself in active peace; she felt she had the time to train the nuns gradually. It was not as if she had to pull them after her 'with a drag-net'; she won them 'by sweetness and it was for their great good.'[1]

When she begged her daughters to let what she said to them speak to their 'inmost heart,'[2] she did so because 'a single person truly on fire with the love of God is more useful than many souls if they are tepid.'[3] Her purpose was efficacious achievement: 'The world is on fire! Christ is being condemned over again and a thousand false witnesses are being raised up against him. O my Redeemer! What is happening to us Christians? Must it always be so, that it is those who owe you most who cause you the most suffering? Those you have chosen as your friends, who have you near to them, to whom you give yourself in the sacraments, are they not ashamed that you have endured such torments for them?'[4]

Each Carmelite must substitute herself for those who had no love for God, or very little, for those who did not pray or prayed badly, and must give herself completely for the salvation of the world and of souls, for the Church and its priests.

'Sisters,' said Teresa, 'that is what you are called to; that is why you are here together; that is what your business is, that is what your desire must be and the object of your tears and supplications.'[5]

A few women, then, had made a vow to follow 'the evangelical counsels with the utmost perfection possible.'[6] The first of these counsels was: 'Pray without ceasing.' That might be expressed as to work without ceasing, build convents without ceasing, but the work would be worth no more—and no less—than the workman.

Mother Teresa guided her daughters along the way of perfection as her own experience had taught her. She spoke to them in practical

---

[1] Sb, V, c. xi–16. [2] Sb, C, c. vi–4. [3] REC, iii, 18.
[4] Sb, C, c. i–3. [5] Sb, C, c. i–5. [6] Idem, 2.

terms and her purpose was a very concrete one: the discovery and conquest of God's kingdom and its spread among mankind. Not for their own glory, but as the vanguard of the Church militant and to help a suffering world which had lost its bearings.

Enclosure, silence, recollection—all were necessary for the satisfactory accomplishment of the 'precision work' they had undertaken —to grind in well the cogs of the essential virtues—as the earth needs to be hardened by frost and pressed well down if the seeds beneath it are to germinate.

The virtues in question are three:

'The first is to love each other; the second, detachment from all created things; but the most important, although I have mentioned it last, is true humility which includes all the others. . . .' [1]

And the Mother added:

'Those who, without possessing these virtues, think themselves very contemplative, are much mistaken.' [2] 'Right thinking helps a good deal towards the accomplishment of noble deeds.' [3]

Love—Like the Gospel, the Epistles and all the saints, Teresa spoke of the love of one's neighbour and, in her tireless search for perfection even in the minutest detail, she found new terms in which to express it. She was talking to women and she had a bad opinion of women: she could not have expressed herself with more conviction: ' Anything can be harmful to weak women like ourselves. . . .' [4] 'It is enough for me to be a woman for my wings to drop off. . . .' [5]

She knew how the common life lived in an enclosed convent sharpened both the need for affection and one's susceptibilities:

It would be a terrible thing, very hard to bear, to be only a few in number and to get on badly together. May God's goodness never permit such a thing! [6] Sisters, the time for childish games—'you love me . . . you love me not'—has gone by. [7] I am older . . . I have worked a longer time . . . someone else is better treated than I am. . . . To dwell on such thoughts or make them the subject of conversation is a pest. [8]

On the occasion of even the slightest word that may cause enmity, one must hasten to apologize, pray much, not turn one's grudge into a point of honour. Ah! 'these little points of honour' (*puntillos de honra*) which for so long had been Doña Teresa de Ahumada's stumbling

[1] Sb, C, c. iv-4.   [2] Idem, 3.   [3] Idem, 1.
[4] Sb, C, prologue, 3.   [5] Idem, c. x-8.   [6] Sb, C, c. vii-9.
[7] Idem, c. xx-4.   [8] Idem, c. xii-4.

block! Teresa of Jesus exclaimed: 'My blood freezes when I think of it! If it were like that with you, you could consider yourselves as good as lost and that you had driven the Bridegroom away from his house—in that case cry to His Majesty for help and remedy the matter.' [1] And she uttered the first of her terrible anathemas:

> Let the prioress watch; if she sees a nun upsetting the house, let her endeavour to send her to another convent. God will provide the dowry. Cast out the plague-bearer, cut down the branches as far as possible; if that does not suffice, tear up the roots; and if that should prove impossible, the one who is causing the trouble must be kept in the prison cell and not come out : that is better than exposing the rest to the danger of infection. For it is a great evil! I would rather see our houses on fire and for us all to be burned! [2]

To help one another, to be compassionate, 'not only to show good-will but tenderness with it,' [3] to be merry with the sisters during recreation 'even if you don't feel like it,'[4] to look after the sick, to serve in the lowliest tasks—Mother Teresa put all this on just as high a level as contemplation of Our Lord, or mental prayer. 'What does it matter whether we are serving him in the one way or in the other?' [5] Divine love is inseparable from the love of one's sisters. True affection, which has nothing in common with earthly attachments, helps us to make progress. Perfect love does not hesitate to warn those who are following the wrong path of their mistake, it avoids flattery as much as it does secret blame, and submits to criticism without bearing a grudge. One cannot hide anything from true friends: 'They see the little faults,' and Teresa who, even though she was prioress, did not cease to be a woman talking to women, used an expression which was especially applicable to defects in textiles: *Las motitas ven.* . . . Tiniest blemishes are seen. . . . [6]

Throughout her life Teresa implored her nuns to reprove her when she deserved it and she accepted criticism humbly.[7] All her life long she showed each Carmelite how she must 'preach by deeds, since the Apostle and our lack of knowledge prevent us from preaching by word of mouth.' [8]

But how was one to achieve, in love and detachment, this combination of firmness and gentleness, this doing away with the 'black point of honour'? By one supreme virtue on which all the others depended: the knowledge of self.

---

[1] Sb, C. c. vii–10.   [2] Idem, 11.   [3] Idem, 7.   [4] Idem, 7.
[5] Idem, c. xvii–6.   [6] Idem, c. vii–4.   [7] FR, L. IV, c. vii.
[8] Sb, C, c. xv–6.

The knowledge of self—'Self-knowledge is the bread which must be eaten with every dish, even the daintiest . . . there's no nourishment without that bread.' [1] The Mother never ceased to insist on the extreme importance of clear self-knowledge. Hers was a strong character, progressively released by prayer and divine grace from the weight of what a psychoanalyst would call her self-punishing complexes. When she took as her motto the three words: 'To act, to suffer, to love,' [2] the quest for suffering did not signify a morbid tendency: 'Try us, O Lord, you who know the truth, in order that we may know ourselves!' [3] Suffering alone shows our true strength, or, on the other hand, what an illusion our self-complacency is. For Teresa of Jesus to suffer was to learn to know oneself.

But her prudence and good sense were such, she had known so many people—herself included—whom the shame of finding nothing good in themselves had driven away from the Lord of all mercies instead of bringing them close to him in childlike abandonment, that she immediately added a rider that would comfort the scrupulous: 'This bread must be eaten with moderation; once the soul is submissive, when she has seen clearly how little she gives in exchange for the gifts given to her by so great a King,' what need is there for her to spend further time over this? 'Let us go on towards something else, towards whatever the Lord places before us. . . .' [4]

For 'the understanding must be ennobled in order that self-knowledge does not rob us altogether of our courage.' [5]

Humility—For Teresa, the depths of humility lay very close to the highest of honours, of which for a long time she herself had had no experience: 'If I had understood, as I do now, that my soul's tiny palace contained so great a King, I shouldn't have left him there so often alone, I should have stayed with him from time to time and, moreover, I should have made an effort to keep his house in less dirt and disorder. . . .' [6] It was in this way that the Mother who wielded the broom so energetically and compared sin to spiders' webs—she was a good housewife and a courteous hostess—referred to the presence of God in man.

'Humility is to keep within the bounds of truth,' [7] she said. 'The truth is magnificent: we are nothing, but God dwells in us and God is everything.' 'Worse than the beasts as we are, we don't understand our

---

[1] Sb, V, c. xiii–15.
[2] SEC, R, xxxvi, p. 64.
[3] Sb, M, III, c. i–9.
[4] Sb, C, c. xiii–5.
[5] Sb, M, c. ii–8.
[6] Sb, C, c. xxviii–11.
[7] Sb, M, VI, c. x–7.

soul's great dignity and we insult it by bringing it down to the level of the vile things of this world. . . .'[1] 'Let us beware of the false humility which refuses to recognize the gifts which God has so generously bestowed upon us: Let us understand clearly, absolutely clearly, about this: God grants them to us without any merit on our part and therefore we should thank His Majesty. . . . The richer we find ourselves, knowing all the time that we are really poor, the more progress we make in true humility.'[2]

The effects of this union of the humble soul with God are wonderful. Teresa returns to her liking for tales of chivalry and draws upon that source to explain these effects to her nuns more clearly: 'If an insignificant peasant girl married the King would not their children be of royal blood? When Our Lord gives a soul the great grace of uniting himself to it so intimately, what fruit, what heroic acts will not be the result.'[3] But for Teresa of Jesus a heroic act is no longer what it was for Teresa de Ahumada, a sacrifice quickly over, the 'cheap' way of gaining heaven, but the perfect accomplishment of every single action, even the most ordinary.

'It is the humblest among you who are the most perfect,' she said, 'not those who are favoured in prayer or with ecstasies.'

And it was to mortify herself that she added: 'I am glad to give this advice, but it is counsel which contemplatives will find humiliating.'[4]

This slow transformation of women far from perfect into the brides of Christ, into the servants of all in the world who suffer, this training of the character, of heart and soul, to live on the mountain tops of spirituality, this ' precision work' in which the adaptation of body and mind to the spiritual life consists, was part and parcel of the primitive Rule of Carmel.

The anchorites of Mount Carmel claimed to be the direct heirs of the prophet Elias; for long centuries these Fathers of the Desert had worn garments of plaited palm fibre. It was they whom Teresa wanted to imitate when she had to resign herself to not dying a martyr's death. About the year 1200, Albert, Patriarch of Jerusalem, had given them a Rule and Constitutions, and from the end of that century onwards, protected by the crusaders, they continued to found numerous monasteries in Europe, frightening in their austerity but nurseries of saints, until the great plague of 1348: the few friars who survived, feeling a little sorry for themselves, relaxed the observance. It was thought that

---

[1] CTA, xix.   [2] Sb, V, c. x-4.
[3] Sb, CAD, c. iii-9.   [4] Sb, C, c. xviiii-9.

now humanity had grown weaker it could not bear the rigours imposed by its ancestors without danger and, in 1482, Pope Eugenius IV attenuated and mitigated the primitive Rule.

The fasts, which had lasted from the feast of the Exaltation of the Cross until Easter, *i.e.* seven months, were reduced to three days a week, except during Advent and Lent.

Perpetual abstinence from meat was likewise reduced to three days a week.

The coarse habit was replaced by one of fine cloth; they no longer went barefoot. Formerly obliged to seclusion and perpetual silence, the friars were now authorized to talk to each other freely in the cloisters.

As to the nuns, not only did they visit each other's cells, but visitors, both pious and worldly, thronged the parlours, and the sisters were allowed to absent themselves from their convent.

Teresa adopted the primitive Rule in every single one of its requirements. What was called her Reform was in reality a return to the observance of the ancient Order of Carmel. She restored in her convents the character of laboratories of spiritual culture in the strict sense of the term. She would not even allow her daughters—bound as they were by vow to live by the work of their hands—to have common workrooms: this would be a pretext for chattering and thus for dissipation. A Carmelite must work alone, in her cell, seated on the ground. She might speak only at recreation and even there a little rattle was frequently shaken to remind one of the presence of God. The enclosure door shut on her for ever. For her rare visitors she remained invisible behind the barrier of grilles, curtains, veils.

To be solitary, silent, despising the body and its needs, but gay as children; humble, but conscious of their soul's dignity; submissive, but to spiritual things; in love, but with Christ; deprived of everything, but queens of the world, 'for those who trouble about no worldly thing are rulers over all;' [1] that was was the pattern Teresa of Jesus set for Our Lady's daughters.

'This house is a heaven if there is one upon earth.' [2] The Mother who initiated her daughters into mental prayer by first of all teaching them to say 'Our Father, who art in heaven . . .' well, commented on the beginning of the *Pater* with her magnificent logic: 'You know that God is everywhere, it is clear that where the King is there is his court; in short, where God is, is heaven. You will allow that where His Majesty is, there is all glory. St Augustine says that he sought him everywhere and found him in himself. Do you think it a matter of

[1] Sb, C, c. ii–5.   [2] Idem, xiii–7.

small importance for a soul who wants to open her heart to understand this truth, to see that she has no need to go to heaven to speak to her eternal Father and enjoy his presence, that it isn't even necessary for her to raise her voice? She has no need of wings to go and seek him: all she needs is to be alone and contemplate him in herself. . . .' [1]

Not only was the house a paradise on earth, but each Carmelite carried her paradise within herself.

[1] Idem, xxviii–2.

XI

A WRETCH AMONG ANGELS

IT was still dark when the little bell rang, giving out its cracked sound: five o'clock in the morning. The Mother Prioress of the convent of St Joseph of Carmel made the sign of the cross and got up; she listened and heard sounds of her convent awakening.

A voice cut the silence: 'Praised be Jesus Christ, praised be the Virgin Mary, his Mother! To prayer, Sisters! Let us praise the Lo–o–o–rd!'

The vibration of the young, high-pitched voice was prolonged on a single note, with one sheer intake of breath: it was Isabel de Santo Domingo. . . .

A brief pause, then another voice: 'Praised be Jesus. . . .' The more solemn, slightly husky timbre of a woman of mature years: Úrsula de los Santos.

Two voices rang out at the same time from the far end of the cloister, vibrating in harmony: '. . . To prayer, Sisters! . . .'

In imagination Teresa of Jesus could see the cell doors opening in the light of dawn and her daughters on their knees as the day came into being. At the beginning of each day it was her delight to hear these chants rising to God from Carmel, as from a tree full of nests, nests which were full of song-birds. That was why she always came out last. The sky above the patio was tinged with a blue still milky-pale when the Discalced Carmelites and their Mother Prioress made their way to the chapel, to the accompaniment of a heavy swish of moving frieze.

Mental prayer and the little Hours: Prime, Terce, Sext, None. Then Mass.

After breakfast, which was about nine o'clock, each nun went to the work assigned to her.

The cell was quickly swept and put in order. The straw pallet, which the planks scarcely raised above the level of the red-brick floor, was shaken and the thick frieze which did duty for bed-linen put back in place. The warm brown colour looked well against the white-washed wall whose only decoration was a large cross. The rough wood door formed a brown mass, the window a patch of blue. In a corner stood the blue and white earthenware pitcher and basin in use everywhere for one's ablutions at that time. On a narrow piece of board stood a few books. On the floor was a cork mat which did duty as a seat. That was all. Nothing more. But the 'nothing' was so clean that it positively shone.

It was there that any Carmelite who had no particular office assigned to her worked at her spinning in silence, to earn her bread and that of her sisters.

But 'with your eyes on your Bridegroom. It is to him you must look for your food. If he is pleased with you, even those who love you least will give you something to eat. Even if you were to die of hunger, blessed the nuns of St Joseph's! . . . Leave all anxiety about food on one side, then, otherwise everything is lost. Abandon this care to him who is Lord both of revenues and those who possess them: we are here at his command, his word is truth, and heaven and earth will fail before that fails us. . . .' [1] 'He never fails those who are in need. Either you believe this or you don't believe it; if you believe it, why kill yourselves with worry?' [2] 'There was a time when I trusted the world's aid; I see clearly now that all that is worth no more than a few sprigs of dried rosemary. . . .' [3]

Before the bell rang for dinner a short time was spent in the deepening of self-knowledge: the examination of conscience.

The refectory was rectangular, with narrow tables arranged round the sides. Along the white walls the Carmelites sat on wooden benches, each one with a spotless serviette, stiff because perfectly ironed, in front of her. The earthenware drinking-bowl which was lifted with both hands formed a splash of blue, the wooden utensils, the bread, provided patches of light colour. The huge black cross hung over all. Vegetables, eggs or fish were eaten in silence. From a pulpit constructed in the recess in the wall formed by one of the windows, a sister read aloud, her black veil standing out against the blue of the Ávila sky.

White: walls and coifs. Brown: the habits, the wood-work. Red: the tiles of floor and roof. Blue: a few pieces of earthenware, the sky. Such are the only colours found in these Carmels. And over all that, the sun of Spain.

When there was only one egg, it was kept for the most delicate among them, they vied with each other as to who was strongest, each refusing to eat it.

When there was nothing in the turn and the purse was empty, Prioress Teresa of Jesus made her daughters come to table all the same

[1] Sb, C, c. ii-1, 2.   [2] Idem, c. xxix-2.   [3] R, iii, p. 17.

and she spoke to them of God in such wonderful words that they
forgot their hunger.

At that time at St Joseph's there were none of those lay-sisters
whom the Mother was later to call so delightfully 'those with the
white veil'; the choir nuns shared all the household tasks. Teresa used
her privileges as prioress only to take upon herself the hardest tasks.
Her 'week in the kitchen' was a red-letter week for them all. 'She did
all she could to give them a treat' [1] and Our Lord sent her the wherewithal to do it. In her opinion, to make the best possible use of what
God gives was one way of praising him.

'Daughters, don't let's give way to disappointment when through
obedience we are occupied in external things. If your job is in the
kitchen, don't forget that Our Lord is there in the midst of the pots
and pans!' [2]

So much was this the case at St Joseph's that one day Isabel de Santo
Domingo found Teresa in front of the kitchen stove in ecstasy:

'Dear God! Our Mother will upset the little oil that's left to us on
the fire!'

But, although she was rapt to heaven, her feet were firmly planted
on the ground. Teresa did not loosen her grip of the handle of the
frying-pan one whit and the eggs went on sizzling. . . . [3]

She was Martha and Mary in one.

Úrsula de los Santos was over forty: it was late to begin to mould
oneself to obedience, especially for one who had been mistress of a
household and responsible for the upbringing of a family. Teresa
accordingly watched her closely and saw to it that the ordinary trials
of religious life were multiplied in her regard: Ursula came off with
flying colours.

Did the prioress feel that this nun was not entirely free from
mental reservations? However this may be, she decided one day to
put her through an extraordinary test and was fully determined to
deprive her of the habit if she showed a want of docility.

She stopped her abruptly in the cloister:

'Oh dear, Sister, I *am* sorry for you. Go and get into bed: it's
essential.'

She felt her pulse, behaving as though she found her very ill.
Úrsula de los Santos went to bed. When they came to ask her how she
was, she replied:

[1] SEC, F, p. 7.   [2] Sb, F, c. v–8.   [3] SST, vol. III, pp. 78–9.

'I am very ill.'

'What is the matter? Where are you in pain?'

Ursula did not hesitate.

'Sisters, I know nothing about it, but Mother Prioress says so.'

Teresa was not yet completely satisfied. She went to see the patient herself and took her pulse again.

'Oh, dear me! Sisters, send for a barber quickly! She will have to be bled.'

The barber came and bled her; Úrsula de los Santos' only response was complete and perfect obedience.

After this, the Mother loved her with an especial love 'so much did the bleeding of this good nun contribute to the extraction of self-will from these convents. . . .' [1] 'Any one wanting in obedience shall not be a nun here, . . .' [2] said Teresa. 'The way of obedience is the way which leads most quickly to absolute perfection.' [3] The logic of this was obvious. 'Obedience is the true means of submitting one's will to reason.' [4]

In short: it is essential to know how to obey if one wants to command and particularly if one wants to command oneself. A daughter of God must show obedience, just as a soldier must. Teresa did not forget that she came of a warrior race; she used to give her nuns examples from military life: 'Soldiers must always be prepared for their captain to send them where he will. . . .' [5] And her summons to spiritual exercises rings out like a trumpet blast: 'Mental prayer, Sisters, or if that is impossible, vocal prayer: holy reading, colloquies with God.' [6]

And what about María de Ocampo who had promised 'her inheritance' to help in the foundation of St Joseph's convent? She came to join the others on St John's day 1563. She had been 'the most elegant and the best-dressed among those with whom she associated. Her fine dresses went to make altar frontals, chasubles and other things needed for the chapel. . . .' [7] Her famous 'inheritance' settled one of the convent's debts and paid for the erection of a few hermitages in the orchard 'where one could give oneself to prayer'. The paintings on their walls inspired devotion. The Mother Prioress would not allow María de Ocampo's father to give more.

María de Ocampo now ceased to be: Sister María Bautista had so completely overcome vainglory and her own will that when Teresa

---

[1] SEC, vol. V, p. 94, n. 1.   [2] Sb, C, c. xviii–8.
[3] Sb, F, c. v–10.   [4] Idem, 11.   [5] Sb, C, c. xviii–3.
[6] Idem, 4.   [7] JA quoted SEC, vol. V, p. 9, n. 3.

ordered her to go and plant a rotten cucumber, she merely asked:

'Vertically or horizontally?'

'Horizontally. . . .' [1]

That was the way obedience was practised. But María Bautista's obedience in no way diminished her common-sense, as she showed when the prioress asked her to give her opinion: the well-sinkers alleged that to dig the well more deeply in the hope of finding drinking water would be 'a waste of money.'

'Let them try. Our Lord will certainly have to send us someone to provide us with water, and the food for whoever he sends: it will be easier for His Majesty to let us have water here and he will not fail to do so. . . .' [2] As it turned out, good fresh water was found and the well was named María Bautista. . . .

His Illustrious Lordship Don Álvaro de Mendoza, Bishop of Ávila, became very fond of St Joseph's. Someone had just given him a life-sized crucifix and he had this taken to the convent to show the Discalced nuns, for he was sure they would find it moving. He returned later to fetch it and as he was talking to Mother Teresa at the parlour grille, the sound of the chanting of litanies reached their ears, although it was not the customary hour for this exercise:

'Lord, Lord!'

'Stay with us!'

'Jesus crucified!'

'Stay with us!'

The sound of the voices came nearer and the nuns came into the parlour in procession, headed by two sisters carrying the large crucifix with much difficulty:

'Jesus crowned with thorns!'

'Stay with us!'

They were chanting in all seriousness and their pageantry was without the slightest tinge of impertinence. Teresa blushed with embarrassment and, begging Don Álvaro to excuse the nuns, she began to scold them forthwith. The Bishop, however, laughed heartily:

'Good! Let them keep it then!' [3]

Miracles are the due reward of innocence. When the most naïve among them—for María de San José was noted for her childlike simplicity—asked the crucifix:

[1] Sb, F, c. i–3.　　　　[2] Sb, C, c. i–4.　　　　[3] SST, vol. I, p. 83.

In the Convent at Malagón

In the Convent of St. Joseph at Ávila

MEDINA DEL CAMPO
Fortifications

'Lord, what is your name? You are sometimes called "Christ of the Agony" or "Christ, our Saviour," but what name are we to give you for this crucifix?'—she was in no way surprised when Christ, the friend of the childlike and simple, answered: 'Call me the holy Christ of love. . . .'[1]

When money ran very short the nuns contented themselves with dry bread, but there was never any lack of wax candles for the altar and everything connected with divine worship was as exquisitely perfect as possible. A visiting priest was scandalized:

'What! A scented towel to wipe one's hands before saying Mass?'

Teresa, her fine face lighting up with fervour, took the blame on herself:

'It is from me my daughters get this imperfection. But when I remember the way Our Lord reproached the pharisee for not receiving him with sufficient honour, I could wish that everything here in the church, from even its very threshold, were perfumed with sweet waters. . . .'[2]

The construction of a larger church was clearly indispensable. Teresa called the depositrix:

'How much money have we?'

'Mother, *un cuarto*, a farthing.'[3]

'That will please him greatly,'[4] and she put the work in hand. For in the absence of even a sprig of dried rosemary, God would provide.

María Álvarez Dávila y Salazar was one of Mother Teresa's nieces: of the highest ranks of nobility and as beautiful as one could wish. One September day she invited her friends to go out with her: the ladies went in litters, the gentlemen on horseback. She was a very splendid figure, María Dávila, 'attired in much silk and gold and all the magnificence one could desire.'

She led the cavalcade in the direction of St. Joseph's and there stepped down from her litter; the enclosure door opened and Teresa, who was waiting for her, appeared carrying a crucifix. María kneeling 'kissed the feet of the crucifix fervently, then without turning round to acknowledge her friends' farewell, she allowed Teresa to close the door behind her and divested herself forthwith of her fine apparel. . . .'[5]

María Dávila thus afforded much astonishment to all the nobility and gentry of the town.

[1] Idem.   [2] Y quoted SEC, vol. II, p. 499.
[3] MJE quoted SEC, vol. II, p. 292.   [4] Idem.
[5] FR, L. II, c. 5, and B.

But María Dávila had ceased to be: all there was in her stead was a young Discalced Carmelite, Sister María de San Jerónimo.

One night after Matins when Teresa had stayed behind to pray, she saw the five Marías, the two Isabels, Ursula, Antonia, Ana and Petronilla come into choir in procession, carrying lighted candles and preceded by a crucifix carried by the youngest. They were singing hymns, followed by this strange couplet:

> You clothe us with apparel new,
> Heavenly King!
> Should creatures vile infest our frieze,
> Delivrance bring![1]

As a very special favour, they had just obtained permission to wear the roughest frieze even next to the skin, with a view to greater mortification. In future they would wear no more linen and even the handkerchief would be of coarse material. 'But fearing lest such coarse wool should be infested with lice, with the image of the Crucified at their head and in deep recollection they came to pray God to spare them such an unclean pest!'

Touched—and amused, Teresa answered their *coplas* by improvising a reply. And in the chapel of St Joseph's could be heard a curious concert, 'against impertinent little creatures':

> *Teresa*:
> These tiresome creatures much disturb
> in time of prayer
> Minds which are ill establishèd
> in things of God.

> *All*
> Should creatures vile infest our frieze,
> Delivrance bring!

> *Teresa*
> You who've come here prepared for death,
> Yield not one whit,
> And such vile creatures great or small,
> Fear not at all.

> *All*
> You've clothed us now in livery new,
> Heavenly King.
> Should creatures vile infest our frieze,
> Delivrance bring!

[1] SEC, vol. VI, pp. 117-19.

'From that day onwards not even one such creature was ever seen either in the habits or in the gauze veils.' [1] And they called the Christ who worked the miracle the Christ of the lice.

Stories like this were told with every freedom to the hum of the spinning-wheel at recreation—unless in their great joy the nuns broke out into songs and dances or the playing of the flute and tambourine. These 'hermits' were by no means gloomy; at St Joseph's the atmosphere was enlivened by the poetry and music which entered into everything; as Teresa said, 'all that is most necessary to render our life bearable.' She took part in it all but never left off her spinning. One day, a sister who had finished her work took up a spool and wound the thread on to another empty spool.

'What are you doing, Sister?'

The child had to admit that she wanted to spare herself the shame of being idle in the prioress's presence.[2]

For the Mother never allowed herself any rest, but was always spinning, weaving, sewing or darning. She found the curtains drawn behind the parlour grilles a convenience, for she was thus able to work with her hands while discussing convent business.

Don Francisco de Salcedo, 'holy gentleman' as he was, was slightly irritated by this.

'Mother, you don't listen to what I say. It's impossible to listen when you're spinning so fast.'

'Am I not obliged to do so? Isn't it my duty to do everything in my power to feed my daughters?'

He proposed a bargain: when he came to see her he would pay her the equivalent of an hour's work on condition that she did not inflict on him the sound of the spinning-wheel humming behind the black curtain. After this, when he went away, he deposited the amount of his debt in the turn, with the parlour key. . . .

It was with distaste that Teresa obeyed the order P. Báñez gave her to set down in writing, as her daughters wished, the day-to-day counsels she gave them. Why must she always be forced to spend her time writing? She had only just finished the second version of her autobiography which she had revised at the request of P. García de Toledo. Were they always going 'to prevent her from spinning'? [3] So in the matter of what she called 'the little book' (*el librillo* . . .) on the *Pater noster*, later to be known as the *Way of Perfection*, she placed obedience before every other virtue.

---

[1] SST, vol. III, p. 82.   [2] B.
[3] Sb, V, c. x–7.

About 11 o'clock at night, when Matins and Lauds were chanted, the nuns of St Joseph's retired to their cells. They knelt down on the threshold, as they had done in the morning. The youngest sister gave three knocks and on two notes chanted a *saetilla* [1] composed of a few lines providing a theme of meditation for the night:

> Sister!
> You will die only once,
> If you go astray . . . woe betide you!
> Sister!
> No man can escape death,
> Neither poor man, king nor pope. . . .
> Sister!
> In a deep dark tomb
> Endeth the joy of this world! [2]

The prioress went round the cloister, stopping to bless each nun as she passed. One after another the doors closed. Teresa, last of all, did not close hers until the portress handed her the bunch of great keys which locked up the convent.

The browns, blues, the russet red, the white even, all the colours of Carmel became indistinguishable in the darkness.

In the little convent all was darkness and silence except for the light of a smoky oil lamp coming from the prioress's cell.

For she was not going to let writing prevent her from spinning any longer: she would take the hours from her sleep. Seated on the ground in front of the stone block which served her as table she wrote the *Way of Perfection* for her daughters.

The 'little book' included, in addition to the counsels on asceticism contained in the first fifteen chapters, a treatise on mental prayer in ten chapters—although the word 'treatise' is very pedantic in the case of a woman who all her life long sought to avoid any display of learning—and finally a commentary on the *Pater* showed how vocal prayer could lead souls to supernatural prayer.

Teresa wanted to cure her Carmelites of an evil of the day, the mechanical repetition 'of many vocal prayers said very rapidly as if one were dispatching a duty; they are convinced they have got to recite them every day, so much so that when the Lord puts his kingdom into their hands, they do not accept it.' [3] 'You do more by saying a single word of the *Pater noster* from time to time. . . .' [4] 'The Lord attaches

---

[1] The *saeta* (lit. 'arrow') is a cry pronounced in a long modulation something like an Arab chant.
[2] EM, p. 157.   [3] Sb, C, c. xxxi-12.   [4] Idem, 13.

no importance to our hurting our heads with a multiplicity of words when we speak to him. . . ."[1] You must understand what you say . . .'[2] 'and understand to whom you are speaking. . . .' [3] 'When I say the word *Credo*, it seems to me reasonable to understand and know in what I believe; and when I say 'Our Father,' to understand who this Father is and the Master who has taught us this prayer is a work of love. . . .'[4]

She does not preach or become excited, the tone is natural, affectionate and yet firm, the plan is absolutely clear. To this framework of the interior life she brings the same accuracy as she does to the organization of the material life of the convent, down to the last detail. Her sentences have the ring of her conversation about them and have caught something of the sound of her voice. On paper she questions those who are asleep not far away from her, proving that they are always in her thoughts: 'What are we to do in that case, Sisters?' 'Sisters, have you ever noticed? . . .' [5]

When she wanted to show that a thing was blameworthy, she did not hesitate to quote her own example: 'I sometimes imagine I am quite detached from the world . . . but at another time I find myself so attached to things which I should have despised the day before that I don't recognize myself. . . . Sometimes I think I have a lot of courage and would not refuse anything in God's service; but then comes another day when I could not kill an ant for God if you tried ever so little to prevent me. . . .' [6]

The acknowledgement of her mistakes could not harm a prioress who made herself not only mother to the nuns but their sister and who gave the example of trying to acquire self-knowledge. They were so near to her heart, her Discalced Carmelites, and she expected so much from the four young ones, María Bautista, María de San Jerónimo, Isabel de Santo Domingo—these three scarcely twenty—and Isabel de San Pablo, not eighteen. The Lord was already endowing them with so much perfection, overwhelming them with such high graces that she felt 'covered with confusion' [7] in their presence. For Teresa of Jesus remembered how many years it had taken Doña Teresa de Ahumada to reach, as they had, the stage of 'finding her consolation in solitude and of looking upon visits as something painful. . . . If one of them has permission to live apart in a hermitage, she considers herself the most favoured. God has his purpose when he gives his daughters a courage in his service far beyond the courage of women. . . .' [8]

[1] Idem, xxix–6.   [2] Idem, xxiv–2.   [3] Idem, 6.
[4] Idem, 2.   [5] Idem, xxxviii–4.   [6] Sb, C, c. xxxviii–6.
[7] Sb, F, c. 1–6.   [8] Idem, 6.

What was his purpose? What was so much courage for? Were they not contemplatives? Did not the world consider women who did nothing but pray, useless? It was this that made Mother Teresa stress the significance of their vocation: 'Although the ensign does not fight in the war, he is none the less in the thick of the danger, he holds the standard and cannot defend himself. He will not let go of it even if they hack him to pieces. Contemplatives are like that. Their rôle is to suffer like Christ and to raise the standard of the cross on high. If they loose hold of the flag, the battle is lost!' [1]

'Completely humble and considering obedience a joy, these hand-maids of the active virtues are truly blessed. . . .'[2] 'As to the joys of prayer, raptures and visions, we must wait until we get to the other world to know what all that means. . . .' [3]

For a moment the flow of the pen was interrupted. Teresa was now reflecting, as she was always inclined to do, on her own miseries: '. . . miserable sinner that I am in the midst of these angels. . . .' [4]

---

[1] Sb, C, c. xviii–5.   [2] Idem.
[3] Idem, 7.   [4] Sb, F, c. 1–6.

PART THREE

GOD'S KNIGHT ERRANT

'Our Lord will never abandon those who love
him when their venturing into the unknown
is for him alone.'

PASCAL: *Pensées*, ch. iii

'To have courage for whatever comes in life,
everything lies in that.'

Autobiography, ch. iv

'Let us risk our life, for he who will lose his life
shall best find it.'

Poems, xix

I

THE BIRTH OF THE FOUNDATIONS

OUR Mother is going away!'
When they learnt at St Joseph's that Mother Teresa was thinking of leaving Ávila to go and found other convents, her nuns were filled with dismay.

She did not try to console them: instead she fired them with enthusiasm for her work.

'Can the Order of Our Lady of Mount Carmel be limited to one poor convent? Is each of us to save herself alone? Even for thirteen Discalced Carmelites, is it enough for us to give ourselves to prayer and penance, considering ourselves worthy of the bread we eat only if we have earned it by the work of our hands, and saving just ourselves? No. The world is still burning!'

The prioress reminded them of P. Alonso de Maldonado, the Franciscan who, on his return from the Indies, his face weather-beaten from wind and spray, had made the whole of their tiny church re-echo with his cry of alarm.

'Millions of souls are being lost in these conquered lands where the sword does not always clear away the obstacles in the path of the cross!'

Over the mighty empire of all the Spains the sun never set but it did not dissolve the darkness of violence, of greed, of everlasting death. From Flanders too there came tales of churches pillaged and desecrated, of profanations of the sacred Host. Whereas the daughters of Our Lady of Mount Carmel were at rest in the lap of their father St Joseph, busy spinning the cocoon of their new life.

'I say to all of you who are fighting under this standard, do not sleep, do not sleep, there is no peace upon the earth!'

'And since like a mighty captain our God willed to die, let us follow him, we who have slain him. . . . Do not sleep, do not sleep, for God is no longer upon earth!'

'Oh, what blessed warfare! Let no one desert! Let us risk our life, for he who will lose his life will find it best!'

'Let us follow this standard, Christ is marching before us!'

'Be fearless! Do not sleep! There is no peace upon earth!'[1]

Teresa already saw herself at the head of legions of fighting angels. And then she wept. For whole days and nights she wept in the hermitage of Christ at the column, beside herself with grief and help-lessness. 'A poor weak woman like myself could do nothing.'[2] Nothing, nothing but weep? 'Don't let's think that everything is done by much weeping, but let us put our shoulders to the wheel.'[3]

Prayer in the first place. Prayer can be warfare, silence a fortress, and mortification, strategy; a soul centred in God is as mighty as armies on the march, and women who are silent and still under their black veil can fight for the peace of the world by making every single thought, every single sacrifice 'an heroic act.'

Teresa of Jesus could be said truly to love God only from this moment when her heart, grown larger now, embraced the whole world; now she loved all mankind and would have given her life to save the least among them. 'He who loves not his neighbour loves not you, O Lord!'[4]

Alas! Only a poor insignificant woman and her sisters! So much fervour, so much austerity already: was it possible to increase it? Teresa mingled her blood with her tears.

This continued until one evening Our Lord appeared to her with a most tender expression as if he wished to console her, and said:

'Wait a little, daughter, and you will see great things. . . .'[5]

At this time Philip II was so desirous of reforming monastic life in his dominions that he invited the General of the Order of Our Lady of Mount Carmel, P. Juan Bautista Rubeo, of Ravenna, to come and investigate the means of carrying this out. He was received with very great honour. The 'Most Reverend Master General' visited Castile. At Ávila, the Bishop, Don Álvaro de Mendoza, did not fail to bring to his notice the example of a return to the primitive Rule afforded by the convent of St Joseph, which he took him to see. He was amazed to find these 'nuns so different from all the others, clad in frieze, wholly unostentatious, wearing sandals, humble, mortified.'[6]

During his stay in Ávila, he frequently returned to this oasis of pure and austere life. And this great prelate, whose face had, as well as a slight puffiness about the cheeks, something of the nobility of feature of the ancient Romans, called Teresa of Jesus *la mia figlia*, 'daughter mine.'

---

[1] P, xxix.   [2] Sb, F, c. ii–4.   [3] Sb, M, VI, c. vi–9.
[4] Sb, E, ii–2.   [5] Sb, F, c. i–3.   [6] JA, p. 238.

On his departure he left her a letter patent:

We, Fray Juan Bautista Rubeo of Ravenna, Prior and Master General . . . to the Reverend Mother Teresa of Jesus:

There is no good merchant, labourer, soldier or man of culture who does not take care of, look after, employ all solicitude over and go to much trouble to enlarge, his house, his honour and all his possessions.

How much greater should be the efforts made by the servants of God to extend their work to other places, to build churches and religious houses and do all that is necessary to serve souls and for the glory of the Divine Majesty!

To the Reverend Mother Teresa of Jesus we grant the faculty and power to set up everywhere in the kingdom of Castile convents of our holy Order, where the nuns will live in accordance with the primitive Rule, the habit and other holy customs being those in use at St Joseph's. . . . Let them wear brown frieze. . . . If frieze cannot be found, let some other coarse stuff be used. And we shall give them vicars or commissioners to govern them.[1]

Then a second letter patent:

'It is understood that our authorization is for the whole of Castile, Old and New. . . .'[2]

Finally, a third letter patent from P. Rubeo marked one of Teresa's greatest triumphs: she was authorized to found houses of friars under the primitive Rule, to the number of two to begin with. Here the principle of penance, together with that of deep prayer, would not be allowed to fall into disuse.

Only men could preach and spread these principles; only men could undertake the spiritual direction of the Discalced Carmelite nuns. In that matter, too, Teresa had experience to guide her. She knew only too well the damage which 'the half-educated and timorous'[3] could do and how much she herself had suffered from want of understanding on the part of her confessors. 'What a lot of time I've lost through not knowing what to do! I am terribly sorry for those who, when they reach this state, are alone, without help. . . .'[4] She had known so many who, with God's grace, were soaring upwards in the spiritual life like eagles until they were constrained by some timid director to walk 'like chickens with their feet fastened together!'[5]

For the spiritual direction of the daughters of Carmel, she wanted priests who were both intelligent and experienced. 'If they are learned

---

[1] SEC, vol. V, pp. 333–4. [2] Idem. [3] Sb, V, c. xx–21.
[4] Sb, V, c. xiv–7. [5] Sb, V, c. xxxix–12.

as well, so much the better.' [1] But she considered the first two qualities the most important: 'It is no light cross to submit our intelligence to someone who hasn't very much himself. Personally, I've never succeeded and I don't believe one ought to do it.' [2] 'God preserve us from foolish devotions!' [3]

In his letter patent P. Rubeo gave a perfect résumé of Carmelite prayer:

> We desire that all religious who are sons of this Order be transparent mirrors, burning lamps, flaming torches, and shining stars to enlighten and help those in the world who go astray. We therefore particularly desire that they should devote themselves entirely to continual and familiar converse with God and that, consecrated as they are to prayer, contemplation and holy meditation, they should strive to be so closely united with him that their spirit, though still fettered by the body, already dwells in heaven. . . . Forgetful of themselves, wholly absorbed in those frequent and sublime flights of the spirit in prayer, which it is impossible to define for they are extraordinary, their light travels quickly, whether, since it is inherent in the soul it is indistinguishable from it, whether it withdraws to its inmost centre, or whether it moves, rises, descends, in such a way that the understanding cannot grasp it: it leaves tears in the eyes, but in the heart the most refreshing and profitable dew.
>
> Urged, then, by the desire of extending our Order, it seems to us our duty to grant the petition we have received that we should authorize the foundation of certain houses of friars; they will celebrate Mass, pray, chant the Divine Office; will devote the requisite number of hours to mental prayer, meditation and other spiritual exercises, and will accordingly be known as houses or monasteries of contemplative Carmelite fathers; they will also be a help to the others and will live in conformity with the primitive Constitutions. [4]

It was indeed given to Teresa of Jesus to see 'great things': without money, without support, without houses, without friars, she was given the mission of peopling Old and New Castile with Carmelite houses. From now onwards there would be no rest for Mother or daughters.

In agreement with P. Baltasar Álvarez, Medina del Campo was chosen for the first foundation. Teresa took six nuns with her, two from St Joseph's and four from the Incarnation; among them were Isabel Arias and Teresa de Quezada who embarked on the adventure despite the opposition of all their relatives.

---

[1] Sb, V, c. xiii–16.   [2] Idem, 19.

[3] Idem, 16.   [4] SEC, vol. V, p. 336.

The time came to say goodbye. The Mother would not show her feelings except to Our Lord. She retired to the hermitage of Christ at the column, the place where she had received his great promises. She begged him that on her return she might find the house holy and recollected, as she was now leaving it.

On the occasion of every departure she was to experience a heart-ache which she always succeeded in concealing. This time the pain of parting was severe. Ávila said that Mother Teresa was madder than ever; even the kindly Bishop had no encouragement to offer. But what were obstacles, however great, to such a fervent will, such wonder-fully forthright energy as hers? Her enthusiasm and tenacity in action found expression in a strength that was almost unbelievable: '. . . A firm and very determined act of the will not to relax until the end was attained, come what might, whatever happened, whatever hardship there might be, whosoever grumbled, even if one were to die *en route* or one felt the trials were beyond one's courage, or even if the world should fall to pieces!' [1]

She put considerations prompted by human reason on one side and decided once for all that it was no use being guided merely by natural wisdom: 'it's a hindrance. . . .' [2] For her the difficulty dis-appeared from the moment she took the decision to conquer it: 'at the beginning the effort it costs is only small.' [3] What this woman, who was always in poor health, called 'a small effort' were enormous labours in which she would cheerfully take her share. Hesitation was not part of her character: she knew at once what she wanted and she set to work straightway. When circumstances obliged her to mark time, she held on without allowing her determination to weaken by one iota.

Neither the talk in her native city nor the apparent coolness of her bishop in any way diminished her courage. She commissioned the prior of the convent of friars of Mitigated observance in Medina, P. Antonio de Heredia, to find a house for her, hoping that Our Lord would take in hand the business of paying for it, for on the day of departure she had to say:

'I've scarcely a *blanca* in my pocket; and who'd give credit to a gadabout like me?' [4]

Don Quixote also was to travel *sin blanca*, for he had never read in tales of chivalry of a knight errant carrying money with him. Teresa of Jesus had had too close an acquaintance with Amadis of Gaul

---

[1] Sb, C, c. xxi-2.   [2] Sb, V, c. xv-6.
[3] Sb, F, c. xiv-5.   [4] Sb, F, c. iii-2.

and Esplandián in the days when she was Doña Teresa de Ahumada to be troubled because she had not a well-filled purse.

Teresa was a great Castilian: in the course of her journeys where she is continually plunging into fresh adventures, she often reminds one of that other Castilian, Miguel de Cervantes, who a generation later would write the work in which the soul of his country was to become incarnate: its ideal of heroism in the person of a great madman attacking windmills, its practical realism in a good honest peasant.

Says Don Quixote:

'Don't you see coming towards us on a roan horse this knight in a golden helmet?'

'I see only,' answers Sancho Panza, 'a man mounted on a reddish-brown donkey like mine; he wears something shining on his head. . . .' A village barber using his shaving dish as a hat.

But Teresa, who prided herself on being 'not only poor in spirit, but completely mad' [1] for the love of Christ, also said: 'I am much more worried about what men can take from us than about what the devils can take from us . . .' [2]; she said that nuns whose prayer gave rise to peculiar manifestations should be made to eat meat: 'let us mind that her sanctity does not arise from melancholy. . . .' [3]

Whilst Miguel de Cervantes was to immortalize in two characters as different as possible from each other, the manifestation of the soul of Spain at its two most extreme human tendencies, Teresa of Jesus condensed in her single person by a miracle of tension, and for all future time, Spain's ideals and Spanish realism.

At the time when she began her great foundations Teresa was fifty-two. Religious life had in no way stifled that which had made her life in the world such a brilliant success: she was still beautiful, gay, lively, more eloquent than ever and endowed with a charm which it was useless to try and resist. In her, one experience did not efface a previous one, each merely added something to her amazing personality without taking away or destroying anything of it.

Teresa was determined not to allow the maladies of every sort from which she suffered continually and of which the daily vomiting was the least painful of consequences, to be an obstacle. During the five years of enclosure at St. Joseph's she had matured; without her even being aware of it, her very high state of prayer had equipped her for action. She was free now, in full liberty of spirit, mistress of herself

---

[1] Sb, C, c. ii–5.   [2] CTA, cxxxiv.
[3] CTA, lxxxvii. Cervantes was born in 1547—Tr.

because she was detached from all egoism, pride or self-interest: brave with the courage of her race, bold 'with the boldness God gives to the ant.' [1]

At break of day the streets of Ávila awoke to the sound of the screeching and jolting of three heavy carts; they contained the few essential household articles for the installation of the future convent of Medina del Campo, and a few nuns, proud of 'their leader.' [2] Servants and Julian de Ávila, the chaplain, followed on muleback. It was the 13th August 1567. The bells of every church rang out the angelus, as they had done for the birth of the babe Teresa, for her flight to martyrdom with her brother Rodrigo, and for the departure of Doña Teresa de Ahumada, accompanied by her brother Antonio, for the convent of the Incarnation. She was not alone this time, any more than she had been on the previous occasions: she was taking with her in the grey light of dawn souls who were on fire with love and fervour.

[1] Sb, F, cii–7.   [2] FR, L. II, c.v.

II

A FRIAR AND A HALF

THE sáme day at nightfall the little group, worn out by the jolting of the rickety carts along the bad roads, arrived at Arévalo, where they were to halt.

One of Teresa's friends was waiting for her: he whispered in her ear that everything was going as badly as possible, there was now no house for her, the one which Antonio de Heredia had rented for her was next door to a monastery of Augustinian friars who refused to have a convent so close to them, lest the good people round about should divide their alms into two portions.

Teresa begged him to keep the matter secret.

Her daughters from St Joseph's, María Bautista and Ana de los Ángeles, would go through fire and water for her, as would her cousins Ana and Inés de Tapia, but the others who had come from the Incarnation, Teresa de Quezada and Isabel Arias, were not imbued with the fighting spirit of the daughters of the house of Cepeda y Ahumada. Teresa was beginning even then to prefer to keep the difficulties for herself alone; she felt it was quite enough to have to face them without having to brace up the fainting courage of others in addition. But the idea of giving way in the face of difficulty never so much as crossed her mind: they would install themselves at whatever cost and would end by coming to an understanding with these Augustinians.

What they had to do now was to get in secrecy into the house to which they had been denied entrance, but Mother Teresa was handicapped by all the paraphernalia of her carts, her mules and her nuns. In order to eliminate noise, the little band was reduced to two nuns only, with P. Antonio de Heredia who had come to meet the foundresses and Julian de Ávila who would have died of grief had he missed such an expedition. A man as much devoted to the cause of the foundation as he was to gossip, he was itching to have adventures to recount:

The Medina del Campo foundation! What a business! We arrived at Medina at midnight; at the entrance to the town we had to get down and walk, for our only remaining cart made a din in the night calculated to awaken the entire population. There we were in the streets, friars and nuns, laden with the sacred vessels and vestments necessary for saying the first Mass and fitting up the chapel: we looked like gipsies who had been robbing churches; if we had run into a police patrol we should have spent the rest of the night in jail. Luckily the only people who saw us were the sort of rogues who prowl about in the dark because they have good cause to prefer night to day. They were ready with a few pleasantries of the usual sort. We didn't utter a word but stepped out briskly.

We had to wake up the caretaker and summon him with all urgency to open the house and clear it for us. O Lord! We had scarcely got in when we thanked God with all our hearts: he saved us in the nick of time from six bulls for the next day's *corrida* which were dashing madly across the town to the arena.

It was nearly dawn. You should just have seen the prioress, the sisters, all of us, some with brooms, others on ladders busy putting up hangings or fixing the bell in place. We had no nails and it wasn't the moment to go and buy any. Mother Teresa made good use of those she found in the walls; somehow or other the place was cleared and the porch began to look more or less presentable.

All that now remained was to get the Vicar-General to come and give his confirmation that the convent was being founded in accordance with the Bishop's authorization: they got him out of bed.

The altar was dressed, the chapel well decorated, but all the light we had was one poor candle and in the darkness we might well wonder if the installation of the chapel really had been made inside the walls and not in the middle of the street. . . .

As soon as it was daylight, we joyfully pealed the bell for Mass, one stroke after another. Those who heard the peal came in to find a convent sprung up during the night. They were left speechless with astonishment. Soon there were so many people that our little porch was filled to overflowing.

The nuns had to make way for the crowd but where were they to go? Fortunately one staircase had not been pulled down, and they took refuge there, hiding behind the door. The chinks in the woodwork served them as choir to follow the Office, parlour to receive visitors, confessional to confess their sins and prison to weep in. . . .[1]

Such was the account of these memorable events given many times over by Julian de Ávila. Daylight revealed that the house consisted only of a few half-crumbling walls. The Blessed Sacrament would be exposed right in the open in a town where the fair attracted merchants from all over Europe, many heretics among them, at a time when the

[1] JA quoted SEC, vol. V, pp. 352-3.

Lutherans were asking for nothing better than the opportunity to commit sacrilege.

They had never seen Mother Teresa of Jesus happier—or in greater distress. She was happy because once Mass was said, the Convent of St Joseph of Medina del Campo was well and truly founded, whether the Augustinians liked it or not: the Vicar-General's approval anticipated any attempt at expulsion on their part. But all the same His Majesty was in great danger. Teresa did not sleep and through a fan-light kept vigil by the Blessed Sacrament.

It was going to take no end of time to reconstruct the dilapidated house. Where were they to lodge in the meantime? Medina, on the high tide of prosperity, was full to overflowing with travellers and visitors. There was nothing to let, then, and they had no money at all.

The Lord touched the heart of a merchant, Blas de Medina, and he offered the 'wanderers' a storey in his house and a room 'large and gilded,' for use as a chapel, until their convent should be ready.

The Lord also raised up benefactors for them.

And all the little group managed to live and the work of reconstruction went forward satisfactorily. The Tapias and their two companions from the Incarnation rejoined the infant community. Teresa made their beds, cleaned and swept their cells, saying to María Bautista who was helping her:

'Daughter, it is only right that we should wait on these ladies who have been good enough to come and help us. . . .'[1]

Teresa had already made some friends at Medina del Campo. The Carmelite friars of St Anne's monastery of Mitigated observance frequently came to see her, in particular the prior. P. Antonio de Heredia had legitimate reason to hope that he would eventually attain the very highest rank in the Order of Our Lady of Mount Carmel and people saw in him a future provincial. He was by no means displeased at this and his complete self-satisfaction was expressed on his countenance. He was tall, with a handsome face and fine carriage, as careful of his person as was possible for one who, while he never forgot he was of gentle birth, was also a friar; at the same time this former student of Salamanca was a good religious, 'studious and fond of his cell.'[2]

His meeting with Mother Teresa made a deep impression on him: the Carmelite's black and very much worn veil, her habit of coarse frieze—she insisted on wearing a darned one—her cheap, common rope-soled sandals, her joy in sacrificing every comfort and convenience, to which she had been as much accustomed as he, reminded

[1] CP, vol. III, p. 292.   [2] Sb, F, c. iii–16.

him that he too had wanted to gain heaven by an austere life. She who was already known as the *Madre Fundadora*, the Mother Foundress, received him in the gilded room of Blas the merchant which did duty as parlour in addition to its other use, unless sometimes he chose to go with her to the scene of the work on the dilapidated house: she superintended the work of reconstruction with an energy that was astounding in a woman. The convent began to take shape. It was something like a country cottage, it was so rustic—some compared it to a golden-brown loaf or a honeycomb—but solidly built around its patio with good, light cells and vaulted refectory. Each time Antonio de Heredia was increasingly sorry to leave Mother Teresa and in his monastery of well-fed, well-housed friars, the permitted comforts of the Mitigation seemed to him a heavy burden. The Mother spoke of Our Lord with so much love and a fervour that was so contagious that he burned to do more in God's service. Theologian as he was, he marvelled to hear her say things about prayer that were so sublime and yet in perfect conformity with reason. He experienced a joy that was unusual for him and was convinced that the Carmelite was enlightened by the Holy Spirit. 'She expressed herself with a force that was more than human without departing from her infinite sweetness and charity.' [1] And so the day when, with the sole idea of asking his advice, she spoke to him of P. Rubeo's letters, authorizing her to found two monasteries of men in conformity with the primitive Rule and of the difficulty in which she found herself for want of friars, Antonio de Heredia exclaimed:

'I will be the first.' [2]

Teresa thought that the brilliant prior was joking, and laughed heartily: could he seriously be considering a change that would be so hard for him, especially after fifty-seven years of comfortable existence? But he insisted, thus displaying more humility and spirit of penance than might have been expected of a friar so nice in his ways and dress and noted for the artistic taste with which he decorated his cell.[3] The Mother did not fail to tell him that she did not think him made for this heroic undertaking:

'Each one has his own way, Father, and you are following the one which suits you. No doubt you do aspire to austerities. . . . But there is a "but" . . .'[4]

The prior was obstinate. He announced his intention of entering with the Carthusians: he even had the Provincial's authorization. No

[1] SEC, vol. I, p. 87, n. 1.   [2] Sb, F, c. iii–16.
[3] SEC, vol. V, p. 406.   [4] Idem.

austerity frightened him, he was ready to take his oath on it. Teresa, who was not to be satisfied with words alone, asked Antonio de Heredia to try to keep to what he was promising for a whole year, during which he would practise the most severe penances. Her satisfaction at having one friar at least to count on was not unmixed with anxiety.

One day, however, there arrived a young Carmelite friar who 'pleased her much'[1] from their first meeting. Juan de San Matías had just said his first Mass at St Anne's monastery. Since then he had felt such a strong call to the solitary life of a hermit that he, too, had decided to enter the Charterhouse of Paular where the cenobitical life was carried out with the utmost possible austerity.

Teresa knew that Juan de San Matías was the son of a *hidalgo*, Gonzalo de Yepes, who had been cast off and 'abhorred' by his family for having married a girl as beautiful and virtuous as she was poor, so poor that she earned her livelihood by weaving silk. And this grandson of one of the men-at-arms of John II, this nephew of an Inquisitor at Toledo, with three of his relatives canons at the cathedral, had likewise become an artisan. He died young and Catalina was left alone to bring up her children with the utmost difficulty on the earnings from her weaving, at which she worked day and night.

Juan, the fervent and emaciated young friar who stood before Teresa, was the youngest of Catalina Yepes' sons. 'Fathers whose name carried weight' had spoken highly of his learning and piety and one of his companions had even added 'wonderful things about his kind of life.' Teresa, however, was surprised to find him so small—his height was less than five feet—as she was at the breadth of his forehead and the fire in his dark eyes. She who was such a good talker also knew how to listen: she let Fray Juan de San Matías talk freely and she praised God for what she heard. For himself, although he belonged to the Mitigated observance, he kept the primitive Rule of the Order. Not only was he unafraid of its rigours, but he was not prepared to live a life that was not austere.

The eager spontaneity of Teresa's character would not allow her to wait for a second interview to tell him about the great project of the Reform; it was not necessary for him to ask her to allow him to be one of the first Discalced: her face flushed with joy, she 'begged him earnestly'[2] to be patient a little longer before entering Paular; Our Lord could not fail to give them a house in which to found this monastery of Carmelite friars soon. Would it not be an additional perfection for him to be able to serve God as he wished without doffing the habit of

---

[1] Sb, F, c. iii–17. [2] Idem.

a son of Our Lady, Mother of God, whom since childhood he had called 'the Morning Star'?

He gave her his word that he would wait, but with an impetuosity not unworthy of Teresa herself this boy of twenty-four added:

'On condition that I haven't to wait too long. . . .' [1]

That evening Mother Teresa was full of joy and as always when she was particularly happy, the salt of her Castilian wit broke out into a quaint phrase:

'Daughters, I have a friar and a half.' [2]

But the half friar was not tiny Fray Juan. If he alone had been in question, with God's help, without a *blanca*, without a house, she would have set out that very day to found her monastery of Discalced Carmelite friars. She only delayed a little because she was 'less satisfied with the prior. . . .' [3]

She saw Juan de San Matías again. The better she knew him the more she liked him. 'Although he is small, he is great in the eyes of God. . . . He is full of good sense, well fitted for our kind of life and so I think Our Lord had predestined him to it. There isn't a friar who doesn't speak well of him for he has lived in a great spirit of penance. It seems as if Our Lord is leading him by the hand and in spite of a few differences in the course of this business—I alone was the cause for I have allowed myself to get irritated with him—I've never come across any imperfection in him. And he's courageous.'[4]

Such is, in brief, the picture of the relations of the Mother Foundress with him whom she afterwards called 'my little Seneca' and whose logic and stoical independence 'irritated her' more than once. But years slipped by and she still had not discovered any imperfections in Juan de San Matías, now become John of the Cross. His courage continued to make her marvel and in the end she saw him 'reach to the greatest height of sanctity a human creature can attain to in this life.' [5]

Good Julian de Ávila summed up the matter: 'In this town of Medina del Campo, a sort of fair where you find everything, the Mother found the cornerstone of her monasteries of Discalced friars.'[6]

[1] Idem.   [2] SEC, vol. V, p. 30.   [3] Idem.
[4] CTA, x.   [5] Quoted BRJ, p. 316.   [6] SEC, vol. V, p. 406.

III

THE WORLD'S GREAT ONES

DOÑA LUISA DE LA CERDA had been 'very fond' of Teresa of Jesus ever since the time she had been her guest on the eve of the foundation of St Joseph's at Ávila; she offered her hospitality whenever she had business in Toledo. In her house Teresa went about so cheerfully and simply, taking such good care not to betray the secrets of her inner life by any outward show of feeling, that when the daughter of the Duke of Medinaceli began to think of gaining a little merit by founding a convent on her property at Malagón, she said:

'It must be a convent of Carmelites of the Reform. I did think of María de Jesús, but I don't want to have such a great saint to found my house. . . .'

An opportunity of humility for Teresa! No, indeed, she was not such a great saint! The penances imposed by María de Jesús at the convent of La Imagen seemed to her so little calculated to advance spiritual progress that she agreed to spend three months at Alcalá de Henares, in the hope of moderating her excesses.

'Exact much in the way of the practice of virtue but not in that of penance,' such was the principle she enjoined. She added: 'This perhaps proves that I am only a mediocre penitent.' What it proved was her intelligence: to sublimate one's instincts instead of ruthlessly crushing them calls for as much lucidity as it does strength of soul. Formerly, when at the Incarnation, Teresa had practised corporal macerations with an ardour that was truly terrible; the walls of her cell were bespattered with her blood. But in every excess the devil can find a foothold and she now saw that to submit one's will absolutely to all the prescriptions of the Rule was a better thing than to ill-treat the body. In the hierarchy of perfections she placed obedience above austerity.

Her high state of prayer and the signs of heaven's favour would have remained her secret alone, if the raptures which came on her in public had not betrayed her and if her fear of being the victim of illusion or deceived by the devil had not brought her to give an account of her visions to her confessors. She strove to compensate a reputation which made too much stir for her liking by an attitude that was very simple and even gay.

She liked to disappoint the hopes of those who came to see her moved solely by curiosity. When she was in Madrid, staying with Doña Leonor de Mascarenhas, former lady-in-waiting to the Empress Isabel and governess to Philip II, a Portuguese, all the pious people at court—for piety was in the fashion—flocked to meet 'the saint of Ávila.' They hoped at least to see her work a miracle, fall into ecstasy or be lifted off her feet and carried up to the ceiling. But all Teresa of Jesus let them see was her modest and courteous graciousness with perhaps a touch of studied simplicity. Those who expected to hear sublime phrases from her lips were very much surprised to hear her exclaim: 'What fine streets there are in Madrid!'—or talk only of the rain or the fine weather.[1]

But the Descalzas Reales, where Teresa went to visit Princess Juana, the King's sister, were delighted beyond words:

'God be praised! He has granted us to see a saint whom we can all imitate. She talks like us, sleeps and eats as we do, and her conversation is unpretentious. . . .'[2]

If Doña Luisa fell into the error of thinking that a pleasing manner was incompatible with being a 'great saint,' María de Salazar made no such mistake.

The little maid of honour who on the Mother's previous visit had slipped pious verses into her hand was now twenty; she was still charming, just a tiny bit over-keen about literature and Latin, but most gifted. It was when Teresa visited Toledo to discuss the Malagón foundation with Doña Luisa that she accepted as a novice the girl who was to become María de San José, the best loved of all her daughters and one of her most remarkable prioresses. 'Her tact and sweetness always attracted me to her,' said María. 'Her wonderful life and the way she spoke would have moved the heart of a stone. . . .'[3]

Teresa was firmly opposed to Doña Luisa de la Cerda's wish: a convent could not find sufficient to live on at Malagón. Who would buy the sisters' work there? Doña Luisa offered revenues which Teresa firmly refused: Carmelites were to depend for their daily bread, as they did for their spiritual sustenance, on no one but their Father in heaven. P. Domingo Báñez had to intervene. He blamed Teresa for obstinacy in refusing to found a house in a place where Our Lord would be well served merely to avoid breaking a law about work which she herself had laid down. The holy Council authorized her to accept revenues on condition that the nuns possessed nothing as

[1] SEC, vol. V, p. 72, n. 2.
[2] Idem, p. 133, n. 4.
[3] MJ quoted SEC, vol. V, p. 218, n. 3.

individuals: was not her attitude as much an attachment as any other, an attachment to her own idea of poverty?

She was obliged to yield. Thus at the outset of her work of foundation she was often forced to accept patrons, benefactors or benefactresses. She strove to do without them as much as possible, preferring that her houses should have to struggle with difficulties rather than be enslaved to the caprices of the great.

In exchange for the revenues they gave or the houses they bought, the patrons of a convent would reserve the right of entry there for subjects of their own choosing and wanted to impose other hampering restrictions. When such patrons were reasonable and sincere, like Doña Luisa de la Cerda or the Bishop of Ávila's sister, Doña María de Mendoza, the Foundress's tact could smooth away the difficulties, but with the Princess of Éboli, benefactress of Pastrana, events took a dramatic turn.

For Teresa of Jesus did not give in to the great ones of this world. The solicitude of which she was the object on the part of her noble protectresses 'was enough to kill' her, and to her 'if it is not with God and for God, all rest is wearisome.'[1] She always spoke her mind; the Bishop himself, Don Álvaro de Mendoza, did not come off scot free when he thought it best to remain neutral in the fierce quarrel with the relatives of Doña Casilda de Padilla who, at the age of twelve, had run away from her husband to enter Carmel: 'It seems to me that Our Lord defends his daughters better than Your Lordship defends your subjects.'[2]

As to Teresa, no one in the world would force her to take a subject with whom she was not completely satisfied. She proved her greatness as foundress and organizer by her determination only to accept as novices those who were first-class from every point of view.

. . . If Your Ladyship commands me, there's nothing more to be said, I shall obey. But I do ask Your Ladyship to reflect seriously and to want nothing but the best for your house. Where the nuns are few in number, the quality must be proportionately higher. I can find subjects everywhere, but I haven't dared to take one—for Valladolid—for I want them perfect. On my own account I shall not accept either of the two of whom you speak to me. I find in them neither sanctity, courage nor talents sufficient to be an advantage for the house. And if the house is to lose by them, why does Your Ladyship want us to take them? If it's simply to extricate them from a difficult situation, there's no lack of convents. . . . For

[1] Sb, V, c. xxvi–1.   [2] Cf. CTA, liii.

the love of God, I beg Your Ladyship to consider all these points and not to forget that the good of all must always be preferred to the interests of one person alone. If Your Ladyship commands this thing, your orders will be obeyed, but, should matters not turn out well, the entire responsibility will be yours. May Our Lord arrange the matter for his greater glory and may he enlighten Your Ladyship.[1]

An unmistakable refusal nicely sandwiched in between two compliments. The benefactress, this time Doña María de Mendoza, did not insist. One of the candidates had only one eye which caused Teresa to declare:

'I don't want any one-eyed nuns!'[2]

There are cases where charity consists in putting the good of all before the interests of one person alone. Too many convents were simply a refuge for poor girls who were no use in the world—this was one of the causes of their laxity: in the reformed Carmels Teresa wanted there to be room for nothing but the love of God. At the beginning there were thirteen nuns in each, later twenty-one, but no more: there was no room for mediocrity or for concessions; the brides of Christ must at least have the qualities which any ordinary man has a right to expect in his wife, and fervour in addition. On this point Teresa never yielded in the slightest degree.

'The Lord showed me such great favours while I was there and that in turn gave me so much liberty of spirit and made me so despise what I saw, that in my dealings with these great ladies whom I might have considered it an honour to serve, I kept as much liberty as if I had been their equal.'[3]

'She spoke to them with a "natural majesty," '[4] just as if she had indeed been one of them.

She never put aside this natural majesty, even in her relations with the King.

The Princess Doña Juana undertook to transmit to Philip II a message which Our Lord had given Teresa for him. It concluded thus: 'Remember, Sire, that Saul, too, was anointed, and yet he was rejected!'[5]

In her *Autobiography* she addressed sovereigns as if she too were a queen:

Blessed is the soul to whom Our Lord gives an understanding of his truth! What a realm that would be for kings! They would do far

[1] CTA, xxxiv.
[2] SEC, vol. VII, p. 85, n. 2.
[3] Sb, V, c. xxxiv-3.
[4] FR, L. IV, c. i.
[5] Quoted LV, p. 433.

better to strive to acquire that, rather than to seek great power.
What righteousness there would then be in their kingdom! How
many evils would be averted! . . . In those conditions no one
would fear to lose life or honour for the love of God. . . . To increase faith in souls or to enlighten heretics, such a king would
willingly lose a thousand kingdoms. For to gain a kingdom of which
there shall be no end is a more advantageous thing. . . .[1]

The King, Don Felipe, received the Carmelite's message 'respectfully.' This king was only too ready to lose 'a thousand kingdoms' to
gain one, and the saint's words did but echo a dispatch which he
charged his ambassador in Rome to communicate secretly to the Pope:

. . . I would lose all my realms and give my own life a hundred
times over rather than suffer the least schism in religion or in the
service of God; I have not the least intention of reigning over heretics. I intend to try to smoothe out the religious difficulties in the
Low Countries without recourse to arms, if it is still possible, for I
see clearly that a war would involve the country in total devastation;
but if matters cannot be put right without armed intervention, I am
resolved to take up arms and take part in the battles myself; nothing
shall hinder me, neither the ruin of this country nor that of the lands
I possess elsewhere.[2]

Teresa of Jesus used love to bring about God's triumph, the King
thought he could bring it about by bloodshed; Teresa passed her life
in penance and prayer for the redemption of the heretics whom the
King was causing to be massacred; Teresa hoped that the King would
make Spain a beacon light, but he made it a stake. Saint and king used
the same words but with different meanings for they lived on different
planes.[3] Had Teresa been able to form some idea of the world's
intrigues, she would have hesitated and trembled to advise the mighty
and would have shuddered to learn of the veneration the Duke of
Alba, who had shed so much blood, had for her; she would have
begun to wonder to what cruelties the reading of such a work of love
as the account of her life, which he was so eager to learn about, might
move him.

The political unity of the vast kingdom which was now about to
break up was too closely linked with its unity of belief for the work of
spreading the Gospel not to take advantage of the opportunity of using

[1] Sb, V, c. xxi-1. [2] Quoted SH, p. 229.
[3] For a different view of Philip II, see Gachard: *Lettres de Philippe II à ses Filles* (Paris, 1884)—Tr.

military methods: people could only fight with the weapons they were familiar with. The intermingling of the spiritual and temporal in government has always had the most disastrous consequences and Philip II made a further mistake when he replied to the proposal to abandon the Philippine Isles, which were ruinous to colonize, more as if he were a monk than a king: 'To win a single soul to God, I would sacrifice all the treasures of the Indies and if that were not sufficient I would throw in Spain, too. . . . For to me and my descendants the Holy See has transmitted the mission of the apostles, which is to preach the Gospel; so that it may triumph to the ends of the world and beyond . . . without the intervention of any hope of gain.' [1]

Philip II ruined Spain without succeeding in making the spirit of the Gospel triumphant in the world, for it was not without reason that Christ commanded Peter to put back his sword into its sheath. An army of mercenaries even if Friars Preachers walk before it will never open men's hearts to the word of Christ. In their convents Mother Teresa and her daughters fought more effectively.

Teresa of Jesus made use of the great and powerful but never ceded one inch of her independence or judgement. 'What it was necessary to say was said and their faults were pointed out to them with no small courage.' [2] Only the fear of hurting others restrained her, but when the good of souls was in question she turned such fear aside. There is no doubt that of all the devout ladies of high degree who, because they revered her, imagined they had the right to give her orders, Doña María de Mendoza was nearest to her heart, and yet she was the one whom she most liked to take up sharply: 'I hope to find Your Ladyship more mistress of herself: you have the strength of character. . . . Your Ladyship would gain from being with me, just as I gain from the presence of the Father Visitor. As my religious superior, he tells me the truth about myself, and I'm willing to do the same for Your Ladyship, for I don't lack courage and am accustomed to your not minding my frankness. Ah! If Your Ladyship had as much nobility of soul as of bearing, how lightly you would esteem what are called trials!' [3]

She sugared the pill with a dusting of compliments, for God himself had taught her how little case should be made of creatures however good they may be, and how it is sometimes necessary to use a grain of diplomacy.[4] Great ladies and powerful lords gave large sums to her convents. She was grateful to them for doing so, but did not fail to

---

[1] Quoted SH, p. 153.   [2] FR, L. IV, c. i.
[3] Cf. CTA, xxxv.   [4] CTA, cclxx.

tell them that 'to give *reales* is nothing: you scarcely feel what you give. . . .' [1]

Doña María de Mendoza and her brother the Bishop of Ávila gave her *reales* but they also gave her constant proof of deep friendship. Don Álvaro was so kind to the reformed Carmel that Teresa was afraid he would get into debt through helping them. Her letters telling him of the affairs of the Order are a mixture of respect and fun, of piety and of intelligent instinct for business:

'Your Lordship is surrounded by holy people, you should then recognize those who are not holy and you forget about me. But in heaven I think Your Lordship will see that you had a duty to this miserable sinner. . . .'

The good Bishop's brother, Don Bernardino de Mendoza, had offered the Mother Foundress a fine house in Valladolid to set up a convent there, but Doña Luisa de la Cerda insisted so strongly on her beginning the Malagón foundation that she agreed to do so. Doña Luisa gave them adequate revenues and a house which enabled the nuns to live decently and with some convenience.

Accordingly Teresa left Toledo and set out for Malagón along the road which passes over the high rocky hills, sloping down again to the bottom of the valleys where the vine and olive grow in the drab ochre-coloured or reddish earth. It is the road to the south along which, village by village, the granite-built houses of Castile give place increasingly to façades limewashed in white or blue with geraniums climbing up the balconies.

Teresa took with her in her completely closed cart two of her nuns from St Joseph's and four from the Incarnation.

After a few days in Doña Luisa's mansion—absolutely necessary to allow time for the Mother Foundress to superintend the final preparations herself—the convent of St Joseph of Malagón was inaugurated on 11th April 1568.

Inaugurated, but not altogether to Teresa's liking. Too close to the square where the markets and fairs with all their din were held, it afforded insufficient possibility of silence and recollection. . . .

The whole village took part in the opening celebrations, particularly as the Carmelite, distressed at the ignorance of the village girls there, had sent for a woman who was 'a good Theatine,' that is to say, well acquainted with the methods of the Society of Jesus, to teach them to sew and other useful hand-work: 'under this pretext she was

[1] CTA, xiv.

also able to teach them Christian doctrine and how to serve God well, all things very profitable to them.' [1] Teresa thus showed that in this case she considered work as important as prayer; at that time this was tantamount to a revolution.

But Don Bernardino de Mendoza died suddenly very shortly after having partially redeemed a frivolous existence by his gift of the Valladolid convent. Teresa would have stayed on at Malagón but Our Lord called her to order: she was leaving a soul to linger suffering in purgatory. So she set off with all possible speed, although nothing was ready for the new foundation.

All the haste in the world could not shorten the length of the journey and Teresa was forced to make certain détours: she went back towards Toledo, passed through Ávila where she collected María de la Cruz, Antonia del Espíritu Santo—of the 'shock troops' of St Joseph's—and Isabel de la Cruz, a future prioress, and stopped at Medina where His Majesty's injunction became even more pressing. 'This soul is suffering greatly. . . .' [2] She finally arrived at Valladolid at the beginning of August.

It was a fine house standing in the midst of vineyards and lovely orchards, but situated outside the town itself, at Río de Olmos, on the banks of the river and surrounded by unhealthy swamps.

Ought she to hesitate? There was no time, Our Lord urged her forward: Don Bernardino would not go to heaven until the day the first Mass was said. Tertian or quartan fevers notwithstanding! The authorization of the Ordinary was slow in arriving; Teresa decided to do without it and hastened to have a Mass said, not expecting, however, that the promise of heavenly glory for Don Bernardino would be fulfilled before the day of the official foundation. Doubtless Our Lord intended to do without official authorizations: at the Communion, behind Julian de Ávila who was holding the sacred Host, Teresa saw 'Don Bernardino, his face resplendent with joy.' [3] He thanked her for what she had done to release him from purgatory and went up to heaven. Teresa, in ecstasy, was caught up to heaven with him.

It would have been bliss to stay there. When she came to her senses again after such raptures, which she endeavoured to disguise from those around by asking for a glass of water or some remedy for her heart trouble whereas the radiant expression of her face deceived no one, she resumed the routine of daily life, but sorrowfully: it was for God's sake alone that she took up the heavy burden again.

[1] CTA, vi.   [2] Sb, F, c. x-3.   [3] Sb, F, c. x-5.

The house at Río de Olmos was delightful, but the Carmelites caught marsh fever there. It was essential to move elsewhere. What did it matter if the installation was already finished? They would begin over again.

Doña María de Mendoza gave them another house in Valladolid itself: grilles, enclosure, chapel, cells, offices, were set up anew. Teresa took special care that in each new convent founded the practice of perfect recollection and exact observance of the Rule should be established.

One day the bell failed to ring at the appointed hour; she was angry:

'If things are like that while I am alive, and when I am present, what will they be when I'm dead?' [1]

It was necessary that she should learn to desire to live, in order that the Reform should be established on unshakable foundations.

[1] SEC, vol. V, p. 79, n. 2.

IV

SO MANY CROSSES!
SO MANY SKULLS!

W HILE she was talking things over with Doña María de
Mendoza at Valladolid, or while at Alba de Tormes the
Duchess, Doña María Enríquez, invited her into what
might be called the holy of holies of earthly riches, one name, 'Duruelo,'
was refreshment and joy to Teresa of Jesus.

At Alba de Tormes the Carmelite could not suppress a slight
shudder as she entered the small room where the treasures of the Dukes
of Alba were displayed. Everything around her shone, glittered,
sparkled; there was nothing but the fiery gleam of jewels with their
lustre and brilliance: 'What good can this heap of objects be?' And
then she praised the Creator for the variety of the 'things' his creatures
had made. The Duchess drew her attention to the gold chasing, the
magnificent diamonds, the purity of the emeralds, expecting that
Teresa would admire them, and was very much astonished when she
said shortly afterwards:

'There was so much to see that I've forgotten everything, I've retained no more impressions of these jewels and precious stones than if
I had never seen them and I couldn't tell you what they were like." [1]

But as long as she lived she never forgot the poorest thing she had
seen in the world: the little village of Duruelo, scarcely twenty hearths,
situated in the depths of a valley of Old Castile and, in this hamlet, a
casita, whose ceiling was so low that one had to stoop to go into the
lean-to which served as choir, so poverty-stricken a place that it reminded one of the stable at Bethlehem. But Our Lord poured forth
his spirit and his grace there in overflowing abundance and the first
two subjects of the Order, Fray John of the Cross and Fray Antonio
de Jesús lived there 'in great joy.' [2]

For at Duruelo the first monastery of Discalced Carmelite friars had
just been founded.

A nobleman had offered Teresa a tumbledown old place in this
isolated village, so far off the beaten track that when she went to visit

[1] Sb, M, VI, c. iv–8.   [2] Sb, F, c. xiv–3.

it accompanied by Antonia del Espíritu Santo and Julian de Ávila, the two Carmelites and their chaplain wandered about all day, jolted by their mules under the August sun which beat fiercely down on man and beast. 'When we thought we had arrived, we had still as far to go as we had already travelled. . . . I shall never forget how tired we were nor what confusion we were in. . . .' [1]

At nightfall they came to an oasis—green chestnut trees and running water, but they did not find the peaceful rest they had hoped for: songs and shouts, the thrumming of tambourines and the shrill sound of the flute came from the house where shepherds, tillers of the fields, farm labourers and gleaners were celebrating the harvest. When the Mother appeared at the door with her black veils, very erect in her darned habit, the din ceased but only for a few minutes: and it was in this din that she visited the dirtiest and most cluttered-up place she had seen in her life: later on, she would see many others.

A brief glance sufficed. When Teresa had made up her mind, no disappointment could damp her enthusiasm. Her talent for organization immediately began to work:

> The house consisted of an entrance porch of reasonable size, a room with a lean-to and a small kitchen: that was the whole of our monastery. I calculated that it was possible to make the chapel in the porch, the choir in the lean-to and a dormitory in the room. My companion, although a much better person than myself and one who had a real love of penance, would not allow me to think of founding a monastery in such conditions. She said to me: 'You can take it for granted, Mother, that not even the most fervent would be able to put up with it. Give it up.' [2]

But in the church where she spent the night to escape from the noise and dirt, the Foundress could see with her imagination the Carmel rising from the wretched hovel where peasants drunk with 'the wine of the earth' were dancing with the girls.

She hastened to Medina del Campo with all possible speed. The prior, Antonio de Heredia, had shown an admirable constancy in the year of trial, Teresa was beginning to change her opinion of him; and Juan de San Matías, who had indeed been practising mortification by controlling his impatience, would not have to wait much longer.

Immediately upon her arrival Teresa sent for her friar and her half-friar and kept back nothing of the deplorable state of the little house. It was the prior who first exclaimed:

[1] Sb, F, c. xiii–3.   [2] Idem.

EL PADRE FRAI IVAN DE LA CRVZ

Que importa que se apresure la muerte contra los Justos i Santos
arones, plantados alas corrientes de las aguas de la gracia; si en el breve tiempo de
vida produzen tantas hojas, flores, i frutos de buenas obras, como si uvieran vi
do largos años? las de un joven anciano, avemos de recoger en un corto Elogio.

del

ST. JOHN OF THE CROSS
(From a lithograph in the collection of
Don Ramón Menéndez Pidal)

St. Teresa's Place in the Refectory

THE CONVENT AT MALAGÓN

Jars of St. Teresa

'Not only am I willing to live there, but in a pigsty if it should be necessary.' [1]

Teresa's heart almost burst with love for the poverty of the thing, the stuff of which saints are made.

Dear God! How small a thing are buildings and exterior comforts in our inner life! Fathers and Sisters, I ask you for the love of God to be always very modest and not to want vast and sumptuous houses. . . .[2] Great houses are ill suited to poor, insignificant people like ourselves. . . . Remember that everything will crumble to pieces on Judgement Day and it isn't right that the house of thirteen poor women should make a lot of noise when it falls. . . . I have seen more spirituality and exterior joy when the body has scarcely the bare necessities of life than when it has all it wants in a great house. We only live in a cell. What does it matter to us whether it's spacious and well built or not? We don't spend our time there looking at the walls. We shall not always live in it, our time there will be no longer than our life on earth. . . . To live poorly, like our good Jesus, requires only a small effort and that a pleasant one. . . .[3]

Fray John said nothing, but he offered to set out immediately.

That day, Teresa gave her nuns the rough brown frieze, and the habits of the Discalced friars were cut out and made up.

The following day, the Mother Foundress, behind the parlour grilles, in the presence of the nuns in their long white mantles as, lighted candle in hand, they sang the *Veni Creator Spiritus*, herself gave the habit to Juan de San Matías. He solemnly renounced the Mitigation, promising to live according to the Rule of Our Lady of Carmel, in obedience, chastity and poverty.

And, barefooted, at long last slave only of his vows, at last free from the fetters of the world and material things, he who would in future be known as John of the Cross, wended his way to the *casita* of Duruelo.

The prior Antonio de Heredia who was now Antonio de Jesús joined him there soon afterwards.

It was Fray John of the Cross who was 'the first.' Fray Antonio was not too well pleased at this and John in his charity allowed him the pleasure of boasting that he was Discalced before anyone else. He was also quite willing for him to be prior of the Duruelo house, but quietly stood out against the twists and turns given to the primitive Rule by a man who had lived more than thirty years in the Mitigation. That was why Mother Teresa put all her energies into obtaining Constitutions for

[1] Sb, F, c. xiii-4.   [2] Sb, F, c. xiv-5.   [3] Idem.

the friars, 'for some were of one opinion and others of another,' and the Foundress was often ' considerably troubled by their differences.' [1]

All this did not prevent Antonio de Jesús from chaffing Fray John because he had received the habit at the hands of a woman, the very same who, at Valladolid, when she was superintending the completion of the construction of the enclosure, instructed the young friar on the manner of life in monasteries of this sort, and on everything else, 'our mortifications, as well as our fraternal friendship and the recreations which we took together.' [2] In these directives as in those Teresa of Jesus gave her nuns, the keyword was 'moderation.'

Afterwards when Fray John of the Cross, now Padre John, was away in distant Andalusia (it was only in the beginning that all the Discalced Carmelite friars were called Fray), she remembered the rapt attention with which he had listened to her words. 'He was so perfect that I could have learnt more from him than he from me; however, I did not take the opportunity, for I was busy explaining to him the manner of life of the sisters.' [3] There is a note of regret in these reminiscences: it would have been delightful to listen to him who at that time called himself her disciple but who was already imbued with the spirit that would make him the 'Father of her soul'; but it was urgent to get on with the work of construction.

A few months later, taking advantage of a journey to Toledo, the Mother Foundress went a little out of her way and arrived one fine morning at Duruelo. They did not expect her, but she found the prior, Antonio de Jesús, in front of the monastery busy sweeping, like a simple lay-brother, his face lit up with the joy that comes from casting aside vainglory. He led Teresa towards the chapel:

> I was amazed at the spirit which God had infused into the place. Two merchants who had travelled with me did nothing but weep. There were so many crosses! So many skulls!
> I shall never forget a little wooden cross above the holy-water stoup. The picture representing Christ which was glued to it, though only of paper, inspired one with more devotion than if it had been an exquisite carving. . . . On either side of the chapel Fray Antonio and Fray John had erected two hermitages so small that they could only sit or lie prostrate there; they had filled the hermitages with hay, for it was very cold and the roof was almost touching their heads; through two garret windows they could see the altar; they had a stone for pillow, their crosses and their skulls.

[1] Sb, F, c. xxiii–12.   [2] Sb, F, c. xiii–5.   [3] Idem.

I learned that after Matins until Prime, instead of going to rest they remained there so absorbed in prayer that they sometimes came into chapel for Prime with their habits covered with snow, without noticing it. . . .[1]

In 'this little stable of Bethlehem,'[2] Teresa found once more the spirit of the Fathers of the Desert, with their austerity and love.

This house, which was now spotless, whitewashed, the dust laid and the floors polished, to conform with the Foundress's ideas of cleanliness, had already become an object of reverence to the good folk of the neighbourhood. These friars who went out preaching the Gospel for ten leagues around, always barefoot whether in puddles of water or in the snow, made themselves so much loved that 'it was wonderful to see the peasants bringing baskets with bread and all they required to eat.'[3] And Teresa thought herself in paradise, as did Julian de Ávila who was privileged to spend several days there.

Each of the brethren praised the austerity and perfections of the others. It was well known that Fray John took more pleasure in eating dry bread than if he had been eating pheasants. And he surpassed the requirements of the primitive Rule in austerity. One day when, ill and almost exhausted with fatigue, he had begged Fray Antonio de Jesús to allow him to take his collation a little sooner than usual, he was so remorseful at having thus yielded to the demands of his wretched body that he was not satisfied with accusing himself of it in Chapter; at supper-time his brethren saw him come into the refectory with bare shoulders and discipline in hand; he threw himself on his knees on some broken tiles which he had scattered over the floor and scourged himself until he collapsed with weakness and pain on the ground, which was red with his blood.

Antonio de Jesús sent him to his cell to pray God to forgive men their wretchedness.

This story and others like it frightened Teresa: 'Weak and vile as I am, I begged them not to give themselves up to penance with so much rigour. . . . I was afraid the devil might take this means to make an end of them before what I hoped for from these Fathers had been effected. . . .'[4] It was not the first time she attributed excessive mortification to the inspiration of the devil. 'He sees the harm they can do him so long as they are alive and leads them into the temptation of giving themselves up to crazy penances to destroy their health. . . .'[5]

[1] Sb, F, c. xiv-6, 7.　　　　　　　　　　[2] Idem, 6.
[3] Quoted SEC, vol. V, p. 111, n. 1.　　　[4] Sb, F, c. xiv-12.
[5] Cf. Sb, F, c. xiv-12.

The idea of having to live reasonably because one was living for God was already taking root in her. But neither her entreaties nor her reiteration of the word 'moderation' were listened to. Perhaps she was mistaken? She was always ready to believe she was wrong when her opinion did not coincide with that of 'wise and learned' men. Was she not 'so wretched, so base, so weak and miserable, of so little worth,' [1] a woman in short? What met her eyes at Duruelo was like a scene from the Bible and all she heard there, the converse of seraphim. She left 'in a state of immense interior joy.' [2]

Her steed jogged along the road to Toledo. The Mother Foundress's silence was one long interior thanksgiving.

The merchants who were her travelling companions talked indeed but found no other subject of conversation than their edifying visit:

'I would not exchange what I've seen there for all the goods in the world,' said the one who had hesitated to make this détour along the bad, rough roads.

The other declared that so much virtue and poverty seemed to him more enviable than all his riches. [3]

But neither the one nor the other turned his bridle, renouncing his ducats in order to be happy rather than rich.

Teresa heard them vaguely and refrained from smiling. For she reflected that in this world there must be saints but there must be merchants too, and that it is already no small thing when a merchant amid his satiating riches experiences from time to time a longing for extreme poverty.

[1] Sb, V, c. xviii–4.   [2] Sb, F, c. xiv–11.   [3] Idem.

V

THE MERCHANTS OF TOLEDO

EVERY merchant who had become rich by honest means, trading in Córdoba leather or in Toledan swords and cloth, intended to enjoy the goods which his prudence and his flair for business had earned him in reasonable measure, but, no less reasonably, in the evening of life, before giving up his soul to God and rendering him a strict account, he divested himself of his heaviest ingots in order to mount up to heaven as lightly as a poor man.

It was this that decided the pious and wealthy Martín Ramírez, merchant of the city of Toledo, to found after his death a church, with several ecclesiastical benefices: without doing his heirs any great injustice, he would thus be well provided for and favourably regarded as far as eternity was concerned, just as he had been prosperous and honoured in this world.

When Martín Ramírez was 'struck down by a fatal illness,' P. Pablo Hernández, a Jesuit and a great friend of Mother Teresa, explained to him that the foundation at Toledo of a convent of reformed Carmelites would be a more novel and at the same time more efficacious means of appealing to the Judge before whom he must appear. The merchant died before he had had time to take the necessary legal steps, but he charged his brother, Alonso Álvarez, 'a godfearing and prudent man,' [1] to open negotiations with the Mother Foundress.

Teresa arrived at Toledo on 24th March 1569. She brought with her only two of the 'young ones' of Ávila, Isabel de San Pablo, and Isabel de Santo Domingo who was to become one of the most energetic prioresses of the Reform. Julian de Ávila had caught fever at Valladolid and so had to forgo the joy of adding to his series of travel diaries. Gonzalo de Aranda replaced him: he was a silent man and left no reminiscences.

Doña Luisa de la Cerda received Teresa most warmly and put two rooms at her disposal, thus providing a cell of recollection in her wealthy mansion. Teresa had a great deal to do: Alonso Álvarez conducted the negotiations with her through his son-in-law, Diego Ortiz,

[1] Sb, F, c. xv–2.

known as 'the Theologian,' who had as much talent for legal quibbles as he had for discussions on thorny points of doctrine. He wore out the Foundress's inexhaustible patience, though she never refused to listen to his wearisome arguments when he brought his little boy of four with him. She told the porter:

'Always call me when Martinico comes with his father: I like that child, he is virtuous already.' [1]

She adored children, and, strict as she was when it was a matter of observance of the Rule, she would go against the letter of her own Constitutions to receive in her convents girls of nine, twelve or fourteen, destined eventually for the religious life, whose naïve sayings, charm and piety she never wearied of talking of. When Diego Ortiz announced once more that his search for a site for the convent had failed, Teresa consoled herself with Martinico.

The authorization, too, was slow in arriving. These authorizations caused the Mother Foundress endless worry. Besides the brief which the Master General of the Order had given her, she had to have authorization from both the town and the Ordinary, not to mention the goodwill of the other Orders in the city which it was necessary to strive to acquire; for if the Augustinians, Franciscans or Mercedarians could not prevent her from founding a convent, through the influence they exerted they could make things difficult for her.

That was why Teresa decided that in future she would take possession of the buildings of her future convents like a thief in the night, as it were: once the first Mass was said, both neighbours and reluctant authorities would yield to a *fait accompli*, with sometimes perhaps more fuss and threats and sometimes less. In the course of the negotiations, her diplomacy generally won over in the end even the most ill-disposed. 'The Foundress had a horror of lies and her diplomacy was beyond reproach. I have never seen anyone more skilled in the art of disclosing nothing she wished to hide, yet without lying. . . .' [2]

The situation at Toledo was complicated by the absence of the Archbishop: Bishop Bartolomé Carranza was awaiting the result of his trial in the secret dungeons of the Inquisition: in his *Commentary on the Catechism* numerous propositions had been instanced in which strict censors thought they could perceive a flavour of Lutheranism: he concerned himself in popularizing the words of Christ himself and the theologian Melchor Cano found in him 'a taint of illuminism' because he affirmed that there were people of good sense and measured judgement, so good, so devout, that one could put the entire Scriptures

---

[1] SEC, vol. V p. 117, n. 3.　　　　　　[2] JG quoted SEC, vol. V, p. 94, n. 1.

into their hands as safely as one could into those of many learned men knowing Latin; 'not that I claim that learning has not its place in Scripture, but because the Holy Spirit has his disciples whom he helps and enlightens.' [1]

It was then that the Grand Inquisitor Fernando Valdés published his *Index* which prohibited the translation into Spanish and the reading of the majority of works on mysticism: 'illuminations' of the spirit were to remain the prerogative of the clergy or of privileged souls who had the advantage of being directed by a learned confessor. It seemed impossible to allow the ordinary faithful to practise mental prayer. There was a solid prejudice of caste. Ten years after these events, Teresa of Jesus' troubles were a consequence of this prejudice.

So a man who was neither illustrious nor of noble birth had the audacity to want to be the patron of a convent! That was no more possible than to allow a carpenter's wife to practise a high degree of mental prayer.

In the Archbishop's absence, the head of the Council of government of the archbishopric of Toledo, Don Gómez Tello Girón, was all powerful. He it was who was informed of the incredible pretension of the deceased Martín Ramírez and his heirs. Unkind comments ran about like wildfire and Teresa knocked on closed doors: Doña Luisa de la Cerda herself became reticent and cool.

But Rubeo, the Master General, had enjoined on the Mother Foundress not to discourage the benefactor: the fact of having bought things to sell them again did not make an honest man unworthy of acquiring a good place in heaven. He wrote to her:

. . . Avarice, cause of innumerable crimes, devours one's neighbour's work, grasps everything for oneself and is never weary of coveting. Nations eaten up by this vice are in peril, and souls too fond of earthly riches, those who spend on pleasure what they acquired without toil, are put in the centre of the earth and justly punished after being sentenced by the Most Just Judge.

That is why men who fear God, afraid of being caught in the snare of riches, give the greatest part of their gains to the Church.

You, Reverend Mother Teresa, must not be surprised that the noble and devout *caballero* Martín Ramírez, wanting to be united with Jesus Christ and his holy Mother in paradise, has given away a part of his goods to this end. . . .[2]

The Master General did not hesitate to class as ' noble and a

[1] Quoted BA, p. 132, n. 2.   [2] Quoted SEC, vol. V, p. 424.

gentleman' a merchant who belonged to the only aristocracy which counts: that of a generous heart.

Mother Teresa rated work too highly to despise those who had not acquired their riches 'without toil'; she esteemed merit above birth, 'for, before God, titles and functions will not count.' Diego Ortiz, ill at ease in his rôle as benefactor, was more intransigent than he would otherwise have been because more than one *hidalgo* took it upon himself to humiliate him; there were points on which the Foundress could not give way and it was not her fault if all negotiations between her and the merchants were finally broken off. And the promised 12,000 ducats took wing.

There she was, then, in Toledo, without patrons, without any to give security for her, without a house, without money, esteemed of little account by the mighty men of this world, but determined not to admit defeat. To the two Isabels she said:

'Now that the idol of money has crashed to the ground, I consider this foundation more certain than ever. . . .'

Once more, human help had proved itself to be worth no more than a few sprigs of dried rosemary: but once more His Majesty would show his power.

Teresa began to look for a house on her own account. Without anyone's support she endeavoured to approach the Governor, who obstinately refused to receive her. Fortunately for the business in hand, the churches were at that time a kind of forum or fair-ground; business less innocent than the foundation of a new convent was transacted there. Teresa waylaid the Governor near the altar where he was accustomed to hear Mass and begged him to come and speak to her in the chapel where she had withdrawn to avoid prying eyes. 'Our Lord gave her a great spirit of determination.' [1]

Although he was a very serious man and conscious of his exalted dignity, she infused so much charm and sweetness into what she said and spoke to him with 'such a great and holy liberty' [2] that, first of all surprised and then won over to her, he listened to all she had to say:

'It is hard that women whose only desire is to live in austerity, perfection and enclosure, should be prevented from serving Our Lord by those who are not caused the least inconvenience by all that and who think of nothing but living out their days comfortably. . . .' [3]

She added 'many other things besides,' and, finally, this:

'If this foundation fails merely because of Your Lordship, do you

---

[1] Sb, F, c. xv–5.   [2] FR, L. II, c. iii.   [3] Sb, F, c. xv–5.

think you can justify yourself over the matter when you have to appear before Our Lord?' [1]

Teresa was so 'gentle and charming,' [2] even when she was threatening an ecclesiastical Governor with the thunders of the Most High, and made such a deep impression on Don Gómez Tello Girón that he granted her the authorization she asked for forthwith, on one condition: the convent was to have neither revenues nor benefactors. In this way he hoped to prevent her from raising merchants to the rank of patrons of Carmel.

She went away delighted, 'as though she had everything, although she had nothing.' [3] She had only three or four ducats left. 'Teresa of Jesus and three ducats are nothing, but Teresa of Jesus, three ducats and God are everything.' [4]

She eagerly spent her last ducats: two pallets, a blanket, and two pictures for the future chapel, one of which showed Jesus falling under the weight of the Cross, the other Our Lord in prayer, seated on a rock. This was the bare minimum for three poor little nuns: the wherewithal to pray and to sleep.

But 'as to a house, there was no sign of one at all.' [5] As was her wont, Teresa toiled, laboured, acted to the utmost in the measure of her resources and even beyond and then, imperturbable, she waited for the accomplishment of the promise: 'Knock and it shall be opened unto you.' Knock, that meant work.

Did she see in a youth who came up to her one day in a church the chosen instrument of the promise's fulfilment? In both appearance and dress he was more like a *pícaro* than an honest man. When the two Isabels saw him come up, they stood round their prioress ready to defend her: these Toledan churches were frequented by people whose devotion must be accepted with a certain reserve and Teresa had already been the subject of attack by a woman who used her fists and who accused her of having stolen one of her clogs. What with crooks on the look-out for an easy prey and thieves who were satisfied with a purse, there was every need to take care: but what danger of this kind could a poor woman who had nothing and who when she was attacked gave praise to God, incur? She got a lot of fun out of the incident of the clog.

The poor fellow greeted her politely, said that his name was Andrada and that he came on behalf of Fray Martín de la Cruz, a Franciscan and a friend of the Mother Foundress.

[1] FR, L. II, c. iii.   [2] Idem.   [3] Sb, F, c. xv-6.
[4] Quoted BRJ, p. 71.   [5] Sb, F, c. xv-6.

'Fray Martín told me: Go and find Mother Teresa of Jesus, put yourself at her disposal, help her all you can and even more than you can.' [1] Having no money, living rather in poverty and wretchedness, he could only give what he had, his person, his obedience, his knowledge of even the most remote corners of Toledo and agile legs to take him all over the city with rapidity. Finally, no small measure of the gift of the gab with which to make inquiries of all and sundry.

Teresa listened to what he had to say with a kindly smile and asked her nuns not to forget any of the directions through the labyrinth of narrow streets to the place where she could find the youth who said he was 'her servitor' when needed.

The honesty both of what he said and of his face pleased Teresa greatly: she loved ordinary folk and persons of low degree so much that she did not forget Andrada's offer, but when she wanted to send for him to ask him to look for a house, Isabel de Santo Domingo and Isabel de San Pablo, after having had a good laugh over it, looked at each other with dismay:

'Mother! You're not going to get that man here? What will the porter say? What will Doña Luisa say? And her attendants and the servants! You've got a strange messenger, just the sort for Discalced Carmelites! What hope is there that a man in rags and tatters can find a house when rich merchants, a canon of the cathedral who was the son of a Governor of Castile, and so many other important persons have sought one in vain?'

'Don't talk like that,' said Teresa. 'What harm could people think of poor pilgrims like ourselves? Fray Martín is a saint: he has sent me this youth Andrada, he had his reasons and they were good ones. I will see him.' [2]

Nobody ever dared answer the Mother's 'Don't talk like that.' Andrada came. When he replied: 'A house? Nothing easier. I will find that for you,' Isabel de San Pablo shrugged her shoulders to convey to Mother Teresa that the poor fellow certainly had not all his wits about him. But a few days later, when the three Carmelites were hearing Mass in the Jesuit church, he came up to them:

'The house is found.'

He had brought the keys with him; they set off eagerly to look at the house and found it exactly what they wanted.

Teresa was never gentler than when she had good cause to triumph:

'His Majesty is proving to us that we must take care not to consider

[1] Idem.   [2] FR, L. II, c. xiii.

it an honour to rub shoulders with the great ones of this world, but with those who are poor like the apostles were! . . .' [1]

But she laughed to herself when her daughters begged her not to let Andrada see that their entire household possessions consisted of only two pictures, two pallets and a single blanket: they were afraid the poor fellow might lose interest when he found they were even poorer than he was. . . .

The little convoy which was to see to the removal and make the foundation formed as soon as night fell: it consisted of the two Isabels, Andrada and a Calced Carmelite friar who carried the vestments and sacred vessels which the monastery of Mitigated observance lent them. All the money Teresa had was one hundred reales borrowed from the wife of Doña Luisa de la Cerda's butler. [2]

They spent the night sweeping, cleaning and arranging the house, making primitive attempts at decorating the wretched place. There was no room for a chapel: the altar was erected in a room to which the faithful could only have access through the house next door, which likewise formed part of the buildings of the future convent. But the two women who were living in it had not been told for fear of gossip. They were awakened by great bangs on the wall: Andrada and the Calced friar were breaking through their partition. When they saw them appear they thought they were in hell and broke into loud complaints. Teresa succeeded in calming them down by a well-balanced combination of soft words and ducats.

At dawn all was ready. Doña Luisa de la Cerda and her ladies took their places in the chapel as the little hand-bell used for the elevation was ringing to announce the first Mass: there was no proper bell. But a small child who was passing by in the street, when he saw the altar lighted up, the palms [3] and the pictures, exclaimed:

'Blessed be God. How lovely it all is!'

'For this exclamation of praise alone coming from the lips of such a little angel, I consider myself well repaid for all the trouble this foundation has given me,' said Teresa to her companions. 'It was God's will that the agreement with Alonso Alvarez should come to nothing in order that this foundation should be built solely on work and poverty.' [4] 'Andrada, a poor boy, found the house for us, the humble wife of a servant of a great house has given the necessary money; finally, upon all these poor people comes the blessing of a little child.'

---

[1] CTA, ccclxxx.
[3] It was Palm Sunday—Tr.

[2] FR, L. II, c. 13.
[4] Sb, F, c. xv-8.

She was thinking of the stable at Duruelo, of Fray John of the Cross, of Fray Antonio de Jesús, and gave thanks to God.

At last the three Carmelites were alone in the convent of the Glorious St Joseph of the city of Toledo and were now well and properly enclosed. The menu for this day of rejoicing consisted in a few sardines which they were slightly regretting being unable to grill for want of a little wood, when providentially they found a faggot in the chapel. They cooked their meal on a borrowed stove. A paper with a stone on top lest a breath of air should blow the salt away served them as salt cellar.

Teresa was delighted: up till then had not her love of poverty been that of a person who had never lacked what was necessary? Toledo was the means of her initiation into absolute poverty—'the arms on her standard.' [1]

One night—the nights in May are still fresh at this altitude—she was cold and asked the nuns to cover her up. They laughed heartily:

'Mother, you already have all the coverlets there are in the house, that is to say, our cloaks. . . .' [2]

Teresa was touched and amused at the same time. She laughed with them.

Teresa of Jesus had wanted to negotiate with merchants. What she now said, was:

Such great poverty when the lady who was so fond of me was at hand in her own house may seem incredible. I don't know what the cause of it was except that God doubtless wanted to show us the benefits of this virtue. I asked Doña Luisa de la Cerda for nothing, for I don't like to bother people and fortunately she did not notice our extreme lack of everything. I owe her a great deal more than she could have given us. . . . [3]

Our inward joy was so great that I often remind myself of all Our Lord told us was involved in this virtue. Our poverty was the means which brought us to blessed contemplation. This did not last long for people soon began to give us what we needed. This made me as sad as if a lot of gold and jewels had been taken away from me. I saw that the nuns were sad and asked them why:

'Mother, what could the reason be except that we are no longer poor?'

From then onwards my desire for poverty increased and I felt all the richer for not caring about temporal goods. When they are lacking, interior riches increase and they indeed satisfy us more fully and bring us a much greater peace. [4]

[1] Sb, C, c. ii–7.   [2] FR, L. II, c. 13.   [3] Sb, F, c. xv–13.   [4] Idem, 14.

In the midst of all this difficulties arose with the owner who did not want her premises turned into a convent. The wife of an eldest son, *i.e.* an heir, a powerful woman and given to intriguing, she stirred up the ecclesiastical Council. The Governor, Tello Girón, was away and so could not confirm his verbal authorization, the whole of Toledo was indignant 'at the audacity of an insignificant little woman,' [1] in founding a convent against the will of the notables of the town. She was threatened with excommunication if she continued to have Mass said.

In her, bad news or any other blow merely aroused fresh fervour. The blood coursed more quickly through her veins and her maladies disappeared. Toledo, all its annoyance notwithstanding, found a woman whom nothing could move despite her meekness; to threats she gently replied that she would obey although she was not obliged to do so. But whether she was holding her own or, as the case might be, putting up undaunted passive resistance, whether she was suffering from cold, or hunger, she worked with might and main for the completion of what had to be done to the house, so that those of her daughters who were to form the community might come soon; whenever she was free from the necessity of defending her cause in the parlour, she worked with her hands, not even allowing herself respite for prayer and contemplation: to serve is also to pray.

On Pentecost eve the ecclesiastical Governor Tello Girón returned and the Council calmed down. The work on the buildings was finished, the owner appeased and the nuns arrived and installed themselves. Teresa took her place in the refectory 'so glad to think that at last she could rejoice in the Lord for these wonderful happenings, that she could not eat, she was so overwhelmed with joy.'

At that moment they came to call her: a messenger from Ana de Mendoza y la Cerda, Princess of Éboli, was asking for her urgently in the parlour.

[1] Idem, 11.

VI

ANA DE MENDOZA Y LA CERDA, PRINCESS OF ÉBOLI

THE whims of Ana de Mendoza y la Cerda, Princess of Éboli, were commands: she had known Teresa of Jesus at Toledo when the latter was staying with her aunt, Doña Luisa de la Cerda, and her immediate caprice was to have in her duchy of Pastrana a convent which she herself had founded, just as she would have demanded a farthingale overnight from a fashionable dressmaker.

She sent a carriage which was not to leave without bringing back the Mother Foundress.

Teresa gave the princess's suite a meal and, leaving the refectory, hurried to the chapel. She fell on her knees:

'O my delight,' she prayed, 'Lord of all creation, my God! How long must I wait to enjoy your presence? What relief do you offer those who find no rest in this world but in you? Oh how long life is! And how painful! O life which is no life at all! Oh for solitude alone! Oh where does the remedy lie? How long, O Lord, how long, how long? My only good, what am I to do? Must I desire not to desire you? O my God, my Creator, you hurt without anointing the wound!' [1]

She could bear no more. For what was she asking for, this daughter of Our Lady of Carmel? Simply to live enclosed, cloistered by God himself. The number of those who were enjoying silence and peace in her convents increased every day—Ávila, Medina del Campo, Valladolid, Toledo, besides the friars at Duruelo. But Teresa herself? Each time she was just beginning to hope to enjoy it, she had to leave.

And yet nothing equalled the joy of them all when, as each foundation was made, the sisters at last found themselves separated from the world by thick walls and a whole host of grilles, bolts and locks, Constitutions and prohibitions. There no earthly noise, no human being could touch them, there, 'trampling the world beneath their feet,' they were free, queens and mistresses of the kingdom of the spirit. How could they breathe elsewhere? 'A fish thrown on the bank cannot live: similarly souls made for the living waters given by the Bridegroom die

<hr>

[1] Sb, E, vi-1.

when caught in the meshes of the world, if they are not thrown back into the living water. . . .'[1]

Perhaps she had not deserved to enjoy the solitude she preferred to all else? For when scarcely on the fringe of her oasis, she had to turn back to what she 'abhorred,'[2] all the bustle of people and business and money. She would have made light of all the work of the foundations if it had not been for having to see all these men and women of whom she had to form an opinion, whom it was necessary to solicit or get rid of, to charm or to win over, to circumvent or to dominate: this meant an adjustment of oneself to the sphere of the infinitely small, whereas her soul was attuned to the infinitely great.

'Pity on me, pity on me, Lord! This exile is very long and in it the heavy penalty of unsatisfied desire for God is exacted. O sweet refreshment of the lovers of God! O suffering! Pity on me, Lord!'[3]

She begged Our Lord, who was her Counsellor, to dictate to her a letter of refusal which would not offend the Princess: for the sake of the Order, she could not displease Doña Ana nor her husband, Prince Ruy Gómez, the most powerful man in Spain after the King.

A friend of Philip II in childhood, the Portuguese Ruy Gómez da Silva had remained his intimate counsellor throughout the years. The King, who wished to honour him, had, however, not made him an attractive present in giving him Ana de Mendoza y la Cerda, one of the greatest names and fortunes of all Spain, for wife. She was the great-grandchild of Don Pedro González de Mendoza, Cardinal Archbishop of Toledo, himself the son of the illustrious Marquis of Santillana, the famous warrior and one of the best poets of the fifteenth century.

'The mighty power of Pedro González de Mendoza was such that he was surnamed "the third king of Spain" at a time when the other two were no less than Ferdinand and Isabella the Catholic, and his vitality was so superabundant that after making the kingdom resound with his political, social and military exploits, he left several natural children.'[4]

The Princess of Éboli had inherited the turbulence of her distinguished ancestor. She was famous for her beauty although she had only one eye, which flatterers expressed by saying that she 'had only one sun'; that one was sufficient to enlighten the court of Spain and the world. She was no less famous for her quarrelsome, haughty and unscrupulous nature. She was now thirty. The King had no illusions about her: 'She wants everything that comes into her head and sticks

---

[1] Sb, F, c. xxi-46. [2] CTA, xxx.
[3] Sb, E, xv-1, 2, 3. [4] MA, vol. I, p. 167.

at nothing to gain her end; her rages and ill words are unparalleled for one of her rank.' The court feared the sting of her tongue and her husband had made up his mind once and for all not to contradict her. To alienate Doña Ana was to alienate Ruy Gómez; to alienate Ruy Gómez was to alienate Philip II.

Our Lord dictated no letter to Mother Teresa: he ordered her to leave for Pastrana, for the journey was more important than she thought it was. He added that she was not to fail to take the Rule and Constitutions with her.

Teresa of Jesus' joy in obeying was so great that it cut short all regret. When in accordance with the divine plan she went back into the world she did not leave God. Rather, he went with her.

On the way she was obliged to pay her respects at the court: the King's support was essential to her, especially for the monasteries of friars. At that time the sight of Teresa in the streets of Madrid, soliciting the help of lords and princes, was not uncommon.

Her reputation was already so great that Doña Leonor de Mascarenhas herself had gone to the trouble of trying to recruit subjects for the Discalced Carmelite friars and held Mariano Azaro and Giovanni Narducci in reserve for her.

If little Fray Giovanni, going straight from the studio of the painter Sánchez Coello to the 'desert,' showed 'a great simplicity in worldly matters,' [1] Mariano Azaro looked down on the world from the height of great birth and privileged intelligence. A Neapolitan, Knight of the Order of St John of Jerusalem, formerly Master of the Palace to the Queen of Poland, he was in addition a great geometer, a great mathematician and one of the best engineers of the day.

Mariano and Giovanni were living as hermits in the 'desert' of Tardón, from which the engineer was called away somewhat too frequently for his liking by Philip II. After the victory of St Quentin which was partly due to his work, the King summoned him to construct a canal connecting the Tagus with the Guadalquivir. When the work was finished he returned to his solitude.

At present he was preparing to leave for Rome. Since the Council of Trent, hermits had to be incorporated in some already existing Order and Mariano wanted to persuade the Pope to permit him to remain in the 'desert' with his companion.

When Teresa learnt from Doña Leonor that, not content with observing silence and solitude, they were practising penance, abstinence, fasting and mortification and living by the work of their hands

[1] Sb, F, c. xvii–6.

and not by begging, she was delighted: was not this the essence of the primitive Rule of Carmel?

She showed Mariano Azaro the Rule and Constitutions which Our Lord had told her to bring: he could save himself the trouble of asking for exceptional treatment—a step which did not go hand in hand with perfect obedience—and, as a Discalced Carmelite, live far away from a world 'lost by reason of its cupidity.' [1]

Averse as he was to the company of men, Mariano Azaro avoided that of women still more: was he to exchange his hermit's robe for a Carmelite habit at the first bidding of a person belonging to this crafty sex? He said he would like to sleep over it but God disturbed his sleep and, before dawn, he had made up his mind and 'was very much astonished that he had changed his opinion so quickly, particularly under the influence of a woman.' [2] Our Lord's command was wonderfully clear. He had just received from Prince Ruy Gómez a very good hermitage situated in Pastrana itself. Did not Teresa of Jesus' invitation, coming as it did at this identical moment, prove that this hermitage was destined to become the second monastery of Discalced Carmelite friars?

When the Mother Foundress left Madrid, she took with her two more friars, and the 'Rose of Lebanon,' Beatriz Brances, a friend of Doña Leonor de Mascarenhas, who was to take the Carmelite habit at Pastrana under the name of Beatriz del Sacramento.

At Pastrana there was a fuss about authorization as usual; but a warm welcome from the Prince and Princess.

Delays, as usual: the Princess had had the house demolished all except the walls and was setting herself enthusiastically to the task of getting it rebuilt. But Teresa and her nuns were lodged in the palace and their rooms were shut off from the noise of the world and the chatter of attendants and valets by thickness after thickness of heavy curtains of magnificent splendour.

Much work, as always. But quarrels, as never before: the Princess was punctilious about her rights and the ceremony she considered her due. Teresa found the necessity of concealing what she really thought and of not always having direct access to the Princess, trying. The King of Kings had treated her with less formality: 'With him I can speak as with a friend, although he is the Lord God, because he is not like those whom we have here who display their power even when it is based upon a sham authority. . . .' [3] Ana de Mendoza insisted on presenting

[1] Idem, 9.   [2] Idem.
[3] Sb, V, c. xxxvii–5.

as a subject a certain Sister Agustina, but the Mother Foundress did not
want nuns already formed to the observance of another, and different,
Rule. The Princess now haggled over the amount of revenue she had
offered the day before, the next day quibbled over the regularity of the
allowance, finding a hundred and one points for discussion which she
tried to turn into points of dispute. It would have been like founding a
convent on a volcano if the Prince had not used the wonderful and
kindly forbearance acquired during his married life to persuade the
haughty Princess to yield to the requirements of holiness.

Having a freer hand for the monastery of friars, the Prince was so
generous that the skill of Mariano Azaro and four hundred ducats were
employed to bring water to the top of the hill where the hermitages
were grouped; in this way it was possible to make delightful kitchen
gardens and orchards, gay with the songs of birds. Taking advantage
of this generous zeal, the Discalced friars gave themselves the luxury of
cells that were more like tombs than dwelling-places for the living.
Everything was so rough, so austere, decorated with crosses and skulls
as at Duruelo, 'that even the most sluggish devotion came to life there
and the hardest hearts softened.' [1]

The Prince paid secretly for all the work done, 'so that the village
should not cease giving the friars alms,' and also that Doña Ana should
not get too touchy about his generosity.

The Princess's nuns sewed the habits the Prince's friars were to
wear: Mariano Azaro became Fray Ambrosio Mariano de San
Benito, and Giovanni Narducci, Fray Juan de la Miseria. Neither of
them wanted to be ordained priest, because they wished to be employed
only in the lowliest tasks.

P. Antonio de Jesús came to Pastrana to establish perpetual adoration there: night and day, two friars would remain in prayer before
the Blessed Sacrament. 'He implanted this holy exercise so well there
that it is still practised as fervently as it was at the beginning . . .
And all the friars there live in the enjoyment of abundant heavenly
consolation. . . .' [2]

The foundation of the convent of nuns took place on 28th June
1569. The Princess provided the chapel with gold and silver vestments,
together with an amazing abundance of relics.

With a great pealing of bells, in solemn procession, amid shouts of
enthusiasm, with singing and dancing, amid the rhythm of litanies of
which the responses were taken up by the crowd, Teresa of Jesus, the
prioress Isabel de Santo Domingo, the sub-prioress Isabel de San Pablo

---

[1] SEC, vol. VI, p. 126.   [2] Idem, p. 127.

—always the two Isabels—followed by their sisters in white mantle and black veil, entered their convent.

The crowd of religious, noble lords and ladies, and villagers was immense; the demeanour of the Prince was recollected; the Princess in her splendour was more than ever like 'a precious stone set in the enamel of nature and fortune,' as the madrigal of Antonio Pérez, the King's secretary and her admirer, would have it.

The ceremony was as edifying as it was gorgeous. The court and the town talked for a long time to come of the opening of this convent which had been constructed, financed and equipped by Ana de Mendoza y la Cerda, Princess of Éboli, who had now no further cause to envy her relatives, Doña María de Mendoza and Doña Luisa de la Cerda: she, too, had her Carmelites now. . . .

Mother Teresa of Jesus was so weary of courts and courtiers that she refused to found a convent at Madrid: eager to get back to the poor again and her merchants, she set out with all speed for Toledo.

Up to the last the Princess was to prove no friend to her. She had insisted on her taking her carriage and a priest saw the Carmelite getting out of the luxurious equipage in front of the convent. He asked for her in the parlour and insulted her:

'So you're the saint who is deceiving everybody and going about in a carriage?'

This priest was mad and he went on to add all the words of abuse which came into his head.

Teresa, thinking he was in his right mind, listened to him humbly, without seeking to excuse herself: 'You are the only one courageous enough to point out my faults.' [1]

From that day she travelled only in the poorest and most uncomfortable carts.

[1] FR, L. IV, c. xvii.

VII

MOTHER TERESA AND HER DAUGHTERS

THE Mother Foundress was not to remain idle long at Toledo. With more pleasure than she had obeyed the orders of the Princess of Éboli, she answered the appeal of the Rector of the Jesuits at Salamanca and set off to found a convent in the great university city. She took the prioress, María del Sacramento, away from Malagón but took no one else with her: experience had taught her that two women, if already accustomed to hardships, could deal with the difficulties much more easily when they had not to bolster up the courage of timid young sisters. But even when Teresa of Jesus set out on her travels in secret, priests or laymen—the latter perhaps *caballeros* or merchants—who considered it an honour to escort her, would join themselves to her company. All these people formed a gay and motley cortège around her closely covered cart: there were *hidalgos* in doublets with their short, brightly coloured capes; commoners enriched by trading and no less gaily attired, who adjusted the steady trot of their hacks or the ambling step of their palfreys to the pace of the mules of the churchmen; ecclesiastics all in black, each wearing the monumental hat known as the *teja*, and on his nose the enormously large spectacles which travellers used to protect their eyes against the sun and dust. As to the friars, Our Lord was their support throughout the many miles they covered on foot or on donkey-back.

Such were the knights serving this 'dame errant'[1] who enlivened all of them by her conversation and who was more charming to the humble folk, serving boys and muleteers, than to churchmen or nobles. 'She was full of gaiety,' but the merry conversation was always interspersed with remarks which turned one's thoughts to heaven.

Among the travellers affectionate familiarity was the rule and Teresa showed so much gratitude towards anyone who rendered her some slight service that all were delighted to help. And yet, if this unusual company 'edified' some people, many otherwise good Christians—especially pious women—assumed a strait-laced air or openly blamed the Carmelite, whose passage disturbed the towns and

[1] SEC, vol. V, p. 6.

villages of Old Castile too frequently, brought the evil talkers out on to their doorsteps and too often furnished idle tongues with subjects for gossip.

But God's service was more important than the fear of chatter:

'So long as God is praised and a little better understood the whole world can cry after me!' [1]

Teresa of Jesus did not hesitate to go considerably out of her way to visit the Carmelite houses which were within reach. *Hidalgos*, merchants, priests, friars, servants followed her: the gossips too.

To reach Salamanca she went through Ávila. Each time she came back to St Joseph's, the first of her foundations, she was deeply moved:

'I come back to my mother. . . .'

This time, the prioress, María de San Jerónimo, formerly the lively María Dávila, presented two novices to her.

One, Ana García, was the daughter of peasant folk. As a child she had lived on such intimate terms with Our Lord that she would apologise to him when the other children asked her to join in their amusements: 'I am going to play and I'll come back straightway. . . .' Later she deliberately frightened off her first admirer by appearing with a towel on her head instead of an elegant head-dress. When she was twenty she had a vision which resulted in her entering Carmel. In a dream she saw herself in a small convent remarkable for its poverty but where the silence was permeated through and through with the love of God. She asked for something to drink: nuns dressed in a habit made of heavy, coarse brown stuff held out an earthenware pitcher to her; never had her thirst been slaked by fresher or cooler water. From this description the priest in her village recognized the convent of St Joseph of Ávila and spoke to the prioress about Ana. It had just been decided to add two lay-sisters to the community and the young peasant girl was sent for. She recognized the house down to the last detail, even the earthenware pitcher. That was how Ana de San Bartolomé became the first Carmelite lay-sister.

The Foundress loved this simple, timid girl as soon as she saw her. Ana had so much good sense that later on she made her her secretary; and she was so gentle and loving that Teresa chose her as her infirmarian and inseparable companion.

The other novice was as brilliant as Ana de San Bartolomé was humble. Born at Medina del Campo, Ana de Lobera was now twenty-five: her passage through the world had been so striking and her reputation for beauty such that she was surnamed 'the queen of

[1] Sb, M, VII, c. i–2.

women.' [1] And queen she remained even in the cloister, on account of
her talents, energy and the high degree of spirituality she attained. Her
entering St Joseph's was also marked by a miraculous sign: in a picture
of Our Lord in the Hermitage of Christ at the pillar, she recognized
the face and eyes of a beggar who had asked her for help one day.
She had given him an alms and went her way, but moved by his look
of sorrow and at the same time of love, she turned her head to look at
him again. He had disappeared. It was from this moment that she
detached herself from everything which had hitherto constituted her
pleasure. Teresa, like a water-diviner finding water, immediately sensed
the exceptional value of Ana de Jesús and determined to make her
novice-mistress of the future convent of Salamanca.

The Mother Foundress and María del Sacramento arrived at
Salamanca on All Saints eve, October 1570. All the furniture they
brought was a bundle of straw, for 'where we have straw we have
beds.' [2] A house had been allocated, but the tenants, a band of students,
only left the place with loud protestations late in the evening. The two
travellers went into it worn out, numb with cold, scared by the noise
and din of a town where the fact that they were future doctors of the
university did not prevent the students from behaving like hooligans.
With fatigue added to everything else, María del Sacramento was
seized with terror in this unfamiliar house which had been pillaged by
its young inhabitants. In the darkness, broken only by the yellowish,
tapering point of a candle flame, disturbing shadows flickered on the
walls. The poor woman wandered tremblingly from room to room
amid confusion and disorder like that of Judgement Day, making the
sign of the cross at every step and sprinkling holy water while all the
bells of the town tolled: it was the night of All Souls.

Mother Teresa long remembered this arrival. The thought of it
made her laugh and she made her nuns in Ávila, Valladolid and in all
her convents laugh over it too. They often begged her to tell the story
once more:

> María del Sacramento could not forget that the students had been
> furious at leaving; she imagined they must be hiding in the lofts and
> dark corners to frighten us: it would have been easy, there was plenty
> of room. . . . We shut ourselves up in a room where I had thrown
> our bundle of straw and spent the night under two blankets someone
> had lent us.

[1] SEC, vol. V, p. 193, n. 1.   [2] Sb, F, c. xix-4.

When my companion saw that the door was fastened, she grew calmer as far as the students were concerned, although she kept on looking round anxiously. But the devil put into her mind ideas calculated to upset me in my turn. I am so weak that it doesn't take much. I said to her:

'What are you looking for now? No one can get in.'

'Mother, if I died suddenly, what would you do here all alone?'

She was so much in earnest that her terror communicated itself to me; I have always been afraid of dead bodies, even when there was someone else with me.

All this time the bells were tolling without interruption for, as I have said, it was the night of All Souls, and it was only too easy for the demon to scare us by childish fancies. . . .

Fortunately, I was dropping with sleep:

'Sister, if that should happen, I should have to think what to do. Just now, all I want to do is to sleep. . . .'

We had just spent two very bad nights and soon sleep remedied our fear. . . .[1]

Teresa needed all her gaiety to keep her going: this foundation at Salamanca was so beset with difficulties that years later the community was still looking for a suitable place to live; they could not succeed in extricating themselves from the tangle of litigation which one of the owners of the house, Don Pedro de la Banda, delighted in. The Foundress wrote to this quarrelsome man: 'May Our Lord give Your Grace a little calmness. . . .'[2] And in tactful words she reminded him of the shortness of this life: 'Anxiety about this world's goods should not turn our thoughts from thinking of our heavenly home. . . .'[3]

And yet it was there, in the midst of a thousand preoccupations, that she began to write the story of her foundations. God had commanded her to do so and the order was confirmed by her former confessor P. Ripalda, whom she met once more at Salamanca where he was Rector of the Jesuits. She began on 23rd August, 'feast of St Louis, King of France,' grieved by 'her want of talent, her clumsiness, the absence of peace and quietness in which to write, and her bad health. . . .'[4] 'My style is so heavy that I fear to weary others and myself as well. . . .'[5] To her objections Our Lord replied: 'Daughter, obedience brings strength.'[6]

And so she obeyed. In the meantime she had to go and found a convent at Alba de Tormes, under the patronage of Teresa de Layz, and under the invocation of Our Lady of the Annunciation. Every-

---

[1] Sb, F, c. xix-4, 5.   [2] CTA, xlviii.   [3] Idem, xlvii.
[4] SEC, vol. V, Prologo, 5.   [5] Idem, 3.   [6] Idem, 2.

thing there, however, went well, and she was able to work quickly. The foundation took barely a month at the beginning of 1571, and she was then able to return to Salamanca and sustain the courage of her nuns there.

The prioress of Salamanca was her cousin, Ana de Tapia, the daughter of her uncle Francisco; she had at last left the Mitigation and in the wake of Teresa had become Ana de la Encarnación. The sub-prioress, María de Cristo, María de San Francisco, Jerónima de Jesús, and two novices, Ana de Jesús who had at last arrived from Ávila, and Juana de Jesús, completed the initial nucleus of the community.

Teresa was always very fond of her novices. In motherly words she anxiously inquired about Juana's health, for she seemed to have 'such a tiny face.' [1] Ana de Jesús shared her cell, and Teresa watched her as she slept and traced little crosses on her forehead; she gave her her new cloak and kept the old one for herself.

One by one and by her own example she inculcated in them the great principles of Carmelite charity which bring so much gentle sweetness to the bedside of the sick, following Christ's counsel: 'The prioress who did not provide for the welfare of the sick would be behaving like Job's friends. God is trying them for the good of their souls, but she would be exposing them to the danger of losing their patience.' [2] Teresa ordered Ana de la Encarnación to eat meat, for she considered her overtired and in poor health.[3]

We can see her at the bedside of the dying 'caressing each one's face with her gentle hand, and encouraging them with loving words,' and no one had more sympathy than she for people's troubles and sufferings. She was the consoling angel of all her daughters, of all the people around her, and even of strangers whose complaints she listened to— she who never complained herself—'with supernatural pity.' [4] According to her view of things, the stronger we are the greater our obligation to stoop in tenderness towards those to whom a mere nothing often causes great suffering.

For her, each one of her nuns was a soul walking along the royal highway. There are no weights and measures in the Kingdom of the spirit and often a slight effort on the part of some is evidence of more virtue than great ecstasies on the part of others. She always refused to be considered holy because she had visions and raptures, constantly repeating: '*Yo que soy ruin* . . .' 'Vile as I am . . .' and gave continual proof of humility. She never failed to ask the opinion of the

---

[1] CTA, li.   [2] SEC, R, ix, p. 45.   [3] CTA, li.
[4] Cf. Sb, C, c. vii–5.

sisters and, what is more, she conformed to it. During her visits to the various convents she did not allow the nuns to come to her for things but sent them to their prioress, to whom she showed as much respect as if she herself had been her subject too. As far as the business of the Order and of the foundations, her correspondence, her charge of souls and bodies permitted, she took time, even if she had to take it from her sleep, to ply her distaff, to take her share like the others in providing for the needs of the community.

When, with her naturally quick tongue, she happened to hurt a sister by the way in which she reproached her, or by one of the ironical remarks that sometimes escaped her, she would prostrate herself at her feet and ask pardon. She did the same when she was at fault herself; the nuns at Malagón related that one day when she had made a mistake in reading an Office, she prostrated in the middle of the choir before their eyes: they were so touched that amid their tears they forgot to signal to her to rise again. And she signed her letters to the prioresses, those prioresses whom she had formed herself: 'Your Reverence's unworthy servant.'

That was her way of acting when she alone, the human personality called Teresa of Jesus, was in question. It was quite another matter when the Order was in question, and she required the same twofold manner of acting from her prioresses: she required that they should be exacting, firm, capable of severity and even hardness. The Mother Foundress's anger was short but terrible and of pitiless clarity; it never signified a loss of self-mastery, but an energetic intent to have things as they should be. Her letters are full of such expressions of displeasure, as sharp as her spoken words, since she never read over what she wrote; from one letter to the next her anger died down but the will which had prompted it persisted, made itself felt and triumphed. The fullness of her forgiveness blotted out every feeling of irritation or resentment, and she prayed particularly for those who might have reason to fear they had incurred her displeasure.[1]

She was a mixture of gentleness and of unswerving justice. Her skill in the art of dealing with human nature, and her understanding of the most complex characters were unparalleled. Her nuns at Salamanca never wearied of hearing her explain the deepest things of spirituality: they would spend the recreation listening to her. Without neglecting her spinning Teresa would go on talking and although she herself was no stranger to ecstasies, she warned them against the danger of seeking such a state, and denounced its false imitations.

[1] CTA, ccciv.

'I've known more than one, and persons of no small virtue, who spent seven or eight days in a state they thought was rapture: the most simple spiritual exercise affected them in such a way that they let themselves lose consciousness, convinced that they would otherwise be resisting Our Lord. . . .'

And the Foundress added, in that way she had of not mincing matters:

'In the end it's enough to kill them or send them mad if no remedy is applied. . . .'[1]

One sister asked how this condition of unconsciousness differed from rapture:

'The appearance is the same. But rapture, or union with God, is of short duration, its benefits are immense, it leaves the soul bathed in interior light, the understanding has no part in it, Our Lord acts on the will alone. In the other case everything is very different: the body is a prisoner but understanding and memory remain free; these faculties function in a disordered sort of way. . . .[2] In my opinion the soul has nothing to gain from such bodily weaknesses. . . .'[3]

And she advised the prioress 'to forbid such long fits of unconsciousness categorically,'[4] . . . and to forbid fasts and penances in the case of nuns whose prayer caused such bodily peculiarities, and to give them some office 'whose exercise would take their minds off the matter.'[5]

She was afraid lest some collective state of exalted but diseased imagination might occur in places like enclosed convents where women were eager to distinguish themselves in the eyes of God—if indeed their abnormal state was not due to the fact that they simply wanted to be important in the eyes of the community or in their own. Accordingly she never tired of repeating:

'The one who is humblest and most mortified among you is the most spiritual.'[6]

At that time melancholia was doing immense harm in all the convents of Spain. The doctors were powerless to cure these cases of what we should now call neurasthenia, the victims of which were subject to alternate fits of violence and depression, aggressiveness and self-pity, and all nuns were greatly afraid of this malady. Mother Teresa taught her prioresses how to recognize and reduce it as far as possible, and suggested remedies.

'Melancholia begins by overclouding one's reason. What limit is

[1] Sb, F c. vi–2.   [2] Idem, 4.   [3] Idem, 5.
[4] Idem, 5.   [5] Idem.   [6] Cf. R, iv, p. 26.

there to our passions when reason is not in control? Those who have this disease think they are quite well and consider the prioress more sick than they are. . . .'

For her descriptions Teresa could, unfortunately, find no lack of examples:

'Before all else they want their own way, say everything that comes into their heads, find in others faults which justify their own, and are content only when everything is to their liking. When passions are not mortified, what happens if there is no barrier by which to restrain them? . . . The prioress must then govern not only their interior but their external life and her mind must be as clear as that of the patient is clouded, she must force those who will not submit of their own free will, and not give way to pity, for to do that would be misplaced kindness. A single nun with melancholia can upset a whole convent.' [1]

Teresa who loved others so much showed that she also knew how to save a situation by severity, when it was necessary:

'This evil,' she wrote, 'is without remedy if passions are not controlled by every possible means: by punishments, if words are not enough; if punishments do not suffice, by severer penalties; if one month's imprisonment has no effect no hesitation must be shown in imposing four months: it would be doing the greatest possible good to these sick souls.'

Regretfully the Foundress admitted:

'Believe me: after having tried all sorts of remedies, I find no others than these. The prioress who through pity gave complete liberty to those suffering from melancholia would bring about an intolerable situation, and such nuns would have already done much harm to their sisters by the time we think about curing them. . . . It is a serious disease, it is sometimes necessary to purge the humours by medicines and the patient must then stay in the infirmary. A prioress must manage them without their being aware of it, and with a great deal of motherly compassion. . . .'

It was in things like this that Teresa of Jesus showed her skill in the guidance of souls and her knowledge of character:

It looks as though I'm contradicting myself for I've spoken of austerities. Such nuns must be made to feel that they will never get their own way, obedience must be imposed on them, they would be in grave danger if they thought they were free. But the prioress must avoid giving them orders which would provoke them to disobedience for they have not the strength of self-mastery. She must lead

[1] Sb, F, c. vii. The whole section concerning melancholia.

them without their knowing they are being led and with love. For
them the best remedy is work and they must therefore be allowed
only a short time for mental prayer: it's the imagination, which in
most of them is very unstable, which does them the greatest harm.
In the case of every disease, one either recovers or dies: one doesn't
die of melancholia, but one gets cured of it only by a miracle. Those
who suffer from it taste death a thousand times in the way of afflic-
tions, imaginations, scruples, which they call temptations. If they
refused to take themselves seriously they would obtain relief at once.
In very truth I am terribly sorry for them. . . .

Teresa of Jesus, hidden away in her Carmel in about the year 1571,
thus anticipated the future work of psychiatry. Deeply impressed, her
daughters begged her to devote a chapter of her book of the *Foundations* to the treatment of those suffering from melancholia. They were
thinking of the time when she would no longer be with them, their
Mujer Grande, the woman with the mighty intellect and the big heart:
whom would they find to understand them then, if the future retained
no record of her intuitions and her genius? And they were proud of
having been received in these convents where she would accept no one
whom she considered mediocre:

'I won't have nuns who are ninnies,' [1] she said.

And about a prospective postulant whom she found too ready to
give way to tears, she said:

'Perhaps I shall take this cry-baby. . . .' [2]

Gay herself, she liked others to be gay. All her nuns knew that
'foolish devotions,' 'gloomy saints' were not to her liking any more
than she approved going on praying 'until one is exhausted.' [3] Her
laughter was so infectious that when she laughed the whole convent
laughed with her.

At Salamanca as in all her convents, when the bell rang for
recreation, if the Foundress hurried away to her cell, the novices, her
spoiled children, would bar the way:

'Mother . . . Isn't Your Reverence staying with us? . . .' [4]

While they got on with their spinning, they chatted and composed
coplas which the young ones declaimed or sang very charmingly.
Teresa improvised poems which her nuns memorized as she recited
them; one can feel the rhythm of the music beating in that of the verse
and sometimes even, in the exclamation which cuts a strophe, one can

[1] CTA, vi.   [2] CTA, liv.   [3] SEC, vol. VI, p. lii, n. 3.
[4] Quoted BRJ, p. 73.

feel the *desplante*, the lunge forward which was a feature of the popular dances:

> *Vertiendo esta sangre,*
> *¡Dominguillo, eh!*
> *Yo no sé porqué. . . .*[1]

The songs are illustrated by finely drawn illuminations in which the Virgin Mary appears as the daughter of a notable:

> *¿Es parienta del Alcalde,*
> *U quien es esta doncella?*
> *Ella es hija de Dios Padre,*
> *Relumbra como estrella. . . .*[2]

Ana de Jesús was professed at Salamanca. Such bridal feasts brought out all Teresa's warmth and fervour, and her love for the Child Jesus, whose statue Ana carried in her arms and called 'the Bridegroom', broke out into improvisations as fresh as the bouquet of a village bride:

> *Oh dichosa tal zagala*
> *Que hoy se ha dado a un tal zagal*
> *Que reina y ha de reinar.*
> *Ya yo, Gil, estoy medroso,*
> *No la osaré más mirar,*
> *Pues ha tomado marido*
> *Que reina y ha de reinar. . . .*[3]

For Teresa of Jesus tenderness and gaiety were such innocent manifestations of the love of one's neighbour and thus of the love of God that even at recreation fervour took possession of her and she became incapable of resisting the urge of the spirit. She would begin to dance, turning round and clapping her hands as King David danced before the ark, and as the girls of her country and those of her Carmels still dance to-day; the nuns accompanied her 'in a perfect transport of spiritual joy.'[4]

---

[1] Shedding this blood, Dominguillo, eh! I know not why (P, xv).

[2] Is she of the Mayor's kin?
Who can this maiden be?
She is daughter of God the Father
And bright as any star.

[3] How happy is this shepherdess
For she has to-day given herself to a shepherd
Who is royal and will continue to reign.
As to myself, Gil, I am afraid.
I shall never dare to cast eyes on her again
For she has taken a husband
Who is royal and will continue to reign.

[4] SEC, vol. II, p. li.

Years afterwards, when Ana de Jesús accompanied by Ana de San Bartolomé came to France to found Carmelite convents there, the French nuns, to their great astonishment, saw the venerable Mother 'more like a seraphim than a mortal creature executing a sacred dance in the choir, singing and clapping her hands in the Spanish way, but with so much dignity, sweetness and grace that, filled with holy reverence, they felt themselves wholly moved by divine grace and their hearts raised to God.' [1] These sacred dances were in the pure tradition of Teresa of Jesus.

A new novice entered at Salamanca gifted with a voice as clear as crystal and such a delightful inventive genius for music and verse that Mother Teresa often asked her to sing. One Easter evening, when she had been very sad all day, she asked Isabel de Jesús for a *cantarcillo* at the after-dinner recreation.

With a voice like an angel's, she sang to the tune of a *villancico* [2] the exquisite words:

> *Véante mis ojos*
> *Dulce Jesús bueno,*
> *Véante mis ojos*
> *Y muérame yo luego.*

> *Vea quien quisiere*
> *rosas y jasmines*
> *Que si yo te viere*
> *Veré mil jardines. . . .* [3]

The harmony of the words, the music, the nuns so pure and lovely beneath their black veils, the novices with their coifs like dove's wings, the beautiful April evening, a veritable apotheosis of the Resurrection, all this moved Teresa of Jesus so profoundly that she felt her limbs become icy and cold and fell into ecstasy—María de San Francisco caught her in her arms.   They carried her to her cell unconscious.

When she recovered consciousness, 'in pain and with her hands as

---

[1] BM, vol. II, p. 313.   [2] Christmas carol.

[3] May my eyes behold thee,
Good and sweet Jesus,
May my eyes behold thee,
And then may I die.

Let him who will delight his gaze
With jasmine and with roses,
If I were to see thee,
A thousand gardens would lie before my eyes.

it were dislocated,' [1] she experienced in every bone an intense burning feeling which caused her to break out into impassioned verse.

It was to this we owe one of her finest poems: *I die of being unable to die.* . . .

> *Vivo sin vivir en mí*
> *Y de tal manera espero*
> *Que muero porque no muero.* . . . [2]

From that time onwards, when the Mother was rapt in God, her daughters surrounded her softly singing Isabel de Jesús' *cantarcillo*. For Teresa their voices were mingled with those of the angels.

[1] SEC, R, xv, pp. 97–8.

[2] I live without living in myself
And in like manner wait
For death because I cannot die.

(Cf. Peers: *Complete Works of St Teresa of Jesus*, Vol. III, p. 277 and n. 4—Tr.)

VIII

MANY DEVILS

'I FEAR a discontented nun more than I fear many devils. . .',[1] said Teresa of Jesus. An order from the Apostolic Delegate, the Dominican, P. Pedro Fernández, was to oblige her to confront one hundred and thirty discontented nuns.

One hundred and thirty nuns of her old convent of the Incarnation at Ávila. One hundred and thirty women of all ages, for the most part of noble birth, but poor, and dissatisfied at being poor. It is true that many among them were wise virgins, but the majority behaved like virgins—with a touch of foolishness. One hundred and thirty Carmelite nuns of Mitigated observance, very well satisfied with their laxity, and to whom the thing which they had been dreading ever since the foundation of the convent of St Joseph, had happened: somebody was coming to 'reform' them against their will. And it was their former companion, Doña Teresa de Ahumada, who was being forced on these hundred and thirty women obliged to live within the confines of a house too small for their number and with plenty of leisure to arouse one another to indignation.

'What grave fault have we committed that our right to elect our prioress by vote should be taken away?'

'They're giving us the only one whose reputation all over Spain is enough to make one tremble.'

No more visits, grilles everywhere, no more going out, an end of gossiping in each other's cells, a frightful fast, penances enough to make one shudder, the discipline till the blood comes through the broken skin, dry bread or the prison cell for the least disobedience, the slightest lateness in chapel, the least inattention, the smallest infraction of the Rule—that Rule that was originally made for hermits in the desert and not for poor girls many of whom would have preferred marriage to the convent, if so many young men had not gone overseas with Cortés, Pizarro, or Almagro. Why had not this Teresa de Ahumada been condemned to life imprisonment when her disobedient behaviour had so well deserved it a few years ago!

Newcomers questioned the older ones:

[1] CTA, clxxv.

PASTRANA

The Square in Front of the Palace of the
Princess of Éboli

TOLEDO

'You knew her: what was she like?'

Some spoke of her gaiety, of her straightforwardness, of her compassion. Others spoke in the same breath of her love of God and of the gentlemen whom she received in the parlour. All declared that she saw Christ and Our Lady and that she fell into ecstasy or was raised above the ground.

'And that comes from God?'

'Great theologians have admitted that it doesn't come from the devil.'

In any case, she had found life at the Incarnation too pleasant and had gone off to found houses more like prisons than honest convents.

Even the youngest remembered the scandal of the foundation of the convent of St Joseph, the lawsuit which had lasted years, stirred up so much talk and finally made so much commotion that it had done more harm than good to the cause of religion.

Doña Teresa's present mission was to impose her yoke and her austerities upon the convent of the Incarnation.

Displeasure at having to accept the requirements of the primitive Rule was aggravated by the humiliation of the position, and the most fervent, even those who would one day be willing servants of the Reform and follow Teresa of Jesus, as so many of their sisters had already done, protested as angrily as the others.

As to Teresa, she did not hide the fact that she would have preferred to found four convents rather than reform even one. Particularly this one. The Rule of her convents was made for twenty-one nuns at the very outside. How could one make one hundred and thirty angry nuns live in silence? How could one form them to recollection and obedience? One might as well try to reform hell and its legions.

One hundred and thirty women! The Mother Foundress did not conceal the fact that she had a certain contempt for her own sex. How much tittle-tattle, foolish nonsense, exhibitionism, gossip, touchiness, how many lies small and great, how much over-sensitiveness, how many exaggerations would she not have to put up with before she had dominated all this by kindness! When she had occasion to praise a novice, it was for being 'far removed from the affected ways and childish behaviour of women, in no way inclined to scrupulosity, and very straightforward.' She was too familiar with the convent of the Incarnation not to know she would not find there the good, honest, 'ordinary' virtues she required of the Discalced Carmelites.

Appalled at the idea of finding herself 'in this Babylon' once more, she temporized and in spite of her resolute character, Teresa, whose courage never failed her, wondered if there might not be some way of escape. She had good reasons for not going immediately: P. Pedro Fernández's order reached her right in the midst of a reorganization of the convent of Medina del Campo. Was she to leave her nuns and the work she was doing there, to impose herself where neither her presence, nor fervour, good order nor peace was desired? She had logic on her side.

But one day when she was begging God's help for her brother Agustín, the most warlike of the handful of *conquistadores*, the one who seemed to forget, as he made war against the Araucanians in Chile, that he had to win heaven as well, she ventured to say:

'Lord, if I saw one of your brothers in such danger, what would I not do to save him?'

To this imprudent entreaty, Our Lord replied:

'Oh, daughter! daughter! Those in the Incarnation are my sisters and yet you delay! Take courage, and remember that I want it; it is not as difficult as you suppose. Resist no longer for my power is great!' [1]

Not only did Teresa hesitate no longer, but, in spite of the lateness of the hour and the coldness of the weather, she decided to set out immediately. How was she to find a means of transport? A water-carrier agreed to lend her two mules and in this way she covered the twenty leagues separating Medina del Campo from Ávila. [2]

While waiting to take up her functions at the convent of the Incarnation, she installed herself at St Joseph's where she enjoyed a delightful interval of peace. She took Ana de San Bartolomé, the little lay-sister, into her cell and found great joy in talking about Our Lord with this timid, simple girl who was yet so fervent and so intelligent. In her naïve way Ana said to the sisters:

'You are like angels. But the Mother Foundress is a seraphim aflame with the love of God and her neighbour.'

The Foundress, however, had chosen Ana de San Bartolomé to share her cell for the same reason that she had taken Ana de Jesús at Salamanca: both were heavy sleepers and Teresa was anxious that no one should witness her raptures which were sometimes accompanied by heavenly music.

On 6th October 1571 Mother Teresa of Jesus came to take up her office as prioress at the Incarnation. The Provincial, P. Ángel de Salazar, a Carmelite of the Mitigation, was to induct her.

[1] R. xx, p. 53. [2] B, vol. I, p. 461.

Perhaps he was tactless: the matter would no doubt have gone off better if the Foundress had been left free to act with her customary discretion.

The reading of the letters patent was received with jeers: one hundred and thirty women jealous of their liberty—for the best of them it was a case of wanting to serve Our Lord in *their* way, and for the others the undisguised wish not to be deprived of the delights of the parlour, of going out, of wearing trumpery worldly jewellery over the habit—protested with a single voice and claimed their right to vote.

The Vicar Provincial grew exasperated:

'In short, you won't have Mother Teresa of Jesus?'

Amid the unanimous cries of 'no,' however, was heard the voice of Doña Catalina de Castro:

'We want her and we love her!'

This energetic affirmation afforded a slight respite which was sufficient to rally to the cause of Teresa a few timid souls who had not dared to swim against the stream; they, forcing their way through the barrier of rebels who continued to vociferate, tried to enter the choir in procession, preceded by the crucifix and the new prioress, as the ceremonial demanded. But the opposition, momentarily put out of countenance, now strengthened its defence, and P. Salazar gesticulated and harangued in vain. Finally those who stood up for Mother Teresa and those who, shouting for all they were worth, cursed and abused her, came to blows.

The tumult and scandal were such that you might have thought the whole convent was tumbling about your ears: the police were sent for with all urgency.

Teresa of Jesus, the occasion of the tumult, strove to mollify P. Salazar's anger and made excuses for the rebels:

'It is not surprising. . . . It is very hard to force anyone, no matter who it is. . . .' [1]

With the help of the constables, the party of those trying to sing the *Te Deum* increased in numbers, the Mother Prioress was finally able to enter the choir and everyone followed her.

Teresa had remained so calm on this veritable battlefield, clasping tightly in her arms the statue of her father St Joseph, which had accompanied her on all her foundations, and in her compassion had so completely dominated all violence and vexation that she was able to go to Communion next day without going to confession first. The

[1] FR, L. IV, c. i.

hundred and thirty who all had on their conscience ill words, ill-natured blows or at least unchristian thoughts, were amazed:

'Was it possible that Teresa was a saint after all?'

When the first chapter was held, on entering the room where for twenty-seven years she had been 'an insignificant little nun,' she absent-mindedly went and sat down in the seat she had formerly occupied. Her forgetfulness caused her infectious laugh to ring out; the whole convent relaxed in general hilarity. How natural she was! And how humble!—admitted her enemies. And many whispered:

'She really is holy!'

No, she would not impose herself on these poor nuns who really had the right to choose their prioress, nor would she take upon herself to reform them by force. She was not going to domineer from the prioress's stall and bring about the rule of fear in the spacious and delightful house which she had formerly left with regret. . . .

At this moment she left the choir for a few minutes to return carrying a statue of Our Lady which was very beautiful, more than three feet high and magnificently attired in embroidered and brocaded silk. She put Our Lady in her place in the prioress's stall. She then gave her the keys and sat down at her feet.

'Ladies, here is your prioress: Our Lady of Mercy. . . .'

She spoke with so much sincerity, good sense and kindness that the hardest hearts melted 'like wax in the sun.' [1]

She remembered that she was a daughter of this house and that she was suffering as much as her sisters from the imposition which made her prioress against their will. But was it not her duty, as it was that of all of them, to obey prelates?

'I am here only to serve you and to make things as pleasant as I can. I hope Our Lord will help me to do this. . . . As to the rest, any single one among you can help me to reform myself. Don't be afraid of my Rule for although it's true I've been living with the Discalced, I think I know, by the grace of God, how one should live among those who are not of that condition. My desire is that we should all serve Our Lord in sweetness. . . .' [2]

In this way she infused feminine charm into the application of one of her principles which rings out with the boldness of a statesman's maxim: 'Moderation in government is a great thing.' [3]

---

[1] MP quoted SEC, vol. II, p. 107.
[2] SEC, vol. II, p. 216.   [3] Sb, F, c. xviii–6.

IX

'A PRIORESS INDEED . . .'

'MAY the Holy Spirit be with Your Grace, and may he show you as much charity as you displayed promptitude in bringing us Don Francisco's alms!'[1]

It was in these terms that Mother Teresa thanked the steward of Francisco de Salcedo, who had just sent her an important consignment of poultry. Sixty-two birds: 'But the poverty of this house is such, there are so many sick people that all that was very necessary.'[2]

The holy gentleman had constituted himself purveyor to the convent of the Incarnation as he was to St Joseph's: vegetables and chickens from his farm, bottles of *aloja*, the drink made of honey and spices which those suffering from fever appreciated so greatly, came to the two convents in abundance. The tiniest salad or basket of quinces filled Teresa of Jesus with joy and gratitude; the convent of the Incarnation was so wretchedly poor that the number of nuns and, still more, of secular persons had greatly diminished, for P. Rubeo, the Master General, had forbidden them to receive novices: they would have been in danger of dying of hunger there.

And so the new prioress began by transforming herself into a kind of quartermaster-sergeant: had not the first miracle of Our Lord Jesus Christ been to give wine to the guests at a wedding? Did he not give bread and fish to the multitudes who followed him on the mountain? Did he not put the petition for our daily bread before that for the forgiveness of our sins or for protection against all evil? Man does not feed 'on bread alone,' but it is right and proper that he should receive his just portion of it.

The Mother Foundress, who had established her Reform on a basis of nuns earning their daily bread and who scolded prioresses who contented themselves with merely making known the fact that they were in need, found herself constrained to appeal to charity to feed these hundred and thirty nuns who were too poor to provide for themselves and too aristocratic to work with their fingers. Before they could be reformed they must be fed: it was hunger that was largely responsible

[1] CTA, xli. [2] Idem.

for the disorder in this miniature world of the convent of the Incarnation; it was in order to avoid starvation that the nuns often went off to their families for months at a time, or perhaps to stay with one or other of the convent's rich benefactors; the reason they flocked so eagerly to the parlours was because there was as much opportunity to stave off one's hunger there by munching the dainties brought by one's visitors, as there was to chatter.

The Duchess of Alba, Doña María de Mendoza, Doña Magdalena de Ulloa—who was known as God's almoner, for she had given more than five hundred silver ciboria to the churches of the Asturias and more than 16,000 ducats for the redemption of captives—played the rôle of Providence at regular intervals, but this did not deter Teresa from asking her sister Juana, whose resources were very modest, for a few reales for her own subsistence: from the convent stores she took only her bread and considered even that was taking too much.

Poor Juana boasted of the prosperity of her farm-yard that year! 'Send us some turkeys, since you have so many.' [1] Teresa scrutinized the accounts and signed the book of expenses daily; the strictly necessary must be considered fully sufficient, for the convent was in debt: it was essential to pay the debts, and they were paid and paid in full.

The Foundress sent for Isabel de la Cruz, formerly Isabel Arias, from Valladolid. Like herself, Isabel was a former member of the community of the Incarnation and knew the spirit of the convent. Assisted by her as sub-prioress, 'with a proper measure of diplomacy' [2] she set on foot the necessary reforms gradually and gently. She treated the nuns like restive fillies, pulled on the reins, but did not fail to offer a morsel of sugar hidden in the palm of her hand. To the poorest, those who had no inheritance—there were eighty of them—she gave one real each week; they were as much amazed at her tact as at her kindness: this small sum of money restored the dignity of those who were poor, and made them independent, far more than their past liberties had ever done.

For the era of anarchy was over. For Lent Teresa abolished all visits, not even making an exception for parents. In that house it was a revolution. But the habitual visitors to the parlour would not take no for an answer. One gentleman, tired of hearing the extern sister answer that the nun whose 'devout gentleman' he was would not receive him, took with him to the very door of the monastery a group of young riders to whom he swore that even if he had to confront the prioress

[1] CTA, xxxvi.   [2] FR.

herself, they should all be admitted in triumph to the parlour. Accordingly he summoned Teresa of Jesus to come and speak with him.

The Foundress settled herself behind the grille, with her spinning-wheel—for she never stopped spinning, unless the visitor was a prelate—and without a word of impatience allowed him to continue to pour out his flood of abuse and ill words until his eloquence dried up of its own accord.

Then she spoke—a few words but unanswerable ones:

'In future Your Grace will leave this convent in peace. If Your Grace persists, I shall appeal to the King.'

The blusterer left the convent abashed and his friends were so much surprised at the tone in which he said: 'There's no trifling with Mother Teresa of Jesus and we shall have to give up the parlour . . .', [1] that they forbore to laugh at his discomfiture.

The report of this incident soon spread round the City of Saints and the saints approved.

From the very beginning of Lent the mortifications which the nuns spontaneously practised in the refectory were 'worthy of all admiration' [2]—the youngest brought Teresa the worldly trifles to which they were still attached—a ring, a mirror, a fan; these hundred and thirty women who had really had their youth taken from them, and who tried to snatch what they could of it at recreation time by worldly dancing, delighting in the latest songs and music, gradually came to prefer to all that the conversation about God, the angels, or heaven which their prioress enlivened with as much wit as spirituality.

'All this goes on in great peace. We should praise Our Lord for the change which has taken place in them. It's those who were the most rebellious who are now the most pleased and who show their pleasure most. There really are great servants of God here and all make progress.' [3] They no longer say: 'A change is worse than death. . . .' [4]

Teresa was sad in spite of her success: she longed for her reformed convents where a round dozen of sisters in perfect recollection obeyed every stroke of the bell and lived in silence. Ávila's icy climate suited her so ill that she could not understand how she came to be born there. Moreover, the dignified simplicity of social relationships seemed to have disappeared in the City of the Knights as it had in the rest of Spain, the most insignificant *hidalgo* now insisted on being addressed

---

[1] Idem.   [2] Idem.
[3] CTA, xxxiv.   [4] CTA, xxxi.

as 'Don': 'In Ávila now, one finds nothing else than that and it is disgraceful. . . .'[1]

Now it is necessary to address as Illustrious those who were formerly called Magnificent. . . . It's almost necessary to erect a faculty where they teach us how to address the people to whom we write and how we should speak to them; in some cases the margin has to be placed on one side, in others on the other. . . . I've seen so many complete changes in these matters that I no longer know how to go on. . . . I pity spiritual persons who for the highest of reasons are obliged to live in the world: they have a heavy cross to bear. . . .[2]

The seething agitation at the convent of the Incarnation was more painful to her than the trouble of her foundations. She had to be ceaselessly on her guard and had no one in whom she could confide. She who was by nature so spontaneous, in this convent experienced nothing but tension and constraint. The whole time she was loved and honoured by some, suspected or decried by others. At that time it was hardly thought fitting for a woman to display so much energy. Quite recently the Dominican Provincial had asked P. Báñez:

'Who is this Teresa of Jesus of whom they tell me that she's very attached to you? It doesn't do to rely on the virtue of women. . . .'[3]

'Your Paternity is going to Toledo, there you will be able to see her and discover for yourself that it is with reason she is held in high esteem. . . .'

In Toledo, the Provincial, Juan de Salinas, saw her more or less continually throughout Lent and heard her confession nearly every day. He cleverly contrived not to eat his words by declaring to P. Báñez:

'You informed me wrongly when you told me that Mother Teresa was a woman; i' faith she's a man and one of those most worthy to wear a beard.'

This Father showed that he did not know much about women: for Teresa of Jesus was never other than womanly in all her struggles just as much as she was in the intense manifestations of her love of God. But at that time men were little disposed to admit that women had any capacity at all for strength or wisdom. It took both Teresa and her daughters to convince another Dominican, the appointed Apostolic Visitor of the Discalced Carmelites, P. Pedro Fernández, that they were capable of living in accordance with evangelical perfection.

---

[1] CTA, xciii.   [2] Sb, V, c. xxxvii–10, 11.
[3] SST, vol. II, p. 505.

It was not one of the Mother Foundress's least merits that she proved by her example and that of the Carmelites she formed, that 'heroic deeds' are not incompatible with charm and graciousness.

When Teresa exclaimed in protest: 'From foolish devotions may the good Lord deliver us,' she did not attribute such things solely to women, any more than she assigned to them the exclusive prerogative of the 'childish nonsense,' superstition, scruples, pettiness for which she blamed them: in her eyes the 'most serious of men' were not free from such things. In men as in women she complained of unfaithfulness in little things, of self-complacency, blaming such matters all the more severely in those who in that age were the nation's warriors.

> In the case of insignificant little women like myself, weak and possessing but little courage, it seems to me that it is what one would expect that God should grant them to taste of his sweetness. . . . But when I see servants of God, men of weight, learned, intelligent, making a fuss because God does not give them devotion, I am, I must say, disappointed. If Our Lord grants it to them, of course, let them receive it and esteem it highly . . . but if they lack it, they must not be troubled and must understand that since His Majesty does not grant it to them, it is not necessary for them, and let them remain masters of themselves . . . many have begun but never persevere to the end; it is, I think, largely the fact of not embracing the cross from the beginning that makes them distressed for it seems to them that they do nothing. What His Majesty wants are our acts of will. But the afflictions for which we ourselves are responsible only disturb our souls; if such persons cannot make progress in one hour, four will make no difference to them. . . .[1]

Mother Teresa's spirit of determination, her courage in the face of reality, whether in the spiritual sphere or the material, was no masculine prerogative but that of a great mind and a fine character.

The Visitor, P. Fernández, esteemed the Foundress very highly, a fact which he concealed from her as much as he could. Grumbler as he was, he pleased Teresa of Jesus who liked those who treated her without indulgence: 'He keeps me alive, I do not think he is mistaken about me as others are, for God has made him see what a trifling thing I am; at each step, he catches me in some imperfection and this is a great consolation to me; and I do my best to let him know all of them.'[2]

Perhaps this great humility conquered the Apostolic Visitor's intransigence. Although when he spoke to her he did nothing but

[1] Sb, V, c. xi–14.   [2] CTA, xxx.

blame, he sang her praises when he had to argue about her with the Duchess of Alba, who wanted her at Alba de Tormes. 'The hundred and thirty nuns at the Incarnation all live together in as much peace and holiness as the ten or twelve in your convent. This has greatly surprised and pleased me. And it is solely due to the Foundress's presence. If she were missing for a single day, all that has been gained here would be lost. . . .'[1]

If Teresa had known about this letter, she would have replied in the same phrase as she used in writing to Doña María de Mendoza: 'It's my prioress who is working these wonders!'[2]

In point of fact Our Lady of Mercy had remained in the prioress's stall where Teresa had put her on the first day. Every evening it was to her she gave the keys of the convent. In the sub-prioress's place she had put St Joseph. The nuns accused this good saint of revealing all their small imperfections to the Foundress and so they christened his statue 'the chatterer' (*el parlero*) and alleged that St Joseph's mouth was always open. Our Lord began to bestow so many graces on this house that the Mother of God appeared there, in her prioress's stall, surrounded by her company of angels; she remained throughout the singing of the *Salve Regina*.

And then, so that the last might be first and her 'poor dears at the Incarnation' might have expert guidance along the royal road of mental prayer, Teresa gave them Fray John of the Cross as confessor.

She sent for him urgently from Pastrana, where he had been brought with haste from Alcalá to teach the Prince of Éboli's friars that moderation was a virtue. Wherever there was some great and difficult task to be done, Fray John was sent for urgently.

The friars of Pastrana 'seemed men of stone rather than flesh.' They spurred one another on and the church re-echoed with the sound of the blows with which they struck their breasts; when the spirit moved them or when they were inflamed with a kind of mad fervour, they could not restrain their cries, whether it was a matter of the public avowal of their sins or of a manifestation of their love of God. Some were so abundantly endowed by Our Lord with the gift of weeping that the flow of their continual tears carved deep furrows on their wrinkled and ascetic faces.

Mortifications, penances, disciplines were carried to the point of madness. Matters grew to such a pitch that the bare back of a novice was scourged as he knelt in front of a pile of unseasoned wood, in the expectation that fire from heaven would unfailingly come down if the

[1] Quoted SEC, vol. II, p. 247.   [2] CTA, xxxiv.

novice were very holy or very well beaten. Had that not happened in the case of the prophet Elias, father and model of all the Discalced?

Their feet were so tumefied by the cold and wounded by the stones 'that they were like egg plants. A newcomer, Fray Jerónimo de la Madre de Dios, discouraged, despite his zeal, by such violence and roughness, was on the point of giving up his vocation as a Carmelite.' [1]

Fray John of the Cross had been commissioned to restore some sense of measure and moderation to these fanatics. He displayed so much skill in turning this mad zeal to nobler ends that Mother Teresa judged that no one would be better able to excite fervour in lukewarm nuns than he would. This Father seemed to her to be the man who always struck the right chord.

[1] JGP, Dial. 1, p. 21.

X

CHRIST'S BRIDE

'LADIES, I'm giving you as your confessor a Father who is a saint!'[1]

It was in these terms that the prioress, Mother Teresa of Jesus, introduced to the convent of the Incarnation, the little dark man emaciated by penances: Fray John of the Cross. Although he was thirty he seemed a very young man, so clear and pure was the look in his dark eyes. 'His bearing was calm and extremely modest, his mere presence was an invitation to composure. His countenance reflected something regal that was not of this world, and he inspired love and respect at the same time.'[2]

The Foundress had had a small hut built for him outside the enclosure but in the immediate vicinity of the convent: he had no time to lose in going to and fro; the work was considerable and urgent: the confessions of one hundred and thirty nuns to be heard at least once a fortnight besides their direction, ranging from the choice of their reading to orientation in the ways of spirituality.

And they had to be led individually: the Foundress and Fray John had the greatest respect for the liberty of souls: each one had her own particular way. 'Our Lord gives each soul its own grace, in that I do not interfere.'[3] No collective methods then, but detailed personal direction, save for the indication of the great lines of mental prayer and in the observance of the essential virtues, love, humility, obedience, silence. 'A soul under constraint cannot serve God well, and it is through that that the devil tempts them,'[4] said the Mother.

Fray John of the Cross echoed her words:

'It is better to leave expressions of love to develop naturally and fully, in order that each one may profit by them in her own way and according to the abundance of grace. . . .'[5]

The nuns of the Incarnation were thus called to a state of union with God, but in perfect freedom: the Foundress showed them the joys of this state and Fray John the difficulties. He wanted souls to reach the very summit of spirituality even if everything collapsed or

---

[1] BRJ, p. 130.   [2] JJ, p. 786.   [3] Sb, V, c. xxii–8.
[4] CTA, cccli.   [5] JCC, Prologue.

crashed about their ears, even if events did not justify their expectations: to disturb oneself effects nothing. . . .[1]

He subdivided mental prayer into three parts:

1. An imaginative representation of the mysteries on which one is to meditate;

2. An intellectual consideration of the mysteries represented;

3. A loving rest in and attention to God. That was where one gathered the fruit, where the door of the mind opened to divine illumination. One passed from natural to supernatural knowledge when the soul put itself into this state of rest which was peaceful, loving and calm at the same time.[2]

Representation, consideration, illumination, love: the Foundress, in counterpoint, illustrated the theory of what he said by realistic images:

'I am sure that Our Lord is not displeased that we should find delight and consolation in contemplating his actions and meditating on his words, just as a king would be delighted to see a good little shepherd boy naïvely look at and admire his rich brocades and wonder what this can be and how that was made. . . .'[3]

Fray John insisted on strict control of the imagination, for contemplation must not be confused with the fantasies of the humours or melancholy. And in this matter, too, he was in agreement with Mother Teresa. He blamed all seeking for sensations, and affirmed that far from being a sign of perfection in mental prayer, the pleasures found therein are a sign of weakness. And if he spoke to them 'of the multitude of sweetness which God has hidden for those who fear him and of the torrents of delight which he will give them to drink,' it was in order that they might feel more surely 'the weight of glory to which the Bridegroom predestined you, on the particular day of eternity when he decided to create you. . . .'[4]

The weight of glory. . . . The Foundress was not exempt from the severities of the confessor of the convent of the Incarnation. She in no way sought to elude them but accepted them in all humility although to tease rather than to mortify her, Fray John one day said to her:

'When you make your confession, Mother, you have a fine way of excusing yourself. . . .'[5]

There is even reason to suppose that he was more severe for the prioress than for the most insignificant nun in the convent: was she

---

[1] JCS. [2] JJ, p. 517. [3] Sb, CAD, c. i-8.
[4] JCC, c. xxxviii. [5] SST, vol. II, p. 390, n. 1.

not herself more severe towards those she loved most? When Office was over, the confessor ordered Mother Teresa to remain on her knees long hours in the chapel: she had to repent of experiencing too much delight in the love of Our Lord, those *gustos*, those pleasures that she was the first to proscribe. She bowed herself down in prayer and wept as much for the graces God showered upon her as for her sins. Yet what could she do about it? She in no way sought visions or other divine manifestations and did not solicit either the words she heard or the delights she experienced. God loved her, he had chosen her and drawn her to himself almost by force in this very convent more than twenty years ago, while she was still vacillating between heaven and earth; she was as little responsible for those raptures of the spirit as the water when the sun absorbs it and changes it into clouds.

What did Fray John think on Palm Sunday when Teresa, as she communicated, was seized with rapture to such an extent that she could not swallow the Host? When she recovered consciousness her mouth was full of blood which was running down her face—the very blood of Redemption—she experienced an overwhelming sweetness and Our Lord said to her: 'Daughter, I will that my blood be profitable to you. . . . I shed it for you in great pain, make your greatest delight of it. This is my way of returning the invitation which you have always made me on this day.' [1]

For more than thirty years it had been Teresa's custom to communicate on Palm Sunday to prepare her soul to give Jesus a place of sanctuary: 'the cruelty of the Jews towards him seemed to me so great, they had allowed him to go so far away to eat after having given him such a great welcome, that I prepared myself so that he might dwell with me.' [2] On that day she took no food until three o'clock in the afternoon and gave her portion to the poor.

Could Fray John be displeased with such simple tenderness? Despite the fact that her thirst was slaked with blood from the chalice, that she was fed with bread by the hands of Christ himself, drawn close to the Father who spoke 'very pleasant words' [3] to her, jealous, indeed, of Mary Magdalene but consoled by the Son of God: 'she was my friend while I was on earth; it is you I have chosen now I am in heaven' [4]—despite all this he whom the Foundress called 'my little Seneca' was none the less cautious: these emotions and visions seemed to him too earthy: for him 'the soul, unified and transformed by

---

[1] SEC, R, xxvi, pp. 56-7.   [2] Idem.
[3] SEC, R, xxv, p. 56.   [4] SEC, vol. II, p. 61, n. 1.

abundance of heavenly gifts and riches,'[1] must have 'subjected the passions and mortified the natural appetites.'

Fray John considered that Teresa was still too fond of these joys; and so, out of love, he let nothing pass which he judged to be an imperfection, just as a lapidary lets nothing pass in the diamond he cuts. And so he ended by drawing her away from the matrix-ore of these *gustos*, which too closely resembled this world's joys. And he caused the precious stone to sparkle with the fire that leaps up to meet the light which shines in the darkness and which man will never know until he is reborn of God alone.

One morning at the time of Communion, John of the Cross 'broke the host to give part to another sister,' said Teresa. 'I thought he did so to mortify me, not through want of hosts: I had told him how much I loved big hosts although I knew quite well that Our Lord was wholly present in the smallest particle. His Majesty said to me: "Fear nothing, daughter, nothing can separate you from me." He made me understand that that did not matter.'

Then he appeared to me in an imaginary vision, as he had done before, but in the very depths of my being. He gave me his right hand and said to me: 'Look at this nail: it is the sign that from to-day you are my bride. Until now you had not merited that; in future you will be jealous for my honour not only because I am your Creator and your King, but as my true bride. My honour is yours: your honour is mine.'

The action of this grace was so powerful that I remained out of my senses. I was as it were stupefied and asked Our Lord to enlarge my littleness or else not to give me such an immense favour, for my natural weakness could not bear it. I spent that day in a state of inebriation. Great benefits have come from it since, but also an increase of confusion and distress, for I do not serve as I ought to serve after having received such a great grace.[2]

Such was the mystical marriage of Teresa of Jesus. Her sisters, greatly moved by seeing such marvels in their convent, never again approached the Communion grille, 'blessed bridal couch of such espousals,'[3] otherwise than with awe.

Fray John had cut the slender but still solid thread which bound Teresa to her own will; free at last from the weight of dead matter, detached from herself, bound by no desires, she had accomplished her transfiguration.

[1] JCC, c. xi. [2] SEC, R, xxv, pp. 63–4.
[3] SEC, vol. II, p. 111.

She gave expression to the ardent bonds of love of this mystical marriage in her *Conceptos del Amor de Dios*, or *Thoughts on the Love of God*.

Everything goes to prove that she wrote these clear, impassioned pages at Ávila.[1] It was at Ávila that Our Lord said to her: 'Do not fail to write down the teaching which I give you, so that you do not forget it. You greatly desire to have the teaching of men in writing: why do you think it is waste of time to write down that which I give you? A day will come when you will need it.'[2]

From the first pages of the *Conceptos* she emphasized her act of obedience to the divine command by answering Our Lord's question directly: 'I hold well employed the time which I shall devote to treating of a matter so divine that I do not deserve to hear it.'[3]

From the account of her visions and certain passages of the *Conceptos* there emerges a dialogue between bride and Bridegroom, and sometimes she likes to remind him of the most wonderful of his promises:

Christ: My honour is yours, your honour is mine!
Teresa: He will take charge of my affairs and I of his![4]
God the Father: I have given you my Son, the Holy Spirit and the blessed Virgin here. What can you give me?[5]
Teresa: What can I do for my Bridegroom? What could anyone so clumsy as I do? Waste the graces you have given me. . . .[6]
Christ: Do you imagine, daughter, that to be in a state of joy is meritorious? The only way to merit is to act, to suffer and to love.[7]
Teresa: Stay me up with flowers. It does not seem to me that that is asking for death, but more to consecrate one's life to serve him to whom one owes so much. . . .[8] Let Bridegroom and bride be no longer two but one single will, not so much in words or desires but in acts.

Such was indeed the case. In future Teresa's sole delight would be to act for the Bridegroom and with him, in voluntary renouncement of pure contemplation:

[1] P. Silverio de Santa Teresa dates the *Conceptos* between 1571 and 1573 at Ávila, Salamanca or Medina del Campo. P. Bruno assigns to them the year 1574. But the likeness between this book and the spiritual notes made at Ávila during the time she was prioress at the Incarnation is too great for it to be possible not to admit that it stems directly from them. Moreover, is not this commentary on the *Canticle of Canticles* the very panegyric of the mystical marriage? She must have written it towards the end of her stay in Ávila and perhaps finished it at Segovia.

[2] SEC, R, xxviii, p. 58
[3] Sb, CAD, c. i–8.
[4] Sb, CAD, c. iv–8.
[5] SEC, R, xxv, p. 56.
[6] Sb, CAD, c. iv–11.
[7] SEC, R, xxxvi, p. 64.
[8] Sb, CAD, c. vii–1.

The soul asks that she may accomplish great things in the service of Our Lord and of her neighbour and for that she is more than content to forgo her pleasures. For although they fully understand all they will lose in this existence which is more active than contemplative, Martha and Mary never fail to act almost simultaneously when the soul is in this state. One's contemplative life expands into activities which seem exterior and when the works of the active life spring from this root they produce lovely and fragrant flowers: they spring from this tree of the love of God alone, for him alone, without anything of self-interest and the fragrance of these flowers spreads all around, for the good of many: it is a fragrance which does not evaporate quickly and it produces great effects.[1]

Contemplation was no longer to be an end in itself: it was becoming a force for action, in action.

And because Teresa of Jesus no longer sought for anything but the Kingdom of God, all the rest was added unto her: efficacious action and joy.

Despite the calm and peaceful tone which she forces herself to adopt in these *Thoughts on the Love of God*, a commentary on the *Canticle of Canticles* written for the nuns of the Incarnation—this much can be surmised from the precautions she takes not to discourage, by making too many demands, those who are not yet entirely detached from the world, and from the circumspection, delicate tact and discreet allusions to which she has recourse to detach them from it —her bridal love breaks out and is carried away on the tide of the Bridegroom's love:

> . . . A sort of divine intoxication, oblivious of what it wants, what it says, what it demands. . . .[2] He wants to fill her to over-flowing, to delight her still more, he changes her into himself, and like all those who faint away through excess of pleasure and joy, she remains as it were unconscious in the divine arms and on the divine breast. She no longer cares for anything except to abandon herself to joy, nourished by the divine milk. . . . This heavenly inebriation by which she is delighted and terrified at the same time . . . this holy madness. . . . *Thy breasts are better than wine* . . .[3] entirely saturated in the ineffable greatness of God. . . . My Bridegroom, a single drop of the precious wine which you give me makes me forget every created thing. . . . Let me gaze at my Beloved and he at me. . . . I beseech you, O God, by the blood of your Son, to give me this grace: *Kiss me with a kiss of your mouth!* [4] . . . And what can I do for my Bridegroom? [5]

---

[1] Sb, CAD, c. vii–3.
[2] Sb, CAD., c. v.
[3] CC.
[4] Idem.
[5] Sb, CAD, c. v.

The younger nuns at the Incarnation badly needed to purify their idea of love in this way. At first they had irritated Teresa considerably by their tittering: they were mature in years but had never really grown up:

'I remember having heard a wonderful sermon on these delights of the bride in her intercourse with God; there was so much laughter and what the preacher said was so very much misunderstood, because he spoke of love, that I was appalled.' [1]

Teresa was like the woman of Samaria 'who so well understood Our Lord's words and took them to heart that she left Our Lord himself to go and bring the people of her village to him and as a reward for her great charity she merited to see the great good which he wrought in that place. The holy Samaritan woman inebriated with the wine of God, went through the streets crying aloud. At last they listened to her and the number of those who went to Our Lord was very great.' [2]

Teresa wrote the *Conceptos*, her expressions of love, at the order of her Bridegroom, Christ, but with the authorization of her confessor. Fray John of the Cross knew all about the work, discussed it with her, and his answer to this mysticism of love issuing in action was the arguments which he was later to develop on this same theme of the *Canticle of Canticles* in his *Cántico Espiritual*; but he gave pride of place to Mary rather than to Martha:

When the soul has reached this state of loving union, it is not fitting that she should busy herself with external actions even for God's service, for this may fetter her in this life of love in him. For a little of this pure love is more precious in his eyes and for the soul—even though it seems one is doing nothing—than all other actions put together. That is why Mary Magdalene hid herself in the desert for thirty years to give herself wholly to this love. . . . Consequently, when a soul has in herself a particle of this high state of solitary love, to occupy her in external or active things, however important, and even if only for a short time, would be to do her great harm. [3]

The spiritual marriage of Teresa of Jesus, the state of soul which resulted from it, to which she gave expression in the *Thoughts on the Love of God*, mark the difference between the mystical way followed by the prioress and that followed by her confessor. For her, to love was to act. For him, to love was to immerse oneself completely in contemplation.

The difference, however, in no way impaired their deep communion of thought. Teresa was fully aware that she owed much to the

[1] Sb, CAD, i–5. [2] Sb, CAD, c. cvii—6. [3] JCC, c. xxviii.

spirit and virtue which Our Lord had given Fray John,[1] ' people consider him a saint and in my opinion he is one and has been all his life.' He was then and always the Father of her soul. As to him, it is touching to see him turning gradually towards action after the Mother Foundress's death, as if he did not want to lose anything of that precious heritage. The directives which he gave to prioresses were framed so closely upon those of Mother Teresa that he even borrowed her homely expressions: ' Watch carefully whom you accept in the beginning for those who come afterwards will be like them. . . . Tell the sisters that since Our Lord has chosen them as the first stones of the building they must take care as to what sort of people they really are. . . . In a beginning like this, let them set out anew along the way of perfection, in all humility and detachment both within and without, not childishly, but with a stout heart.' [2]

Mother Teresa would have smiled tenderly had she read her little Seneca's letter to Ana de San Alberto, Prioress of Caravaca: 'I am in Seville, busy with the removal of our sisters who have bought a very suitable house; although it has cost 14,000 ducats, it is worth more than 20,000. They are installed there and the Cardinal will place the Blessed Sacrament there with all solemnity on the feast of St Barnabas. I intend to establish another house of friars here before I leave. . . . About the feast of St John, I leave for Ecija where by the grace of God we shall found another, then I go to Málaga and finally to the *junta*. . . .'

Thus Fray John also became a Father Founder.

Distinct both in temperament and in their ideas of the mystical life, Teresa and John become identical when they are carried beyond themselves by the flight of the spirit.

In the little parlour of the Incarnation with its red-tiled floor, prioress and confessor often spoke together. About the state of soul of his spiritual daughters, Fray John could be as precise as the Foundress usually was. On the subject of spiritual illuminations Teresa could be as free from all earthly bonds as Fray John.

One day—it was the feast of the Holy Trinity—seated one each side of the grille, he on a chair and she on her bench, they were speaking of the essence of the Three Persons in One, 'this marvellous operation,' [3] when Beatriz de Ocampo, who was looking for the prioress, saw her on her bench indeed and Fray Juan in his chair, but both in ecstasy and Fray John, borne upwards by the flight of the spirit, was touching the ceiling.

---

[1] CTA, x.   [2] JC quoted SEC, vol. VI, p. 213.
[3] SEC, R, xxxiii, p. 62.

But both knew that perfection does not consist in such wonders.

'Humility, always humility,' said Teresa of Jesus. And John of the Cross echoed: 'Humility.'

The 'poor little nuns of the Incarnation' thus travelled along the path to heaven guided by one who was 'heavenly and divine,' Fray John. P. Pedro Fernández, taking advantage of this situation, did not let the Mother Foundress rest. He sent her to Alba de Tormes, recalled her to Ávila and finally sent her back to Salamanca to transfer the nuns to a new house. P. Antonio de Jesús was commissioned to accompany her, as well as a few nuns—quite a little escort—and naturally, Julian de Ávila. Once more in Ávila people would talk of nothing else but Teresa of Jesus and Julian! Teresa laughed heartily over it.

It was August and to avoid the heat they decided to start at nightfall.

Things began badly: first Antonio de Jesús, and then a servant girl, fell head foremost from their mounts.

And afterwards it was not much better. Julian de Ávila gave an amusing account of the journey to anyone who cared to listen:

It was very dark, the donkey which was carrying the money intended for Salamanca got lost and could not be found in the darkness; with all our searching and the falls we had in the pitch-black night, it was after midnight when we reached the inn. Next morning, a servant went out to look for the donkey we had lost and found her lying on the side of the path: her load was intact.

The next night we lost much more than the donkey, although she was said to be carrying five hundred ducats. . . .

What did he mean?—They lost Mother Teresa in person.

It was still dark and we were travelling in two groups: the one our holy Mother was with, and for the sake of their honour I won't say of whom it consisted, left her in the street of a little village, asking her to wait for us, and went off before the others; but when it came to finding the Foundress again, they couldn't remember where they had left her.

We kept on asking each other: 'Is the Mother with you?'

They replied: 'No!'

'She is with *you* then?'

'She was with us, but she isn't now. Where has she gone?'

We were thus in every kind of gloom and darkness, that of the night, which was thick, and that which was much darker still of finding ourselves without our Mother. We didn't know what to do: should we go forward or go back? We separated once more, some to look for her whom we had lost, others to call her with great cries in the hope that she would answer us from one point or another.

'Madre Teres–a–a–a–a–a!'

'Madre Teresa de Jes–ú–u–u–u–s!'

After a long time of suspense and anguish we saw our Mother coming with her companion and a peasant whom she had got out of his house and induced to set them on the right road by giving him four reales. He went back very pleased with his money and we still more so at having recovered all our riches, and merry at having these adventures to tell.

We stumbled upon an inn so overcrowded with muleteers that they were even sleeping on the ground, and it was impossible to take one step without treading on harness or on sleeping men. At last we found a small space for our holy Mother and the sisters we were bringing with us, although there were not six feet of empty space; to fit in at all they were obliged to stand up. Such inns had one good point about them, that we impatiently awaited the hour of our departure. . . .[1]

At Salamanca Mother Teresa was busy with the reconstruction of a house which was destined later to cause them a lot of trouble, but what did it matter? They had to provide for present necessities. More than twenty workmen erected 'more than two hundred yards of partitions,'[2] to make the cells and enclosures. The Mother Foundress directed operations and the workmen found, as she herself thought, 'that experience had given her a good knowledge of these matters.'[3]

She had the art of infusing any work with encouragement; Pedro Hernández, the head carpenter, told all his life afterwards how Mother Teresa would sometimes appear at the top of a skylight giving orders that all the workmen were to be brought something to drink. One day, he considered that her generosity was involving her in too much expense—a measure of wine cost a real and a half—so he sent only for a maravedi's worth and poured it out sparingly, but when he poured what he thought was the last drop, the jar was still full.[4]

Their thirst slaked with miraculous wine, how could workmen and masons be lacking in courage?

When this house was finished, there were fresh departures and fresh arrivals: Alba de Tormes, Medina del Campo, finally Ávila but for a very short time, for the turmoil over the foundations which had died down for the past three years was to begin again.

[1] JA quoted SEC, vol. VI, pp. 148–9.   [2] CTA, xlvii.,
[3] Idem, 41.   [4] SEC, vol. V p. 157, n. 2.

XI

THE SHADOW OF THE GRAND
INQUISITOR

MOTHER Teresa set out for Segovia carefree: all the indications for this foundation were good. The less attention she attracted, the better she felt on these journeys and this time she had with her only Fray John of the Cross, Julian de Avila, Isabel de Jesús—the nun who sang the *cantarcillo* at Salamanca—and a layman, Antonio Gaytán[1] : only four companions but very capable ones.

A widower and a man of some means, Antonio Gaytán had developed such a zeal for the reformed Carmel and Mother Teresa, that he had begged her to make use of him for whatever the Order needed: it was not necessary to use this sort of language twice to the Mother Foundress and from that moment Antonio Gaytán had no respite. He put a duenna at the head of his household, entrusting her with the upbringing of his daughters, and went off to accompany Teresa of Jesus.

As they went along the road he learnt principles of spirituality adapted to the needs of the daily life of a good layman: as Teresa saw things, just as in the world there are different climates, seasons and changes of weather, so the needs of each one's spiritual life vary according to temperament and occupation. She reassured him when he complained of the slow progress he made in prayer: 'Don't be in any way troubled about it, that is not your fault. . . .'[2] 'Don't tire yourself out by too much thinking, don't be distressed by your failures in meditation. The greatest grace God gives us is that of praising him without ceasing, and to do all we can that others may praise him. . . .'[3]

She had a dangerous mission for him: the secret removal—we might almost say abduction—of the fourteen nuns of the convent of Pastrana, victims of the extraordinary Ana de Mendoza y la Cerda, Princess of Eboli.

The Prince had died a year before. His wife had not been able to resign herself to being a widow like other widows: she took the Carmelite habit in Madrid—a habit which she had had patched

[1] Sb, F, c. xxi–4.　　　[2] CTA, lxvi.　　　[3] Idem.

beforehand—from the hands of the same priest who had given the Last Sacraments to her husband whom she loved to such an extent that she would have preferred not to survive him. Leaving in the lurch the pledges of this love, her ten children, she got into a completely closed cart, in imitation of the holy Mother Teresa, and, renouncing Satan, who did not, however, renounce her, she set off for Pastrana.

When the prioress, Isabel de Santo Domingo, was informed of her arrival in the middle of the night, she exclaimed:

'The Princess in the convent! This house is lost!'[1]

She did not come alone: like the widows of India who climbed on to the funeral pyre with all their suite, she brought a number of girls, her maids, and demanded that they should be admitted to the novitiate with her.

She demanded. All the woman knew was how to demand. A strange way for a Carmelite to talk. But this was only the beginning.

For Sister Ana de la Madre de Dios—such was the name she took in religion—neither rules, Constitutions nor bells existed and still less did she dream of obeying in the slightest degree. Her idea was to speak when she wanted to, receive visitors, go out; she had her cell made to communicate with the street. She insisted on being treated with all the honours due to her rank, ill-treated the prioress and openly snapped her fingers at chaplains, confessors and visitors:

'What have friars to do with *my* convent?'

In the end she caused so much scandal that they had to tell her it was too great an honour for a poor convent to have her among them and that the court alone was worthy of her: and this Isabel de Santo Domingo made her understand, politely, but firmly.

Ana de Mendoza, so-called of the Mother of God, did not fail to understand the meaning which lay behind these courteous words, exclaimed that they were turning her out and appealed to the King; she found herself put in her place once more, and this time with less regard for her feelings, in the world of sinful women who were only half repentant: Philip II, beside himself, now called her 'a notorious female.'

'Your first duty', he intimated to her, 'is to look after your children.'

Once back in her palace she sought for something to amuse her and found it: to persecute the poor Discalced nuns; the least of her cruelties was to suppress the revenue which she had undertaken to give them, which was tantamount to imposing famine upon them, for nobody could help them in this isolated village.

[1] SEC, vol. V, p. 139, n. 4.

Mother Teresa with her sympathetic nature felt the sufferings of her nuns keenly and if she only took one sister for the Segovia foundation, it was because she intended to bring the Princess of Eboli's victims there.

Everything augured very well indeed for the new convent: a 'great servant of God,' Doña Ana de Jimena, had a house ready where the first Mass could be said immediately. The Mother arrived as usual *sin blanca*, but Providence would not fail to provide for the purchase of a suitable and permanent house: the good Lord had never failed them yet.

And so Teresa of Jesus was musing over these details, as one likes to do in a carriage bearing one swiftly towards an objective the fulfilment of which is already in sight, when Julian de Ávila came and asked her to let him see how the document in which the Bishop authorized her to found this convent was drawn up.

'A document? I haven't one. Isn't a Bishop's verbal authorization sufficient?'

The mules had difficulty in climbing the steep slopes of the Guadarrama, the cart jolted violently and, in addition, Julian de Ávila began to be sulky and scold:

'The Bishop is away. It only wants the Vicar-General to be the sort of man who's particular about papers. . . . Anyhow, don't let's think any more about it!'

At Segovia they got into the house at nightfall. Next morning they rang their bell, Julian de Ávila said the first Mass and installed the Blessed Sacrament: whatever happened, the convent of St Joseph of the Carmel of Segovia was founded. But what a fright followed! The worthy chaplain, without any false pride, told the story:

The Vicar-General came in, and I never saw a man more angry. He shouted, wanting to know who had put the Blessed Sacrament there. The nuns had already withdrawn to the enclosure and as to myself, confronted with a rage like this, I took refuge under a staircase. The man happened to pick on Fray John of the Cross.

'Father, who has put *That* there? Take *That* away as quickly as possible, while I ask myself ought I to put you in prison or not?' [1]

He didn't do so because it was a friar, but if he had noticed a poor little ecclesiastic like me, I'm sure he would have sent me there.

The Foundress remained unmoved by this scene: she scarcely worried at all once the first Mass was said: all her worries were 'before.' She stood up to the Vicar-General with as much boldness as

[1] JA quoted SEC, vol. VI, p. 194.

courtesy. He did not dare to suppress the convent, but in order that his prohibition of the saying of Mass should be observed, he left a constable there who frightened everybody considerably.

The storm was violent but quickly over: it was possible to prove to the Vicar-General the authenticity of the verbal authorization given by the Bishop and everything was then in order.

That is to say Julian and Antonio Gaytan were free to set off on their expedition to Pastrana. They took five carts with them.

The nuns were ready. On Mother Teresa's advice, for some time now the prioress had made a note each time of everything the Princess gave them, both in the way of ordinary things and sacred vessels and vestments. Isabel de Santo Domingo, who was as great an expert in legal niceties as if she had practised nothing else all her life, sent for the *Corregidor* and a notary public and, inventory in hand, gave back everything which did not form part of the convent's original possessions: what was left of the poor nuns' belongings amounted to very little.

The two rescuers, priest and layman, scaled the walls in great secrecy, and, very excited at playing such an important part in an adventure where it might be said that heaven was in conflict with the court, slipped silently into the convent. The first thing was to consume the sacred species, then, fortified with the Bread of the strong, the nuns followed their rescuers in single file, walking on tiptoe and with the utmost caution, invoking God, but in their hearts alone. The silence which preceded dawn seemed like the silence of an ambush: anything might be expected from such a powerful and vindictive enemy. Good Padre Julian admitted that to escape as they were doing took more courage than if they had been able to make a frontal attack on their enemy.

The carts were waiting a good way off in order not to attract attention in the village. At last the fourteen nuns got in, and the fugitives were able to get away from Pastrana amid a great clatter of galloping mules, cracking of whips and shouting of muleteers.

With the exception that they were all nearly drowned crossing the Tormes which Julian de Ávila compared to the sea, they arrived at Segovia safe and sound after several days' rapid travelling along roads as hilly and uneven as any in the world.

Teresa was overjoyed and showed it and she appointed Isabel de Santo Domingo, who had given such magnificent proof of wisdom, courage and wit in her dealings with Doña Ana de Mendoza, prioress of the convent at Segovia.

And it was thought that the matter was ended.

But if the Princess had not sent her myrmidons in pursuit of a few poor nuns, it was because she was holding in reserve a more sensational revenge.

How did she know, at the time of the foundation of the houses in Pastrana, that Mother Teresa had written an account of her life? Teresa of Jesus kept this autobiography, which was written solely at the command of her confessors and for them alone, secret; she had been on her guard against letting slip the slightest hint of it to the Princess, more than in the case of anyone else. And how did it leak out that the Foundress had brought a copy with her? The imprudence— for her ill intention is not proven—of an Augustinian nun whom Ana de Mendoza had forced the Foundress to accept and who was indeed promptly sent away, was to blame. This excitable lady was seized with so violent a curiosity over the book that she did all she possibly could to get hold of and read it. She tried to coax Teresa, but the Foundress was firm and persisted in her refusal. Feeling herself snubbed, Ana got excited, stormed and appealed to Ruy Gómez who begged Teresa to give permission for the sake of peace: finally Ana did not hesitate to swear that no one but she and her husband would read it. Besides, why should they mind her seeing it so much? Had not her aunt, Doña Luisa de la Cerda, had a copy in her house?

Teresa of Jesus had been forced to give way.

Persistent in all matters of spite or envy, the Princess was quite the contrary in the fulfilment of her pledged word: in Palencia the account of the *Life* of Mother Teresa lay about on the tables of the palace; the court and the servants had full leisure to derive edification from or to ridicule it: much amusement was derived from Teresa's visions and they were laughingly compared to the deceits in which the devil entangled Magdalena de la Cruz. The echo of all this ridicule even reached Madrid and the Princess did not fail to add her grain of spice; for an entire season one of the court's greatest amusements was to introduce this subject of conversation in which Ana de Mendoza's wit sparkled as did her spite.

So Mother Teresa thought she could tear her innocent nuns away from her, did she? The Princess of Éboli gloated over her denunciation of the *Autobiography* of Teresa of Jesus to the Inquisition and affirmed that the book contained 'visions, revelations and the setting forth of dangerous doctrine.' [1]

While this one-eyed lady was weaving her network of intrigue

[1] SEC, vol. I, p. cxxiii.

Teresa was enjoying the quietude of souls which are innocent and pure; she was very far from imagining to what lengths hatred and wounded vanity could go. She had just bought a good house for the Carmel of Segovia and had installed her nuns there with the usual ceremony for taking possession of a house: followed by the nuns singing *Laudate Dominum omnes gentes*, she went from room to room ringing a little bell and opening all the doors. They set up an altar in this place where in future no spirit would reign but that of Christ.

This convent was as humble and poor as she liked to have them, with low ceilings under the red roof-tiles, for 'thirteen poor little women, the least corner is sufficient. . . .'[1] The cells opened on to the patio. It was there that one day Fray John of the Cross was so transported with love at the sight of a picture of Christ falling under the weight of a cross in the form of a wine-press that he went totteringly to embrace the great dark cross which stood out against the white wall of the cloister and fell into ecstasy.

The Foundress could talk with the Father of her soul in peace and enjoy solitude in a cell at the top of the house where she frequently shut herself away. 'It is a long time since I've been able to isolate myself like this and I find it a great consolation.'[2] Her nuns surrounded her with an affection which, even if it was sometimes indiscreet was always sweet to her affectionate nature, so affectionate that the word 'love' was perhaps the one she uttered most frequently. 'I want to do nothing but love,' she said, 'there is no better remedy than love. . . .'[3] Because she herself loved so truly and sincerely, she found it natural that others should love her truly and sincerely too.

When Ana de la Santísima Trinidad who naïvely followed her everywhere discovered her praying in her cell at the top of the house Teresa scolded her with an indulgent smile:

'You little ferret! Won't you ever leave me alone?'[4]

These indiscretions had a happy consequence: Teresa of Jesus had brought to Segovia the little notebook containing the *Thoughts on the Love of God* and showed it to her confessor, P. Diego de Yanguas. This father was no less famous for his unpolished, sturdy virtues than he was for his commentaries on St Thomas. He read it and said:

'What's the good of using up your energy writing things like that? Throw it in the fire.'

Teresa did not answer, her face betrayed not the slightest emotion, a fire was lighted and she threw the sheets of paper into it.

[1] Sb, C, c. ii–9. [2] CTA, lxx.
[3] SEC, R, v, p. 32. [4] SEC, F, p. 178, n. 2.

P. Yanguas was 'animated with the zeal of St Paul who ordered women to be silent in the church of God: that is that they should not preach in the pulpit and must not write books.' [1] But that was not all: the Inquisition showed particular severity in everything touching on knowledge of the Scriptures. One of the accusations which had told heavily against the *Alumbrados* of Toledo had been that they met in groups, secretly, to comment on the Holy Scriptures 'in hidden corners'; they were even called 'disciples of secret doctrines and of hidden places. . . .' Teresa always took the greatest possible care to specify clearly that the Scriptures brought her great consolation when expounded to her by theologians whose holiness was equalled by their learning, but she made no allusion to any direct reading: yet the quotations she made from the Bible and her constant references to it prove that she knew it very thoroughly. She affirmed that the words of the Gospel made her more recollected than the most learned books,[2] and Our Lord himself said to her: 'All the evils of the world come from ignorance of the truths of Scripture in all their clarity, of which not one jot nor tittle shall fail. . . .' [3] But this did not prevent her interrupting a prospective postulant at Toledo whom she had just accepted, when the girl said she would bring her Bible with her:

'Child, stay where you are! We don't need you or your Bible! We are ignorant people who only know how to spin and to obey. . . .' [4]

In the heyday of the Grand Inquisitor Don Gaspar de Quiroga this was wise, and there was more prudence than narrow-mindedness in P. Yanguas' attitude. Fray Luis de León was shortly to be thrown into prison for having translated the *Canticle of Canticles* into Castilian at the request of one of his penitents:[5] he remained there four years.

One can imagine P. Diego's fear when confronted with Teresa of Jesus' vehement 'little notebook.' He defended himself against the charge of having behaved in an intransigent way by claiming to have spoken only in jest and to test the Mother's obedience: he never imagined that she would so eagerly throw into the flames such a wonderful little book 'which contained nothing against faith.' [6]

He little knew how the Foundress loved to obey or her total absence of literary vanity.

---

[1] SEC, vol. IV, pp. liv–lv.   [2] Sb, C, c. xxi–4.
[3] Sb, V, c. xl–l.   [4] SEC, vol. V, p. 129, n. 1.
[5] Largely because the penitent was indiscreet; the MS. was for her own eyes only—Tr.
[6] SEC, vol. IV, pp. liv–lv.

However, the text was saved: one of the 'ferrets' had copied the manuscript secretly. Teresa imagined that the whole thing was destroyed and thought no more about it. Each of her retreats on the threshold of a foundation contributed in increasing measure to detach her from all created things. From Segovia she wrote: 'I am freer, interiorly, day by day. . . .'[1]

At this time the Inquisition in Ávila was looking not only for her *Autobiography* but for all her other writings. P. Domingo Báñez, determined to support Mother Teresa with his weighty authority, took the book which had been denounced to the Inquisitors himself, after having made a few very slight emendations; he added a few pages of approval.

When Teresa learned what danger she was in, she was in no way troubled:

'God knows with what sincerity I have written what is true.'

Moreover, in all her books, great and small, did she not proclaim her fidelity to the Church, always and in every way? In the account of her *Life*: 'to tear the devils to pieces in defence of the very least of the teachings of the Church. . . .'[2] In the *Interior Castle*: 'If I said anything not in accordance with the truths of our holy, Catholic and Roman Church, it was through ignorance and not malice. . . .'[3] In the *Way of Perfection*: 'In everything I hold to the truths of our holy mother, the Roman Church.'[4] In her spiritual conversations with her confessors: 'I submit myself to the correction of the Church.'[5]

Submission for her was simply love.

What she felt more was the anxiety of her daughters and she reassured them by reminding them:

> Let nothing disturb thee,
> Let nothing affright thee,

or else she gently shrugged her shoulders:

'¿*Que más da*—?What if things are so?'

On leaving Segovia to return to Ávila, she stopped at the cave in which St Dominic had dwelt. She remained there prostrate in prayer for so long that her little escort grew impatient. With all her charm and graciousness she apologized: she had been kept by the holy Friar Preacher who had appeared to her. He had promised to help her in everything and especially in her foundations.

What had she to fear from anything or anybody, even from Inquisitors?

[1] CTA, lvi.   [2] Sb, V, c. xxv–12.   [3] M, Prologue.
[4] Sb, C, Prologue.   [5] SEC, R, i, p. 7.

XII

JERÓNIMO GRACIÁN DE LA MADRE DE DIOS

ACROSS country that might be described as greyish-blue in colour, sharply delineated in the cold light, as with an etching-tool, the carts screeched their way as they clung to the sides of the Sierra Morena. At each turn of the wheel, stones from the side of the track loosened and rolled down into the void, rebounding from rock to rock, awakening in the depths to which they fell echoes which made ten valiant women shudder.

The seven convents of Carmelite nuns which Mother Teresa had founded so far had been situated 'in her part of the country' within about twenty or thirty leagues of Ávila in one direction or another; now, in February 1575, she was venturing further afield, to Beas, on the borders of Castile and Andalusia, in the province of Jaén. Dismayed by the distance and the prospect of travelling across high mountains, she had finally allowed herself to be persuaded by the persistent piety of the donors, the two Godínez sisters, ladies of noble birth, and by the attraction of a climate which was particularly mild and pleasant. She took with her the two most faithful among her loyal friends, Julian de Ávila and Antonio Gaytán and with them Gregorio Martínez who had known her at Medina del Campo and had followed her. Ana de Jesús, the beautiful Lobera girl known as 'Queen of the World,' was one of the party, as was also María de San José, formerly Doña Luisa de la Cerda's little waiting-maid. In addition there were Isabel de San Jerónimo, whom P. John of the Cross had cured of melancholy, Ana de San Alberto, María del Espíritu Santo, María de la Visitación, Isabel de San Francisco, who wrote so well that Teresa asked her to be Carmel's chronicler, tiny little Leonor de San Gabriel, so charming and affectionate that she was always *mi Gabrielita* to the Mother Foundress, and lastly Beatriz de San Miguel: when quite a child Beatriz had cut off her fair curls and brought them to her mother in a box:

'I'm leaving you this finery and I want to go to God.'

It was she who held the child Jesus in her arms, he went with her on all journeys.

For days the rickety, jolting carts jerked their way across the sierra. There was no end to the zigzags, steep ascents and abrupt falls. The mules went more and more slowly, less and less surely, and the drivers themselves seemed to have no lungs left as they shouted their *¡Ar–e–e–e–e!* to spur on their beasts.

The Mother, through a chink in the wooden planks which closed in her cart, saw a certain anxiety in the looks of the muleteers who were hesitating; a moment later they tackled a steep slope which might have been all right for goats, but was in no way intended for their wide, heavy carts. She scented danger.

Like the captain in a storm giving orders to reef the sails and lash the tiller, the Foundress ordered her nuns to suppress the fear they had good reason for feeling, and not to loose hold of their faith in God's protection:

'Those men no longer know where they're going. Let us be-take ourselves to prayer, Sisters, let us ask Our Lord and our father St Joseph to guide us!' [1]

Then a voice rose from far away, from the very bottom of the ravine, the voice of an old shepherd who was used to making himself heard at an immense distance:—'Sto–o–op! sto–o–o–p! You will overturn and roll down the precipice if you go that w–a–a–y!'

Amid the clatter of wooden shoes, scraping over the stones, of men tugging frantically and brutally at the reins, of the jingling of harness, of screeching axles, of the clash of wheels, the carts made an abrupt halt whilst the shouts of the muleteers were echoed in the mountains around: 'Sto–o–o–p! *¡Par–e–e–en! ¡Par–e–e–e–e–n!*'

The panic of men and beasts lasted a few seconds, followed im-mediately by a great hubbub of questions, affirmations and exclama-tions: they were well and truly lost in the Sierra Morena! Actually, they were slipping down into an abyss! The voice coming up from the depths of the chasm had saved them. But how were they to get out of their present situation? How were they to turn round on the narrow path between the rock and the chasm? How were they to find the right road again?

With hand over mouth, trumpetwise, they shouted to the bottom of the precipice: 'Where can we pa–a–a–ss?'

And the bottom of the precipice answered:

'Go gently backwards, there's no danger in that. If you go back a hundred turns of the wheel, you will find the right track ag–a–a–i–i–n!'

[1] AJ, quoted SEC, vol. VI, p. 200 and the whole account of the journey.

The voice hovered in the silence and echo gave it back as a very clear mirror gives back a reflection.

A servant who went to reconnoitre came back declaring that the right track was indeed at the point indicated: it was concealed by a boulder which could be moved without great difficulty. While some of the men in the escort set to work to clear away the boulder the others tried to find their invisible rescuer. They shouted as loud as they could, peered into the depths of the chasm, one of them even tried to climb down it: all to no purpose. Where was this shepherd hiding? The air was so diaphanous that it was possible to distinguish the tiniest stone as far as the eye could see, and the sierra was so barren, the light so penetrated to every part of it that it seemed impossible to hide there.

Teresa's countenance was radiant with love amid her tears and confusion:

'I don't like letting them go on looking,' she said to her daughters: 'they will find nobody. But we can't tell them that the voice we heard is our father St Joseph's answer to our prayers.' They had still one day more of mountain travel, but from then onwards everything was so easy and the beasts moved so quickly that the muleteers grumbled and swore.

'Driving mules who fly is strange work.'

On the banks of the Guadalquivir the Carmelites were preparing to get down from their carts to cross the river, when they found themselves transported to the opposite bank: it was no longer possible to hide from anyone that heaven's angels were carrying the holy Mother in their arms. . . . [1]

The excitement this supernatural event caused was such that all the clergy of Beas in surplices, with all the inhabitants, children included, walking in procession with the cross at their head, came out to meet Teresa of Jesus; the party was preceded by horsemen who made their horses perform 'all the courtesies in the world.' [2] They escorted her to the church which she entered to the chanting of the *Te Deum*, in the midst of all the nobility of the place and all the notables in festive attire.

Such were the miracles which brought joy. But there was a miracle of a different sort: the new convent, which adjoined the parish church, was installed in what had been the assistant priest's house and the nuns were authorized to follow the Offices at the parish church through a small window. This authorization annoyed a certain Alonso

[1] Idem.   [2] FR.

SEGOVIA
View of the Cathedral from the Convent

Inside the Convent at Valladolid

de Montalvo so much that he did not hesitate to go off to Madrid to get it suppressed. He came back very proud of himself:

'The window will be closed up in three days or else my eyes will be closed. . . .'[1]

Three days later his eyes were closed: he died suddenly. As the psalmist says, it is thus that the just shall rejoice when he shall see the retribution of the wicked.

The veneration and enthusiasm which Teresa inspired bordered on delirium and the convent of St Joseph of our Saviour of Beas, inaugurated on 24th February, became a nursery of saints.

The two Godínez sisters who had given the house and 6,000 ducats, took the veil there under the names of Catalina and María, de Jesús.

Of the two it was Catalina who had the strong personality: Catalina Godínez, or 'pride converted,' was the subject of a picturesque story of the kind Teresa loved to write.

At fourteen she had been so proud of her beauty, her fortune and her name, that she was annoyed at what she considered the lack of ambition on the part of her parents when it came to the matter of her marriage: they were contenting themselves with an heir, the eldest of a great family, for her. She did not understand where she got so much pride from but she found the thought of being tied to a man humiliating; she would have liked her lineage to begin from herself alone![2]

God was going to make use of her pride to win her to himself. One evening when she was thinking over her prospects of marriage, raising her eyes her glance fell on the crucifix and in a flash she understood that God alone was a spouse worthy of her. She was a strong character: she made a vow of chastity and poverty on the spot. The devils, from whose clutches she was escaping, then made such a din in the house that her father, awakened by the noise, came downstair in night attire and sword in hand.

Her parents did not allow Catalina to enter a convent, and persisted in trying to force her to marry; to frighten off her suitors, she secretly went to the farm buildings, wet her face and exposed it to the sun to spoil her complexion, like Peau d'Âne.[3] All the time she could snatch from her mother's strict supervision she spent in prayer and she got up at night and groped in the dark to kiss the feet of the sleeping servants: she asked their pardon for the fact that she was forced to let herself be served by them.

[1] RD quoted SEC, vol. V, p. 192, n. 3. [2] Sb, F, c. xxii–5.
[3] A character in one of Perrault's fairy tales.

She suffered from all sorts of diseases but was miraculously cured. The death of her father and mother left her free and she was at last able to obtain from Mother Teresa the foundation of a Carmelite convent at Beas of which she and her sister María would bear the cost.

She had learned of the existence of the reformed Carmel from an angel: she had seen herself in a great room of some convent, whose only light came from the candles which about fifteen nuns veiled in black were holding in their hands. When Catalina asked them to which Order they belonged, without breaking silence they raised their veils and she saw their radiant smiling faces. The day she took the habit she recognized in her new companions the faces she had seen in her dream.

But it was certainly not because there she lived in the Golden Legend atmosphere that Mother Teresa said afterwards that she had never been happier than at Beas: it was at Beas that she met Fray Jerónimo Gracián de la Madre de Dios.

'I shall never spend happier days than those I lived with my Paul. . . .' [1] That was her nickname for him, for it seemed to her that, like the apostle, he was alternatively 'on the mountain tops or in the depths of the sea,' [2] so easily did his enthusiasm turn to discouragement. She also called him 'my Eliseus' [3] because of his head which was 'large and bald.' She wrote to P. Rubeo, Superior General of the Order: 'Gracián is like an angel . . .'; [4] and to the prioress of Medina del Campo:

O Mother, how I wish you had been with me just lately! Without exaggeration they have been the best days of my life. Gracián has just spent more than twenty days here. I tell you that I have not yet appreciated this man at his proper value. In my eyes he is perfect and for us better than anything we could ask God for. I hope Your Reverence and your daughters will pray His Majesty to give him to us for religious superior. I shall then be able to have someone else to refer to besides myself for the government of these houses; I've never seen so much perfection joined with so much meekness. . . . Julian de Ávila is mad about him and all here are the same. He preaches wonderfully. [5]

Teresa of Jesus was so excited that she almost seemed like Doña Teresa de Ahumada again. She declared that her soul only found peace in God or with the one person who understood her: 'All the rest is

[1] CTA, cxviii.   [2] Idem, cclvi.   [3] SEC, vol. VII, p. 189.
[4] CTA, lxxiv.   [5] Idem, lxxii.

such a heavy cross to me that I cannot bear it. . . .'[1] Although she was sixty she was full of enthusiasm. Given her generous nature and the constraint under which she had lived, this was not surprising. Even those who thought her visions and her voices wonderful found them a little awe-inspiring: P. John of the Cross judged that they were due to a feverish imagination and a result of too much clinging to the pleasures of divine love, and Teresa herself sometimes wondered if they were not a trap of the devil. To her it was as painful to be considered a saint as it was to be regarded as a sort of curiosity, and that was why among the novices she loved the gayest best; their affectionate familiarity gave her a sense of repose, relaxation and tenderness.

As to Gracián, when Teresa disclosed to him the secrets of her interior life, he was in no way surprised at her deep intimacy with Our Lord; as a man of learning, and with the support of Scripture for his opinion, he approved. This was an immense relief and consolation to the Foundress, to whom her very happiness was so often the cause of suffering: 'May he be blessed for ever!'[2]

Because he gave her a sense of security and peace, he meant much to her and soon became indispensable.

And then he was not 'dour': even in the first days of their acquaintance he made her laugh.

There had been quite a few clothings at Beas, among others that of Gregorio Ramírez who took the name of Gregorio Nacianceno. Julian de Ávila contented himself with asking P. Jerónimo Gracián if he would give him the scapular of the Order to which the good chaplain had devoted himself without counting the cost.

The Father Vicar grouped the novices in the choir behind the grille, made them sing the *Veni Creator* as was done at clothings and to all intents and purposes seemed to be going on with the ceremony. His sermon, on the beauties of monastic life, lasted an hour. Julian, poor fellow, was in despair: could they make a friar of him without his having asked for or wishing it? Were they going to force him to take a vow of poverty when he had several sisters to keep? But perhaps Mother Teresa had had a revelation about him, commanding that he too should discard his shoes and put on the coarse frieze? If that were so, how could he resist the command of Our Lord? 'He turned pale, went red, perspired, was much upset,'[3] but when the sermon was over P. Gracián merely gave him the scapular.

Julian de Ávila's account of his panic delighted the nuns, the

---

[1] Idem, ccclxvi. [2] CTA, civ.
[3] JG quoted SEC, vol. VI, pp. 201–2.

Foundress laughed heartily over it, more pleased than ever with her Paul, her Eliseus, her Gracián.

With him she was able to take an easy tone and give rein to her vivacity, without feeling obliged to keep back some amusing retort or spontaneous expression of affection. To him she could write: 'You amused me very much and made me laugh. O Father! Your Reverence had no need to swear, not even like a saint and still less like a cart driver, for that's what I understood you to say. . . . I leave the matter, reminding Your Paternity that you have authorized me to judge and to think what I please. . . .' [1]

She loved him as a mother or a sister, as a saint who had reached such a degree of purity that on her lips the strongest expressions of love could not be misunderstood. If her soul had not been as clear as crystal, she would not have dared to use them: 'What a pleasure it would have been to give him a meal when he was hungry as he said he was!' [2] 'He is stout and in good health. Thanks be to God!' [3] When he signed one of his letters: 'Your dear son,' she was full of delight. 'You amused me so much when you wrote *Your dear son*! And I immediately said to myself that you were perfectly right!' [4]

She was concerned about him, his fatigue, his health, his clothes, his moods, and finally she rejoiced in the extreme goodness of the 'Master of the house' (*el casamentero*), Christ himself, who had linked them in so close a friendship that death would not separate them, they would be united to all eternity.[5] And the thought of P. Gracián helped her to praise God better.

If she begged him—not without a spark of innocent malice—not to fall off his donkey, if his failure to write frequently inspired her with the wonderful saying, 'where there is love, it doesn't sleep like that . . . ,' [6] if for certain prioresses—María de San José, for instance, with whom Gracián later formed a close friendship—she felt something very much akin to feminine jealousy, all this, which proves that Teresa of Jesus was human, in no way implied that her heart was not completely filled even to overflowing with a love which swallowed up all lesser affections: that of God and of her Order.

Had not P. Gracián the same ideas as herself, her tastes, her method of directing souls? 'Your Paternity is absolutely right as to what you consider necessary for the reform when you say that souls are not to be won by force of arms like bodies. May God keep you near me, for I like you very much!' [7]

[1] CTA, ccxxviii. [2] Idem, cxl. [3] Idem, clxxxi. [4] Idem, cxlvii.
[5] CTA, clx. [6] CTA, ccxc. [7] CTA, clx.

The fact that such a strong expression of feelings escaped her caused her some uneasiness, but one day, after Communion, she was transported in spirit to a flowery meadow, so lovely that it reminded her of the images of the *Canticle of Canticles*: 'I saw my Eliseus there, not as he really is, a trifle too sallow, but beautiful in a way not of earth: he had on his head as it were a crown of large precious stones; numerous maidens walked before him with palms in their hands, singing canticles to the praise of God. I opened my eyes wide. . . . I thought I heard angels singing and also little birds which brought joy to the soul. And it was said to me: "This man is worthy to be among you."' [1]

Who then was this wonderful person to whom heaven itself gave letters of credence?

Aged thirty when he met the Mother Foundress at Beas, P. Jerónimo Gracián de la Madre de Dios was already Apostolic Visitor of the Discalced Carmelite friars and of the nuns of Mitigated observance in Andalusia. Very learned, gifted with persuasive eloquence, with childlike gaiety and austere as a desert father, he 'charmed' by his perfect manners, gentle and kindly ways, while his even temper made relations with him easy and pleasant.

He was preparing to enter the Society of Jesus when he got to know the Discalced Carmelite friars; to the habit of Ignatius Loyola's sons he preferred that of the sons of Our Lady and he took it at Pastrana.

He had always had a most tender devotion towards the Blessed Virgin and christened a statue of Mary which he frequently visited as a young man in one of the Madrid churches, *mi enamorada*, my sweetheart. It was this gift of pious gallantry that predestined him to be Teresa of Jesus' 'dear son.'

He was tender-hearted and had great delicacy and, although possessed of all the qualities which make for success in the world, was so little made for the world that nothing ever cured him of his ingenuousness. He was destined by his family to hold high office at court: the call of God was more peremptory than that of the King, more so even than the duty of helping his nineteen brothers and sisters to find means of livelihood. For although his father had been secretary to Charles V and his brothers Antonio and Tomás secretaries to Philip II and Luis secretary to the Queen-Regent of Sicily, the good graces of these sovereigns in regard to their important personnel were so capricious and so meagre that this family of high functionaries was as poor as it was honourable.

[1] SEC, R, xliv, p. 73.

Jerónimo Gracián was the man whom the Foundress needed: 'Although he was not one of the first, he came at the right moment: I should often have regretted having undertaken so much if I had not had such great confidence in God's mercy. I am referring to the monasteries of friars, who quickly fell away from perfection because they were not set up as an independent province and were governed by the Mitigated.' [1]

Whom had the Foundress to count on? The two 'first' friars of the Reform, Antonio de Jesús and John of the Cross, seem to be indicated. But P. Antonio lacked common-sense, he was touchy and given to romancing; as to P. John, the incomparable angel of the *Dark Night*, he still sought to escape the all-absorbing effort which foundations meant, with their worldly contacts, business and diplomacy: it was only much later that he adapted himself to all this. And then, Teresa could not manage him as she pleased: even the most intelligent saint cannot manage an archangel.

On the other hand she could manage P. Jerónimo Gracián.

Mother Teresa bent P. Jerónimo Gracián de la Madre de Dios to her will by the means all women employ, be they saints or sinners, geniuses or fools, to bring men under their domination: she vowed obedience to him, promised to do only what he commanded all her life long, unless it should be anything against God or the ecclesiastical superiors to whom she had duties. She likewise undertook to hide from him nothing of her interior life, or of her sins—in short, she put him 'both interiorly and exteriorly' [2] in the place of God.

After this, it only remained for P. Gracián to submit.

As quickly as possible the Foundress wrote to Philip II begging him to divide the Mitigated and Discalced Carmelite friars into separate provinces: she had at last found the man who could assume responsibility for the reformed Order: ' . . . A Discalced father named Gracián whom I've just seen. . . . Although quite young, he is of such a kind that I have greatly praised God for him; I think he has chosen him for the good of our Order.' [3]

Teresa was going to crush him whom she had chosen as her master under the weight of the work; she was pursuing one single aim: the autonomy of the Discalced in relation to the Calced, of her friars who had returned to the primitive Rule vis-à-vis the friars who were remaining under the Mitigation, of her fathers clad in frieze as against those who wore fine cloth. She had dedicated herself to this work

[1] Sb, F, c. xxiii-12.   [2] SEC, R, xl, pp. 69-70.
[3] CTA, lxxvii.

until death. And of this work, P. Jerónimo Gracián was to be the instrument.

The Foundress revealed her inmost heart when she wrote to the prioress at Valladolid, her cousin María Bautista: 'It's a curious thing, I'm no more troubled about loving him so much than if he were not a person at all. . . .' [1] Indeed for Teresa, with her mind set on the realization of her plans, he was not a person, but more than a person: he was the best tool she had to carve her foundations out of the granite.

[1] CTA, lxxxvii.

PART FOUR

THE GREAT STORM

'I saw a great storm of trials and difficulties. . . .'

Relations, xxxvii.

I

THE ROAD TO THE SOUTH

THE Mother Foundress's one wish was to return to her Promised Land, Castile, but P. Gracián asked her to go and found a convent in Seville.[1] As she hesitated, he gave her a formal order to do this, with good reasons for his request: the support of the Archbishop Don Cristóbal de Rojas had been obtained, the new convent would be filled with novices with good dowries: the Sevillan girls seemed only to be waiting for Teresa of Jesus' arrival to take the Carmelite habit, and everything would be for the best in the richest city of all the Spains.

Such arguments did not quieten Teresa's apprehensions: Andalusia frightened her. She dreaded the climate, the customs, the inhabitants, the revolts—it was hardly five years since Don Juan of Austria had crushed the last Moorish insurrection with no little difficulty—and she feared the rabble of adventurers whom the ships leaving for the Indies attracted to its ports.

P. Gracián intoned his usual panegyric:

'Its wealth, its grandeur, its majesty are like the sun . . . it is the place of exchange, the gateway to and port of the Indies. . . . There is nothing in the world like what you see at Seville: when the galleons come into port, one hundred, nay two hundred carts, each drawn by two yoke of oxen, transport the ingots of gold and silver to the Royal House of Commerce for the Indies.'[2]

'All this gold is of no interest to us,' said Teresa.

Gracián described the rich dress of the inhabitants, the silks covered with thickly raised, padded and incrusted embroideries; wool was not used at all, but everything was of velvet, taffeta, damask and brocade.

And when the Foundress frowned slightly:

'It only depends on us, on Your Reverence, and the riches which are now used for so much vanity and frivolity will be given to the support of our Order.'

'Don't they say,' objected the Foundress, 'that the streets of Seville are less safe than the passes of the Sierra Morena? The folk there are

[1] CTA, xciii.   [2] Lope de Vega.

idle ruffians and quarrelsome. . . . Don't they call Seville "the Babylon of the Great Sea"?'

She also knew that among this crowd of foreigners heretics would insinuate themselves and get to work and that Lutheran propaganda there was intense, the Inquisition more suspicious than in Castile, repression more active even than at Valladolid and so cruel that it was better not to have to prove one's innocence before the tribunals.

But Teresa of Jesus had made a vow of obedience to P. Jerónimo Gracián de la Madre de Dios. She was forced to yield and to quicken her preparations for departure, for it was May and her health would not have stood the journey in the great heat.

She left Ana de Jesús, whom a Provincial would one day dub 'captain of prioresses', in charge at Beas. John of the Cross considered Ana de Jesús an angel of the highest order and Teresa herself declared: 'Ana does the work and I have the credit. . . .'

Sin blanca, as usual, Teresa borrowed a little money for the journey from the convent of Malagón: she asked only for what was strictly necessary, for P. Gracián declared that the generosity of the Andalusians could be relied upon. She chose six nuns from the community at Beas: Isabel de San Francisco, María del Espíritu Santo, Isabel de San Jerónimo, Leonor de San Gabriel, Ana de San Alberto and lastly the future prioress, María de San José. Not only intelligent, but brilliant, brought up in the best circles of Toledo, with Doña Luisa de la Cerda, María belonged to an élite as much on account of her learning as of her birth; she spoke Latin and made no secret of it, and she wrote to perfection in prose and verse and was only too willing to show people what she had written. Teresa, who preferred a proverb in good popular speech to a Latin quotation, teased her about her pedantry, but after her own fashion which consisted in dressing the scratch with a kind word: 'I wonder why I love you so much. . . .' [1]

Teresa of Jesus never took a nun away for a new foundation against her will. María de San José, whose assignment on their departure from Castile was to be prioress of Caravaca, was consulted:

'Would you give up Caravaca, where you're sure to be well lodged and have sufficient money, to share the risks of this Seville foundation with us?'

María de San José asked if she would be prioress of one or other of these houses in any case: through humility she would have preferred to have no position of honour:

[1] CTA, clxxiii.

'Sister,' replied Teresa, 'you will be prioress, for when there are no thrushes we have to eat blackbirds. . . .'

'In that case I choose Seville.'

The Foundress broke into a triumphant laugh:

'You wanted it! Let come what will come!' [1]

The energy and staying power of a young prioress would be put to good use in an enterprise like this.

So now the carts were once more prepared for the journey, just as a ship is equipped for a long voyage. In each cart, which was covered over so that nobody could guess it was carrying nuns who were travelling the world over the better to renounce the world, the hourglass was hung up; it would remind them that conventual life was interrupted neither by mountains nor valleys; the little bell to announce the hours of prayer was put within reach of the Foundress's hand; lastly they piled up the provisions and the water-skins.

At dawn on 18th May, after Mass at which all communicated, the carts took the road to the south. Julian de Ávila, Antonio Gaytán, Gregorio Nacianceno followed on muleback. P. Jerónimo Gracián de la Madre de Dios had left for Madrid.

The sun beat down on them so fiercely that from the very first day the provisions went bad—although there was no meat among them—the very water was not fit to drink and everything had to be thrown away. What did it matter: the first halt in a flowery wood was so delightful that Teresa, who never felt the presence of God anywhere so much as when confronted with a beautiful landscape—she then forgot everything in praising her Creator—returned to her cart where the heat was suffocating with great reluctance.

A regular routine was observed on the journey. The Foundress rang her little bell at ordered intervals, and the rhythm of prayer kept pace with that of the mules to the accompaniment of the steady grind of the enormous cart-wheels right through the midst of the wood.

The little bell was also rung when it was time for silence. Then the *mozos de mulas*, the *arrieros*, the cart-drivers themselves kept silence: one word from Teresa had been sufficient for them to agree to abide by the convent discipline. The sounds along the road, the distant sheep-bells only made the silence of the daughters of Carmel more perceptible. Precious silence: it is in silence that the soul embraces God and that God embraces and instructs the soul; just as Solomon's temple was built without any sound of axe or hammer, so Our Lord builds his dwelling-place in us in silence.

[1] MJ quoted SEC, vol. VI, p. 243.

A further ring of the bell and Teresa, still radiant from her prayer, offered the *arrieros* a wineskin filled with 'wine of the earth' to reward them for having kept silence so well. Then they began their songs again and also, in the innocence of their hearts, their oaths.

For their siesta the party halted under the shade of some eucalyptus trees or under a bridge; this was the moment for gaiety, even when it meant having to dislodge a drove of pigs from the little shade there was. Teresa had a most lively and picturesque way of speaking, and her sense of humour enlivened all the various vicissitudes of the journey and even their very worst misfortunes. Whether she was teasing Antonio Gaytán on his attachment to this world's goods—the good man was not very successful in concealing his anxiety as to how things were going at his house in Alba de Tormes—or Sister Leonor de San Gabriel on her small stature, she never hurt anyone's feelings and was always amusing. And when the conversation turned to more spiritual matters, she inflamed all her companions with the love of Our Lord. She improvised *coplas* which the nuns sang:

> Let us travel towards heaven,
> Nuns of Carmel . . .[1]

But along the steep uphill road to heaven, she never lost sight of the sharp stones by the wayside and saw to it that those whose souls were in her charge did not injure themselves on them.

The first night they slept in a hermitage on the stone floor, for, counting on the generosity of the Sevillans which P. Gracián had promised them, they had not even brought pallets. In the morning they unpacked the sacred vessels and the vestments, the only luggage they had of any value, and Julian de Ávila said Mass before they started on their way again.

As they advanced southwards, the sun beat down on them more and more fiercely, and the heat which had accumulated under the tarpaulins covering the carts was so appalling that the nuns could talk of nothing but the sufferings of hell and purgatory: to win heaven at the price of innumerable hardships was to earn the right to live for ever where it was cool. All six showed so much courage that Teresa was delighted.

'With nuns like you, I would not mind going to the land of the Turks!'

All they had to eat during this journey was a little bread, some beans and a few cherries, and that when they were not obliged by

[1] P, cx.

circumstances to go without anything at all. Thirst was their worst suffering: the Andalusians sold their water at as high a price as their wine. But Teresa only said:

'May God give us much to suffer for him, if only in the way of fleas, wicked little boys and bad roads!' [1]

Whatever danger or unforeseen circumstances might arise, the Mother Foundress maintained order by insisting on the observance of the Rule and Constitutions. As they were crossing the Guadalquivir, the force of the current swept away one of the ferry-boats which was carrying two of the carts. The sisters pulled at the haulage ropes which broke ; miraculously the ferry-boat drifted on to a sand-bank. The travellers were now far away from any inhabited place, night was falling and the guides no longer knew where they were. . . . 'O God, we thank you for the bad roads!'—Teresa organized conventual life on the banks of the river as if the circumstances were in no way unusual, when all the goods and chattels of this convent now at the full mercy of the elements consisted of a statuette of the Child Jesus, six flasks of holy water and a few prayer books. They sang Compline and were preparing to sleep under a rock when a riverside dweller came to their assistance, not without uttering all sorts of abuse at both nuns and friars. But he led them back to the right road again and they were able to continue the journey as far as the halt they had planned.

Their worst terror was the inns, those *ventas*, noisy with the shouts of drunken men, with the harsh twang of guitars, the click of castanets and the thrumming of tambourines, or ringing with loud songs or sacrilegious or obscene oaths.

In the midst of all this din and clatter Teresa caught fever and became delirious and they had to find her a bed. The loft was so dirty—'Thank you, dear Lord, for the fleas!'—the bed so hard, the sun darted its burning shafts so fiercely through the slits in the tiles, the wet bandages applied to the patient's forehead were so unrefreshing and the din so terrifying, that she begged them to take her back to her cart: she would suffer less there.

They continued their journey towards Córdoba where they arrived in the early morning: the gipsies were already watering their horses at the fountains while they pestered the girls who were filling their jars with the aid of a long reed, with *piropos*.[2] From the bottom of their closed carts, those who saw nothing of the external world caught the sounds of a life quite different from that of Old and New Castile: voluble, excited, restless, bustling, and all this was whirring around

[1] CTA, lvii.　　　　　　　　[2] *I.e.* flattering compliments.

these lumbering carts which had come from beyond the sierras and were covered with dust and laden with mystery. Leaping up on the wheels in spite of the whips of the *arrieros*, some of the urchins managed to raise the tarpaulins; their laugh showed their sharp white teeth in swarthy faces.

The Foundress heard this noisy din going on all round her and could not contain her distress. Prepared even to forgo Mass, she would have liked to flee from this devilish town: Julian de Ávila disagreed, arguing on strictly theological grounds: all they had to do was to find a quiet church on the other bank of the Guadalquivir. But when the carts got to the bridge, the gates were still closed: the *Corregidor* kept the keys himself; when they ran to ask him for them he was still asleep, but they did not scruple to disturb his slumbers.

The excitement of the crowd, however, was growing greater; when access to the bridge was obtained it was found that the carts were too wide: the part that would not go across was accordingly sawn off. The amusement of the gaping crowd turned to frenzy: 'Thank you for the wicked little boys, dear Lord!'

The seven Carmelites and their escort of friars and laymen at last reached the church which Julian de Ávila had described as so quiet and peaceful! The feast of the Holy Spirit was being celebrated there, not only by a great procession but with dancing; the arrival of the nuns clad in frieze, with their white cloaks and black veils, was an unexpected attraction which proved such a sensation 'that if bulls had come into the place there wouldn't have been more commotion.'

All this upset cured the Foundress's fever. She could not get away from the place sufficiently quickly; the little band left as if in flight from their pursuers, in the full heat of the day. The siesta was spent under a bridge. At evening the hermitage of Écija seemed an oasis of prayer and amid the songs of the birds there Teresa, in the presence of Our Lord, renewed her vow of obedience to P. Jerónimo Gracián.

The respite was brief. In the *venta* at Albino, their only food a few sardines preserved in brine and not a drop of water to quench their thirst, the poor nuns thought themselves in the antechamber of the devil himself: certain 'devilish' individuals began to quarrel among themselves and, blaspheming for all they were worth, hurled themselves at each other weapon in hand: forty swords flew about, clashed, flashed like lightning in the sun, muskets were fired; in the middle of this cannonade the sisters rushed out of their cart and into Mother Teresa's to die by her side. She calmed them by laughing at their fright and proved right, for these furious madmen suddenly disappeared, no doubt in fear of the constables.

Teresa, God's knight errant, and her daughters arrived at Seville on 26th May, after eight days of a journey full of unexpected adventures which María de San José and Julian de Ávila vied with one another to recount. They all praised God who had provided them with wicked little boys, fleas and bad roads, giving them all kinds of mortifications for makeweight.

II

THE RICH CITY OF SEVILLE

PADRE AMBROSIO MARIANO ARAZO DE SAN BENITO was waiting for the Foundress and her nuns in the house he had rented for them: it was a tiny little hovel, very poor and very damp, situated in the Calle de las Armas, right in the centre of the town. The women who had been living in it gave it up for the nuns, but it did not seem to occur to anyone that the newcomers might be in need of some help in a strange town: nobody sent them a mouthful of bread or even a jar of fresh water.

They did, however, find there a few odd things for their use, of which María de San José has left us details:

'Firstly, half a dozen old wicker hurdles which P. Ambrosio Mariano had got from the monastery of Los Remedios; placed on the ground they served as beds; two or three straw mattresses, very thin and in bad condition, were kept for our Mother and the most delicate among us. There were neither sheets nor blankets, but we had two pillows which we had brought.'

So much for the bedding. As to the furniture and utensils:

'In the house we found a fibre mat, a small table, a frying-pan, one or two candlesticks, a mortar, and a pail for drawing water from the well. We were rejoicing over this initial help towards our household equipment, to which must be added a few plates and jugs, when the neighbours who had only lent their things for the day, came to take back, this one her candlestick and another her pail and table, so that we had absolutely nothing left, neither frying-pan nor mortar, and they even took away the rope for the well. . . .' [1]

The sudden and forced disappearance of the poor goods of this world seemed so comic an interlude to the travellers that they forgot their difficulties and laughed heartily over it.

Teresa of Jesus had compared the soul to a garden and the different forms of mental prayer to the different ways in which water irrigates, refreshes and fructifies the soil. With what exultant joy did she speak of abundant showers of rain! When August with its heat was wasting

[1] MJ quoted SEC, vol. VI, p. 241.

away her country of Castile, it was still possible to find an ice-cold spring in some high place or in the hollow of a rock. To her the love of God himself was refreshment: 'O living fountains of the wounds of my God!' [1] But 'the scorching heat of Seville' [2] burnt up and dried Teresa's very soul: 'We are burnt up here as if we were in hell. . . .' 'I have never been so cowardly and faint-hearted as I was then; I did not recognize myself. My confidence in Our Lord, indeed, never failed, but my character seemed to be so different that I understood that Our Lord was leaving me to depend on my own resources to show me clearly that if I had had courage hitherto, it was not to my own merits that I owed it.' [3] 'I am there, but I want you to know how small a thing you are without me. . . .'

From the moment she arrived she was blinded by the sun's reflection against the white walls; everything one touched was moist with heat, the least breath of air carried the smell of plants dying for lack of moisture or the heady perfume of jasmine which had lost its colour from the heat. She was distressed at the 'abominable sins' which stalked abroad in these lands where the very climate corrupts the soul: 'It seems as if the devils are better placed to lead us into temptation there.' [4] There was something about the place one could not explain— things seemed aggressive and the people evasive. 'The lies which are ordinary current coin here! It's enough to make one faint!' [5] 'I'm not made for the people of this country. . . .' [6] 'Seville either drives you away or swallows you up,' says the proverb. The Babylon of the Great Sea did not swallow up Teresa of Jesus.

P. Mariano himself was no longer the same as he had been in Castile. When the Foundress told him that it was necessary to say the first Mass and expose the Blessed Sacrament the very next day, he was evasive: it would be better to wait and see.

Worried for three days by the impatient Foundress, he finally admitted that the Archbishop, Don Cristóbal de Rojas, whose authorization they had taken for granted, now declared 'that it did not please him'[7] to give permission for this convent to be founded. He would willingly welcome Mother Teresa on condition that she dispersed her nuns among different convents in Andalusia which were in great need of someone to give them the example of a more recollected life. But foundations—certainly not: particularly without revenues.

Alas for the egoism of the rich! Was it possible 'that in such a

[1] Sb, E, ix–2. [2] CTA, lxxii. [3] Sb, F, c. xxv–1.
[4] Sb, F, c. xxv–1. [5] CTA, xciv.
[6] Idem, xciii. [7] Sb, F, c. xxiv–16.

wealthy town there were less facilities than anywhere else for a foundation'? [1] All the sounds Teresa heard were those of traffic or amusements. Who thought of God, indeed, in the excess of passion, the fever of adventure and intrigue, the confusion which made the great Mediterranean port a tower of Babel? They did not seem to have any thought of becoming Carmelites, these Sevillan girls with their bewitching chatter and fiery eyes, and were more anxious about their lovers than the salvation of their souls. Some of them did, indeed, come to see the Foundress, but after taking one look at them with their carefully adjusted circular gowns and high head-dresses, or showing only one eye under the shawl with which they were wrapped according to the custom of their country, she felt that they were not suitable birds for her dovecot.

She would have been only too glad to go back to Castile, but there was no money for the journey: she had only one solitary *blanca* left in her pocket and nothing to sell except the tarpaulins which closed in the carts; and in this city bursting with gold there was nobody to lend them a few ducats. With great difficulty P. Mariano managed to get enough money to enable Julian de Ávila and Antonio de Gaytán to go back. When she said good-bye to them, Teresa honoured Gaytán with the title of 'my good founder,' he had helped her so devotedly. He was fortunate in being able to go back to the waters of the Tormes, to his house at Alba, built of grey stone as became his rank, and to his small daughter whom the Foundress called 'my little pest,' and whom she loved so much.

By dint of insisting, in the end P. Mariano wrung permission from the Archbishop for Mass to be said in the Calle de las Armas, but he forbade the Blessed Sacrament to be exposed, the bell to be rung or the house to be given the external appearance of a convent: this was tantamount to condemning the nuns to feed on prayer alone, for who would know of their existence? Where were the munificent Andalusians, so much boasted of when Teresa and her nuns left Beas? Seville was either the most miserly of cities or the most neglectful of the affairs of God. One great lady, however, 'whose eyes followed the saints with longing and who opened her heart to the needy,' [2] gave to them generously, but she applied the laws of charity so thoroughly that, so that her left hand should not know what her right hand was distributing, she charged a *beata* to provide for the needs of the Discalced Carmelites anonymously: linen, crockery, pots and pans, money to buy oil and fish. This duenna had her favourite poor, her

<hr>

[1] Sb, F, c. xxv–1.   [2] MJ, quoted SEC, vol. VI, p. 241.

prostitutes, whose souls seemed to her to be in greater danger than the nuns', and so Doña Leonor de Valera's alms went to the prostitutes.

All this time the sisters were sleeping very badly on their wicker hurdles, eating nothing but potatoes, and there were days when one small loaf fed the whole community as if by miracle.

Teresa could not shake off her sadness. She to whom Our Lord himself had revealed that poverty is a patent of nobility for entering his kingdom was nevertheless anxious and distressed. For she had come to Seville against the will of God: that was her secret and the reason for her discouragement. At Beas, Our Lord had commanded her to found a convent in Madrid; she had confided in P. Gracián who, setting aside the divine command, maintained his decision to send her to Andalusia.

'Obey your superior,' Christ had said to her, 'but he will have to bear the consequences.'[1]

That was why the Foundress was not at peace in Seville and why she said: 'No foundation cost me more hardships and my greatest sufferings were interior ones.'[2]

She felt the storm coming and was afraid.

The General Chapter of the Order had just opened in Italy and Teresa knew that Gracián would be criticized there; what there was human in her anxieties about him added to her trouble. She had warned her nuns against earthly attachments with a clearness of vision which allowed her to make no mistake: 'Our will is wholly occupied in hoping they won't die; if they have a headache we are upset; when they have trials to bear we are impatient; and so on with everything else. . . . What unhappy affection, and I do not speak here of guilty affections, from which God deliver us!'[3]

At Seville Teresa found herself under the influence of two affections that were intense: that for María de San José and that for Jerónimo Gracián. Gracián was absent and she knew he was in danger. Maria was with her, but elusive, reticent, too often presuming on her office as prioress to oppose her will to that of the Foundress. Already one could admire—or blame—in her an art of manoeuvring things, a talent for good administration which later earned her some of Teresa's famous 'terrible' letters; she called her a 'vixen' and said of her: 'In the Seville house I see a greed I cannot tolerate and the prioress is more clever than her office demands. I told her when I was there that she never acted towards me without malice. She has made me suffer very

[1] TC quoted SEC, vol. II, p. 324.   [2] Sb, F, c. xxvi-2.
[3] Sb, C, c. vii-2.

much.'¹ But all reproaches seemed useless: 'it was like running up against steel.'² She did not spare her ratings and was afterwards ready to beg her pardon, just as in her letters reproaches alternated with praise and expressions of tenderness: 'I am unbearable with those I love, for I should like you never to go wrong in the slightest degree . . . and bad as you are, I should like to have many prioresses like you.'³ In these reconciliations María remained distant: 'I treated you as my dearest daughter and it hurt me not to find the same love and simplicity in you.' The very faults of this favourite daughter were faults only to be found in great prioresses and Teresa of Jesus exacted much. Later the Foundress was to regret these differences, so cruelly did she feel María de San José's absence; in the half playful tone which enabled her to get many truths over to her correspondents, she wrote to her that she would be very glad to make the journey in order to quarrel with her as much as she wished. Perhaps she was more exacting than María de San José was imperfect.

She was not at all satisfied with the Andalusian novices. She was highly delighted with their skill as embroidresses, for she so much liked a woman to be clever with her fingers, but her love of frankness could not get on with their disposition to intrigue and duplicity. There were not many of them, moreover; among those who, according to P. Gracián, were impatiently waiting for the Foundress's arrival so that they could take the habit, only one had entered the day the first Mass was said. Beatriz de la Madre de Dios was tiresome, but the Apostolic Visitor and P. Mariano had promised to get her admitted to Carmel. She had been persecuted and even tortured in childhood, and this had left her with a thirst for revenge which she did not succeed in mastering properly.

She was barely seven when one of her mother's sisters took a liking to her and thought of leaving her her property. Her servants who coveted this prize for themselves decided to eliminate her as a rival and accused her of having ordered them to buy sublimate with which to poison her aunt. Sent back to her parents, little Beatriz was whipped every day for more than a year, and the least of the ill treatment to which she was subjected was to sleep on the bare ground. God avenged her of those who calumniated her by permitting them to catch rabies; seized with remorse, before they died they confessed their lie. But their false swearing left something behind: on the first occasion of her hand being asked in marriage, she told her father of her desire to enter religion, but he thought she had committed some sin

¹ CTA, ccxc.　　　　　² Idem.　　　　　³ Idem, cccii.

which made her fear to accept a husband and he subjected her to such violent treatment, going as far as to hang her—and from this she escaped only by the grace of God—that she was in bed for three months unable to move. Her mother, said Teresa, was a good Christian.

The Seville Carmel refused more than one of these daughters of the south. One, however, was admitted as to whose name Carmelite charity has been silent. She was 'an important *beata* already considered as good as canonized by the whole town. . . .'[1]

The Foundress had hesitated:

'If she doesn't work miracles, sisters, we shan't come out of the affair without losing prestige. . . .'[2]

The unfortunate woman [relates María de San José] was holier still in her own eyes, and as she got no praise from us, the severity of the Rule being the touchstone which reveals the true value of all that shines in appearance only, she was soon dissatisfied with us and we were even more so with her. There was never any means of getting her to conform to the Constitutions; she was forty, very authoritative, and had a wonderful way of getting out of every difficulty: when she refused to eat the same food as we, she pleaded illness as an excuse, alleging that she was swelling and that we could read in Galen that those dishes were not good for her; on other occasions she pleaded that she was not used to it—nor to the great heat there is in these provinces. Our Mother told us we must put up with her and not annoy her, in the hope that time would correct all that; she even authorized her to go to confession and to talk with priests who were her friends. . . .[3]

Who would have thought that this wily person, who from the corner of her eye watched every movement and gesture of the Castilians, was effectively contributing to the creation of an atmosphere of hostility to them in Seville? For suspicion and opposition were daily more perceptible.

And that without any human hope of its coming to an end; after three months' stay in a city of wealth, no one had yet come forward to offer to help the Foundress in Our Lord's name.

Heaven sent her all she lacked by the hands of those who were most dear to her: her brothers Lorenzo and Pedro arrived from Ecuador. Lorenzo was as rich in gold from the Indies as he was in good dispositions.

In the parlour, behind the grille, one August day Teresa of Jesus lifted her veil as Carmelites are allowed to do in the case of close

[1] MJ quoted SEC, vol. VI, p. 243.   [2] FR, L. III, c. vi.
[3] MJ quoted SEC, vol. VI, p. 243.

relatives: her brothers could look upon the face of the sister who, when they left her, was young and beautiful but torn between the world and God; they found her so radiant with inner light that the ravages of thirty years had left scarcely a trace upon her bodily appearance.

As to herself, her deep feeling did not prevent her from being amused at the gorgeousness of these Indians: [1] the serious-minded Lorenzo had acquired ostentatious habits in this country where his important position obliged him to live on a grand scale; how gorgeously he was dressed! Even the children, Lorencito and Francisco, the neck confined in starched ruffs, spread out fingers stiff with rings over their velvet clothes; Teresita, their little eight-year-old sister, was smothered in brocade and carried a fortune in emeralds on ears, chest and fingers. But since Teresa had received the finest precious stones of his kingdom from her heavenly Bridegroom, jewels of earth no longer impressed her. And she laughed: the contrast between these wealthy relatives and the wretched parlour in which she was receiving them was a perfect subject for merriment.

Teresita was surprised to hear a saint laugh: her father who was devout but not a saint, laughed but seldom. . . . The nephews were delighted: they had been a little afraid on their father's account, for his age and character inclined him to austerities, of the influence of this wonderful relative of theirs, the reformer of an Order already austere into one more austere still, and of whom people said that her cell in Ávila bore the trace of the blood of her disciplines. But this Reverend Mother spoke with more charm than anyone they knew and when she named God it was to praise him and say that he was good.

When the time came for them to go, Teresita did not want to leave the convent: they had to promise her that she should come and live with Aunt Teresa. And if Lorenzo rattled his doubloons a little noisily during the conversation, it was to declare that in future he would make himself responsible for the entire expenses of the convent and for the purchase of a house.

A few days later the nuns had beds, some utensils, and finally food to eat, while an awning stretched over the patio made the heat more bearable.

Teresita, in a frieze dress of suitable size, trotted about the convent 'like a friendly sprite' to the great joy of the sisters who at recreation never tired of hearing her tell 'stories of the sea and the Indians.' [2] A brief respite. . . .

---

[1] Spaniards who went to the Indies and returned were known as Indians—Tr.
[2] CTA, lxxix.

III

THE FULMINATIONS OF THE MASTER GENERAL

IN insisting that Mother Teresa of Jesus should go and found a convent in Seville, the reverend Apostolic Visitor, P. Jerónimo Gracián de la Madre de Dios, had disobeyed Our Lord. He had also disobeyed the Master General of the Carmelite Order, the Most Reverend Father Juan Bautista Rubeo.

It was not the first time that he had put the decisions of the Master General on one side, and yet one could not accuse him of rebellion for he found himself in a difficult position, caught between Scylla and Charybdis, *i.e.* between Philip II and the General of his Order. The persecutions of which Discalced friars and nuns were to be the butt for nearly five years can be attributed to no other cause, though it must always be remembered that the ill-will of the Calced friars made matters worse. This ill-will was to degenerate into hatred, as happens when there are differences between brethren. In an age when women were thought little of, the Mitigated friars could ill brook the striking success of Teresa of Jesus' Reform. The veneration with which she was surrounded, the general admiration which her sons and daughters aroused, were a perpetual stumbling block to the Mitigated friars and at the same time the example of the austerities of the Discalced was a thorn in their flesh: it was becoming far too obvious that the Mitigated were well clad, well shod, abundantly fed, comfortably lodged, and, above all, unmortified. They had been particularly upset at the return to the primitive Rule imposed on the convent of the Incarnation in Ávila: was this thirst for austerities going to spread to all their monasteries one by one? They were certainly in need of it: in Seville itself had not the police found 'two friars in a house of ill-fame' in broad daylight? 'They were taken to prison publicly, which was very bad; for,' added the Foundress who recounted the fact, 'weaknesses don't surprise me, but I could wish that some regard were had to honour.' [1]

When a Discalced friar, P. Gracián, was made Visitor of the

[1] CTA, lxxiv.

Mitigated there was panic and a state of war ensued. Barbarous excesses in penance, such as those of the Pastrana friars against which Teresa had protested and inveighed through the intermediary of John of the Cross, justified the Calced friars in their own eyes. When they decided to bring to nought the Foundress and her frenzied friars and ecstatic nuns, they were convinced that what they were striving for was for the good of the Order. The nomination of P. Gracián supplied them with a pretext which had every appearance of being an unanswerable argument.

It was the King, Philip II, who in his zeal for monastic austerity wanted to carry Teresa of Jesus' Reform into the very heart of the Mitigation: his zeal was so great that he considered P. Rubeo was moving too slowly. He got the Pope to agree that through the Nuncio, Ormaneto, he should appoint two Visitors, P. Pedro Fernández for the province of Castile and Fray Francisco de Vargas for Andalusia. Both were Dominicans.

Such Visitors were directly dependent on the crown and on the Holy See, which could give them orders directly contrary to those of the Carmelite Master General.

P. Fernández, who was extremely tactful, managed this delicate situation without any difficulties and succeeded in making himself acceptable to the Calced friars; he contented himself with placing a few Discalced among them, instructing the former to initiate them into a more austere way of life.

In Andalusia the matter was quite different. P. Vargas decided to found a considerable number of monasteries of Discalced friars who were to give an example of strict observance as practised by the disciples of Fray John of the Cross and Fray Antonio de Jesús. The Nuncio ordered these foundations, but the Most Reverend Master General of the Order, Rubeo, had not authorized them. Such was the situation P. Gracián found when the powers of Apostolic Visitor were delegated to him by P. Vargas.

To obey the Sovereign Pontiff, his Nuncio and the King, therefore, he had to act in formal opposition to the Superior General of his Order. To accept, he needed as much courage as he did coolness.

He left Pastrana with P. Mariano and set off for Andalusia: there, both received an imperious order from P. Ángel de Salazar, Provincial of the Mitigated or Calced Carmelites, and their Provincial also, for Calced and Discalced were not divided into separate provinces, instructing them to return to their monastery in Castile, under pain of being considered 'rebellious and contumacious.' One can understand why Mother Teresa made the separation of the two branches of the Order her essential objective.

Gracián set aside this command in virtue of his apostolic commission and continued his mission in Andalusia which the Nuncio confirmed.

If only P. Gracián and P. Mariano had deigned to follow Mother Teresa's advice when she begged them to inform the General, P. Rubeo, of the complicated situation in which they found themselves! She knew perfectly well that one could always count on a good reception from this worthy man if one went to him with frankness and confidence. But the Visitors, being young, thought they knew better than the old Foundress, they turned a deaf ear and the first P. Rubeo heard of their 'rebellion' was the violent protest of the Calced friars.

His anger was terrible. That was it then, was it? His most cherished sons, his beloved *figlia*, were setting themselves up against him? Against Gracián and Mariano he obtained a brief of recall, which he kept in reserve in order to hurl at them with more effect at the General Chapter of the Order which was about to take place at Piacenza in Italy.

Thus, the position of the convent at Seville was that it had been founded at the command of an Apostolic Visitor whom his superior was preparing to denounce; and because of this circumstance, Mother Teresa of Jesus appeared equally guilty.

She had no opportunity of clearing herself in time: if the letter in which she tried to defend herself and above all to defend Gracián had not reached the Master General with inexplicable delay, her spirited, sincere and skilful defence might perhaps have saved everything. All she could be blamed for was that she charged Ambrosio Mariano with errors of judgement for which Gracián was nevertheless partly responsible, but she did not become aware until much later of the blunders of her favourite. She said to P. Rubeo: 'We quarrelled, particularly Mariano and myself, for he is extremely impulsive, but Gracián is like an angel; if he had been alone, things would have turned out differently. . . .' [1]

We are surprised to find the Mother Foundress's perspicacity at fault. But no woman could bear entirely alone the crushing burden which had been hers for years. It was in 1574 that she wrote for the first time: ' . . . I am old and tired.' [2] Eight or nine months later 'she met Gracián and saw in him the man capable of supporting and succeeding her. He was far from having her intelligence, diplomacy and,

[1] CTA, lxxiv.   [2] CTA, lx.

above all, her lights, but it was necessary that she should be convinced that someone else could accomplish what she could no longer undertake alone. Her work was slipping from her by its very extension. Which of us would not have done as she did in like circumstances?

In this letter to P. Rubeo, she repeated for the second time and in the self-same words: ' . . . I am old and tired . . . all this has meant for me an effort beyond my strength. . . .'[1] This admission—it cannot be called a complaint, for we are talking of a woman who never complained—was to become a kind of refrain which fell from her pen the whole time she was in Seville.

To her explanation of the facts, she added in her long missive to P. Rubeo loyal and warm expressions of her affection for him, but it was too late, too many slanders and misunderstandings had been accumulated for him to be touched by what she said: 'I would have Your Lordship know first of all, for the love of Our Lord, that all the Discalced put together are nothing to me in comparison with Your Lordship's very habit. That is a fact and I would give my eyes to save Your Lordship the slightest displeasure.'[2]

It is possible for an angry man, even if he is holy, to refuse to believe in the sincerity of such ardently expressed feelings. Moreover, the Chapter at Piacenza was drawing to a close and nobody could now prevent the fulminations from taking their full effect.

Such was the state of affairs.

We left Lorenzo de Cepeda trying to buy a house in which the convent of St Joseph might be installed. Since his arrival the fast of the Carmelites had been as prescribed by the Rule and not the result of their extreme indigence.

It was November 1575: P. Gracián had arrived in Seville and the orders of the King and the Nuncio Ormaneto were definite: he must visit all monasteries of the Calced Carmelites.

The return of her 'dear son' only caused Teresa further suffering: the Calced friars were in revolt against what they considered an intrusion, and 'a person of weight has told the Archbishop that they would go so far as to kill him.' Methods of violence were not infrequent at this period when God's law was not always successful in overcoming strong passions even in religious houses. The Foundress reassured herself when she remembered that some Franciscans who were dissatisfied with their Visitor had nevertheless not killed him. . . . But when P. Gracián presented the Nuncio's brief at the *Casa*

[1] CTA, lxxiv.　　　　[2] Idem.

Grande of the Calced friars in Seville, he found them, said María de San José, prepared to defend themselves with arms. A scuffle broke out and such cries were heard behind the closed doors that they came to tell 'our Mother' who was at prayer with all her nuns, that P. Jerónimo Gracián had been assassinated. But she was not left to the mercy of false news. Our Lord calmed her panic:

'O, woman of little faith! Calm yourself, for all is well!'[1]

There was in point of fact more noise than real harm done, but Teresa was so frightened that for a long time afterwards she begged Gracián never to take his meals with the Calced friars, nor in their neighbourhood, lest they should poison him.

The nameless novice with the reputation for sanctity had left Carmel, furious when she realized that so many austerities were above her strength. Teresa of Jesus was glad she had gone and did not reflect that to mean souls revenge is sweet. Opportunity was not wanting. For although the Archbishop sometimes visited Mother Teresa, won by her charm which was made up of so much human graciousness of every kind subordinated to divine grace—he sent wheat and provisions to the convent—the Sevillans did not seem to have got over their suspicions. The folk around eyed with no goodwill this house where Mass was said without ever a bell ringing to call the neighbours to join in the prayers: there seemed something suspicious about it.

An event occurred which gave them their answer: one day, causing great excitement in the Calle de las Armas, the Inquisition and its train descended upon the 'foreigners.' Contrary to custom, everything was done with 'the most scandalous' publicity.[2] They came in great numbers. Judges and notaries entered the convent of St Joseph, while constables and servants stood about in groups in the street or mounted guard before the exits.

They searched the house and questioned Teresa of Jesus, who was always at her best under trials, whereas the nuns were in a panic. The heads of accusation bore visible trace of the calumnies of the proud *beata*, the novice as to whose name Carmel would be silent for all eternity, the one who preferred to defame the Carmelites rather than own herself defeated by their virtues.

The Foundress was suspected of nothing less than of following the shameful principles of the *Alumbrados*: that could have far-reaching consequences for a woman whose writings had been delated and whose ecstasies, which were supernatural manifestations, attracted dangerous attention.

[1] SEC, vol. II, p. 82, n. 4.   [2] LO, vol. VI, c. xxx, art. I.

Their very poverty was made a subject of complaint against the nuns: not having sufficient veils in which to present themselves at the parlour grille, they passed the few they had to each other and this was interpreted by the spy-novice as 'a ceremony.'

After receiving Holy Communion they turned to the wall to make their thanksgiving, for the communion grille was in a patio where the sun beat down fiercely: this was another suspicious rite.

It was alleged that the Foundress forced the nuns to confess their sins to her. . . . Teresa remembered the sly novice who walked about noiselessly and often pushed the door open seemingly inadvertently when she was talking with one of her nuns of spiritual matters, a practice they all loved. What were they *not* accused of? The reformed Carmelites—people said it was a certain fact—fastened themselves together with feet and wrists bound, and practised mutual scourging. . . . 'I hope to goodness they've said nothing else!' added María de San José. . . .

That day the Inquisitors went away as they had come, to the disappointment of the crowd who had hoped to see them take these nuns who had come down from the north away with them. But the situation remained just as serious. The suspension of the trial merely indicated a want of glaring proof: this tribunal always endeavoured to obtain such evidence and usually with success.

The threat restored all Teresa's courage. 'Not only did I experience no sense of trouble, but a joy so unusual that obviously it did not come from myself alone; what King David did when he went before the ark of the Lord does not surprise me, then, I would willingly have done the same. . . . Not to found any more convents, if it had not been for the displeasure of the Master General, would have been a great rest for me.' [1]

For the fulminations of P. Rubeo had just fallen on the Discalced; the decree of Piacenza ordered the dissolution of the monasteries founded without P. Rubeo's authorization, and the friars were condemned to leave within three days, under pain of the most serious penalties: in case of refusal recourse might be had to the secular arm.

As to the Mother Foundress, she was forbidden to proceed with further foundations, was to return to Castile immediately and never again to leave the convent where she chose to be confined. P. Salazar declared her 'apostate and excommunicated.'

Teresa would have liked to set out for Castile immediately: 'They

[1] Sb, F, c. xxvii-20.

think they're hurting me, but to me it's such a great good that I fear the day will never come. . . . It would be great happiness for me no longer to live among the bustle and disturbance of the Reformed. . . . I've often wanted to finish my life in peace: those who are endeavouring to procure this for me think they are causing me the greatest pain in the world, and other like "benefits." . . .' [1]

The Nuncio did not interpret the decree in this way and P. Gracián ordered her at least to finish the Seville foundation.

Never since the grave affair of St Joseph's in Ávila had Teresa of Jesus suffered so much. Her suffering was increased by her horror of Andalusia, she wavered and persisted in trying to honour P. Rubeo by obeying him in preference to anyone else.

María de San José produced an unanswerable argument:

'Your Reverence cannot go. What would happen if the Inquisition which is inquiring into the false testimony of this novice against us should come here to take you and not find you?'

María was right and the Foundress was amused about it:

'Sister, you have a strange way of comforting me in my great trouble: you assure me that the Inquisition is going to put me in prison!' [2]

She was able to laugh again: it was one of her ways of loving submission under the hand of Our Lord.

From this moment joy never left her. María de San José, who shared her cell at night, often heard her praising God in low tones or singing softly: *Magnificat anima mea Dominum.* . . .

She gave thanks for all that hurt, for all that would have slowly crushed another but which she turned into joy on the spiritual plane. Now she was sensitive only where others were concerned, over the grief of P. Rubeo whom unwillingly she had deeply hurt, over the danger with which her nuns and friars and the work she had begun were threatened. *No estamos para coplas,*[3] 'we're in no mood for songs,' he wrote to her niece María Bautista who sent her some verses. At this time Gracián, on whom troubles were falling 'like hail,' no longer found in her the sympathy he expected: when he told her all the evil people were saying of her, her joy was so great that she rubbed her hands together. . . . She was filled to overflowing with the graces Our Lord sent her as was shown by the two accounts of her spiritual life which she was asked to submit to P. Rodrigo Álvarez, the Inquisitor, together with other documents for her case. She was taught sublime truths by Our Lord himself. One day when she was afraid at

[1] Sb, F, c. xxvii-20.   [2] MJ.   [3] CTA, lxxxvii.

seeing so much majesty 'in a thing as base as my soul, I heard: "It is not base, daughter, for it is made in my image."' [1]

He made her understand how God is in all things: 'As an example he gave me that of a sponge which absorbs water into itself. . . .' [2]

Another time when she was thinking 'that this life which deprives us of the marvellous company of God is very hard' and when she said inwardly, 'Lord, help me to bear to go on living,' he said to her: 'Daughter, consider that when life has ended you will no longer be able to serve me as you do now, and eat for me, sleep for me, do all you do for me, as if it were no longer you who were living, but myself. . . .'

It was at Seville that she experienced the desire, 'not to die too soon,' [3] for she longed to serve, more than ever.

Though the world hunted her down, she could have danced like David. She did not even ask that justice should be done her, yet the nameless novice had entered another convent where they considered her mad. And the renown of Teresa of Jesus' sanctity began to spread in Seville.

She was none the less humble on that account. The most bitter mortification that P. Gracián could impose on her was a general confession, for the memory of her sins was torture to her, whereas the customary mortification of going to the refectory carrying a heavy cross seemed 'recreation and delight' to her.

Nevertheless, fervour in the convent ran to extremes. On feast-days the sisters represented the life and sufferings of the holy martyrs 'so vividly and with such fervour' [4] that Teresita, the little niece from America, was terrified on one occasion and had to be taken away. These nuns were fired with impatience for heavenly glory; they felt that persecution would afford them an opportunity of being dispatched straight to paradise by the executioner. The Foundress calmed them down. She knew now that it was more important to live, in order to serve.

The 'business' of the new house was going forward. Don Lorenzo de Cepeda indeed had had to use the right of sanctuary to escape imprisonment on account of disputes with an owner—but was anything else but trickery to be expected in a city which had more than forty courts of justice? The Franciscans were strongly opposed to

---

[1] SEC, R, liv and xlv.   [2] Idem.
[3] Idem, xlii.   [4] Idem, vol. VI, p. 309.

Carmelites settling in their immediate vicinity, but Teresa was not now to be frightened off by such a small difficulty: the nuns entered the house by night; a few of the more timid did take 'every shadow for a friar,' [1] but when confronted with the *fait accompli* 'the friars remained as silent as the dead.' [2]

The house was worth the risk. 'It is of such a kind that the sisters never cease to render thanks for it. All of them say that we have had it for nothing. . . .' [3] Teresa loved to describe it and to point to what was for her its principal attraction: 'The orchard is very delightful and the view extremely fine.' 'A house from which one can see the galleons is not to be despised. . . .' [4] In the distance they could see the Guadalquivir glittering in the sun.

'Covered with green boughs and white sails. . . .'[5]

In the long letter she wrote to P. Ambrosio Mariano Azaro giving him an account of the completion of this foundation, she passed from one idea to another with an astonishing buoyancy. It was not that she forgot the persecutions. 'I'm very much afraid of this business in Rome. . . . I should like to see our business about the Discalced settled—the separation of the Reformed and Mitigated into two provinces—for Our Lord will now no longer tolerate the behaviour of the Calced, and all these troubles will come to an end. . . .' But the feeling of triumph was dominant, together with a certain natural satisfaction at having overcome so many obstacles. It was in a playful tone that she addressed P. Mariano: 'God help us! What a fine state you are in, leading people into temptation! It must be very virtuous to write to you. . . . When I consider how entangled the situation in which Your Reverence left me was and how you ignore it all, I don't know what to think, except cursed be the man, etc. . . .' [6] The etc. cut short what might have been the lamentation of Jeremias, and Teresa gave free rein to her joy. Joy which was perhaps a little exuberant and which one would attribute to a sort of plenitude of physical well-being after a strain if we were not talking of a woman who was more or less a confirmed invalid. Her style is that of someone young and full of vigour. She is sixty-one, but her phrases are charged with enthusiasm, fervour, humour, feeling, they explain, describe, chide or bless without a tremor, and her enthusiasm is that of youth.

In María de San José she was to leave a great prioress at Seville. 'I marvel at her courage; she has much more than I have. . . .'

[1] Cf. Sb, F, c. xxv–7.   [2] CTA, xciv.   [3] Idem.
[4] CTA, cccxxvi.   [5] Lope de Vega.   [6] CTA, xciv.

Complaints were forgotten. Teresa contemplated her work and found that it was good.

It was of this joy that P. Gracián wanted to have some lasting souvenir. He took advantage of the presence of Fray Juan de la Miseria to get this former pupil of Sánchez Coello to paint the Foundress's portrait. She had to submit to 'moving neither head nor eyes,' and to holding her hands together at the height of her shoulders. These sittings she found extremely tiresome, and she declared: 'God forgive you, Fray Juan! You've made me ugly and blear-eyed! [1]

He also painted the portrait of Teresita which earned him nothing but praise.

The convent of St Joseph of Seville still had to be inaugurated.

I should have liked them to bring the Blessed Sacrament there without anyone knowing, for I am opposed to causing people pain when it is possible to avoid it—we don't want to humiliate those responsible for the persecution. On the other hand a good deal of solemnity seemed indispensable if the convent were to be made known. The Archbishop gave orders to invite the clergy and decorate the streets.

Our cloister served as an entrance, the good Garciálvarez decorated it admirably as he did the church, too, he set up fine altars and was a very prodigy of inventiveness. Among other things there was a fountain perfumed with orange-flower which impressed us greatly. The magnificent way in which our festival was organized was a great satisfaction to all the nuns, as were the streets so gay with flags and so much music and so many minstrels; the saintly prior of Las Cuevas told me that nothing so fine had ever been seen at Seville. The Archbishop himself installed the Blessed Sacrament.

So you see, sisters, the poor Discalced nuns are honoured by everybody; a short time before, however, you wouldn't have thought there was even water for them, although there's quite a lot in this river. . . .

The congregation was an extremely large one. . . .[2]

What Teresa did not say was that after the procession she knelt before the Archbishop and asked him for his blessing which he gave her; she had hardly risen from her knees when, in front of this extremely large' congregation, the Archbishop of Seville, Don Cristóbal de Rojas, knelt down in his turn and asked Mother Teresa of Jesus, Foundress of the convents of the reformed Carmel, to bless him.

---

[1] JG, PA, D, xiii.   [2] Sb, F, c. xxv-12.

On her arrival in Andalusia, Teresa had been treated as an undesirable person, abused, threatened, dragged before the Inquisition. Now they recognized in her such a perfect portrait of perfection in all its forms that one of the highest dignitaries of the Catholic, Apostolic and Roman Church treated her as one only treats prelates and saints.

That happened on 3rd June 1576. That very night at two o'clock in the morning she who was now called *la santa Madre*, in Seville as in Castile, set out for her place of exile.

IV

EXILE

HER brothers, Don Lorenzo and Don Pedro de Cepeda, her nephews, Francisco and Lorencito, a few lay persons of whom Antonio Ruiz was one, and a few friars, among them Fray Diego who was 'a little angel,' accompanied Teresa of Jesus; her niece, Teresita, the little 'nun' of nine, made them all merry.

Don Lorenzo who even then was pious though still somewhat attached to gorgeous display, horrified at the account of the vicissitudes of the journey from Beas to Seville, was determined that the return should be speedy and not uncomfortable; at his own expense they travelled by good coaches and carried abundant food with them. When there was no room in the inns, they took their meals in the fields, and if the Foundress was frightened on one occasion, it all ended as happily as possible; she hastened to tell Gracián about it:

'We were having our mid-day meal in the threshing barn when a great lizard darted in between my tunic and my bare arm, it was by the mercy of God that he didn't crawl in anywhere else, I think I should have died, considering what I felt as it was. . . . My brother caught the lizard quickly but he threw it from him in such a way that it jumped into the mouth of Antonio Ruiz. . . .'[1]

After a halt at Malagón they reached Toledo by way of Almodóvar. At Toledo malicious tongues chuckled over the style in which the Carmelite was travelling: 'a light woman travelling along the roads with ladies and gallants. . . .'[2]

Don Lorenzo was insistent that his sister should follow him to Ávila immediately. He intended to settle there, and Teresa's plan was also to stay in Ávila, but she preferred to stop for a few days at Toledo: this stay was to last a year.

She loved this convent which she called 'my house of delight,' *mi quinta de recreo*, enjoying the pun: Toledo was the fifth of her foundations—*quinta* in Spanish—and 'house of delight' is rendered by *quinta de recreo*. . . .[3]

[1] CTA, xcv.   [2] V quoted SEC, vol. VII, p. 240, n. 2.
[3] Y quoted LV, p. 131.

'I haven't been so well for years, I can fast like everyone else.
. . .'[1] '. . . They've given me a cell apart like a hermitage, very
cheerful and pleasant, looking on to the orchard. I am very little
troubled by visits, and if I had fewer letters to write. . . .'[2]

If the Mother Foundress had fewer letters to write, she would find
the inactivity terribly irksome. Already, when her instructions had
not been closely followed out she would complain: 'Jesús! What it is
to be far away when all these things are happening!'[3] 'If I were there,
I should soon have given all that a shaking up.'[4]

For from this cell, day and night, she continued to direct all her
convents and all the business of the Reform by correspondence. She
entered into the smallest details, there was no gauze or frieze for the
habits of the nuns in the most distant convents on which she did not
decide, no choice of novice over which she did not give her opinion,
in her way of seeming to advise rather than to command. Moreover
she only remained in Toledo because the posts were better organized
there than in Ávila. All that happened to herself and went on in the
Order during the persecutions went into her letters.

Did her austerity come out in her correspondence? She had the
art of treating serious subjects in few words and clearly and of taking
up again at once the spontaneous tone which makes her smile, her
laugh, the sound of her voice, whether tender or sharp, familiar to us.

All her letters bear traces of having been written under pressure or
in haste; she wrote as people speak when they have both wit, heart,
personality and style, and when they have at their disposal the very
thing that Teresa of Jesus lacked—time. For her enormous correspondence was scribbled in the midst of other occupations: 'Don't
trouble to re-read what you write to me,' she said to her brother
Lorenzo, 'I never do. If I miss out a letter put it in yourself. . . . Since
people understand what I mean, it would be to lose time to no
purpose. . . .'[5]

The quarrels between Calced and Discalced seemed to be moving
towards some sort of agreement and the Foundress was now less
anxious than she was at Seville. The General, P. Rubeo, had sent a
delegate to Spain, P. Tostado, who had failed to wrest from the
Nuncio Ormaneto the desired permission to disturb the reformed
convents: he left for Portugal, where it was hoped he might remain.

Gracián, who was still Apostolic Visitor, 'transforms enemies into
friends'[6] so peacefully that the Foundress was amazed. In the chapter

[1] CTA, ci. [2] CTA, cxv. [3] CTA, xcviii.
[4] CTA, cxx. [5] CTA, clxiii. [6] CTA, cxl.

at Almodóvar which met in August and September, he displayed wonderful moderation and charity. It was decided to go on with the Reform, in spite of the opposition of the Calced friars.

To the Discalced, P. Jerónimo Gracián de la Madre de Dios said:

We are being submerged by a wave of opposition. It does not come from our enemies but from Fathers who are our friends; not from sinners but from good people; their intentions are not evil but very good; it is the most fearsome of contests for our position is weak, whereas our enemies' strength comes from the fact that they are our so-called friends and that they are good and well-intentioned. . . . They seek our ruin under the guise of friendship and unity. . . . They have only too much human power, whereas we lack it, although that of the great Philip who is on our side is mighty.

The divine Power, too, is on our side. It is this divine Power which has brought our primitive Rule once more into the light of day and given to Mother Teresa strength to do things for this Rule which the nations have never before seen. . . . Let us pray to God for our enemies as Christ commands us; let us suffer and be silent for patience is always triumphant in the end and the time will come when they will be the first to preach our observance, defend our institution and uphold our primitive Rule.[1]

The Reformed did not swerve from this attitude.

This is illustrated, among other episodes, by the story of Paterna, where three Discalced nuns were sent to reform a convent of Mitigated Carmelites. Things began so badly that the good Discalced nuns, threatened with death by a lot of seeming mad women, spent the night barricaded in a room, struggling to prevent them from coming in. In the end the counsels of Mother Teresa won over the rebels. She wrote to the nuns who were there to carry out the Reform: 'Don't be surprised that they're not like we are straightway, it would be folly to expect it; don't insist so strictly that they're not to speak among themselves or on other things which are not sins; people accustomed to another and utterly different kind of life might make them commit more sins than they cured them of. Time is necessary, and the action of God, otherwise one will only throw them into despair.'[2]

Nothing disconcerted her, and when they raised a false accusation against one of the three Discalced nuns of Paterna, saying that she was 'a virgin but with child,' she merely said that it was 'utter rubbish.'[3]

And she showed no greater concern at the calumnies which rained down on the sons and daughters of Our Lady. 'I have been very much displeased that our Father—Gracián—should contradict the things said

[1] JG, C, vol. I, p. 557.   [2] CTA, clxiv.   [3] CTA, clxvii.

against us, particularly when they are unjust to that extent. To my way of thinking we should laugh at them and let them say what they will.' [1] She went so far as to declare that 'it is a great imperfection on the part of this Father.' [2]

'It is curious that nothing which happens has power to trouble me, so deeply is the certainty that all will be well rooted in me.'[3]

Yet she unceasingly recommended Gracián to be prudent. 'With time Your Paternity will lose a little of your ingenuousness, though I know it is the ingenuousness of a saint. . . .' [4] She was putting him on his guard and added: 'How unkind I am! But it's all necessary in this life!' [5]

If we had not her correspondence we should have no knowledge of a delightful side of the Mother Foundress's character: a nun's gaiety of the kind that clearly proves that the greatest minds can without detriment keep a childlike spirit in the course of a life hidden in God. 'I've received the coconuts. They're something worth seeing. The sisters are delighted with them and so am I. Blessed be he who made them, for truly they're a wonderful sight. . . .' [6] And Gracián himself proceeded to the solemn opening of the curious fruit in the course of a little ceremony. . . .

It was María de San José who had sent these presents: 'You're no doubt dreaming that you're a queen. . . .' [7] Teresa of Jesus loved sweets made of pink sugar, 'sugar-corporals—how gallant they are,' but what she loved most was orange-flower water and the oil extracted from it, for it enabled her to give *en passant* some of the recipes in which she delighted: 'Orange-flower oil is excellent for heart trouble. . . .'[8] 'For the heart, you must inhale orange-flower water, not drink it. . . .' [9]

One can picture the great excitement of the young nuns at Toledo when these parcels arrived from Andalusia. The sisters there were so skilful at embroidery that Teresa asked them to make her a pall 'all in chain-stitch, small, with pearls and garnets.' Passing from trivial to serious matters, in the same letter she gives directions about a nun who has just died: 'The body of this little saint must be left where it is, in the choir, for we must be buried in the cloister and not in the church.' [10]

Persecutions and a code of names: lest her correspondence should go astray or be intercepted by the Calced friars, she agreed with

[1] CTA, clxxii.   [2] CTA, clxxii.   [3] CTA, cxl.
[4] CTA, cxxxiv.   [5] CTA, cxli.   [6] CTA, clxxxv.
[7] Idem.   [8] CTA, ccxxxiii.   [9] CTA, cccix.   [10] CTA, clxxx.

Gracián on pseudonyms for the principal people they were likely to talk about. There was considerable humour in her choice of these 'war' names and also a sense of metaphor which suggests a slight tinge of *culteranismo* [1] which is present neither in her prose nor her poems. In this she was thirty years in advance of her time. The old Nuncio, Ormaneto, was merely 'Matusalem,' but the Mitigated friars were the 'cats' or 'owls,' because they lived in darkness; the Mitigated nuns were 'crickets,' because of their chatter; the Discalced friars were 'eagles,' because they gazed at God in contemplation, and she called her Discalced daughters 'the butterflies,' because of their simplicity. The Inquisitors were 'the angels' and 'the mighty Angel' the Grand Inquisitor-General, Cardinal Quiroga. This led to phrases like the following: 'The mighty Angel is very pleased to have a niece among the butterflies. . . .' [2] 'Matusalem has decided that our vow of separation from the eagles shall be fulfilled. . . .' [3]

Another person is frequently mentioned in these letters, and he too has his pseudonym: Joseph is the name for Our Lord during this period of strife. . . . 'Joseph has told me. . . . Joseph has assured me. . . .'

Persecution and 'ointments,' 'bottles of rose water,' and confirmation of her unswerving objective: 'I shall devote my life to our erection into a separate province for everything depends on that.' [4] Purges, Persian syrup, and apposite lessons in feminine psychology: 'What you tell me about the habits seems all right. Once it is done it will stay done, after a few days of querulous complaint: if a few are punished the others will be quiet, for women are like that, timid for the most part.' [5]

When P. Mariano tried to make her accept a novice whom she did not want, she told him most energetically that he understood nothing about women! 'Let Your Reverence not meddle with that any more, for the love of God! The girl has a good dowry, she can enter elsewhere and not in an Order where just because they are so few, subjects must be very, very carefully selected. Your Reverence amuses me when you say that you will very soon know her: we women are not so easy to know through and through. You hear our confessions for years and then one day you're surprised at having understood us so little; for in the matter of owning up to their faults women don't know themselves, and you judge them on what they tell you. . . .' [6]

---

[1] A literary movement somewhat, but not entirely, akin to euphuism in England—Tr.

[2] CTA, cvi.   [3] Idem.   [4] CTA, cxlvii.

[5] Idem.   [6] CTA, cxxi.

She gave orders that novices 'who seem just made for us and who will help us to pay our way' [1] were to have preference. . . . There was Blanca de Jesús María, whom she quaintly called 'the one with the gold ingots.' [2] 'Don't take the daughter of the Portuguese if what she's to bring is not paid over, for I've learned that we shouldn't get a *blanca* of it, and we're not living in times when we can take subjects for nothing. . . .' [3] 'I am dismayed to learn that Beatriz's mother is only bringing one thousand five hundred ducats, although she's the sort of girl whom we should gain by accepting even without anything. As regards what you say about the payment of what is due, it is obvious that it would be a very good thing to lighten the charges. If with Bernarda's dowry you can make up 3,000 ducats. . . .' [4]

Was this the woman who was called *la Santa Madre*? All this calculation of dowries and revenues? If her daughters had 'abandoned themselves entirely into Our Lord's arms,' [5] as she did, she would have had no need to have recourse to human artifice. When the convents fell into debt or had not enough to eat, the Foundress was distressed at the sisters' want of faith: 'Your faith in God must be weak indeed if you don't think he's powerful enough to give those who serve him enough to eat. . . .' [6] Then she resigned herself to the task of administration. It was then that she gave such strict directives which she herself was the very first to break: 'As to this little slave, don't oppose her admission in any way. In the case of her sister it's more difficult, but take her too . . . and you will be putting an end to their great difficulties.' [7] 'Give us people who are really worth while and you'll see that we're indifferent to the dowry.' [8] 'She has only 200 ducats: I prefer her to a fool.' [9] 'Take that other novice too, since she is so good; we need many, because many die. They go to heaven, so don't be sad about it. . . .' [10]

Such was Teresa of Jesus' attitude over death, far removed from the pagan pomp and circumstance of everlasting regret. She was once exasperated at having to use a seal representing two crossed tibias beneath a skull: 'I do hope my seal arrives quickly, for I can't bear sealing my letters with this skull, I want to use the seal which I hope he will impress on my heart, I.H.S.' [11] For her, death meant resurrection and therefore joy. When Petronila de San Andrés died 'like an angel' Teresa saw His Majesty, his arms wide open at the head of her bed, and

---

the seraphim welcoming her into paradise [1]; she forbade funeral hymns and composed *coplas* of joy which the sisters sang as they danced round the coffin. Years before she had written about her sister María whom she had loved so much: 'I experienced great joy when I learned of her death. . . .' [2] She had known then that María was hardly a week in purgatory and Our Lord showed her to her as she entered into glory.

Many saints have sympathized, perhaps too much, with the grief of those who were left: Teresa consoled them with infinite sweetness and tact, but also reminded them how fleeting their own existence was: 'Your Grace should consider that you haven't a long life to live; it is all so brief that your solitude will only last a moment.' [3] And she sent the widower two melons 'although they're not as good as I should have liked. . . .'

Thus she softened with a gracious word or a gift whatever might appear hard in her detachment from created things. But, as leader, it was her duty to look to discipline. The discipline she imposed was sometimes severe. 'No sister may go out of her convent, be she prioress or ordinary sister, unless it be for a foundation.[4] Although I have authority to transfer to another convent a sister whom the climate does not suit, the effects of such changes are intolerable; it is better that some should die rather than that all should take harm.' [5] Can this be the same woman who, that very year, had written letter after letter about the illness of the prioress of Malagón, Brianda de San José, worrying about the slightest details. 'I am appalled at your being ordered to get up in this weather. For charity's sake, don't do so; it's enough to kill you, it's painful and difficult even for those who are fat and well. . . .' [6] She made the journey herself to go and fetch Mother Brianda and bring her to Toledo where the climate was milder. She none the less recommended María de San José a vigorous therapeutic to calm an outbreak of nerves: 'A few strokes with the whip will perhaps make her be quiet and won't do her any harm. . . .' [7]

The art of government, which she exercised in so masterly a way, would seem to be the art of contradicting oneself without unsaying what has been said and of yielding without being soft. She was strong enough to afford to be kind without people ever being able to accuse her of weakness. When she was angry it was with a promptitude and energy which left no room for doubt as to the firmness of her character.

[1] SEC, vol. V, p. 127.   [2] Sb, V, c. xxxiv-19.   [3] CTA, clvi.
[4] CTA, lxxxi.   [5] Idem.   [6] CTA, clii.   [7] CTA, ccxxxiii.

After Brianda de San José's departure, there was trouble in the convent at Malagón over a question of precedence which had arisen between Ana de la Madre de Dios who was acting as temporary prioress and Beatriz de Jesús: this proved clearly that Teresa knew perfectly well what she was saying when she said that nuns should not be moved for any reason, except for the needs of new foundations: but when she infringed her own directives and applied the remedy with a strong hand, she knew equally well what she was doing. The chaplain at Malagón learned this forthwith:

'Your Grace's letters have caused me great distress; it is like death to me to think that in one of these houses things are going worse than with the Calced nuns in Andalusia. . . . I cannot do otherwise than blame Your Reverence for it. . . . Your Reverence will see where these quarrellers who cause me such worries end up. I beg you to tell this Beatriz so from me. My state of mind in regard to her is such that I do not even want her named in my hearing. . . .' [1] *This Beatriz* was her cousin-german, but she expected more of those who were her kin than of others.

She went into the details of the dispute and frankly took the chaplain to task: 'If Your Reverence does not undo what the devil has begun to weave, everything will go from bad to worse. I shall be sorry to lose you, but I see that you prefer your peace and quietness to rendering me service.' [2]

The letter was addressed to the 'Very Magnificent and Reverend Señor Villanueva, Licentiate,' a good many titles to give him on the occasion of his dismissal.

It must be admitted that he allowed his penitents to adopt strange customs: 'I've learnt that certain mortifications are practised at Malagón: that the prioress orders the sisters to slap each other when they least expect it; I also hear of pinches. . . . The devil seems to be teaching you the way to destroy souls. And I hear about this only now!' [3] There is every reason to think that if the Mother Foundress had been free to go about, she would have gone like lightning to Malagón.

No one had so much authority as she had for keeping in good order eleven convents of women and numerous monasteries of men, and no one had her tact and ability. To mingle severity and kindness in the right proportion, always to show the widest possible understanding, was what she set out to do and what she did. And so when she was at Toledo unable to move, she wrote very detailed instructions

[1] CTA, clxxxvii. [2] Idem. [3] CTA, cxxxi.

for the Visitors and in particular for P. Gracián. And if she apologized for doing so, it was to give greater force to her recommendations:

> It may seem troublesome for a prelate to investigate all the details he will find here, but it would be much more annoying for him to observe the absence of progress in his subjects if he ignored such details. However good they may be, all this is necessary. Women whom one intends to govern must understand that the person in authority will not give way for anything in the world, will insist on all the rules of the Order being obeyed and will punish their infraction; they must see that he looks to this point particularly and realize that not only will he visit them each year but that he knows what they are doing day by day. . . .[1]

In the convents of her Reform, there was nothing of what went on day by day that the Foundress did not know.

She took up a troublesome Visitor as sharply as she did the too easy-going chaplain.

'You now see the trouble caused by the Acts drawn up by Fray Juan de Jesús. Even to read them made me tired: what would it be if I had to observe them? That is just what my nuns fear: the coming of powerful prelates who overburden and crush them. Believe me, our Rule has no room for these ponderous people, it is already ponderous enough itself. . . .'[2] In Spanish these 'ponderous' prelates, 'ponderous' people, are described by the same term as is used for 'boring' people. The nuance appears in Teresa's letter.

She herself was not one of such boring people. Her laugh rang out, her wit was sparkling. Gracián had charged María de San José to see to it that all went well in the convent of Paterna. 'You must be proud of being "half Mother Provincial" . . . I laugh to see myself overwhelmed with correspondence, so much so that I begin to write impertinences. . . .'[3]

The memory of the misunderstandings with the prioress of Seville had been blotted out long ago, and her letters were now the best of recreations for Teresa. She was delighted at the multitude of details in them, and declared they were her very life, *con esto vivo.* . . .[4] It was with this same María that she playfully pretended to quarrel.

It's all very fine to pretend that there's nobody like Teresita! I would have you know that my *Bela* [Isabel Dantisco, an eight years

---

[1] Sb, MVC, 36.   [2] CTA, cxxxiii.
[3] CTA, clxii.   [4] CTA, cxliv.

old novice, who was Teresa's joy at Toledo for she adored children]
is marvellously clever. With a few poor little shepherd boys, the
other young ones and a picture of Our Lady, she delights us on feast
days and at recreation by her inventiveness and the *coplas* she sings
to us. She causes me only one anxiety. I do not know how to correct
her mouth which is pursed; she laughs very coldly and she laughs all
the time. I make her shut and open her mouth and I stop her laughing. She says she can't do anything about it and that it's the fault of
her mouth. Don't repeat this to anyone but I should like you to see
me engaged in correcting her mouth. I tell you all this to make you
laugh. . . .[1] Ah! what a head your Foundress has![2]

It is true that this little Isabel, *la mia Bela,* was Gracián's young
sister. This family entranced Teresa. When she first met their mother,
Doña Juana Dantisco, she threw on to paper an impetuous letter to
this 'Paul,' 'Eliseus,' 'her dear son.'

I am crazy about her simplicity and clear intelligence, in that she
has the advantage over her son. . . . We were together as if we had
known each other all our lives. . . . Your Paternity amused me
when you authorized me to raise my veil for your mother: anyone
would think you didn't know me, I who wanted to open my heart
to her. I've been wondering which of us two Your Paternity loves
best, and I feel that Señora Doña Juana has a husband to love and
other children, whereas poor Lorencia [Teresa of Jesus gave herself
this name in some of her letters to Gracián] has only this Father in the
whole world. God grant that she may keep him for her consolation.[3]

Not many canonized saints have spoken so warmly and humanly.
A month later she wrote to him: 'Your Paternity must ask God to
make a true nun of Carmel of me, for better late than never. . . .'[4]

What is so remarkable is that in all her words, whether serious or
amusing, as for instance in the account of her *Life* or in the most
sublime pages of the *Interior Castle,* she speaks with deep humility of
her failures and faults and of the trouble the least progress towards
perfection causes her. She was not endowed by nature for sanctity,
but she has *become* a true nun of Carmel, she has become the great saint
of Ávila and one of the most influential minds in the world without
on that account ceasing to sparkle with gaiety, charm and often even
with mischief. For her the sign of the cross really is the *plus* sign; she
loses nothing of what she is and in addition there is the tremendous

working of the Spirit in her, and its extension in the world through her. Teresa de Ahumada + God = Saint Teresa of Jesus.

The most austere penance, the hardest and most exacting life of action, have never altered her womanliness. In her it is womanhood which is purified and sublimated.

And Teresa de Ahumada de Jesús has certainly formed more daughters of Eve for divine love than 'gloomy' woman saints have done.

V

DON LORENZO DE CEPEDA, INDIAN

FORMERLY she used to write: 'Señor. . . .' Now she begins her letters: 'May Jesus be with your Grace.' Formerly she ended: 'Your Grace's true servant.' Now she ends: 'I kiss Your Grace's hands more than once.' The 'Grace' is her brother, Lorenzo de Cepeda.

Already he had been her benefactor: now he was her disciple and her confidant as well. The missives she sent him from Toledo were interminable, for if she directed him in spiritual things, she was also his administrator in temporal affairs.

Don Lorenzo was Governor of the Municipal Council of Quito, Treasurer of the Royal Coffers, Mayor of the capital of Ecuador, and son-in-law of Don Francisco de Fuentes, one of the conquerors of Peru who took part in the capture of Atahualpa. He was a charming man—'my brother will cease to be charming when he ceases to live,' and both serious and devout—'he deserves the name of Carmelite,' said María de San José. He was rich, his lands in the Indies were worth 35,000 pesos, he had brought back to Spain 45,000 pesos in merchandise and saved 28,000 pesos in gold. He had now reached the mature age of fifty-seven but he was just like a small boy where his sister Teresa was concerned.

He dared not move one straw from its place without consulting her. Without her, his surroundings would be all wrong, he would be ill lodged, would throw away all his fortune like so much dust, would lose his soul by making a virtue of laziness and his boys would be very badly brought up.

'Let Your Grace not forget to take no special confessor for the moment, and the least number possible of people for your house: it is better to choose servants one by one than to have to send people away. . . .' [1]

He had rented a house in Ávila: 'Be careful, for I seem to remember hearing that one of the rooms in this house of Hernán Álvarez de Peralta is collapsing: take great care.' [2] Even after conquering the Indies one can let oneself be cheated by a not very high-principled landlord.

[1] CTA, ci.   [2] CTA, clviii.

He wanted to cut a good figure. The vainglory of the father is nothing in comparison with that of his sons. Accordingly his sister hastens to send him a 'memorandum' on the bringing up of Lorencito and Francisco.

> If someone does not take these children in hand immediately, I'm very much afraid that they will soon be just the same as all the other conceited boys of Ávila. Your Grace must send them to the Jesuits at once and make schoolboys of them.
> Your Grace thinks too much about the point of honour, mortify yourself in that. I would prefer that you didn't buy a mule for the present but only a nag to use for journeys and your daily needs. As to these children, they'll do well enough walking: let them get on with their studies.[1]

Teresa was typical of the old Spain, hard-working and serious, sober in its simple and patriarchal way of life; Don Lorenzo and his sons represented the new Spain, Spain beyond the seas, the Spain of easy money, of a life of luxury and idleness. Two epochs came into conflict in these two people who were so fond of each other. Naturally, it was Teresa who won, and the pity was that every *conquistador* on his return to Spain had not a sister Teresa by him, gifted with an equally clear instinct for economy: then the gold of the Indies would not have impoverished the realm.

Three miles away from Ávila, in the valley of the Adaja, Don Lorenzo bought a fine piece of wheat-growing and pasture land: 14,000 ducats.

Almost immediately he regretted it and complained: it would give him a great deal of work. . . . He would have done better to put out his money to interest; the sum properly invested would have given him a good income without any work. The rich man thought he was putting forward an unanswerable argument when he wrote to his Carmelite sister: ' I should then have more time for prayer.'

He was very much mistaken. She broke out:

> Don't let me hear any more of it. You should be praising God for this transaction. Don't imagine that if you had more time your prayer would be better. Undeceive yourself: time well spent in looking after the welfare of your children does not injure prayer. God often gives more in a moment than in long hours: his works are not measured by time. . . . Jacob who was busy with his flocks was none the less holy for that, nor Abraham, nor St Joachim. But we find everything tiring when we want to avoid work. . . .[2]

[1] CTA, ci.   [2] CTA, clviii.

Over there the *conquistador* had acquired the habit of living in grand style and of having slaves to do his work. That was why, rather than work himself he would have preferred to make money work in his stead, in order to provide him with leisure: this did not please Teresa at all, even though the leisure might be devoted to conversing with God: we must serve him 'as he wishes and not as we wish.' [1] 'God has given something better than wealth to your children, he has given them honour' [2]—the honour of these old Castilian families like the Cepeda y Ahumada, the honour of men like their father, Don Alonso Sánchez, who did not think it beneath him to carry out his duties as a country estate-owner. And the Carmelite quietly laughed at the Mayor of Quito: 'Don't you think that collecting your revenues would also give you a certain amount of work?' [3]

Don Lorenzo, the Indian, felt he had had his answer.

So now the sons would be at school and the father busy looking after his lands. Temporal affairs were settled, now for the spiritual.

She got him to read the *Way of Perfection*, particularly chapter XXX in which she comments on these few words from the *Pater noster*: 'Thy kingdom come,' and in this way tried to persuade him to surrender himself to Our Lord's will: this will for him was work. It was not unintentionally that in the Constitutions of Our Lady's Order the Foundress had written: 'Whoever wants to eat must work.' [4]

The disciple made very good progress. In the letters which Teresa wrote him, a fraternal exchange of confidences alternated with the most practical and sensible advice of any she gave:

I must tell you that for more than a week I have been in such a state that if it lasted I should find it more than difficult to attend to so much business. I have begun to have raptures again and this has been painful to me, for it has happened several times in public and at Matins. There is no way either of resisting or of concealing the fact. It causes me so much embarrassment that I should like to hide anywhere I could. I am begging God to spare me this in public; do you ask him, too, for it brings very awkward consequences, and it does not seem to me that prayer gains thereby. I am like one drunk. . . . Let us thank the Lord for one another! [5]

For Don Lorenzo told her about the great graces which Our Lord had granted him too. His sister spoke with her usual prudence: 'I don't know what to say to you, it's more than you can probably understand, and the beginning of many blessings if you don't lose them by your own fault. . . .' [6]

[1] Idem.   [2] Idem.   [3] Idem.
[4] CONS, 24.   [5] CTA, clxiii.   [6] Idem.

She tried however to define this state, using once more the delightfully halting accents of the account of her first ecstasies: 'It is a great suffering without pain, without reason, extremely delightful. . . . It is a wound which the love of God makes in the soul, one knows not where, nor how, nor if it be a wound, nor what it is; it is merely that one experiences a sweet pain, and one complains about it thus:

> Lord, You hurt without wounding,
> And without pain you destroy
> The love of creatures . . .

For when the soul is really touched by this love of God, the love for creatures fades away without any suffering.' [1]

It was in reply to a question her brother put to her when he was extremely troubled that Teresa touched on the very thorny point of the physical repercussions of mystical love; she did so with extraordinary delicacy or, to speak more accurately, with sublime indifference:

Of the disturbed feelings which follow, take no notice; that has never happened to me. God in his goodness has always spared me these passions, but I understand that the soul's keen delight causes a natural movement; if you don't pay any attention, that will wear off by God's grace. Several persons have spoken to me of it.

The tremblings will also disappear; for the soul, when confronted with what is absolutely new and strange to it, is frightened and it is enough to make it afraid. The more frequently these things happen, the more able the soul will become to receive these graces. Your Grace should resist such tremors as much as possible and every external manifestation, in order that such things may not become a habit; that does not help but rather hinders.

The heat you say you feel is of no importance; only it could be harmful to one's health if it were excessive; but it will disappear like the tremors. In my opinion, such things follow the humours and as Your Grace is sanguine, the great movement of the mind, with the natural heat which collects at the apex and reaches down to the heart, can cause them; but, as I say, that adds nothing to one's prayer.

I think I have already dealt with what you tell me: the fact that afterwards you find yourself as if nothing had happened. I think St Augustine speaks of this too: the spirit of God passes without leaving a trace, any more than the arrow leaves a trace in the air. I remember

---

[1] *Sin herir dolor haceis*
Y sin dolor deshaceis
El amor de las criaturas (CTA, clxiii).

now that I replied to you on this point, but I've received such a multitude of letters since those of Your Grace. . . .[1]

Thus Teresa of Jesus showed perfect balance, soaring far above what are called nowadays inhibitions and complexes, yet willingly conceding to nature the place which it will occupy with or without our permission. Better equilibrium could not be found.

And she dealt with such deep questions of the spiritual life, writing off-hand in the midst of an overwhelming correspondence concerning the most varied matters.

The rest of this long letter to Don Lorenzo included two receipts: the art of curing rheumatism and headache by burning sweet-smelling lozenges, and the art of wearing a hair shirt. . . .

'When you find it difficult to recollect yourself at the time of prayer, or when you want to do something for Our Lord, put on this hair shirt which I'm sending you; it excites love, provided you don't wear it on any account after you're dressed, or to sleep in.'

But she has misgivings about her brother's excessive zeal: 'I don't do this without fear. . . .'

'Write and tell me how you get on with this plaything. . . . And I'm laughing: for you send me preserved fruits, cakes and money, and I send you hair shirts. . . .'[2]

Kindhearted as always, the Foundress had her usual joke.

He wasn't very easy to direct, this Don Lorenzo, on account of his very zealousness. Did he not take it into his head to meditate on the horror it would be to be damned? Teresa led him gently back to paradise: 'I don't know why you should desire those fears and terrors, since God leads you by the way of love. The form of prayer which he gives you is incomparably higher than thinking about hell. . . .'[3]

He made a vow of perfection without consulting her. 'That's a fine way to show obedience!'[4] She set about changing his ideas on the subject. In the same way she succeeded in dissuading him from the idea of becoming a friar: 'My brother's monkishness went no further. . . .'[5]

He went so far in the ways of penance that he admitted to wearing the hair shirt for twenty-four hours. 'A new fashion, I don't think the Discalced nuns themselves display as much aptitude. . . .'[6] But she restrained this thirst for mortification: 'God prefers your health to your penances, and that you should obey. . . .'[7]

[1] CTA, clxiii.   [2] Idem.   [3] CTA, clviii.
[4] Idem.   [5] CTA, cxxxviii.
[6] CTA, clxxi.   [7] Idem.

He told her of the outbursts of fervour which seized him at night
and made him get up to pray: 'It won't be a bad thing to sit on your
bed a moment, always provided you have as much sleep as your head
needs, for one can reach the point at which it is no longer possible to
pray at all. . . .'[1]

She insisted: 'It is important not to go without sleep . . . six
hours at least. . . . Good sleep is not one of God's lesser graces. . . .
Don't be afraid to sleep. . . .' And she added: 'I have so much work
this evening that I've been hindered from prayer. I have no scruple
about it, only regret. . . .'[2]

If she considered that it was important for friars and nuns to avoid
the occasions of scrupulosity, she took just as much care to save those
living in the world from them, whether priests or laymen.

Among those who asked her for spiritual direction was a great
prelate who was also a great temporal lord, Archbishop Don Teutonio
de Braganza. Anxious over the continuance of a state of tepidity during
a long period spent in travelling about, he wrote to Teresa of Jesus.

'There's nothing for Your Lordship to fear: the tiredness that
comes from moving from one place to another and the want of
regularity in the employment of one's time are the cause of it. When
Your Lordship returns to your ordered life, the soul will find its
peace.'[3]

One day he confided to her that he felt strongly inclined to
give up mental prayer. The reply she made showed to what
extent she understood the process of thought at the different levels
of consciousness: 'Take absolutely no notice. Praise the Lord for the
desire you have for prayer, believe that your will intends it thus and
that it likes to be with God. When you feel that the tension is too great,
make an effort to go where you can look at the sky, walk for a little,
you won't waste your prayer time for that. Managing our weakness
is an art-and it doesn't do to oppress nature. All consists in the search
for God and the means by which we can draw near him. The soul is
led onwards by gentleness. . . .'[4]

It is obvious that nothing escapes her and that with her as guide
not one jot or tittle of the life of perfection is lost.

She gave to each one only what he was capable of receiving and
bearing: in the name of Christ she never failed in love. During the year
she spent in Toledo, she had the grief of being disappointed by Don
Francisco de Salcedo. The holy gentleman saw almost all his property
swallowed up in a lawsuit and he did not display the courage his piety

[1] CTA, clviii.   [2] Idem.   [3] CTA, lviii.   [4] CTA, lix.

would have led one to expect. But she never thought of blaming him nor of trying to teach him a lesson when what he needed was friendship.

'Pray to God,' she wrote to her brother Lorenzo, 'for him to understand and cease to be worried. That's what happens when we're not entirely detached. But when God has given us this grace, we must realize that we shan't console those who are still in bondage by preaching to them, but rather by showing them that we really feel their grief.' [1]

To-day, when I was thinking that God distributes what is his according to his good pleasure, I was astonished that a man like Don Francisco, who has been serving him sincerely for years, should be so afflicted at losing a fortune which he distributed to the poor much more than he used it for himself. I told myself that in his place I should have cared very little about it, but then I remembered how anxious I was when I saw you in danger at Seville; we do not know ourselves. To flee from all for the sake of All is our best plan if we don't want to be slaves of such low and worthless things; but we should consider that all are not capable of it. . . . [2]

She knew 'that there is no soul such a giant that it does not often need to become a child again.' [3]

And so, seeing that her brother was very tense over his prayer, she made up her mind to give him a humorous lesson, even in the things of God. He asked her for subjects of meditation and the subject she gave him—a phrase she had heard—'Seek for Me in Thee,' had puzzled him so much that he asked the grave Francisco de Salcedo, the even graver P. John of the Cross, and the good Julian de Ávila, to set down what these words of Our Lord suggested to them, as he would do himself, and to send them all to Mother Teresa.

Overwhelmed with work as she was and almost crazy with headache, she sat up that night even later than usual and wrote out a reply to them in the style of the *Vejamen*, the satirical criticism delighted in by students. It was an exercise which formed the great delight of students when they wanted to poke fun at one another.

So that her light way of handling the matter should not annoy, she began by declaring 'that she loves them all very much for they have all helped her in her trials,' [4] and then she distributed some fine rebukes all round.

The holy gentleman was her first victim. Certain passages of his

[1] CTA, cxxix.   [2] CTA, cxxix.
[3] SB, V, c. xiii–16.   [4] SEC, vol. VI, p. 65.

commentary 'please her very much,' but 'I have not the least intention of praising what you have all said.' She criticized his comments appositely and in detail.

'What is worse, if he doesn't unsay it, is that I shall be obliged to denounce him to the Inquisition, which is not far away. For after having said all through his paper: this is of St Paul and of the Holy Spirit, he declares that he has set his signature to rubbish. He must make honourable amends quickly; if not, he will see. . . .' [1]

Julian de Avila 'begins well and ends badly; so he has no claim to credit at all.'

He seems to have understood his subject completely in the wrong way, 'but I forgive him his errors, for he has not written at such length as my P. John of the Cross. . . .' [2]

We can imagine P. John of the Cross letting himself be carried up to the heights, his answer not being a little beside the point but a thousand leagues above it: it was P. John of the Cross, holy and learned as he was, whom Teresa teased most merrily:

> This reply is very good doctrine for anyone making the exercises of the Society of Jesus, but not for us. It would cost us dear not to seek God until we were dead to the world, Mary Magdalene was not, when she found him, nor the woman of Samaria, nor the Canaanitess.
>
> . . . God preserve me from people who are so spiritual that, come what may, they want to turn everything into perfect contemplation. Once this has been made clear, we are grateful to him for having made us understand so clearly what we did not ask to know. That is why it is always good to speak of God, we shall derive the benefit we least expect. [3]
>
> It was the same with Señor Lorenzo de Cepeda whom we thank for his answer and his couplets. For if he says a good deal more about it than he can understand, the amusement he's caused us disposes us to pardon the want of humility with which he meddles in such high things, as he says himself. . . .
>
> . . . I hope they'll all correct themselves: I too will correct myself in order not to resemble my brother in lacking humility. . . . [4]

All accepted the merry 'sentence' merrily, except Don Lorenzo who was ill accustomed to being teased. He gave vent to a few complaints but his sister consoled him:

> . . . I knew you would be cross; but it wasn't possible to give a serious answer; if Your Grace reads the letter carefully, you will

[1] Idem, p. 66.   [2] Idem, pp. 66–7.   [3] Idem, p. 67   [4] Idem.

see that I have not failed to praise part of what you said; without lying, it was not possible for me to speak otherwise of Your Grace's answer. I can assure you that after a day overwhelmed with business and correspondence—it seems as if the devil piles it up sometimes —my head was so bad that I don't even know what I said, I had a bad night and the purge made me ill. It's a miracle that I didn't send a letter I wrote to P. Gracián's mother, to the Bishop of Cartagena; I made a mistake in writing the address, I can't thank God enough that it didn't happen.[1]

These detailed explanations calmed the Indian's wounded vanity.

Teresa ended her letter with a spice of mischief: 'God keep you and make you a saint. . . .'

While the Foundress was at Toledo in this year of grace 1577, a young Cretan arrived there, who was beginning to paint for the church of Santo Domingo el Antiguo saints such as people had never seen the like of before, so much spirituality was there radiating from their faces. His name, Domenico Theotocopouli, was so long to pronounce that the Toledans surnamed him *El Greco*.

[1] CTA, clxviii.

VI

AND THEN HE GAVE HIMSELF UP . . .

AT the beginning of the persecution Mother Teresa of Jesus
had said:
'If God grants the Pope, the King, the Nuncio and our
P. Gracián a year or two more of life, everything will work out very
well. But we're lost if one of them happens to be taken from us.'

But Ormaneto, the Nuncio, died. He had been the most powerful
defender of the reformed Carmel: his power came from his sanctity;
he died so poor that Philip II had to pay his funeral expenses. He was
scarcely in his grave when Tostado left Portugal and returned to
Madrid with all haste; he hung about the court, anxious to be on the
spot and only waiting for an opportunity to exercise his authority as
delegate of P. Rubeo, the Order's Superior-General. The King had
not yet authorized him to visit the monasteries of Discalced friars and
nuns, but he had influence, he was not above intrigue, what could he
not effect?

Teresa of Jesus' call to action took the form of a summons to
prayer in all her monasteries and convents: '. . . in order that whatever is for the greatest service of God may come to pass.'

Toledo set the example: in the patio, in the choir, in the cloisters,
the daughters of the Blessed Virgin walked in procession reciting
litanies of supplication, multiplied their penances and rivalled one
another in fervour:

'Leave no stone unturned,' said the Foundress, *no se descuiden*.

Her call to arms was always: 'Don't go to sleep! Don't go to
sleep!'

And she often added: 'But keep calm.'

For those around her were beginning to lose their heads. Gracián
was frankly nervous and P. Antonio de Jesús not much better. While
both were lodging at Cardinal Tavera's hospital in Toledo, one
evening at Compline time they saw a ghost appear behind one of the
chapel windows: a sort of monstrous octopus with many tails and
enormous tentacles. They hastened to tell Teresa about what they
considered an ill omen, but in their very faces 'she laughed heartily

at seeing the courage of her two squadron-leaders turning into cowardice.'[1]

It took more than a ghost to frighten Teresa of Jesus.

'Señor, we have no bread,' was what good Francisco de Salcedo wanted to write to the Bishop of Ávila in the name of the nuns of St Joseph's: Teresa would not consent. She would not complain, even if she were half-starved and persecuted. 'However great my trials have been in this life I do not remember having uttered words of complaint.'[2]

She had had to leave Toledo suddenly at the beginning of July 1577 and return to Avila to put St Joseph's under P. Gracián's jurisdiction. She found the first of her dovecots in a state of utmost destitution, but her view of famine was the same as of persecution and defamatory accusations: 'I didn't find it too hard to bear.'[3]

But she then received a shock which would have crushed anyone else but her or at least would have made them reel: two of her own side had played false. Two Discalced friars had betrayed P. Jerónimo Gracián de la Madre de Dios!

It was the beginning of a relentless conflict. The Mother Foundress was by turns indignant, sarcastic, demanding her rights, or magnanimous in her all-embracing forgiveness of injuries; but she never complained.

She wrote to the King and her tone was regal in its dignity.

The grace of the Holy Spirit be always with Your Majesty. *Amen.* I have been informed of a memorandum which has been sent to Your Majesty against our Father, Master Gracián, of such a nature that I am horrified at the ruses of the devil and at those of the Calced Fathers; for, not content with defaming this servant of God—he is such in very truth and edifies us all, he doesn't visit a convent where they don't write to me that he has changed the spirit of the house for the better—they are now seeking to throw discredit on these monasteries where the Lord is so well served. To this end they have made use of two Discalced friars of whom one has often shown that he lacked judgement; of him and of other Discalced who are set against Gracián, the Calced friars have tried to make use, by obliging them to instance certain extravagances. If I did not fear the harm the devil can do, I should laugh at the accusations they are making against us Discalced nuns; but from the point of view of the Order it is monstrous.

[1] SEC, vol. VIII, p. 243, n. 2.
[2] *Ibid.*, R, iii, p. 18.   [3] CTA, cxciv.

For the love of God I beseech Your Majesty not to allow these infamous accusations to be brought before the courts. The world is such that even if the contrary were proved, a suspicion of evil might remain.

For the love of Our Lord, let Your Majesty consider this as touching your own honour and glory.[1]

Who were the traitors? Fray Miguel de la Columna, and in particular P. Baltasar de Jesús, whose habit Mother Teresa had sewn with her own hands when he had entered the Order at Pastrana. Turbulent, ambitious and harsh, he could not stand P. Gracián. Already, earlier, the rumour of certain intrigues engineered by him had much grieved Teresa 'as far as his soul was concerned.'[2] The very sight of Gracián was so hateful to him that to avoid him he went to hide himself away 'in his den.'

It was this hatred that those 'clad in fine cloth' had provoked and made use of. Mother Teresa, able to bear it no longer, added a post-script to her letter to Philip II in which she refuted the most dangerous of the calumnies against Gracián.

'If it is necessary, all we Discalced nuns will declare on oath that we've never heard him say or do anything which was not calculated to edify us; he is meticulous about observance to the point that even for chapters, when entering the enclosure would seem indispensable, he habitually stays behind the grille.'[3]

From this paragraph it seems that the Visitor was accused of culpable intimacy with his subjects. Gracián was simple, he did not see evil and still less imagined that anyone could invent evil where there was none. The Foundress who knew the world's wickedness put him on his guard, however: it was the duty of the Discalced friars, spied on by the Calced with extreme malevolence, to be more circumspect than ever.

Teresa of Jesus insisted on this point until she was tired:

. . . . If a friar has to stay in this convent, Your Paternity must tell him emphatically to see the nuns as little as possible. Father, this point must be watched very carefully. I should not even like the chaplain to see them frequently, for although he is excellent, from his very excellencies those who are ill-disposed can draw most unpleasant comments, particularly in small places, and indeed everywhere.[4]

Will Your Reverence kindly believe that everything will go so much better if you see that your daughters have no particular friend-

---

[1] CTA, cxcv.   [2] CTA, lxxix.   [3] CTA. cxcv.   [4] CTA, clxxix

ships, even though the persons in question may be saints. I do not want you to forget this.

All these nuns are young. For greater security, they must not see the friars. There's nothing I fear so much as that for these convents.[1]

There's no reason for seeing a friar without a veil, whatever Order he belongs to, and still less for seeing our Discalced friars like that. One can discuss the things of the soul without lifting one's veil. . . .[2]

When P. Gracián was in Andalusia, Teresa was so much afraid that the Calced friars would poison him that she asked María de San José to serve his meals in the convent parlour, but there again every precaution had to be taken to cut short evil gossip:

'In order not to create a precedent, no one must ever eat in the parlour except P. Gracián, who is in a position of some difficulty; but this can be done without its being talked about. . . .'[3]

It did not take as much as this for the Mitigated friars to attack poor P. Gracián's reputation. They began to watch the penitents he had in the world as much as they did his Carmelite nuns: they then accused him of suspicious intimacy with the Marchioness of Elche and her grand-daughter: he had in fact spent an entire night at Évora 'speaking of spiritual things.'[4]

His ingenuousness played into the hands of his enemies.

A short time after this scandalous memorandum, P. Baltasar de Jesús and Fray Miguel de la Columna declared they had been forced by the Calced friars under threat of all sorts of ill-treatment to sign papers they had never read. Yet these infamous accusations were to pursue Gracián all his life.

As to Teresa, she took the 'fine goings-on' attributed to her and her nuns with her usual good humour.

'I am ashamed of what these gentlemen have said about us: they put us under the obligation of becoming what they depict us as being, in order not to show that they have lied. . . .'[5]

All this was only the beginning.

The new Nuncio, Felipe Sega, had arrived at Madrid. Prejudiced against the Discalced before he arrived, by Cardinal Boncompagni, protector of the Calced, he devoted himself wholeheartedly to the enemies of the Teresian Reform. The impudence of those whom Teresa called *los gatos*, the cats, knew no limits. Already P. Antonio de Jesús was obliged to remain in hiding in Toledo in a garret in the Tavera Hospital and even this did not prevent his being imprisoned.

---

[1] CTA, xcv.   [2] CTA, cccxxxv.   [3] CTA, xcvi.
[4] SEC, vol. VIII, p. 184, n. 2.   [5] MJR, ix.

He was promptly released but the great offensive of the Mitigated against the Reformed was launched.

Sega, the Nuncio, did not withdraw Gracián's mandate as Visitor, but he forbade him to visit even a single convent. The King and the Council of Castile expressed a contrary opinion, without making it abundantly clear that they supported Gracián. He withdrew to Alcalá and then to Pastrana, living as a hermit in austerity and penance, praying in an especial manner for his persecutors and bearing his trials with joy 'like a St Jerome.' [1]

It was the nuns of the Incarnation who provided the first pretext for violence through their attachment to the *Madre Fundadora*: the same nuns who six years before had rebelled against the Reformer, this time rebelled in her favour.

They were on the eve of the election of a new prioress and would have no one but Teresa of Jesus. Tostado had decided otherwise: he sent the Provincial of the Calced friars to preside over the election 'furnished with severe censures and excommunications' for those who gave the Foundress their vote.

Teresa related these facts with so much liveliness and vigour that, in spite of her suffering, woman of wit as she was she could not help laughing at the ridiculous anger of so grave a man:

. . . Taking no notice, fifty-five nuns voted for me. Each time he was handed a vote the Provincial excommunicated and cursed; he crushed the voting papers with his fist, then stamped on them and burned them. The nuns have been excommunicated for a fortnight, they're not allowed to hear Mass or to go to choir, even when Divine Office is not going on; no one can speak to them, neither the confessors nor their own relatives.

Best of all, the day after these forced elections, the Provincial re-turned and ordered them to begin all over again. They replied there was no reason to do so for they had already voted. Thereupon he excommunicated them again. He then called the others, to the number of forty-four, and made them elect another prioress. He appealed to Tostado for confirmation.

There's nothing more to be said, the others are standing firm and claim that they will only obey this prioress as vicar.

That, in short, is what has happened. All are horrified at such a serious wrong. As for me, I have no wish to find myself in that Babylon. . . .[2]

The new prioress imposed by the Calced friars was Doña Ana de Toledo.

[1] CTA, ccx.   [2] CTA, cxcviii.

The confessors to whom the excommunicated nuns had not the right to speak were P. John of the Cross and P. Germán de San Matías. They were shut up in the hut built by the Mother Foundress on the outskirts of the convent. John of the Cross kept Teresa informed of what was happening, succeeding in passing notes to her in which he begged her to intervene; in his opinion nothing was more dangerous for the souls of these poor nuns than the ambiguous position in which they found themselves.

The Foundress wrote letter after letter to Madrid and begged that action might be taken not only to get the excommunication lifted, but that the rebels should agree to obey Doña Ana.

All Teresa wanted was peace and it was of peace that she spoke to John of the Cross when he succeeded, 'hiding himself all the way along,' in cheating the vigilance of the Calced friars, and making a long détour to get to her. This brief interview was a great consolation to them both. Not that they had to seek in each other the courage which they derived from its source, the continual presence of God, but together they tasted 'of the delicious fruit of forgetfulness of self and of all things.'[1]

Through his intermediacy the Foundress was able to send her daughters at the Incarnation injunctions to show submission and pardon; yet the Calced accused P. John of the Cross of inciting his subjects to rebellion.

Rumours ran all round Ávila, that city of gossip.

'. . . The Calced have made an offer to P. John of the Cross for him to put aside the coarse frieze of the Reform and put on the cloth habit of the Mitigation. He has refused. . . .'

'. . . The Calced, who are furious, intend to seize P. John of the Cross and P. Germán by force. . . .'

For three days and nights the relatives and friends of the rebellious nuns and those of the confessors mounted an armed guard around the little wooden hut. The danger seemed averted and they went back home.

But in the night of 3rd–4th December, the prior of the Calced friars of Toledo, P. Maldonado, assisted by constables—the decrees of Piacenza authorized the Calced to have recourse to the secular arm against the Discalced—forced the door and took the two friars away. The Foundress had already said of this prior: 'He's better gifted than anyone for making martyrs. . . .'[2]

The whole of Ávila seethed with indignation:

[1] JC quoted SEC, vol. VI, p. 196   [2] CTA, cciv.

'. . . They've taken them off to prison as if they were male-factors. . . .'

'. . . They've beaten them three times and the worst treatment imaginable has been meted out to them. . . .'

'. . . . Maldonado has dragged P. Juan off to Toledo. . . .'

'. . . The prior of the Calced friars of Ávila has taken charge of P. Germán, who was spitting blood; people saw him. . . .'

'. . . Both are saints. . . . [1]

'. . . P. Juan let himself be taken like a lamb. . . .'

'. . . In the morning he succeeded in escaping from them. . . .'

'In escaping from them? He's got away? He's saved.?'

The crowd of humble folk trembled with awe:

'He didn't flee to avoid martyrdom but he returned to his house near the Incarnation to destroy papers about the Reform. He locked himself in and while the Calced friars were wrestling with the door, he ate the documents which he couldn't destroy otherwise.'

A single shudder of anguish ran right through the city:

'And then? . . .

'And then he gave himself up.' [2]

It was thus by comments passed from mouth to mouth that Teresa learnt of the Calced friars' crime and the mortal danger in which John of the Cross and Germán de San Matías were. She gave vent to a cry of dismay. That very day she sent a letter of rather vehement entreaties to the King:

It is creating a scandal throughout the city. Everyone is wondering where they get the audacity from to act like that in a city so close to Your Majesty's residence; they seem to fear neither civic justice nor God.

I am utterly crushed at knowing that our Fathers are in their hands; they've been wanting to get hold of them for several days; I should prefer to know that they were prisoners of the Moors, then one might expect more pity to be shown. This friar, this great servant of God is so weakened by what he has undergone that I fear for his life.

For the love of Our Lord I beg Your Majesty to have him promptly set at liberty and to give orders so that those who wear the cloth cease to do so much harm to these poor Discalced: they say nothing and submit, it is therefore a benefit for their souls, but the scandal is all over the city. The Calced say they will put them to death, for Tostado has ordered them to do so.

If Your Majesty does not remedy the situation, I don't know

[1] CTA, ccvii.   [2] BJR, p. 163.

where we shall end, for on earth we have no one except Your Majesty. . . .[1]

On earth. But there is a higher Protector than a king. On 7th December she wrote: 'The persecution is of such a kind and so bad that our only hope is to have recourse to God.'[2]

And she prayed with all the abandonment she was capable of:

'. . . I go to the place where I pray and begin to speak to Our Lord whatever comes into my mind quite simply, for often I don't know what I'm saying; it is love which speaks and the soul is so much out of itself that I don't see the difference there is between it and God. Love knows who His Majesty is, but it forgets itself and thinks it is in him without any separation and it talks nonsense. . . .'[3]

O my Joy and my God! What shall *I* do to please you? My service is worthless, even if I were to render much service to God. For why must I remain in this wretched misery? Provided the Lord's will may be accomplished, my soul, what greater benefit can we desire! Hope, hope, you know neither the day nor the hour. Watch, all soon passes, although your desire makes that which is certain seem doubtful, and that which quickly passes, long. Know that the more you strive, the more you will show your love to your God and the more you will delight with your Beloved in joys and delights which will have no end.[4]

O my God, rest from every pain, how I wander![5]

O my soul! What a wonderful strife this pain is and how everything is fulfilled to the letter! *Thus, my beloved is mine and I am his.*[6] Who would dare to separate and extinguish two such ardent flames? It would be labour in vain for now they form only one. . . .[7]

Teresa of Jesus showed so serene a countenance that her niece Teresita was amazed: this was the effect of abandonment to God then? The majestic peace of a soul which divine love poises so high above events that it regards them untroubled and without letting itself be caught in their mesh is very great.[8]

When everything around her seemed to be crumbling away, the Foundress called on God for help. To those suffering persecution she counselled prayer far more than the seeking for human help. But her imperturbable common-sense added: 'Prayer, on condition that one doesn't take time from the sleep indispensable to the body.'

To Gracián who wrote her that he was taking time from his sleep

---

[1] CTA, cciv. [2] CTA, ccv. [3] Sb, V, c. xxxv-8.
[4] SEC, E, xv-3. [5] SEC, E, xvi-2. [6] CC.
[7] SEC, E, xvi-4. [8] Sb, V, c. xx-25.

to think over possible solutions, she advised sleep and prayer, which would be worth far more to him than drawing up plans: 'The graces which Our Lord showers down then are immense, and I should not be surprised if the devil is not trying to deprive you of them. God doesn't give the grace of prayer just when we will it, and when he does give it us we ought to value it; in a second Our Lord will give you better means of serving him than any the understanding could discover. . . . If we go away from God when he wants us, we shall not find him when we want to. . . .' [1]

Teresa obtained peace and endurance in the midst of this 'storm of trials,' [2] for she sought God alone.

The days passed. What was the King doing? Was his aid, like all human aid, just dried rosemary?

Teresa was counting each hour as it passed: already more than a fortnight had gone by since the two Fathers had been taken away, she still did not know where they were or what was happening to them, or if Philip II had intervened. [3]

Fresh rumours reached her:

'. . . They've taken his coarse habit away from P. John of the Cross and forced him to put on the cloth the Calced wear. . . .'

'. . . A young muleteer, when they were taking P. John to Toledo, amazed by his gentleness under the ill-treatment his cruel captors were inflicting upon him, offered to help him escape. . . .'

'He escaped then?'

'No. He refused. He replied that he preferred this opportunity of suffering for Our Lord to liberty.' [4]

He had refused! The same questions over and over again: Where is Fray John? What are they doing with him? And the King. . .? Why does the King not answer? How is it he has not acted?

For the first time a letter from Madre Teresa de Jesús to the King of Spain remained without response.

Philip II was silent, but the devil was furiously busy.

It was Christmas night 1577. A blast from hell extinguished the lamp which Teresa was holding in her hand when she went down a staircase to go to the chapel, she missed her footing, fell and broke her left arm.

'The devil might have done much worse to me,' [5] she said.

She offered her pain for the safety of 'the little saint, Fray John.'

---

[1] CTA, ccix.   [2] SEC, R, xxxvii.   [3] CTA, ccviii.
[4] BR, p. 164.   [5] FR, L. IV, c. 17.

VII

NIGHT'S DARKEST HOUR

WAS the lamp she was carrying when she fell the one by whose light Teresa of Jesus worked in her cell when 'in the darkest hours of the night' she wrote the *Interior Castle* or the *Seven Mansions of the Soul*? It did not matter now: the book had been finished a month before.

The Foundress had been pleased with the account of her *Life*, but the *Mansions* caused her to give vent to a cry of joy: 'It is known for certain that this marvel—the *Life*—is in the hands of Don Gaspar de Quiroga, Grand Inquisitor and Archbishop of Toledo, and that he spends much time reading it; he says that he won't give it back until he's tired of it. If he came here, he would see another book, even better, for it treats of nothing but God; its chasing and enamel work are more delicate; the goldsmith was not so experienced when he produced the first work; the gold in this one is of a higher carat and the stones better set. Carried out to the instructions of the Master Glazier it looks very well from what they say. . . .'[1]

Was this the nun who held humility to be the essential virtue? The same person who at a word from her confessor had thrown the manuscript of the *Thoughts on Divine Love* in the fire at Segovia? The two are one and the same and her twofold attitude only makes her complete detachment stand out the more. Utter humility has nothing in common with the affectations of false modesty. Moreover in her *Mansions* Teresa proclaims: 'Humility means walking hand in hand with truth,'[2] *la humildad es andar en verdad*. It was not herself whom she was praising, but him who dwelt in and inspired her.

Speaking about prayer with P. Gracián in Toledo in 1577, she regretted not being able to express herself better.

'Oh, how well the matter was explained in the *Autobiography* which is with the Inquisition!'

Gracián had just made her draw up the *Method for the Visitation of Convents* and complete her history of the foundations as far as the lively account of the foundation at Seville; in his opinion, as in hers, 'the manner of visiting the Discalced nuns was in a sense taught of God,'[3]

---

[1] CTA, ccv.   [2] Sb, M, VI, c. x-7.   [3] Quoted SEC, vol. VI, p. 34.

and he had been delighted to find the *Foundations* 'very attractive.' [1] Mother Teresa was overwhelmed with correspondence, business, cares, anxious about her sons and him in particular. Excess of work forced this woman of sixty-two to stay up until one or two o'clock in the morning without ever claiming the right to get up later. What did it matter: the Foundress had other difficult achievements to her credit.

However, she mentioned her headaches to Gracián:

'I do not spend a day without hearing much noise in the head and writing makes me feel very ill,[2] for more than six months my head has been in a bad way. . . .' [3]

The doctor had forbidden her to go on writing after midnight and asked her to write as little as possible with her own hand; from then onwards she dictated almost all her letters, but she could not dictate a work of that kind.

'Many torrential rivers falling down into cataracts, many little birds and sounds of whistling, . . .' [4] such was the bucolic but deafening symphony which was rumbling unceasingly in Teresa of Jesus' head when P. Gracián imposed on her the task of writing the *Interior Castle*.

'Note down what you remember, add other ideas and make a new book without naming the person in whom these things have taken place.' [5]

After her wretched health, Teresa pleaded her incapacity, but, being courageous, only laughed as she complained:

'How do they expect me to write? Let the theologians do it! They have studied whereas I am only an ignorant woman. What is there that I could say? I shall use the wrong words and there is a danger of my doing harm. There are so many books on prayer already! For the love of God, let me turn my spinning-wheel, go to choir and follow the Rule like the other sisters: I am not made for writing, for that I've neither health nor head. . . .' [6]

The Foundress was sincere. She knew no Latin in an age when Latin was indispensable and she never quotes in Latin without making mistakes; her horror of anything like pedantry constantly influenced her in her rejection of technical terms and when she is obliged to use them, she hesitates: '. . . What is called, I believe, mystical theology. . . .' [7] '. . . I don't know why it's called illuminative: I suppose the term is used of those who're making progress. . . .' She writes: 'One

---

[1] CTA, cxxiv.   [2] CTA, clxxviii.   [3] CTA, clxiv.
[4] Sb, M, IV, c. i–10.   [5] JG quoted SEC, vol. IV, p. ix.
[6] Idem, p. x.   [7] Sb, V, c. x–1.

who understands fountains,' instead of 'well-sinker,' [1] speaks of 'I don't know what acts,' and does not hesitate to write, 'Here is a comparison which it seems to me I've heard or read somewhere. . . .' [2]

In those days women had no right to be learned and Teresa was far from claiming any such right: even if her humility had not prevented it, her extreme womanliness would have been sufficient to restrain her. 'Our Lord knows the confused state of mind in which I write the greater part of these things. . . .' [3]

'I have been disturbed so many times while I've been writing these three pages, which have taken me as many days, that I've forgotten what I'd begun to say. . . .' [4] This great mystical writer is what the majority of women writers are: a woman, who writes; that is, the work to be accomplished does not give her the right to live differently from the way other women do. Life around her does not come to a standstill because she is writing a book. She knew this only too well and shrank from the overwhelming prospect.

She consulted her confessor who persuaded her with his entreaties: Teresa was incapable of refusing anything that would give her friends pleasure; she liked P. Velásquez very much and he was 'as pleased to come and see her once a week as if he had been made Archbishop of Toledo.' [5] Moreover he would later be rewarded for his faithfulness by being made Bishop of Osma. Teresa gave way.

Once more, through obedience, with the sole objective, a practical and realist one, of explaining to others the way of access to the marvels of the interior kingdom, she produced what was the work of a writer of genius. Her style, brisk and homely as usual, was this time adorned with the most scintillating phrases at her command as she strove to express the wonders of spiritual glory.

It was from obedience that the old Foundress who slept scarcely three hours a night derived her strength. Obedience also gave her light, for nothing is more finely coloured with all the sparkling hues of the prism than this account of the adventures of a soul which set off in self-conquest through the seven mansions of the interior castle until it attained union with God.

It is a question of one's inmost heart, that heart from which we harshly eject ourselves when we say, under the stress of violent emotion or anger: 'That has made me beside myself. . . .' This innermost heart, these Mansions into which those who are farthest from any idea of a divine presence in themselves nevertheless penetrate, for a few brief

[1] Sb, F, c. i–4.   [2] Sb, V, c. xi.   [3] Sb, C, c. xxxv–4.
[4] Sb, V, c. xxxix–17.   [5] CTA, civ.

moments when life forces them to reflect, to examine themselves in order to act afterwards with more wisdom or straightforwardness: 'I have entered into myself. . . .' they say.

This conquest of the soul comprises, in short, the exploration and domination of all the planes of consciousness. He who undertakes it rids himself of the weight of his worldly personality by obedience and humility, in order to obtain access to the highest regions of the spirit; just as the traveller who prefers air to railway travel has to leave his heavy luggage behind. But such a traveller, once his flight is over, finds himself a pedestrian again and this will occur more than once, whereas the soul which has experienced the metamorphosis of the spirit will never lose its wings again.

On 2nd June 1577, then, at Toledo, Teresa sat down in front of the blank paper 'like something completely stupid, not knowing what to say nor how to begin.' [1] 'I am, literally, like the birds who are taught to speak and don't know what it is they are taught to say: they repeat it often enough. If Our Lord wants me to say something more, His Majesty will make it known to me. . . . If I succeed in expressing it, it must be understood that that doesn't come from me; I am not gifted with very much intelligence and I should have no ability for such things at all if Our Lord in his mercy had not given it me. . . .' [2]

Our Lord did want her to say something more: the plan of the work was shown her in a vision: 'God showed her a very beautiful globe of crystal, in the likeness of a castle, with seven mansions and in the seventh, which was in the centre, the King of glory in immense splendour. . . .' [3]

Teresa did more than integrate all she knew and all His Majesty dictated to her into this theme: she was to put into it all she was, including the experience of her life of contemplation and action carried to the highest degree of conscious perfection. Like every other of her works, the *Interior Castle* is an act.

In writing of the effusions of divine love, her way of expression is the mystical language of the time fragrant with perfumes of the *Canticle of Canticles*, trembling with the caresses which the Sulamite exchanges with her Beloved; the setting, 'this delightful and beautiful castle,' [4] this fortress where the King dwells, these rooms where 'the men-at-arms' ready to fight against the enemy who threatens the walls

[1] SB, M, I, c. ii–7.					[2] Sb, M, prol., 2–4.
[3] Y quoted SEC, vol. II, p. 494.			[4] Sb, M, I, c. i–5.

pass to and fro, all remind us that Teresa of Jesus had been very fond of tales of chivalry.

The Mansions: Teresa then regards the soul 'as a castle cut from diamonds or from the clearest crystal';[1] in this castle there are a great many rooms, 'just as in heaven there are many mansions.'[2]

'The senses are the people who live there. . . . Our faculties are the governors, major-domos and stewards. . . .'[3]

The entrance gate to the castle is prayer.

The soul who wanders about in the First Mansion is touched by grace, but so many 'venomous things, snakes, and vipers,'[4] are crawling around her that she does not see the light which is coming from the King's apartments. The devil takes advantage of this darkness to set his snares. The soul will only escape them by persistence in prayer, self-knowledge and confidence in the goodness of her King.

She will prepare herself to enter into the Second Mansion by disengaging herself from business which is not indispensable to her state of life: 'Without a beginning of this sort, I consider access to the principal apartments impossible.'[5]

The soul who penetrates into the Second Mansion is one who already practises prayer faithfully. God invites her so gently to go forward that the poor little thing is in despair at not being able to obey immediately 'and she is more troubled than before she heard the invitation. . . .'[6]

She is afraid and very cold, the light is still faint, temptations assail her like venomous snakes. She trains her will to obey God, begins to practise recollection not by forcing herself,[7] but in all gentleness. . . .

The enemy is at the doors of the Third Mansion, 'it is necessary to eat and sleep armed, in case he should succeed in forcing an entrance.'[8] . . . The soul avoids evil, likes to hear God praised and shows 'excellent dispositions'[9] for good, but love does not yet lift her above vainglory nor above the demands of her immediate temporal interest.

'She is impatient when she finds the door which leads to the apartments of the King, whose vassal she calls herself, closed, but consider the saints who have entered there and you will see the difference there is between them and us. . . .[10] Get beyond your little

[1] Cf. Sb, M, I, c. i–3.   [2] Idem.   [3] Sb, M, I, c. ii–4.
[4] Sb, M, I, c. ii–14.   [5] Idem.   [6] Sb, M, II, c. i–2.
[7] Sb, M, II, c. i–10.   [8] Sb, M, III, c. i–2.
[9] Idem, c. i–5.   [10] Idem, c. i–6.

practices of piety, *obrillas*. . . . Your love must not be the product
of your imagination but be proved by acts.'[1]

Detached from the world, masters over their passions, prompt to
obey, concerned only with their own faults and taking care not to
judge their neighbours, the guests of the Third Mansion live in silence
and in hope.[2]

The great adventure begins in the Fourth Mansion. Here the King
distributes his favours lavishly 'when he wills, as he wills, and to whom
he wills.'[3] The soul must be ready to receive them, as the knight
errant is ready to seize every fresh opportunity. Here, rampant or
venomous creatures merely provide heroic occasions of victory.

'In this Mansion what is important is not much thinking but much
love.'[4] If actions do not follow we have no reason to think that we're
doing anything great.'[5] Here Teresa has the same thought as St Paul
when he wrote: 'Knowledge puffeth up but charity edifieth.'[6]

Mansions of recollection and quietude; there the soul perceives
greater lights, the invitation of the King is a gentle call but so penetrating that she forgets her past errors and thinks only of entering
further into the mansions.[7]

When the soul enters the Fifth Mansion she is affianced to the
King.

'. . . However clumsy the comparison may be, I find no other by
which to make myself understood, but the sacrament of marriage.
For although in what we are saying everything is of the spiritual
order—there is an eternity of distance between the spiritual joys Our
Lord gives and those of husband and wife—there all is love, love of
such limpidity, of such delicacy and sweetness that it is impossible
to describe.'[8]

It is the prayer of union in which the soul labours at its metamorphosis, as the silk-worm spins the cocoon in which it encloses
itself in order to be reborn a butterfly.

'Such union is not yet that of spiritual marriage, but just as in this
world, when marriage is in question it is desirable that both parties
should know and love each other, here the Bridegroom is such that
the soul has only to see him to become immediately more worthy to
give him her hand. . . . She is so much in love that she does everything within her power so that nothing may occur which could break
off these divine espousals. An inclination towards something other

[1] Idem, 7.   [2] Idem, c. ii–13.   [3] Sb, M, IV, c. i–2.
[4] Idem, c. i–77.   [5] Idem, c. iii–9.   [6] I Cor. viii–1.
[7] Sb, M, IV, c. iii–2.   [8] Sb, M, V, c. iv–4.

than the Bridegroom alone would suffice to destroy everything, and that is a loss more immense than it is possible to say. . . .' [1]

In this Fifth Mansion, delight is not all; 'love is never idle,' [2] 'Our Lord wants works.' [3]

In the Sixth Mansion the soul lives in close intimacy with God, and yet she never ceases to desire him. He speaks to her, she is rapt in ecstasy and he raises and draws her to himself 'as amber attracts straw,' [4] 'he wounds her with such a sweet wound that she wishes it might never heal.' [5]

The King gives his bride gifts from his jewels, knowledge of the greatness of God, perfect self-knowledge and perfect humility, contempt for things of the earth unless it is to use them in the service of such a great God. [6]

Teresa wanted to publish throughout the world the wonders 'of the great God of Chivalry,' [7] it mattered little to her that people laughed at her provided God was praised; 'what is to be will be!' [8]

'O Sisters, what folly, but what good folly!' She is no longer afraid of hell, no longer worries about sufferings or glory, her only interest is to love, 'mind and soul in her are one, as the sun and its rays are one.' [9]

In the union described in the Fifth and Sixth Mansions, the soul and God 'are like two wax tapers, so near to each other that wicks, wax and lights form but a single whole, but it is possible to separate them and find the two tapers again. . . .' [10]

In the Seventh Mansion the soul is in God and God is in the soul 'as rain water falling into a river or fountain is only one water in which the water of the river is inseparable from the rain water . . . or like the light which enters into a room through two windows: although divided when it enters, there is only one light.' [11]

Such is the intimate union wrought by spiritual marriage in the secret chamber where His Majesty reigns. 'There the soul and God enjoy each other in an immense silence.' [12]

The words which Our Lord speaks to the soul in this Mansion 'do their work in us,' [13] they have the force of acts. For this high state of prayer, that in which the silk-worm, now become a butterfly, has finally achieved its metamorphosis, operates with one essential

---

[1] Idem.   [2] Idem, c. iv–10.   [3] Idem, c. iii–2.
[4] Idem, VI, c. v–2.   [5] Idem, c. ii–2.   [6] Idem, c. v–10.
[7] Idem, c. vi–3.   [8] Idem, c. i–4.
[9] Idem, c. v–9.   [10] Sb, M, VII, c. ii–4.
[11] Sb, M, VII, c. ii–4.   [12] Cf. Idem, c. iii–2.
[13] Idem, c. ii–7.

objective action: 'It is to that that the spiritual marriage tends: to produce works, works and again works!' [1]

The strength of the bride is increased tenfold, 'not for her own delight but to serve.' [2] Henceforward Martha and Mary are inseparable, for 'how could Mary, always at Our Lord's feet, give him to eat if her sister did not help her?' [3]

It needed the Mother Foundress, the Mother Prioress, the one who while she initiated her daughters at the Incarnation into the art of prayer, at the same time saw that they were fed properly, to translate into concrete terms the transcendent realizations of the mystical life.

When she reaches these heights of the Seventh Mansion, the soul, now both contemplative and active, is at last ready for combat. What could she have to fear? 'Death itself has no more terror for her than a gentle ecstasy. . . .' [4]

Teresa of Jesus had begun to write the *Interior Castle* at Toledo on 2nd June. In the middle of July her departure for Ávila interrupted it, she was only to resume it in September and she laid down her pen on 29th November.

Continually disturbed, harassed, with everything thrown into disorder, in the midst of the great storm of trials, it took her three months to put on paper in her neat handwriting 'whose rapidity was equal to that of a notary public,' [5] and with no erasures, one of the clearest treatises on mental prayer that exists.

In the silent hours of the night. But what nights!

One evening in Toledo, María del Nacimiento had a message to give her and entered her cell. The Foundress, sitting on the ground in front of her low table, her long pen in her hand, was beginning a new manuscript book.

She turned round towards María as she came in and took off her glasses to see her, for she was long-sighted, but before she had even lowered her hands she was caught up in ecstasy and remained so for a long time. María del Nacimiento, full of awe and wonder, remained in prayer beside her.

When Teresa of Jesus came to herself again, the white paper was entirely covered with her writing.

María broke into an exclamation of surprise, but the Foundress silenced her with her brisk and homely '¡Callate, boba! Be quiet, stupid'—and she threw the book into a drawer and turned the key.

---

[1] Idem, c. iv–6. [2] Idem, 12. [3] Idem.
[4] Idem, c. iii–7. [5] JG quoted SEC.

VIII

RESTLESS GADABOUT

THREATS, calumnies, excommunication, imprisonment, sufferings caused by constant noises in the ears, rained down at the beginning of the year 1578 and seemed to prove that he whom the Foundress called 'whiskers'—*patilla*—*i.e.*, the devil, was launching his offensive against Discalced nuns and friars in full strength. This was indeed 'the mighty storm of trials' which Teresa of Jesus had already seen in vision: 'Just as the Egyptians persecuted the children of Israel, so shall we be persecuted; but God will make us pass through the waters as if they were dry land, and our enemies will be swallowed up by the waves.'[1]

Teresa suffered a great deal from her broken arm, but perhaps still more from being hampered in her activity: in future she could never dress herself without assistance; Ana de San Bartolomé became her inseparable companion, she accompanied her everywhere, wrote at her dictation, even helped her to put on her veil. For a woman whom neither sanctity nor age would ever cure of her quickness not only of wit but of movement, all this was a hard sacrifice. At night the good Ana would sometimes stay for hours kneeling outside the door of Teresa's cell, waiting for the moment when she would need her.

God tempered all these sufferings by what were really minor miracles, as on the day when, her mouth parched by fever, Teresa could take nothing but a little melon, if there should be any obtainable. Ana, who was also her infirmarian, was in despair; what chance was there of finding a melon in January? . . . There was a knock at the turn; someone had put in half a melon.

God also lavished spiritual consolations upon her: forced to keep her cell for more than a month, the Foundress could not receive Holy Communion. One of the sisters asked her:

'Isn't that the worst privation for Your Reverence?'

She answered:

'I consider it such a great privilege to have to submit to the will of God that I am just as happy as if I communicated as usual.'[2]

[1] SEC, R, xxxviii. [2] SEC, vol. II, p. 296.

Who, then, of those around her could have dared to fear, doubt or complain?

She never concealed either the danger or the calumnies which cast a slur on them when infamous accusations were made against any one of them. Kept well informed of what went on in the Order, she insisted that nothing of the excesses of the opposition should be kept back from her, or any of the 'fine goings-on' which were imputed to her in person.

When she received news of particularly offensive accusations, she rang the bell which summoned the community, smilingly apologized for having to repeat certain ill-sounding words which had been uttered in the Nuncio's presence by men with a high reputation and read:

'. . . The Calced allege that this old woman ought to be handed over to Whites and Blacks in order that she may have her fill of her evil conduct. For, under the pretext of making foundations, she takes young women off from town to town in order to give them the occasion . . .' [1]

She silenced the murmurs of the scandalized nuns:

'It seems also that we're preparing to leave for the Indies, a few poor little nuns on board a caravel, to found convents overseas. . . . Isn't it laughable? And these holy men are saying many other things about me which I can't repeat. . . .' [2]

The colour mounted on the forehead of the nun whom Teresa called 'the Fleming,' María de San Jerónimo went pale to the very lips, Ana de San Bartolomé and many others burst into sobs. The Foundress consoled them:

'They do me the greatest possible good, for if I am not guilty of what they accuse me of, I have offended God on so many other occasions that the one pays for the other. .. .' [3]

One day, news arrived from Rome itself: it was a matter of particular importance to the Calced that indignation against the Mother Foundress in the papal city should be considerable so that the Discalced should not be granted an independent province.

The Count of Tendilla, a nobleman very much attached to Teresa of Jesus, went to ask authorization for the foundation in Spain of two new convents of the reformed Carmel. The prelate who received him appeared shocked:

'I am surprised to hear Your Illustrious Lordship mention a nun who is as base as she is vile. It is well known that she is a bad character

<hr />

[1] MJ quoted SEC, vol. VIII, p. 286, n. 1.
[2] CTA, cclii.   [3] MJE quoted SEC, vol. II, p. 295.

and has only adopted this pretext of founding convents in order that she may have free rein for her immorality.'

The Count of Tendilla, who was son of the Viceroy of Naples, feared no one; he did not hide the horror and disgust which such outrageous accusations caused him:

'Careful, Father! Don't say anything more, for chaste Castilian ears will not listen to remarks like that about a woman whose holiness is so undeniable that even while she's living Spain holds her for a saint. We Grandees and Lords of Spain bare our heads before her. Your Reverence shocks me and gives me offence.'

The Father sought to find an excuse:

'Your Lordship must forgive me, but I'm merely repeating what they write to me about her from Spain.'

From his correspondence he drew a letter which he handed to the count. It was written in a particular prelate's own hand:

I have often written to Your Reverence about this impostor Teresa and the malice with which she uses the foundation of convents of Discalced nuns as an excuse for the liberty she abrogates to herself to lead an evil life. The justice of Our Lord has just denounced her in the eyes of all: a few days ago when she was pretending to go and found a convent in a certain city of these realms, the closed carriage in which she was travelling suddenly came to pieces right in the middle of the square at Medina del Campo, and the people who were there—a fairly large crowd—could see the said nun engaged in offending God with a certain friar. . . .[1]

Although all sorts of things were said about Mother Teresa, the one whose mission it was to inform her of these fresh lies was very embarrassed. She reassured him with a smile: what is humility worth if it cannot smile?

'Son, I should perhaps do much worse things than that if Our Lord didn't lead me by the hand. All that makes me sorry is to think of the dangers to which the man who says these things is exposing his soul. And I would be willing to put up with much greater insults and sufferings for his sins to be forgiven him.'[2]

Sega, the Nuncio, treated Teresa as a 'restless gadabout,'[3] he declared her disobedient, contumacious, accused her of inventing evil doctrines, of going out of her cloister in spite of the prohibition of the Council of Trent and of teaching, although St Paul had forbidden women to do so. He alleged that she had founded her convents without

[1] PP quoted SEC, vol. VI, pp. 383–4.
[2] Idem.   [3] SEC, vol. V, p. 246, n. 2.

the authorization of the Pope or that of the General of the Order. Yet her letters to this same Nuncio, Sega, are written in all humility.

So much meekness astounded the sisters: their Mother's acts were greater even than her words. They saw that she was radiant with love and forgiveness and sometimes even a halo of heavenly light surrounded her. They went about repeating the saying of the Bishop of Ávila, Don Álvaro de Mendoza: 'Whoever wants to be treated as her best friend by Mother Teresa of Jesus has only to bear false witness against her. . . .'

She denied that she had any merit in this:

'I am so accustomed to it that it is not surprising that I do not feel these things. . . .[1] It's as though I had a block of wood inside me on which the blows rain down without touching my heart. . . .'[2]

The consequences of such calumnies, however, could be most serious; it was in the same year, 1578, that the scandal of the *Alumbrados* of Llerena had just come to light. The whole of Spain was appalled at what the trial revealed of the immorality and shamelessness of these heretics. The Calced were to try to identify Mother Teresa and her friars and nuns with these fanatics. The danger was so great that Teresa of Jesus had some difficulty in persuading her nuns to forgive injuries as she forgave them and to love their detractors as she loved them.

'Our Mother is a saint,' they said, 'and we are only poor insignificant nuns. . . .'

One day, she answered with almost girlish mischief sparkling in her eyes:

Sisters, you must understand that people have only spoken evil of me falsely three times:
The first was when I was young and they called me beautiful.
The second was when they took it into their heads to pretend I was gifted: a great lie, too. . . .
The third of these false judgements was to declare that I have some virtue. This is the most difficult of all for me to bear, for I am the only one who knows how many faults I have.[3]

The little sisters of St Joseph's added to themselves what the Foundress would have held to be a fourth false judgement. 'Our Mother is adorable.'

And indeed she was so, both in the human and the divine sense of

---

[1] CTA, ccv.   [2] FR, L. IV, cxvii.
[3] JG quoted SEC, vol. I, p. 260, n. 1.

the word. To concur in this opinion, it was enough to see her successively get angry, coax, act as a woman of feeling, a great diplomat and a soul truly angelic in an affair which added a great many small meannesses and quarrels to the weighty sufferings of the persecutions.

A Jesuit father, who was a very good friend of Teresa of Jesus, P. Gaspar de Salazar, had talked of leaving the Society to become a Discalced Carmelite. The Jesuits turned the matter into a tragedy. P. Salazar turned out to be two-faced; to prove his innocence he threw all the blame on the Carmelite friars and then and there turned against them in terms worthy of the worst detractors of the Reform: '. . . I wonder how people can say that I want to rule over people where there are more lice about than good rules of life. . . .' [1] For the Father alleged that the Discalced had tried to attract him by promising him honours, though the honours of an Order the best of whose subjects were defamed and hunted down could scarcely be considered an attractive offer.

There ensued between Mother Teresa and the Rector of the Jesuits at Ávila an exchange of letters in which the Foundress's style was more trenchant, more expressive than ever, but at the same time showed wonderful prudence. Gracián was the only one who knew how much the self-mastery cost her:

'The Provincial of the Society wrote me such an unpleasant letter about this matter that I should like to have replied to him more severely than I have done. I would like Your Paternity to know that their threats frighten me so little that I wonder at the liberty Our Lord grants me: I have therefore said to the Rector that when I can do him some service, the whole Society and indeed the whole world will not prevent me, but that I have had no hand or part in what has happened.' [2]

Finally, the whole matter died down; P. Gaspar de Salazar remained a Jesuit, absolved by his Rector, 'as if what he wanted to do had been heresy.' [3] It was important to be on good terms with the Society again but at the same time not to submit to injustice without a protest. Towards the calumniators the Foundress followed a line of conduct which was both dignified and prudent [4]; she felt it prejudicial to the Reform to let herself be attacked unless it were possible to seem to ignore the insults. She therefore concealed from her enemies as much as possible the fact that she knew all about their injurious accusations: but the Rector of the Jesuits had attacked her directly and

---

[1] SEC, vol. VIII, p. 156, n. 1.   [2] CTA, ccxiv.
  CTA, ccxxxii.   [4] CTA, clxiv.

that being so, she would forgo nothing of her pride, the pride of one of Our Lady's daughters, while she meekly asked pardon for not having been wrong. With exquisite *finesse* she delicately worded her reply to Gonzalo Dávila, the Rector who had used her ill:

> It's a long time since I have been so much mortified as I was to-day by what Your Grace wrote, for I am not humble to the point of wishing to be thought proud. . . . Never have I had a greater longing to tear up a letter coming from Your Grace. I assure you that you understand perfectly how to mortify one and to make me understand how worthless I am. Your Grace thinks that I claim to teach others: God preserve me from it! The fault lies in the affection which I bear you which makes me speak to you freely without taking account of what I say.
>
> . . . I make the great mistake of pronouncing on these matters of prayer for myself, Your Grace therefore has not to take account of what I say, for God certainly gives you far greater talents than those of an insignificant little woman. . . .

After having informed P. Dávila about certain details of his inner life, she praised him charmingly, for what holy man is holy enough not to like praise? '. . . I should like my prelate to be like you. . . .'[1] and she admits the point in which she is at fault: '. . . I will correct myself in the matter of following my first impulses, since that costs me so dear. . . .'

This was erasing the memory of these unpleasant events with both good grace and magnanimity. Could the Society continue in its unfriendly attitude after this? One may well wonder, moreover, if it would have behaved so harshly if both Reform and reformer had been in greater favour with the authorities: 'How few friends one has in these difficult times!'[2] 'Trials and persecutions do not cease to rain down on this poor old woman.'[3] Even María Bautista herself, her cousin and the one who had given 'her inheritance' to help in the foundation of St Joseph's and who was now prioress of the convent of Valladolid, had allowed a Calced friar to give the habit to one of Gracián's sisters. 'I do not understand why this little prioress is so anxious to please these friars. . . .'[4] To give way to the persecutors was to betray the Reform.

Such defections were all the more bitter to the Mother Foundress in that she was only really hurt by the attacks of those she loved. Their perplexities, the infiltration of doubt in their minds, the blame

[1] CTA, ccxxxiv.   [2] CTA, cclii.
[3] CTA ccxiii.   [4] CTA, ccxxxi.

prompted by the best intentions, troubled her and caused her great suffering.

With those who were loyal to her, she exchanged innumerable letters, asking their help and advice. The correspondence had to be secret, for the slightest word from the pen of Teresa of Jesus would certainly have been interpreted by the Calced quite otherwise than as she intended. It was a correspondence carried out with haste. Peter, the servant who carried this correspondence, which was always urgent, to and fro, was no sooner back in Ávila than he had to leave again. The Mother was anxious about the risks he was running, his fatigue, and her compassion for him prevailed over the necessity of sending her messages with the utmost possible speed. One day when, without even taking his dinner, he was dashing off to take an envelope she had just given him, she stopped him:

'You won't go out from here until you've eaten two eggs which I've cooked myself. . . .' [1]

She was always ready to believe that she was mistaken and that her friends were right. The most courageous of those loyal to her then had to show her what solid ground she had for her words and actions and sustain her courage.

The most striking testimony came from Ana de Jesús. When the Provincial of the Mitigated friars announced his visit, the good-looking prioress of Beas replied:

> Mother Teresa could not clothe herself in camel's hair like Elias, I grant you; but she exchanged your fine cloth and your gauze for the roughest and coarsest frieze. And she imitates the prophet as far as she possibly can: fasting, withdrawal from the world, penance and prayer. I repeat it to Your Reverence, we would rather die a thousand deaths than separate from our trunk. In my opinion Your Paternity and all the Calced are separated from it: such brethren do not imitate their holy Father Elias, since they seek fine clothing, society instead of the desert, and instead of unceasing prayer, the latest news. [2]

Such uncompromising declarations gave Teresa confidence, and the sisters once more heard her say what she persistently repeated during these years of trouble and violence:

'You see all that is happening? Very well! It is for the best!' [3]

One of her loyal supporters was P. Yepes. He declared that it was God himself who gave her strength and courage. One day when he

[1] SEC, vol. VIII, p. 232, n. 4. [2] AJ quoted BRJ, p. 195.
[3] MJE quoted SEC, vol. II, p. 295.

was discussing recent and serious events with her, all of a sudden he saw that she had completely ceased to listen to the conversation; she came out of this reverie as suddenly as she had fallen into it, and remarked:

'We still have much to suffer, but the Order will not look back.' [1]
He took these words as a prophecy.

In the midst of all this Mother Teresa retained the presence of mind to busy herself with even the smallest needs of her convents. Thus she asked permission for her brother Lorenzo to enter the enclosure at St Joseph's convent in Seville, to make a plan of a 'little oven which the prioress had had made for cooking the meals, which will be a treasure for both friars and nuns if it is as she says. . . .' [2]

The Foundress saw to the installation of this little oven herself and two years later she did not fail to note that it had had to be demolished although it cost 100 reales: it used more wood than they could afford. [3]

Like genius, the service of God is 'an unremitting attention to details.' [4]

[1] Y quoted SEC, vol. II, p. 492. [2] CTA, ccxxiv.
[3] CTA, cccxiv. [4] Disraeli

IX

THE SPELL CAST OVER FRAY JOHN

'I AM no worse than usual,' said Teresa of Jesus, 'trials are health and medicine to me.'[1] Her greatest suffering was the knowledge that her Discalced friars were being hunted, imprisoned and tortured, the Discalced whom she would have wished to be like beings from another world. . . .[2]

Fray Gregorio Nacianceno, prior of La Peñuela, as well as his companion Fray Juan de Santa Eufemia, and Fray Gabriel de la Asunción, were either in prison or had been so and only been able to obtain release with the greatest possible difficulty, like P. Germán de San Matías. P. Juan de Jesús Roca went to speak to the Nuncio, but Sega's only reply was to have him imprisoned in Madrid, in the monastery of the Calced friars.

For such violence Teresa endeavoured to make excuse: 'The Calced go too far, they are blinded by rage. . . . They wouldn't do what they're doing if they stopped to think. . . .'[3] But if they did not know what they were doing they were all the more to be feared. It was for this reason that Teresa of Jesus was so anxious about P. John of the Cross. She had been without news of him for months.

January: 'We don't know where they've taken him. . . .'[4]

March: The Foundress had a presentiment of P. John's sufferings, which were probably all the greater since P. Germán had escaped. 'He is all right, outside. . . . I am in anguish at the idea that the accusations against P. John may even take a turn for the worse. God has a terrible way of treating his friends and in truth he does them no wrong, since that was the way he treated his Son.'[5]

'. . . It's said that Fray John has been sent to Rome. . . .'[6]

April: 'We might remind the King how long our little saint, Fray John, has been in prison. . . .'[7]

May: Teresa made conjecture after conjecture over the complete silence which wrapped the disappearance of John of the Cross in

---

[1] CTA, ccxxviii. [2] Cf. CTA, cxx.
[3] CTA, ccxxiv. [4] CTA, ccx.
[5] CTA, ccxix. [6] CTA, ccxviii. [7] CTA, ccxxiv.

mystery and the 'spells' of the tales of chivalry came back to her mind: 'I am appalled about the spell which seems to have been cast over Fray John of the Cross and at the slowness of all these matters. . . .'[1]

August: Don't forget to see if it's possible to do something for Fray John of the Cross. . . .'[2]

'Remind the King. . . . Don't forget. . . .' Were they troubling so little about him? Although Doña Guiomar de Ulloa who was with Teresa at St Joseph's and wanted to take the habit wept over her Fray John of the Cross like all the sisters, 'by some trick of destiny or other, nobody ever thinks of this saint.'[3]

It was no trick of destiny: P. John had so well succeeded in living as he wished, 'wrapped in silence,'[4] that he passed unnoticed in the eyes of men and was effaced from their memory as he would have liked to be effaced from this world.

He was wont to say to the nuns:

'What we lack is neither writing nor speaking, for usually there is only too much of both, but to be silent and to act. For speaking distracts; silence and action concentrate our mind and give it strength. . . . To suffer, to act, to be silent, to withdraw from the senses by the practice and love of solitude in the forgetfulness of all creatures and all events, even if the world should crumble away.'[5]

Around Fray John of the Cross the world had crumbled away, he was buried in silence, 'a spell cast over him.' Henceforward he spoke to God alone in language understood by God alone, that of silent love.

But God knew where Fray John was: in the convent of the Calced friars at Toledo, imprisoned in a tiny dungeon, his only nourishment bread and water, scourged every day by all the friars in turn. His tunic stuck to the wounds on his shoulders. He endured it all with love and patience, the only thing that saddened him was the thought of the sufferings of Teresa of Jesus.

So pure a countenance and such a gentle look only exasperated his captors, as did the strength which this little man showed. He made them all mad with rage by his habit of remaining silent and perfectly still when the most eloquent of the Calced friars urged him to renounce the Reform and adopt their Mitigated rule. When promises proved themselves of no avail, they resorted to threats and then to blows and insults.

Fray John refused to break his silence.

[1] CTA, ccxxxii.   [2] CTA, ccxlii.   [3] CTA, ccxliii.
[4] JC quoted SEC, vol. VI, p. 210.   [5] Idem.

He spoke only to God, he complained only to him, in such accents that the words of this silent man ring through the centuries:

> *¿A dónde te escondiste,*
> *Amado, y me dejaste con gemido?*
> *Como el ciervo huiste,*
> *Habiendome herido. . . .*
>
> . . . .
>
> *Y todos más me llagan*
> *Y déjame muriendo*
> *Un no sé qué que quedan balbuciendo. . .*
>
> . . . .
>
> *¡Oh cristalina fuente,*
> *Si en esos tus semblantes plateados,*
> *Formases de repente*
> *Los ojos deseados,*
> *Que tengo en las entrañas dibujados!* . . .[1]

Was God hiding himself? 'Where there is no love, put love and you will find love.' Mother Teresa reduced this same axiom to three succinct words: *Amor saca amor,* 'Love calls forth love.'

Fray John *was* love but he found only hatred. Yet the severity around him was loosening. Perhaps the Calced were tired of flogging a frail man from whom they did not succeed in wresting a complaint. On two occasions they saw his dungeon lighted up, but when they rushed to see why, for he was forbidden to have any light at night, the supernatural light disappeared the moment they entered. After that they decided he must either be a saint or a sorcerer. Perhaps they

---

[1] JC quoted SEC, vol. VI, p. 197. The poem, *Canciones entre el alma y el Esposo,* was composed by St. John of the Cross in the prison at Toledo. The translation given below is by E. Allison Peers:

> Whither hast vanishèd,
> Beloved, and hast left me full of woe ?
> And like the hart hast sped,
> Wounding, ere thou didst go. . . .
>
> . . . .
>
> Each deals a deeper wound
> And something in their cry
> Leaves me so raptur'd that I fain would die.
>
> . . . .
>
> O crystal spring so fair,
> Might now within thy silvery depths appear,
> E'en as I linger there,
> Those features ever dear
> Which on my soul I carry graven clear ! . . .

decided that saint was the right word or perhaps they were afraid of making a martyr of this saint. They gave him a less brutal gaoler, a young brother named Juan de Santa María. He gave him writing materials and sometimes allowed him to get a little air in the room adjoining his dungeon. Better still: he loved his prisoner. By giving love, John of the Cross was beginning to obtain love.

He had no thought of escape: in his prison he had suffering, silence and that interior activity which is a tremendous adventure. It was Our Lady who prepared his escape and ordered him to flee.

One day during the Octave of the Assumption she showed him in spirit a window high up in a gallery overlooking the Tagus and told him she would help him to escape through it. She also showed him the way to unscrew his prison locks, both the lock of the dungeon itself and that of the room next door.

He took advantage of the quarter of an hour his warder allowed him to go 'to the humble office' while the friars were in the refectory, to go and identify the window which Our Lady had shown him, although he had to cross the entire convent to do so. That very evening he managed to unscrew the lock and release the padlock.

He waited till everyone was asleep; it was time to make the attempt. The first door yielded at his touch, but two visiting friars were sleeping in the room he had to cross. He hesitated, but could not resist the Mother of God; she ordered him to go straight on, assuring him of her help.

Accordingly he opened the door; as he was pulling it towards him one of the iron bars fell and the noise awoke the sleepers:

'Who's there?' one of them shouted.

The silence reassured them, the Blessed Virgin closed their eyes, stopped their ears, lulled their senses and John of the Cross stepped over their prone forms.

Out of his two old blankets and a strip of tunic he had made a rope which he attached to the window support—a bar of wood—towards which an interior voice had guided him. The voice then ordered him to let himself down into the void. He obeyed, slid down the length of his rope, and arrived at the end to find it was at least ten feet too short.

Hanging by a bare thread above the rocky bank of the Tagus, he wondered where he was going to fall. His confidence in Our Lady gave him the courage to jump.

He landed in a courtyard which he recognized as being part of the royal convent of the Immaculate Conception, belonging to the

Franciscan nuns, but outside the enclosure: only a wall was between him and the Zocodover.[1]

A voice coming from a belt of light said: 'Follow me,' and guided him to the foot of the wall. Fray John looked up; the wall was so high that he was leaning against it despairing of having the strength to scale it, when he felt himself lifted into the air and set down on the farther side, free.

It was still dark. In the market they were setting up the stalls; the vendors, mostly women, burst out laughing at this friar, whose blood-stained rags scarcely covered him and who seemed to have sprung from the walls of the Franciscan convent: less would have been sufficient to arouse their laughter. He escaped from them, darting in between the houses. The light which had guided him had disappeared but great confidence and a great interior light remained.

At five o'clock when the Angelus rang, he knocked at the door of the convent of St Joseph of Carmel.

When the extern sister, Leonor de Jesús, came and told the prioress that P. John of the Cross was there, and was asking her 'to come to his help and hide him, for if the Calced friars caught him again they would tear him to pieces,' Mother Ana de los Ángeles was at the bed-side of Sister Ana de la Madre de Dios, who was very ill but who nevertheless had a wonderful inspiration:

'Mother, I feel so ill that I cannot take my purge without going to confession first. . . .'

A friar could not enter the enclosure except to give absolution to a nun who was too ill to go to the confessional.

So the big door opened for Fray John and closed behind him. It was high time: the Calced friars, who could not understand how the slender rope made of strips of stuff could have borne the weight of a man, did not understand either how this man could have jumped from such a height without being killed; but they were forced to accept the evidence: their prisoner had escaped. At once they rushed to St Joseph's; with an escort of constables, they searched parlour, chapel and sacristy.

The whole convent throbbed with intense but silent emotion, the sisters mingling tears of joy with thanksgivings and prayers. There was none so proud as the infirmarian, Teresa de la Concepción, who had the honour of taking P. John of the Cross his meals. He took only a few pears cooked with cinnamon; the weariness, the joy, above all the emotion at being in the very convent which had been Mother Teresa of Jesus' prison, took away his appetite.

[1] *I.e.* market place.—Tr.

About ten o'clock when the doors of the church were bolted, they were able to shut him in there dressed in a priest's gown which the sisters declared suited him quite well. All wanted to see him and the community spent a very pleasant evening: the nuns took their spinning or needlework to the choir while P. John talked to them.[1]

He did not talk to them about his sufferings and dangers, but about God and about the Mitigated friars whom he considered his benefactors:

'They are free now from the faults which my wretchedness made them commit.'[2]

He also recited in a gentle, monotonous voice the poems he had composed in prison and a sister wrote them down.

Finally he talked to them at length about Our Lady who had set him free, and the delicious fruits of divine love which he had culled in his solitude:

'Blessed nothingness and blessed hiding place of the heart. . . .'[3]
'God's immense benefits fall only into empty and solitary hearts. . . .'[4]

As soon as night fell, one of the canons came at the instance of the prioress to fetch him in his carriage and put him out of the reach of danger in the hospital of Santa Cruz. As soon as he could he left for Ávila.

Fray John saw Mother Teresa of Jesus once again and Mother Teresa saw her 'little saint, Fray John.' He was still 'so wasted and disfigured that he seemed an image of death.'

He was not in the habit of complaining, any more than Teresa of Jesus was:

'As far as I am concerned, don't be in any way troubled, for I am not.'[5]

A cry of protest however escaped from the Foundress:

'I don't know how God permits such things!'[6]

She told Gracián about this meeting in disjointed phrases, scarcely able to speak for the beatings of her heart:

'Your Paternity doesn't yet know all. He's spent these nine months in a dungeon so small that there was scarcely room for him, tiny as he is; all this time he never changed his tunic, although he has been at death's door. Three days before his escape the Superior did give him a shirt of his own; nobody ever saw him.'[7]

---

[1] BRJ, c. xiii.   [2] JC quoted SEC, vol. VI, p. 196.
[3] JC quoted SEC, vol. VI, p. 213.   [4] Idem, p. 254.
[5] JC quoted SEC, vol. VI, p. 197.   [6] CTA, ccxlvi.   [7] Idem.

That was what Teresa of Jesus with her great love of cleanliness said. And she who as a child had wanted to die at the hands of the Turks declared:

'I envy him immensely. It is wonderful that Our Lord should have found him strong enough for a veritable martyrdom like that, and it is important that the matter should be known, in order that everyone may beware of these people.' [1]

She echoed Fray John's sentiments:

'May God deign to pardon them!' [2]

But she also cried out for justice for her sons: 'The Nuncio must be informed of what they've done with our saint Fray John, and without his having committed the least fault, for it is lamentable. Fray Germán must be told, he will see to it, he has a lot of courage for those things.' [3]

John of the Cross did not tell Mother Teresa that he had left his kind warder as a souvenir the only thing he clung to in the world: the little cross of precious wood she had given him when he took the habit and which he always wore under his scapular next to his heart. But he no more regretted parting with this treasure than he did having suffered so much: the ardour with which the Mother Foundress defended him, the warmth with which she begged him to take care of himself, caused him a joy he felt to be too human:

'Let us rather look at the riches gained in pure love on the road to eternal life. . . .' [4]

This moment of relaxation and plenitude was brief. Fray John had to go to the Congress at Almodóvar. Teresa was very displeased about it and complained to Gracián.

'I've been very much grieved to see how much he has suffered and I'm distressed that he is being allowed to go although he is so ill. God grant he does not die. I hope Your Paternity will see that he is well looked after at Almodóvar, and that he's sent no further. I beg of you, do not fail to see to this. See that you don't forget. I tell you that if he were to die, Your Paternity wouldn't have many like him left. . . .' [5]

For Gracián to think of John of the Cross, the Foundress had to remind him how useful he was.

Having thrown off his spell Fray John seemed to be back in it again and Teresa had to keep on saying: 'Don't forget Fray John. . . .'

The raptures of silent love are paid for by men's forgetfulness.

[1] Idem.   [2] Idem.   [3] Idem.
[4] JC quoted SEC, vol. VI, p. 209.   [5] CTA, ccxlvii.

X

A FORETASTE OF THE LAST JUDGEMENT

A FEW days before the escape of Fray John of the Cross a
solemn delegation from the Nuncio Sega waited upon the
prioress of St Joseph of Ávila—thus ignoring the Mother
Foundress although she was there—with a counter-brief: it relieved
P. Gracián of his functions as Apostolic Visitor, and countermanding
all the measures taken by his predecessor, Sega took upon himself
the government of the houses of the reformed Carmel. All this was
conveyed in such a style that Teresa of Jesus, accustomed as she was
to the language of her enemies, could not believe her ears.

Seething with indignation, but at the same time thanking Our
Lord for leading her by the same path of humiliation which he had
followed himself, she snatched up her pen to inform the prioresses of
all the convents: '. . . To see all these outrages. . . . Perhaps the
Nuncio won't leave these wolves as free a hand as they expect. . . .',[1]
she summoned Julian de Ávila and sent him to Madrid forthwith to
acknowledge the Nuncio as her prelate, and to beg him not to hand
over the Discalced to the mercy of the Mitigated.

She kept a cool head and her consternation at this fresh disaster did
not prevent her from taking a broad view of the situation: 'I'm not
too greatly distressed; it's perhaps the way that will best lead to our
being erected into a separate province.'[2]

To Gracián, who had left her in ignorance as to his precise where-
abouts, she penned a letter which began by a deserved rebuke:

Let Your Paternity tell me where you are for charity's sake and
not play the fool when I have something to inform you of: I found
myself in a false position over the cipher Your Paternity changed
without telling me about it. . . . I fear they will try and lay hands
on you; if this should be the case (God preserve you from it!) you
would do better to go away. . . . I am writing to certain persons,
to try and quell the Nuncio's anger in regard to you, letting him
know that we should all obey him with the greatest pleasure, if it
were not that Tostado is waiting to work our destruction. . . .

[1] CTA, cxxxix.   [2] CTA, ccxxxviii.

Anything which is not subjection to the friars clad in fine cloth seems to me acceptable.

'Fear nothing, Father. . . .' [1]

Over and over again she had to stand by and prop up Jerónimo Gracián. This Father was impetuous rather than courageous; he sometimes asked God for trials which he was not big enough to endure and let himself be crushed by the affairs of the Order which rested entirely on him since the Foundress was forbidden to take any action. But he had a wonderful way of getting himself forgiven: 'He's afraid like a man, but he writes like an angel. . . .' [2]

The Mother Foundress had the rare gift of allying the love of solitude and contemplation with the power of leaving such joys aside to 'negotiate' with the world, armed with lucidity, prudence and even astuteness. The success of her undertaking meant for her the realization of God's will upon earth. When she admitted 'I am old and tired, but my desires are not,' [3] she showed how strong was her love of action, under the banner 'of the captain of love, Jesus, our only good.' [4]

Yepes who had lived in her company said that for her difficulties were 'like the spark which falls into the sea only to be extinguished, like the wave which beats the rock only to be broken on it, like the blows which strike the diamond without dulling or injuring it.' [5] It might even be said that this diamond was cut out with many facets and made more precious and sparkling by such things.

One sorrow Teresa of Jesus did feel most deeply: the death of Padre Rubeo, the General who had authorized the foundation of the convents and helped her so much; affirming that she was doing as much for the Order as all the Carmelite friars in Spain, he had formerly enjoined upon her to found 'as many convents as she had hairs on her head.' [6] But it was this same P. Rubeo who afterwards disowned her, abandoning her to her persecutors. It was an injury to her sense of justice, her esteem and affection, but she never tired of trying to find means of showing him that her attitude towards him was unchanged. She had just asked Roque de la Huerta to act as intermediary:

Persuade him not to believe what is said about Teresa of Jesus; for truly she has never acted otherwise than as his most obedient daughter; he knows quite well that she wouldn't lie for anything in the world, he also knows what excitable people who do not know her

---

[1] CTA, ccxxxix. [2] CTA, ccxvi. [3] CTA, ccxxxi.
[4] Sb, C, c. vi–9. [5] Y, L. III, c. xxviii. [6] CTA, ccliii.

can say; let him be willing then to be informed of the truth of the matter, and in his office as pastor, let him not condemn without judgement or without hearing both sides. If he finds what you tell him valueless, let his Lordship punish her, but not leave her under his displeasure; she would prefer any punishment rather than to know he was angry; parents forgive even great faults in their children; how much more readily could he not do so when there was no fault, but only the great effort of founding these convents in the certainty of pleasing him. For besides the fact that he is her prelate, she has a deep affection for him. . . .[1]

P. Rubeo was not to know of this act of filial submission. The news of his death distressed Teresa considerably. She wrote to Gracián: 'The first day we wept our fill, being unable to do otherwise, in great sadness for all the troubles we had caused him, and which he certainly did not deserve. If we had taken him into our confidence over everything all would have been simple. God forgive those who have always prevented our doing so: I wanted to come to an understanding with Your Paternity on this point, and yet you were unwilling to believe me. . . .'[2]

The enmity of Calced for Discalced would never have degenerated into persecution if when the first misunderstanding arose an appeal had been made to the General's great kindness. The Foundress well knew that at that particular time Gracián was to blame; she had begged him enough then to write to P. Rubeo. But she preferred to find excuses for him rather than to own he was wrong and forgive him: such was true charity.

With P. Rubeo's death the last hope of conciliation disappeared. It was necessary to resign oneself to this insidious strife in which intrigue and machinations had as much share as violence, with the Nuncio and Tostado as enemies, while King Philip continued to keep silence. 'The Calced don't think now that they're going against God, for they have the prelates on their side. They don't worry about the King, who says nothing whatever they do. . . .'[3]

Teresa gave Gracián precise directives as to the steps he should take, the people he ought to see, what he should say, and reminded him each time of their essential objective: to obtain an independent province for the convents of the Reform. She flattered him: 'I see that at Madrid Your Paternity gets through a great deal in the day,' but however much he did it was not sufficient and she was forced to admit: 'It galls me not to be free to do what I want done myself.'

---

[1] CTA, ccli.   [2] CTA, ccliii.   [3] CTA, ccxxvi.

She told him quite clearly what she wanted said, with all the respect due to an ecclesiastical superior, in spite of a few little words of impatience here and there, and with a good deal of reserve: 'I see you are right, but. . . .'[1] There was always a 'but.' Gracián, the most supple of her instruments, was yet not a perfect one.

In this month of August when the persecutors' fury redoubled, the Nuncio Sega hurled an excommunication against him. This plunged poor 'Paul,' unhappy 'Eliseus,' into deep melancholy. Yet there it was, the trial he had been asking heaven for! He was obliged to go into hiding. Teresa secretly suffered at seeing her cherished son 'darting like a criminal in between the roof-tops. . . .'[2]

'Our Lord knew how to make me suffer by making the blows fall just where they hurt me most.' But her heroic nature suffered perhaps more when she saw he was afraid. He would drown in a glass of water; she found 'my Paul very silly, with his scruples,'[3] when he asked her if he was obliged to go to Mass: would not the Calced who were lying in wait for him be capable of taking him by surprise and carrying him off? Teresa asked the theologians: no, he is not obliged unless he can do so in complete security. She tried to cheer him up, this would all come right, 'for just as God wills that evil should come forth, so he causes good to come forth too.'[4] Nevertheless he continued to complain: 'If you are as sad as that when your life is not such a bad one, what would you have done had you been Fray John?'

That was indeed a telling comparison. Teresa let it sink in very gently, for her style was so conversational that it evoked the tones of her voice, which to Gracián were always affectionate even when her words were severe. Despite her partiality she was too perspicacious not to sum him up. When he leapt from despair to optimism but without taking any action, she grew irritated. 'Your Paternity really must answer me immediately, don't let's be satisfied with hopes any longer, for the love of God! All are dismayed to see that we have nobody who is working for us, and so the others do as they please,'[5] She announced the arrival of a friend of theirs: 'It seems to me that Your Paternity must see him, even if it tires you.'[6]

He was still the same Gracián whom an imaginary monster had frightened in the hospital at Toledo.

He was now shut up in the Calced monastery at Madrid. But he was treated reasonably well there. Yet he allowed himself to be tempted

[1] CTA, ccxxxii.
[2] CTA, ccxlii.
[3] CTA, cclv.
[4] Idem.
[5] CTA, ccl.
[6] Idem.

by the suggestion that he should leave the Reform. With what pity and tact did Teresa not stoop to his weakness:

> . . . Stand firm in what is right, even if you find yourself in danger. Blessed be the suffering which, however great it is, does not prevail over justice. I am not astonished that those who love Your Paternity seek to remove the difficulties from you, but it would not be kind to abandon Our Lady in these difficult times. . . . God preserve us from doing so. . . . That would not be to escape trials, but to plunge into them, for these will end by the grace of God, whereas those of another order would perhaps last one's lifetime. Your Reverence should think about this.[1]

Yes: what would P. Gracián have done had he been P. John?

There was a rumour that he intended to pass over to the Augustinians. His mother, Doña Juana Dantisco, let him know that if he did so she would no longer regard him as her son. As to the Count of Tendilla, he went and sought Gracián out and with his hand on the hilt of his dagger said to him calmly: 'It appears you want to abandon the habit of Our Lady of Carmel. If that's the case, I've made a vow to thrust you through with my dagger.' [2]

Gracián affirmed that he had never thought of leaving the Reform and that there was nothing in the rumour but calumnies on the part of the Calced. He refused the Count's offer to help him to escape and took fresh courage. Teresa gently made fun of his moods. She herself was busy sending secret messengers to Rome, disguised in order to escape the police whom the Mitigated friars had at their disposal. It was no longer the period of the tales of chivalry, that of the picaresque novel had come into being. The mission her emissaries were entrusted with was to inform the papacy about this war between brethren and to make the Holy Father understand how necessary it was that those who were known as 'the Reformed,' although it was they who were the observers of the primitive Rule and the true heirs of the prophet Elias, should be independent of the Mitigated. She begged her convents to supply the money for this costly expedition. Hopes were high: the year 1578 seemed to be ending in a ray of sunshine.

On 24th December, in the morning, the door of St Joseph's convent had to be opened for the Nuncio's envoys who came to bring Mother Teresa of Jesus a decree. This decree, under threat of the severest penalties, put Discalced nuns and friars alike under the jurisdiction of

---

[1] CTA, cclv. [2] SEC, vol. VIII, p. 274, n. 1.

the Provincial and of the superiors of the Mitigated friars of Castile and Andalusia.

This was the death-blow for the Reform. 'A foretaste of the Last Judgement,'[1] the Foundress said. 'All those who were present, the gentlemen of the law, the theologians, the great lords, were thunder-struck.' The terms of the decree were so violent that Teresa would have liked to stop her ears; but she did not dare either to move or speak.

Pedro, the servant who was on duty at the door when the delegates of Sega, the Nuncio, arrived, rushed out to tell Don Lorenzo de Cepeda, who hurried to the convent, accompanied by the *Corregidor*. What was the good? The Calced friars did not even respect the King; they had got accustomed to doing exactly as they wished and nobody stopped them.

While they read out the terms of the decree, Mother Teresa was look-ing at a paper one of the envoys was holding and expected that a sen-tence of excommunication would be hurled at her, but the Nuncio had contented himself with intimating that she was to be transferred to another convent for the rest of her days. 'If they mean a convent of the Mitigation, they will treat me a great deal worse than they did Fray John of the Cross! Although, to suffer as much as he did, I have not his merits.'[2]

She was forbidden to correspond with P. Gracián.

Teresa of Jesus had faced her triumphant enemies with her wonted dignity and calm; she was even seen to smile at the moment when her suffering was greatest; then she turned away from men to look only at God her Father, whose will it was that her work should thus be brought to naught. But when they had gone she suddenly left the grille without a word to Lorenzo; he saw her draw back into the shadow for the first time bowed down with grief; her daughters moved aside to allow her to pass; dismayed at her silence, they too were mute and had no consolation to offer; the Foundress admitted defeat.

Alone, locked in her cell, she opened the door to no one but Ana de San Bartolomé. Ana brought her something to eat, and, on her knees behind the door, she heard Teresa of Jesus praying in a voice interrupted by sighs and sobs. She was accusing herself of being the sole cause of all the trouble: if they threw her into the sea like Jonas, the storm would cease.[3]

When it was time for Office she came into chapel, walking as in a dream; she knelt down, stiffly; her face seemed turned to stone; and

[1] CTA, cclvii.   [2] Idem.   [3] Sb, F, c. xxviii-5.

from this ashen face tears were falling in such abundance that they made a pool on the ground.

In the evening, however, Ana ventured to go into her cell; they were going to sing the great Christmas Office and she begged the Mother to take something in order not to collapse with weakness. A light meal was ready for her in the refectory. . . .

Teresa shook her head, but leant on the kind little lay-sister's arm and agreed to go with her in order to please her.

For a long time she sat motionless before her plate; nothing seemed to distract her thoughts from the vision of her work in ruins. Ana de San Bartolomé did not dare to insist further. But suddenly she saw Our Lord Jesus Christ standing by the table, wearing a linen garment; he unfolded Teresa's serviette, broke her bread, and fed her himself as one feeds a child, mouthful by mouthful.

He said to her:

'Daughter, eat. I see how many sufferings you are enduring. . . . Take heart: it is nothing. . . .' [1]

Teresa ate her bread forthwith, although the wonder of it all might well have caused her throat to contract.

The spiritual marriage had been a splendid feast in heaven with a great concourse of angels and archangels, but now it was the everyday life of bride and Bridegroom. In the community room there was no one present but a little lay-sister.

They had now loved each other for so many years. For one another, with one another, they had striven and suffered so much! And despite these combats, nay in the very midst of combat they had experienced so many joys! Of their union magnificent things had sprung into being. Bride had never ceased to speak of Bridegroom except with trusting and sincere adoration: '. . . What seems good in his eyes seems good in mine, what he wills, I will. . . . I know not where this wondrous delight will end. . . .' [2]

The wondrous delight was leading her towards Love and Glory which would finally be 'for ever.'

---

[1] RD, vol. I, L. IV, c. xxxii.　　　　　　　　　　[2] CTA, liv.

XI

THE CATHOLIC KING DON FELIPE

IT was a different woman who came into the chapel of St Joseph's while the bells of Ávila were ringing for midnight Mass. The Mother's face, whose ashen hue had so greatly frightened the nuns, was now tinged with the fire of the seven spirits of God. She sang the Gospel of St John in an angelic voice, though ordinarily her singing voice was neither clear nor true. All were amazed to see how quickly she had recovered her lost courage when the responsory of Matins rang out: 'To-day true peace has come down from heaven for us. To-day on the whole world the heavens have dropped down honey. To-day has dawned for us the bright day of the new redemption, the day when the original fault was done away, the day of eternal bliss. To-day . . .'

After this foretaste of 'the Day of Judgement' which had ended in glory, Teresa of Jesus' smiling calm never left her. As early as 28th December, she was writing to Don Roque de la Huerta, one of the Reform's most faithful supporters, a letter which rang with joy: '. . . May this Christmas week, this entering into the New Year be as happy for Your Grace as they are for me by reason of the good news you give me. The first two days I suffered much, but since the morning of St John's day we have all been much consoled.'[1]

Since P. Gracián had been shut up in a Calced monastery, the affairs of the Order at court were in the hands of a newcomer to the reformed Carmel, Fray Nicolás de Jesús María, whom only a year ago Teresa had still been addressing as *el Señor Nicolás Doria* for he belonged to the family of the Dorias of Genoa. A man with an infinite number of irons in the fire and extremely wealthy and powerful, eager for still more wealth and power, his love of banking and other financial transactions had brought him to Seville, which was the centre of commerce between the Mediterranean and the New World. He displayed so much skill in these operations that the Archbishop, Don Cristóbal de Rojas, begged him to put the treasury of the Archbishopric on a sound footing, for somewhat casual administration had made it precarious. He succeeded so well that Philip II hearing of the talents of this Genoese

[1] CTA, cclviii.

banker summoned him to court in order that the public finances might
in turn benefit from his good offices. But into this Ali-baba's cave
Our Lord, too, came like a thief, and to the astonishment of everyone,
the courtier, the man of ambition, the trafficker in gold and silver,
preferred the poverty of persecuted friars to a bishopric which the
King offered him: at thirty-seven he took the Carmelite habit, that
of the Discalced, from the hands of Jerónimo Gracián de la Madre de
Dios.

He put his talent for business and his skill in making a virtue of
necessity if needs be, at the service of the Order; in the eyes of the
Mitigated he came to pass for an eccentric whose wits the yoke of the
Reform had dulled, and when the Nuncio imprisoned those he considered most important among the Discalced friars, he left 'the good
Nicolás' severely alone and free for any business that offered. He
showed marvellous astuteness in living in the very monastery of the
Calced friars in Madrid and for this the Foundress never ceased to
praise him: 'we wrote to each other frequently and discussed whatever
was necessary. The whole time I was in a position to appreciate his
qualities and prudence. I have much affection for him in the Lord....' [1]

P. Nicolás Doria succeeded in concealing from the Mitigated friars
all his relations with the Spanish court and with Rome, and the fact
that he had the entrée to the King's person daily enabled him to set
things in motion on behalf of the Reform. And St Dominic, giving
his blessing to the ruse for the sake of the good cause, sent his hound,
his great black and white Dane, to accompany this cunning Italian to
the very doors of the great: when all danger was averted, the dog disappeared. St Dominic kept his promise to the Foundress that he would
help her, and signs of this sort were a consolation to the daughters of
Carmel.

For there was no lull in the violence of the persecution. It even
extended as far as Seville where María de San José was deposed,
forced under threat of excommunication to hand over the letters of
Teresa of Jesus, and the nuns called on to swear on the crucifix that
the false testimony against them, the Mother Foundress, P. Gracián,
the reformed convents, was the truth and nothing but the truth.

Their Foundress, who was their captain, dispatched an order of the
day that was both valiant and tender.

I would have you know that I have never loved you so much and
that you have never had such a marvellous opportunity of serving

[1] Sb, F, c. xxx-6.

The
Prioress'
Cell in
the Convent
at Soria

A Table in
the Refectory
of the
Convent at
Valladolid

VILLANUEVA DE LA JARA
Entrance of the Convent

Our Lord. To prayer, to prayer, Sisters! And let your obedience and humility shine before men. What fine weather for gathering the fruit of your decision to serve Our Lord! . . . Amid these persecutions uphold the honour of Our Lady's daughters; if you do all you can yourselves the good Jesus will help you; for although he sleeps at sea, when the storm arises he commands the waves and they are silent. . . .[1]

Strive at all costs to be gay. . . . You are with your sisters and not in Barbary. . . .[2]

The new prioress, the Beatriz de la Madre de Dios whose father had wanted to hang her when she refused a husband (who was really to be congratulated), had proved guilty of much intrigue and some treason. Mother Teresa urged the victims to forgive:

Be not without fear, Sisters, for if the hand of God were removed from us what evil should we not commit? Believe me: this sister has neither intelligence nor talent in sufficient measure to be responsible for all the webs she weaves: the devil has been teaching her. . . . May God be with her. Pray for her, pray for her, Sisters, for many saints have returned to sanctity after a fall. . . . Do not show her even the slightest hostility. . . . Believe me, this soul is in considerable distress. . . . Remember me to Sister Beatriz de la Madre de Dios.

The very excesses to which the Calced, urged by their hatred, went were finally to recoil on their own heads: the moment was coming when 'our enemies will be swallowed up by the waves.'

Several Grandees, including the Count of Tendilla, went to the King to tell him that they felt as a personal affront all the insults heaped upon Mother Teresa of Jesus and the reformed Carmel, and the overprudent monarch had to put his reserve on one side. 'Our Catholic King Don Felipe,' sent for Sega:

'I have heard about the war which the Calced are waging against the Discalced Carmelite friars and nuns. I cannot do otherwise than regard such attacks against people who have always practised the greatest austerity and perfection, with the utmost misgiving. I have been informed that you are not helping the Discalced in any way. In future range yourself on the side of virtue.'[3]

The Papal Nuncio could not do otherwise than obey the Lord of all the Spains.

By a brief dated 1st April 1579 he released the reformed Carmel from obedience to Mitigated superiors and placed it under the juris-

[1] CTA, cclxiv.   [2] CTA, cclxxiv.
[3] Quoted SEC, vol. VIII, p. 134, n. 1.

diction of P. Ángel de Salazar who, although himself a Calced friar, was a great friend of Mother Teresa and of the Reform. The whole affair could now be regarded as virtually and happily finished and the Foundress could legitimately exclaim:

'When I consider the means Our Lord has used to turn the malice and cruelty of the enemies of Carmel solely to our advantage, I am speechless with wonder!' [1]

All that was wanting to crown this success was the erection of the Discalced friars and nuns into an independent province.

So now P. Ambrosio Mariano, P. Jerónimo Gracián, P. Antonio de Jesús, and all the other sons of Our Lady came out from hiding or from prison. P. John of the Cross, appointed rector of the College of Baeza, was able to leave Beas and its Calvario where he was answering the questions of the prioress, Ana de Jesús, of Beatriz de San Miguel or of Catalina de San Alberto, giving them what was really an anticipation of the *Dark Night* or of the *Spiritual Canticle*, the wonderful treatises on which he had been working since 1578.

Jerónimo Gracián was no sooner out of danger and worry than in his ingenuousness he once more experienced the thirst for trials. His view of matters did not coincide with Mother Teresa's.

'Leave us in peace for the love of God, for you would not be the only one to suffer them. Let us have a few days' rest. . . .' [2]

María de San José caused her the same kind of difficulty and she hastened to write to her:

'Daughter, let Your Reverence now leave foolish perfections aside, and stop refusing to be prioress once more. We all want you to accept this office again, we have made this clear and you are behaving childishly. This is not Your Reverence's business only, but that of the whole Order.' [3]

Accepting God's benefits with pleasure and gratitude is also submitting to his will.

Teresa did not think it right to take pleasures sadly; to her way of thinking, there was a time for trials and a time for rejoicing. And when the persecutions came to an end she declared: 'As to bodily health, I desire it; but I am satisfied with that of my soul.' [4]

Another thing she said was:

'When it comes to exercising government, I am no longer the same person that I was before: now it is all done through love. I don't

[1] CTA, cclxxviii.   [2] CTA, cclxxi
[3] CTA, cclxxxi.   [4] CTA, cclxxviii.

know whether this is because nobody now gives me cause to be angry or whether perhaps I've come to understand that that kind of action is more efficacious.' [1]

This joy and this progress in love were the fruits gathered by Teresa of Jesus from the tree of the cross. When born out of deep suffering, abundant meekness and gentleness are a remarkable sign of holiness; but for the Mother Foundress they only show their full value when issuing in action.

It was a message of organization and action which Our Lord ordered her to convey to the Discalced one day when she was raised with such force above the earth that in the suspension of her bodily powers she was admitted to the secret counsels of God:

> Tell the Discalced Fathers from me that they must strive to observe four conditions; so long as these are kept, this Order will grow and flourish, but if they were to neglect them, it would become decadent:
> *Firstly*: Agreement among its superiors.
> *Secondly*: That there be only a few friars in each house.
> *Thirdly*: That they have as few dealings with seculars as possible and then solely for the good of their souls.
> *Fourthly* : That they teach by acts rather than by words.

Her Father and Bridegroom thus confirmed and glorified for future ages the work she had accomplished.

Teresa of Jesus had always taught by acts, but her testimony had never been more striking than it was during suffering. Not for one moment, during four whole years, were her acts found to be in contradiction to her words. Not for one moment did she through fear or weakness act otherwise than she advised others to do.

A clear summary, a pure epitome of her mystical works is to be found in her life, particularly during her latter years. Day by day she proved the efficaciousness of her teaching in *The Way of Perfection*, demonstrated that the castle of the soul had indeed Seven Mansions and that His Majesty is there awaiting man in the very depths of his being; it was great thoughts like these which engendered her great actions.

Rhythmic movements of the soul we might call them, attuned to the point of perfection by her continual song of praise to Our Lord and her goodwill towards all men.

Self-renunciation—without which **the** forgiveness of injuries would be difficult, to strive to overcome vainglory useless, and a fruitful surrender to the will of God impossible. When Teresa of Jesus said that everything which is ephemeral and does not satisfy God is nothing, less than nothing, and that she had enough dignity left to count temporal things for very little,[1] she proved it by her deeds.

Liberty: in the security of her conscience, she was free: 'that is a great thing.'[2]

Absence of all fear: because one cannot serve God in a state of anxiety, she elected to live by hope.[3] She sought only the kingdom of God and his justice, throwing all appearance of prudence to the winds, and everything was indeed added unto her. It was perhaps in this total and conscious abandonment of all human affairs into the hands of God that she gave proof of the absolute harmony that existed in her between intellectual and spiritual life. She went forward towards what was most certain, 'for God knows what is best for us';[4] 'he knows better what he is doing than we know what we want.'[5]

She worked, she even schemed, she spared no effort, spent her nights in writing letters and books, her days in ruling, maintaining, encouraging, striving, but when all this was done, 'the most profitable business is to keep silence and to speak with God.'[6] In short, to act as energetically as if all depended on action and to pray as fervently as if all depended on prayer. Always the two inseparables: Martha and Mary.

'Sisters, to prayer, to prayer!'[7] 'And let every serious decision first form the subject of prayer!'[8] 'Let us listen to God as we do to our best friend. . . . When we set out to do his will we have nothing to fear. . . .'[9] 'He takes everything in hand.'[10] 'Christ is a very good friend, for we can look upon him as a man with his weaknesses and sufferings, and he becomes our companion. When we have acquired this habit, it is very easy for us to find him by our side. . . .'[11]

This good friend never left her. It was at the very moments when reason seemed to forbid all hope that Mother Teresa was strongest: friends disappeared or faltered, the King was silent, hatred against the Reform redoubled in violence, there remained only God, but 'God sufficeth.'

And the triumph was overwhelming. So true it is that 'when we begin to place our confidence in human resources, divine help is with-

---

[1] Sb, F, c. xv-15. [2] CTA, xciii. [3] CTA, cdxxix.
[4] CTA, clviii. [5] CTA, cccliv. [6] CTA, clxxv.
[7] CTA, cclxiv. [8] SEC, vol. II, p. 357. [9] CTA, clxxix.
[10] CTA, clxxv. [11] Sb, V, c. xxii-10.

drawn.' [1] 'To do everything himself Our Lord only waits for our decision to abandon all to him.' [2]

What Teresa of Jesus taught by her actions after having affirmed it in words [3] was that in all trials there is no better remedy than love for Jesus, the good lover. Such love is proved in action and it was in the midst of temptations to disobey, to despair, to hate, to lie, to become proud of a success or to let herself be crushed by failure that Teresa as a faithful lover showed her obedience, her unwavering hope, her compassion and her humility.

In her, heaven and earth, palpable reality and the reality which was invisible, natural and supernatural were in perfect balance.

And when she spoke of 'the health of her soul,' the phrase was perfectly accurate.

[1] CTA, ciii.   [2] Sb F, c. xxviii-19.   [3] CTA, cccxvii.

XII

THE *BEATAS* OF VILLANUEVA
DE LA JARA

P ÁNGEL DE SALAZAR'S first gesture had been to restore to the Mother Foundress complete liberty of action: that is, she was once more free to show her obedience in other ways than by remaining shut up in one convent. What were they going to require of her? She wondered about this with some misgiving, and it was not long before she knew: this old woman, worn out by sickness, labour, struggle and penance, was commanded to resume once more the bustle and worry of her journeys and foundations; that and nothing less.

On 25th June 1579, accompanied by Ana de San Bartolomé and a small escort which included a surly friar, she said goodbye to her daughters in Ávila, her niece Teresita and her brother Lorenzo, and to the good and faithful Francisco de Salcedo and Doña Guiomar de Ulloa. Her heart was heavy but she braced herself against the tenderness of the farewells:

'Look at her, poor little old woman! Setting off for Medina del Campo, Valladolid, Malagón, Alba de Tormes, Salamanca![1] I tell you that makes me laugh for I feel I have the courage to do much more than that!'[1]

Mile after mile they went, under the scorching heat of Castile in summer, Teresa not even being able to enjoy the sight of the vast horizons she loved, for the carts were, as usual, closely covered.

Although she had insisted that they were not to make any fuss for her visits, her convents welcomed her triumphantly. She was very touched by her reception and repeated over and over again:

'What have I done to make them love me so much?'

She was delighted to find that these houses were flourishing, particularly considering the poverty of their beginnings.

At Valladolid she received good news: Don Felipe Sega, the Nuncio, had himself asked the King to separate Discalced and Mitigated into two independent provinces. She could now hope to see the fulfilment of her wish—for her, to wish for a thing meant to will it.

[1] CTA, cclxxvii.

But there was a shadow over her joy: she felt the threat of a war
of succession between Spain and Portugal so keenly that she wrote
to her friend Don Teutonio de Braganza, Archbishop of Évora,
begging him to make the one claimant, his nephew the Duke of
Braganza, understand that it was of paramount importance to avoid
a conflict: '. . . If God were to allow things to come to this bad pass,
I should long for death in order not to see it. . . . God grant that the
truth be ascertained without having recourse to such a slaughter. For
in times when there are so few Christians, it would be a great misfortune that they should kill each other. . . .' [1]

In this war there was no more question of 'truth' than there was in
any other, but of those 'dark interests' which horrified Teresa of Jesus.
The war broke out, and Philip II placed at the head of his armies his
old friend the Duke of Alba. He brought him from prison where he
was reading Teresa's *Autobiography* to put him at the head of an
invading army of 35,000 infantry and 2,000 cavalry.

In the height of the summer, the Foundress was able to make a stay
of some two months at Salamanca. There she came back to the same
old struggles to get hold of a house. Of the prioress she said: 'Nobody
helps me so much as Mother Ana de la Encarnación.'

The life of the nuns was so exemplary, their prayer bore such
marvellous fruit, that she thanked the prioress:

'Ana, God will reward you for forming such good daughters for
me.' [2]

There she found Isabel de Jesús once more; in her tender affection
for her she was distressed to find her so thin and called her to her side:

'Come here, daughter. . . . Sing your *cantarcillo* for me. . . .'

And the good sister sang once more in her clear voice the verses
to which Teresa owed one of her sweetest ecstasies:

> *Véante mis ojos,*
> *Dulce Jesús bueno.* . . .
> Let my eyes behold you,
> Good, sweet Jesus. . . .

In November there were fresh goodbyes and fresh departures.
The Foundress arrived at Malagón on the 25th, exhausted by the long
journey but radiant with joy: at last she would have the new buildings
which Doña Luisa de la Cerda had delayed so long to give her. For
the first time since she had been founding convent after convent, she
found herself free to set one up where and as she wanted it.

[1] CTA, cclxxxv.　　　　　　[2] SEC, Vol. VIII, p. 328, n. 2.

Doña Luisa's steward accompanied her when she went up and down Malagón looking for a site:

'Not here: a monastery of Franciscan friars is going to be built here one day. . . .'

They were still wandering about all over the brick-red soil of Malagón to which the Mother Foundress paid less attention than she did to the sky, when by a dove that came and settled on the topmost branch of a leafy olive tree, Teresa recognized the site of her dovecot. . . .

She decided on the plans herself in collaboration with a good architect from Toledo and, together with Doña Luisa, put her signature to what would have been called nowadays an extremely detailed specification. This house was to demonstrate to future generations Teresa of Jesus' taste for simple materials—chalk and brick, beams of unplaned wood—her sense of proportion and arrangement. If the cells were small, the galleries were wide, the passages convenient, the offices practical. The smallest detail showed her talent for organization and that for her a certain regard for hygiene or a desire to facilitate the work which had to be done were by no means incompatible with penance. She installed a filter so that the water might be purer, and great porous jars to keep it cool, as well as a hand-grinder for crushing almonds—an excellent food for her nuns.

The Foundress got up at dawn and went immediately to the site; the contractors told her they thought the work would take six months to complete.

'We shall move in in a fortnight,' Teresa assured them.

And she took over the direction of operations herself. Sitting on a stone bench, despite the cold, she presided over everything; she went everywhere. Leaning on her stick which she was unable to do without since her fall at Ávila, she found the most expeditious solution for every problem as it arose, giving a word of encouragement and even lending a hand. She had no time to go and say her Hours until nearly midnight, but in these circumstances was not work a form of prayer?

And on 8th December, as she had foretold, the nuns made their solemn entry into the new convent which was completely and properly finished. They were so delighted at leaving their dark and miserable dwelling and being able to walk at ease in the light galleries that Teresa, who was as pleased as they were, said they were like little lizards darting in the sun.[1]

She had no wish to leave Malagón. All had not been smooth

[1] CTA, cccxx.

going in her recent journeyings. The persecution and campaign of calumny against the Discalced nuns and their Foundress had left a certain taint in the minds of some; in a small place in La Mancha the Foundress's entry into a church caused a disturbance which interrupted the Mass; when she was seen to go up to the altar people cried out it was sacrilege and the crowd was so hostile that she had to slip out quickly and take refuge in her carriage. She felt such violence now more than she had done formerly; she who loved so much to be loved was gladdened more than formerly by the least sign of affection and was touched by the friendly quarrel which broke out over her between the Duke of Alba and his wife, Doña María Enríquez: which of the two did Mother Teresa prefer? She could cast no vote: for God alone had all her preference.[1]

At Malagón she was surrounded with affection and there was peace.

She wrote to Gracián:

'Here there is no more question of Teresa of Jesus than if she did not exist. I am not therefore thinking of going away unless I am ordered to do so for I've often been in despair at all the foolish things I've heard. When people say about you, as they did over there, that you're a saint, it is very necessary to be one and that's not so easily done. Laugh if you like, but just try producing one: and see if it doesn't cost you more than the trouble of saying it. . . .'[2]

But rest was not to be her lot: P. Ángel de Salazar sent her orders to go and found a convent at Villanueva de la Jara. She must leave Malagón and move on once more.

'Remember me, all of you, before Our Lord, for I am tired out and very old. . . .'[3]

There were nine ladies of noble rank who for years had been living as recluses in the little town of Villanueva de la Jara, situated two-thirds of the way along the road from Toledo to Valencia. They never went out and it was only the two eldest who had the right to draw back the bolts of the heavy door when someone knocked. There was no prioress but each of the nine *beatas* assumed the responsibility of government in turn.

Nine ladies of noble birth, very simple and poor, attracted to the place by the reputation for sanctity of a very curious person, Doña Catalina de Cardona.

[1] SEC, vol. VIII, p. 394, n. 5.
[2] CTA, ccxvii.   [3] CTA, cccvii.

Daughter of the Duke of Cardona, Doña Catalina had been governess to Prince Don Carlos, son of Philip II, and to the famous natural son of the Emperor Charles V, Don Juan of Austria. When she was forty she left the court to live in the desert of La Roda, leading a life of such frightening penance and austerity that her bloodstained hair shirts and the discipline of chains which she took for whole hours on end caused as much consternation as they did admiration. In the cave where she dwelt continually, as if she were buried alive, the devils did not leave her alone: in their attacks they assumed the form of huge mastiffs or of serpents. One wonders if she had a calendar in her Thebaïd, for she was reputed to eat only on Sundays, Tuesdays and Thursdays.

When she decided to take a religious habit she chose the Carmelite one, but not that of the nuns: she insisted on wearing the friars' habit, for this penitent for all her hair shirts could not bear a coif upon her head. Her reputation for sanctity was so great that the Princess of Éboli, always on the look-out for celebrities, sent a carriage to her desert for her and brought her to court where she found her old friends once more.

One day the Nuncio learned of the scandal that was taking place in Madrid: a Discalced Carmelite friar was going about in a carriage with ladies of the aristocracy and leaning out of the window was blessing the crowd. He at once insisted that this friar should be brought to him to be punished for the bad example he was giving and also for his presumption. On arrival, the Discalced friar proved to be none other than Doña Catalina who, accustomed as she was to giving her blessing, blessed the Nuncio as she would have done anyone else. This by no means lessened his anger, but this daughter of the desert in disguise was too great a lady of the realm for him to be able to show much severity.

King Philip had, after all, personally invited her to spend a week at the Escorial with Princess Juana.

He tried to persuade her to enter a convent:

'I am not going to live among affected, sentimental, sugary nuns whose imagination makes our natural weaknesses worse. . . .'[1]

He let her go as she had come, in her friar's habit. On her way back to her solitude—from now onwards very busy with the crowd of pious persons who rushed to see her—she stopped a few days at the Carmel of Toledo; the sisters whose privilege it was to be near her affirmed to Mother Teresa that her very coarse and extremely dirty

[1] Quoted SST, vol. IV, c. iii.

habit exuded an odour of sanctity all the more remarkable 'since in view of the great heat one would have expected an unpleasant smell.' [1]

Doña Catalina Cardona had just died; the account given of the sufferings she inflicted upon herself in Our Lord's name awakened lively feelings of confusion mingled with admiration in Teresa of Jesus; she always reproached herself for being only a mediocre penitent. Fortunately God was watching over her. One day when she was distressing herself at not obtaining permission from her confessor to practise greater mortifications, to the extent of wondering if it would not be better for her to disobey him, Our Lord said to her:

'Daughter, as to that no! The way you are following is the best, for it is sure. You know all the penances she practised? I appreciate your obedience much more.' [2]

Thanks to this very clear order, Mother Teresa of Jesus remained the living example of common-sense spirituality.

Thus it was not without pain that she received the news that the nine poor but noble *beatas* of Villanueva de la Jara, Doña Catalina's fervent followers, wanted her to transform their hermitage into a Carmelite convent: was it going to be possible to make them submit to a rule which had some regard to reason? Up to the present they had been doing what they could: they were already wearing Our Lady's scapular and saying the Office as well as possible, which, in fact, was anything but well: it was their ignorance that was to blame and nothing more, for, not knowing how to read, they spent hours spelling out an Office letter by letter. They fasted seven months in the year not counting the days when they *had* nothing to eat, and plied the distaff to earn their scanty pittance and pay the messengers they sent to Mother Teresa of Jesus at the other side of Castile.

For they would not leave off worrying her. The matter was first broached at the time of her return from Seville in 1576; after that the poor *beatas* added prayers to the requests and negotiations: they made novena after novena, dragging themselves on their knees from the entrance to their hermitage to the altar in the church, the procession being headed by a little girl of five whom one of them, a widow, had been obliged to take into the solitude with her.

The Mother continued to hesitate, but the more she did so the more the *beatas* insisted, so much so that in the end their perseverance triumphed over her scruples. Moreover, during the persecutions, P. Antonio de Jesús had been in hiding with the Discalced friars of

---

[1] Sb, F, c. xxviii–32.   [2] SEC, R, xxiii, p. 54.

La Roda, quite near them, and he had given her information about them: touched by their good will and edified by their fervour, he persuaded the Mother Foundress to come and give them the habit herself.

Teresa decided to bring with her four nuns, chosen as much for their common-sense as for their great lights in prayer, to train the *beatas*; from Malagón she took one of the best nuns of Carmel, Ana de San Agustín, and Elvira de San Ángelo; P. Antonio de Jesús came to fetch them all. The Foundress was delighted to see him again and to find him looking plump and healthy; she declared that trials were certainly good for one's health for she herself had never been better.

They started off. Ana de San Bartolomé was naturally among the party, and it is from her we learn what a procession of triumph this twenty-eight league journey in the month of February 1580 was. They went through Toledo again to collect two other foundresses, Constanza de la Cruz and María de los Mártires.

At Robledo, the house of the duenna (who was known as 'lover of virtue') where the little company halted for dinner was stormed by a crowd of all the pious folk of the place. Two constables were installed to guard the doors, but those whose zeal outran their discretion jumped over the wall: several persons had to be taken off to prison before the *Santa Madre* could get a little rest.

The precaution she took of starting off again next day at three o'clock in the morning, before it was light, proved useless: people were waiting for her everywhere, and everywhere she was acclaimed. A rich farmer had taken up his position along the road and implored her to come to his house to take a collation specially prepared in her honour. From thirty leagues around he had sent for his children, grandchildren, sons-in-law, daughters-in-law, all his relations, all his serving men and women, for Teresa of Jesus to give them her blessing. He had also gathered together his flocks and the tinkling of sheep-bells mingled with the murmur of prayer that went up from this kneeling crowd dressed in their Sunday best. It was a goodly company, not unworthy of Biblical times or of the marriage feasts of Camacho,[1] with all these worthy peasants and the tables all prepared and loaded with meats, but without getting down from her carriage the Foundress blessed the good folk, both man and beast, and went on her way.

The friars of La Roda had arrived first: Teresa found them touching, 'with their bare feet and coarse habits,[2] and almost thought herself in the golden age of the holy Fathers of the Desert' : as an offering

---

[1] See *Don Quixote*—Tr.   [2] Sb, F, xxviii, 20.

they brought her two small but beautiful statues: one of the Blessed Virgin, smiling, and the other of the Holy Child. All the way from the monastery of Our Lady of Succour to Villanueva, it was nothing but streamers, branches of trees and decorated altars. All the people round joined the procession: Ana de San Agustín saw the statue of the Holy Child come to life and move from their Mother to the monstrance and back to the Mother again. . . . The countenance of Teresa of Jesus expressed no surprise. Ana de San Bartolomé who also saw what was happening kept silence. . . . And just as Ana de San Agustín was about to exclaim out loud, the Foundress cut her short with a categorical:

'Silly little child, be quiet!'[1]

Thus preceded by the Son of God, the *Fundadora* made her entry into Villanueva de la Jara amid a veritable whirl of enthusiasm, people shouting and singing and bells chiming, all honouring a few humble Discalced Carmelites for the love of Our Lord.

But she was eager to make the acquaintance of her new daughters, the nine *beatas*, both noble and poor. Behind the thick door of their hermitage the recluses were waiting for her, rather fearful: would she not go away again, appalled at their state of utter poverty? To think this was to misjudge the Mother Foundress. She took to them forthwith, although she could not help being aware of their dirt, as well as of their fervour. The pious creatures had been wearing the same garment —a lay dress but austere in form—ever since their entering upon the life of perfection and they thought they were proving to Our Lord their detachment from the world by scarcely ever washing. And so Teresa began by snatching up a broom and with her good arm she set to work with determination to put the house in order. The community followed her example.

She stayed a month at Villanueva de la Jara and spent it making the wretched house look something like a convent; anxious to make the place as pleasant as possible, she even planted a vine with her own hands.

P. Antonio de Jesús taught the new Carmelites how to say their Hours a little better than by just muttering them, and the sisters who had come from Malagón and Toledo taught them by their example the virtue of obedience and that other eminently Teresian virtue,

[1] I got this story from the oldest of the nuns of Villanueva de la Jara, who in her turn had received the tradition when she was young from the oldest then living. Madre María Margarita del Santísimo Sacramento also told me that when leaving this statue to her daughters Teresa of Jesus told them that in it they would always have 'a very prosperous farm'. . . .

moderation in all things, for only the love of God can be practised to an unlimited degree without danger.

When Mother Teresa went away again, in a convent that was poor indeed, but clean and polished in every corner, she left souls who were already travelling along the road to heaven.

Everything that was difficult or dangerous Teresa put into the hands of God and when action was not possible for her she then did her best to forget such matters. Accordingly she very seldom thought about her *Autobiography* which was still in the hands of the Inquisition. What could she do about it? Nothing. It was therefore useless for her to worry about it: and the business of the Order kept her attention occupied elsewhere.

After completing the foundation of Villanueva de la Jara, she remained in Toledo for some time and took advantage of her stay there to go and see Cardinal Don Gaspar de Quiroga, Archbishop of Toledo and Grand Inquisitor General. Gracián went with her for the purpose of the visit was to ask permission to found a convent of Discalced Carmelite nuns in Madrid, 'without mentioning the book.'

But the Cardinal, a man with a long nose and harsh mouth, whom El Greco has painted with his long white beard standing out against his scarlet robes and a look expressing weariness even more than severity, broached the subject right at the beginning of the interview:

I am very glad to make your acquaintance for I have been greatly wanting to do so: look upon me as your chaplain, I will help you as much as ever is necessary. I want to tell you that a book of yours was presented to the Inquisition several years ago; its teaching was examined rigorously. I have read it all through and I maintain that its teaching is very safe, very true and very profitable. You can take it back again when you like: I give you the permission for which you ask and I beg you to pray to God for me always.[1]

That matter was thus happily ended.

[1] JG quoted SEC, vol. I, p. cxxvi.

XIII

OUR LADY'S ORDER—
AS I'VE WANTED IT

A T sixty-five, Teresa still retained her fresh complexion and an astonishing youthfulness, but at Toledo she almost died of an attack of the widespread influenza epidemic; after this she was greatly changed, and when she got better had become thin and old. She never completely recovered.

In 1580 this influenza epidemic made havoc all over Europe; several of Teresa's friends died of it, among others the holy gentleman Don Francisco de Salcedo, Don Cristóbal de Rojas, Archbishop of Seville, and P. Baltasar Álvarez her former confessor whom she greatly mourned. No one was more loyal in her affections than this woman who was detached 'from all created things.' Ten years earlier she had written to Don Francisco: 'God grant you life until I die, for in order not to be without you, I should obtain from Our Lord that he called you very quickly. . . .' [1] And yet after all he died first.

And in that same year she lost the dearest of them all, her brother and spiritual son, Don Lorenzo de Cepeda. 'I am three years older than he and yet I go on living. . . .' [2]

Teresa, a perpetual invalid, but endowed with amazing resistance, was thus bereaved of her most tried and loyal friends. The hurt went deep and she lamented:

'Why has God left me in the world to see so many of his servants die?' [3] At Valladolid she had a relapse, her heart showed signs of giving way, signs of paralysis of the tongue made them fear she might lose her speech, and the pains in the head and noises in the ear were now incessant. But, most serious symptom of all, she seemed to have lost heart. It was pathetic to watch the woman who had wrestled triumphantly with Sega the Nuncio, with Tostado and with hundreds of Mitigated friars, trying to struggle with herself. Her nuns had always known their Foundress as a daring captain overthrowing the enemy by swift counter-offensive, without stopping for skirmishes against temptations and weakness. But at Valladolid her worn-out body was

[1] CTA, x.   [2] CTA, cccxxvi.   [3] CTA, cccxxxvi.

no longer capable of obeying the demands of the spirit, she recoiled, was afraid, wanted to give way.

She herself analysed what she termed her cowardice: 'To be ill and to suffer great pain is nothing if the soul is alert and praises God, taking everything as coming from his hand. But to suffer on the one hand and on the other to remain doing nothing is a terrible thing. . . . [1] In my weakness I had even lost the confidence that God in his goodness had given me of the necessity of undertaking these foundations. . . .'

Those around her put it down to her age. Was the Foundress too old? No, but she was 'bound by the devil or by disease,' a prey to panic, listless and with no will left.

She was reluctant to go and found the convents of Palencia and Burgos as P. Ángel de Salazar, with no compassion for her state of exhaustion, ordered her. And not only did no one succeed in restoring her courage, but all those around her, even the prioress María Bautista, began to waver.

Yet her listlessness was not such that she did not desire to know God's will. One day, after Communion, when she asked him about it, Our Lord said in a reproachful tone: 'What are you afraid of? When have I failed you? I am the same as I have always been. Do not fail to make these two foundations.' [2]

Teresa exclaimed:

'O God Almighty! How different are your words from these of men! They give me such courage and determination that the whole world would not stop me. . . .' [3]

Teresa of Jesus had uttered her great word: determination. The spirit of determination, the will, in her had acquired such power that from the moment of her decision the whole thing could be taken as accomplished: for 'the Lord helps those who are determined to serve and glorify him.'

She sent P. Gracián on to Palencia in advance; he found so many obstacles that he was quickly discouraged. Happily he also met a nobleman 'of cape and sword,' Suero de Vega, whose zeal was so ardent that he was not afraid to take a holy friar to task:

'He said so much to me of the excellence of a lively faith and of confidence in God, and in such a way, that I caught his fervour. . . .' [4]

That was one point gained. Canon Reinoso also undertook to help, as it proved, very effectively. He was a man 'well built, of fair complexion; his cheeks somewhat bright by reason of an inflammation

---

[1] Sb, F, c. xxix-3.   [2] Sb, F., c. xxix-6.   [3] Idem.
[4] JG quoted SEC, vol. V, p. 270, n. 2.

of the liver which made him more handsome still on account of the freckles which it caused. . . .' [1]

The second point gained happened as follows: From the depths of the sea P. Gracián rose upon the crests of the waves and let himself be carried ashore. In a town which claimed to be too poor to feed a few nuns it was absolutely essential to win over the most adamant of all: the *Corregidor*. Teresa of Jesus had charged P. Gracián to get from this man of flint an authorization which he had so far granted to no one.

'He received me very badly, flew into a rage and said to me in an angry tone: "Go, Father, and let what Mother Teresa of Jesus wants be done quickly. She must be hiding in her bosom a provision from God's own royal Council, for quite against our will and pleasure we have to do everything she wants." ' [2]

This account of the situation seemed so encouraging to Teresa that she decided upon an immediate departure. Once more the devil had raised difficulties which proved only apparent but which were all the more serious because they came from within herself. 'One knows perfectly well that he never succeeds in his purpose, but he makes one worried. . . .' [3] As always, the very clear and definite determination of Teresa of Jesus checkmated him.

And so once more the Mother Foundress journeyed up hill and down dale. Not in covered carts this time but on mule-back, in the winter's bitter cold, through so thick a fog that the riders could scarcely see each other. She reached Palencia in a state of collapse, but next morning, 29th December 1580, the first Mass was said and the convent founded. There, as elsewhere, she had difficulties in bringing off the purchase of a house, and against the opinion of the whole town, she finally installed the Carmelites hard by a certain hermitage known as Nuestra Señora de la Calle—Our Lady of the Street—where such extremely unedifying happenings were going on that Our Lord willed the presence of the Carmelites there to end the scandal.

According to the Foundress it was the prioress, Inés de Jesús, who did everything to bring about this foundation :

'I no longer serve any useful purpose, except perhaps for the stir the name Teresa of Jesus makes.' [4]

St. Joseph's convent of Our Lady of the Street at Palencia was barely founded when she set off to found a convent at Soria in response to the appeal of Doña Beatriz de Beamonte y Navarra—*Beamonte*

---

[1] Quoted SEC, vol. V, p. 271, n. 5.
[2] Idem.
[3] Sb, F, c. xxix–9.
[4] CTA, cccxliv.

being a Spanish form of Beaumont—a descendant of the Kings of Navarre, who placed at her disposal her palace and a revenue of 500 ducats.

Quite a lot of the route from Palencia to Soria lies in the plain, it is extremely well watered, and Teresa just loved it:

'It was a tremendous pleasure for me. . . . I often found companionship in the very sight of the rivers. . . .' [1] For her the spirit of God moved above the face of the waters. One incident in the journey amused her: the Bishop of Osma, who was her old confessor P. Velázquez, sent his bailiff to meet and accompany her, carrying his standard; the crowd flocked up and imagined the nuns were being taken to the dungeons of the Inquisition. Both her humility and her sense of humour derived the greatest amount of pleasure from this mistake.

At Soria as in other places she attended to the organization of the convent down to the last detail, in particular to the strictness of the enclosure.

. . . Behind the parlour grille, there shall be added, set back a little way, a wooden grating made of very thin bars but so close together that the tiniest hand cannot pass through; over this a thick veil is to be nailed. This grating shall only be opened for near relatives and the Mother Prioress will keep the key.
. . . The communion grille shall likewise be bolted. The Prioress alone shall have the right to open it.
. . . A private window will allow Doña Beatriz de Beamonte to talk with the nuns, but a veil shall be drawn if any of her suite accompany her. [2]

Mother Teresa insisted that Doña Elvira, a niece of Doña Beatriz, should come but seldom, 'for she is a young married woman and is dressed according to her station. . . .' It was important that the nuns should not get a longing for worldly attire.

Grilles at the windows looking out on the orchard, grilles in the choir, grilles at even the smallest opening on the world.

But the Foundress was as keen about the health of her daughters as she was about their absolute separation from the world—they were not to live in cells recently built until the walls were perfectly dry!—and their safety: 'When coming out from Matins they should light a little lamp which would last on until morning, for it is dangerous to sleep without a light; so many things might happen! It would be very

---

[1] CTA, ccclxxviii. [2] SEC, vol. VI, pp. 357-8.

dangerous if one of the sisters had an accident and there was no light. A candle with a little twisted wick doesn't cost much.'[1]

The choice of the prioress for Soria astonished P. Gracián:

'Heavens, Mother! Do you know that Catalina de Cristo cannot write and can scarcely read? She knows nothing about administration and will be incapable of governing.'

'Be quiet, Father!'—for if necessary Gracián, too, was silenced like the others—'Catalina knows a great deal about the art of loving God and she is very intelligent: no more is needed to know how to govern and she will be just as good a prioress as anyone else would have been.'[2]

Catalina de Cristo, who was a relative of the Foundress, was a tall woman with a severe face worn thin by excessive mortifications. She had begun by finding the discipline too easy, the straw pallet on her bed too soft, the prayers too short, and the spare diet on fast days too plentiful and too palatable. Her father, most fanatical of men, was haunted by fear of the *Alumbrados*. To protect his daughter from clandestine heretical books and pamphlets, he had discovered a method that was foolproof: not even to show her the letters of the alphabet. Cloistered, as it were, in her father's house, only allowed to go to Mass very early in the morning, she left the church before the sermon, in case the preacher were contaminated by the accursed sect. Catalina de Balmaseda thus grew up without seeing a living soul; far from finding her solitude displeasing, she grew so accustomed to it that she even spent nine months in a cellar and finally obtained leave to enter Carmel.

Mother Teresa loved her all the more because she had had a lot of difficulty to make her see that austerity must be tempered by a little common sense and a great deal of gentleness in regard to one's neighbour; she succeeded, however, and did not hesitate to impose upon her the searching test of governing her sisters and setting the tone of a new convent. And from Soria she was able to write to P. Gracián: 'The prioress is very satisfactory.'[3]

Thus, one by one, often trusting much more to what her intuition told her about the qualities of her daughters than to appearances, Mother Teresa of Jesus formed a circle of great prioresses.

The law of God, the Rule and Constitutions

Point by point, during twenty years of daily observation recorded down to the last detail, attentive to every reaction however slight, to

[1] Idem. Such little twisted wicks are still in use in certain Spanish Carmels.
[2] SEC, vol. V, p. 290, n. 2.   [3] CTA, ccclxx.

the most insignificant details as much as to the most important generalities, modifying one thing, taking into account another, appealing
to experience against tradition and to tradition against some over-
venturesome innovation, Teresa of Jesus achieved in 1581 the final
form of the Rule and Constitutions of the reformed Order of Our
Lady of Mount Carmel.

During the few months she spent at Palencia, this preoccupation
never left the Mother Foundress: the Discalced, met in chapter at
Alcalá de Henares, were to adopt the Constitutions permanently. Up
to the last minute, sending message after message to P. Gracián, she
never ceased putting retouches and amendments.

In the first place she begged them to avoid anything which might
give the timorous a pretext for scruples:

> About the stockings of hemp or frieze, I hope that Your Paternity
> will see that nothing definite is laid down: let it just be said that they
> can wear stockings, otherwise they will make endless scruples. . . .
> Where it says 'hempen cap' just say cloth. And see if you can remove
> the clause which forbids them to eat eggs, and bread at collation: in
> that matter it is sufficient to observe what the Church imposes with-
> out adding anything more. To do so would make them scrupulous
> and so do them harm.[1]

Will men ever understand nuances like these? The undesirable
results of excessive zeal are beyond them and the Mother had no small
amount of trouble to protect her daughters even against P. Jerónimo
Gracián. And she blamed him for it, too, with no hesitation: 'Antonia
has told us so many things ordered by Your Paternity that we're all
scandalized over it. Believe me, Father, these houses are going on very
well, and there's no need to overload them with observances. For
charity's sake, don't let Your Paternity forget this. Just watch very
closely to see that the Constitutions are observed, without expecting
anything more; if they keep them well, they will be doing a good
deal.'[2]

Again, 'for charity's sake,' she begged him not to forget everything prescribed about the wearing of the black veil before the face.

And 'for the love of God,'[3] she begged him to stipulate that beds
and table linen must always be spotlessly clean. She wanted to put
cleanliness in the Constitutions, she loved it so much and considered
it so indispensable, and the friars—not her daughters, happily—
esteemed it so lightly.

---

[1] CTA, cccli. [2] CTA, ccxxxii. [3] CTA, ccci.

She who was called 'mystical doctor' while still alive—a circumstance which was to displease her greatly—made them stipulate that prioresses should be put at the head of the list for sweeping, 'so that they may give good example in everything.' [1] And they were to 'make themselves loved in order to be obeyed.' [2]

A single sentence of the Constitutions showed clearly both her knowledge of the human heart and her sense of justice: 'Never punish until your anger has died down.' [3] And her ever-watchful compassion tempered the rigours of the penalty for those who were undergoing punishment for a 'graver fault.' The culprit must indeed receive the discipline, confined in a cell, 'deprived of the company of the angels,' but, added the Foundress, 'Let the Mother Prioress show compassion and send a sister who can comfort her, and if there is any humility of heart in her, let her good intentions be taken into consideration.' [4]

As to her beloved poverty, she inscribed it in the Rule in terms that were unforgettable: 'Let poverty, ever present, shed its fragrance over everything. . . .' [5]

How deeply these Constitutions bear the imprint of Teresa of Jesus. They start from earth, mindful of the stones along the road, rising progressively, yet surely, step by step, to heaven.

In novices she insisted on 'good health and common-sense,' explaining to someone who expressed surprise at this:

'Our Lord will give them devotion here: we shall teach them prayer. But common-sense? We can't do anything to inculcate that into them.[6] And the devil knows only too well how to take advantage of their want of intelligence. . . .' [7]

On the thorny question of dowries Teresa of Jesus added: 'When the person is satisfactory from our point of view, she should be accepted, even if she can give no alms to the house, as has been done up to the present.'

Eventually, 'the law of God, the Rule and Constitutions of the Order' were adopted at the chapter of Alcalá de Henares. All the Mother Foundress had to do now was to wait 'for them to be printed, so that nobody can change anything.'[8] At the year's close she had the joy of having the book in her hands.

It was at Palencia, too, that she learned that Discalced and Calced had at last been erected into independent provinces by Pope

[1] SEC, CONS, p. 11. [2] Idem, p. 15. [3] Idem, p. 18.
[4] Idem, p. 22. [5] Idem, p. 10.
[6] FR, L. IV, c. xxiv. [7] CTA, cclxxiv. [8] CTA, cccli.

Gregory VII. This bull, given under the form of a brief, set the crown on the Foundress's work. P. Jerónimo Gracián de la Madre de Dios was elected Provincial of the new Province which comprised 'all the monasteries in these realms founded up to the present and all those which shall be founded in the future, whether of friars or nuns, which observe the primitive Rule. . . .'

Teresa of Jesus saw the Reform not only accomplished and achieved but given permanence and perpetuity. 'That was one of the greatest joys I could have in this life. Now we are all at peace. Calced and Discalced, no one will hinder us any more from serving Our Lord.' [1]

Twenty-two monasteries and convents, three hundred friars, two hundred nuns, details the Holy Father's bull, will in future be free, before men as before God, because they will all be subject to one austere unchanging Rule, by means of which they will be born again of God alone.

When the bell wakes the sisters at Palencia, at five o'clock in the morning, Mother Teresa now follows in thought what is taking place in her twelve other dovecots: at Ávila, Medina del Campo, Malagón, Valladolid, Toledo, Salamanca, Alba de Tormes, Segovia, Beas, Seville, Caravaca, Villanueva de la Jara. Our Lady's doves, black veils or white, are going to renew their plumage in the lustral water of prayer and resume their plaintive notes for Christ Jesus.

For Christ, and for those whom he has preferred to all others: sinners, the sick, the desperate, the dying, those who are contending against difficulties, those who are suffering hardships, those who fight, those who want peace, those who seek love and those who find tears.

The Foundress sees columns of light rising to heaven like Jacob's ladder: prayers are rising up to meet the angels, everywhere, and at the same time.

Bells—for work. Bells—for recreation to the hum of the spinning-wheel. Bells for Office, bells for the discipline, bells for penance. Bells for examination of conscience. Wherever she is, whatever she is doing, in every Carmel at the same moment, each Carmelite kneels down and purifies the transparent crystal of her soul, the beauty of which Teresa of Jesus has described, and two hundred souls of crystal purity reflect the countenance of their King.

Only one occupation has no fixed time: the meal. 'The time for eating cannot be arranged, for this depends on what Our Lord sends us. In winter at half past eleven when there is anything to eat. . . .' [2]

[1] Sb, F, c. xxix–32.　　　　　　　　　　[2] SEC, CONS, p. 12.

And at eight o'clock in the evening the bell will ring in the silence: until Prime on the following morning no word will be spoken except to Christ or to the hosts of heaven. And in this silence the rhythmic movement of adoration will be so great that it will refresh the ever feverish world more than morning dew.

The Foundress sees this white guard of love gaining the whole world and, across the ages, thousands of souls who are active in prayer peopling the convents of Carmel.

'God has sufficed' to the Mother Foundress.

She remembers the beginnings, *sin blanca*; the praise, adoration, inebriation with God, would raise her to the clouds if she did not stoop towards the earth, to ponder over the work accomplished. And she wrote to María de San José:

'At last, I can re-echo Simeon's words, for I have come to see Our Lady's Order as I desired it. I beg you then not to ask God for me to live, but that he grant me to go and rest: for the future I am no longer necessary to you.'

Ana de San Bartolomé came into her cell unnoticed; she saw Teresa of Jesus put down her pen every two or three words; she heard her utter deep sighs. From her countenance came such dazzling rays of light that the little sister could scarcely bear their brilliance.'[1]

---

[1] FR, L. III, c. x.

PART FIVE

'BELOVED, IT IS TIME. . .'

I

ÁVILA, 1581

'YOU'LL see what this poor little old woman is ordered to do. . . .'[1]

Scarcely had she returned from Soria when Mother Teresa of Jesus was elected prioress of the convent of St Joseph, at Ávila.

She protested very gracefully, and found abundant reasons why they should choose a more worthy prioress. But Jerónimo Gracían, now Father Provincial, ordered her to show her humility merely by kissing the ground, and while she was thus prostrate he intoned the *Te Deum.*

The Foundress's distaste was sincere: she was overwhelmed by years, her ill-health, the responsibility of all the foundations past and to come. 'They have made me prioress because they're starving. . . . How can I with my age and all I have to do, make a success of it ?'[2]

It was not a spiritual famine, but one of their daily bread. She wrote to her other convents: 'All of you, ask God to give these nuns something to eat.'[3] Once more the Foundress began by straining every nerve to find food for her subjects, convinced as she was that it was useless to deal properly with the souls of poor girls 'who have very little indeed for dinner and nothing for supper.'[1] In this year 1581, it wanted the saints of the city to turn its stones into bread.

For ten years the situation in Spain had been growing steadily worse. The destitution of the convent of the Incarnation in 1571 will be recalled; from the account books kept that year by Teresa at Medina del Campo, we learn that in the course of a week the sisters earned only 11 reales by their work, whilst the expenses in bread, oil, eggs, fish, honey, rice, vegetables and a little mutton for the farm servant amounted to 79 reales. Alms amounted to about 30 reales, not including the gifts in kind which pious people left in the turn.

In 1581 the nuns' work brought in just as little—they were not to fix the prices themselves, but to take what was given them—and the cost of living was five times higher; during Teresa's last journey, Ana de San Bartolomé offered four reales for two eggs and could not get

[1] CTA, cclxxviii. [2] CTA, ccclxxxv. [3] CTA, ccclxxxv

them. Provisions were scarce in Castile: at Toledo the Foundress was distressed at the extreme poverty of the place and if it had not been for the parcels María de San José sent from Seville—even to fish kept fresh inside a loaf during the long journey—the Carmelites would have often fasted quite apart from the Rule. Teresa remarked that one could not find woollen material in this city of materials of all sorts, but, on the other hand, ells of gold brocade: Spain's economy had become unbalanced. Alms to convents were becoming scantier and scantier as well as rarer, for to reduce their expenses without lessening their reputation the *hidalgos* spent as much time as possible on their estates which were so badly cultivated that they brought in very little money, and did not bother about giving to convents.

The curse of gold is a fact: the conquest turned Spain into a new, wealthy kingdom, which had lost the liking for work and acquired that for ostentation. Osuna in the Fourth and Fifth *Abecedarios* paints a lively picture of the times and unmasks laziness as enemy No. 1: 'See these nobles who have fallen from their high condition: they live on in idleness amid hardships. In public they are seen with their long sleeves and every appearance of luxury; at home, they fast on many days of the year, not from devotion but because they have nothing to eat. You tell them, "Take service then with some great Lord, or work." They answer: "God forbid!"'

Spain's second enemy was pride: 'For many *hidalgos* a horse and two grooms would suffice, but in their ambition they want to have two palfreys and a mule in their stable, plus three or four grooms to look after them. And the result? In this noble household nobody eats his fill. . . .'

And Osuna writes again: '. . . A page in sumptuous livery whose hands, ceremoniously raised, bear two dishes of silver placed one upon the other. Preceding this page and his cumbrous burden of silver dishes, walks a major-domo in full dress and staff of office in hand. But if by chance you ask: "Gentlemen, what are you carrying on those dishes?" they will answer you: "A radish!"'

'The squire's aim is to be equal to the nobleman, poor folk dress in Courtrai cloth whereas they ought to content themselves with simple frieze.'

It was at this time that the sorry gentlemen who, in their fine clothes of which the cloak hid the threadbare condition, would use the toothpick with much ostentation whereas they had not dined, were first heard of. The Lazarillos and Rinconetes were replacing the Amadis and Olivantes.

Mistaking wealth for power, Charles V and Philip II had made gold the instrument of their policy of expansion; mercenaries proved even more expensive than spies. As to the nobles, who were fighting only for glory and maintained their regiments with their own money, they ruined themselves to follow the Emperor. In such devotion pride, too, had its share: 'The Duke of Bejar, having learnt that the Emperor willed to go and fight against the Turk, passing through the gate of Salamanca journeyed until he came up with the Emperor in Spires, with such a great display of arms, and such a show of men and riches that the foreign princes could not help but notice the Spaniard and marvel, but his household and descendants have felt the effects of it down to this day. . . .'

Throughout the whole country people chose to dream rather than pay attention to keeping accounts: like those who when they are expecting ten pounds make projects that would cost twenty and get thirty pounds into debt. Montezuma's treasure which Cortés brought back was not sufficient to pay for a single one of Charles V's journeys.

Wars without ceasing, a ruined fleet, an idle and extravagant nobility, too many functionaries, the abuse of pensions and perquisites, in short every Spaniard expected that a little of the royal gold should find its way into his purse, while the King expected the galleons to pour the gold of the Indies into his coffers; often, however, the English, French or Dutch corsairs helped themselves first.

If the Grandees managed to live on loans and mortgages, the state of the people was wretched. Already 'the merchants are leagued together and organize monopolies. In time of famine, speculators buy up all the corn which arrives in the ports and sell it again very dear. The wealthy landowners of Burgos centralize all the wool of Castile and send it away to France or England. As a consequence, whole families are deprived of their means of livelihood and all the spinners and weavers are thrown out of work. . . .'[1]

Mother Teresa, who could keep accounts as well as dream, estimated at 300,000 maravedis the income necessary for a convent to subsist, *i.e.* so that thirteen nuns—or twenty-one at most—accustomed to fasting, should not die of hunger.

Of the fourteen convents of Discalced nuns which remained out of the fifteen founded by Teresa of Jesus in nineteen years, those where the nuns did not lack essentials were rare. Such happy exceptions were due to the fact that the people round happened to be extremely

[1] RO, O, p. 26.

charitable—as, for instance, at Palencia, or to unusual gifts for administration and managing money which a prioress happened to possess—
such was the case at Valladolid, thanks to María Bautista. Mother
Teresa however teased her on the tendency she had to 'hoard,'[1] to
'provide for her small house without considering the good of all.'
At Caravaca, Alba, Beas, even at Seville which the imprudent management of Beatriz de la Madre de Dios had put into debt, the Carmelites
knew something of what famine meant. But the Ávila convents
remained the poorest; at the Incarnation the last elections had passed
off very quietly, 'for famine has turned these nuns into lambs. . . .'
But want does not always have this sedative effect and Teresa was
determined to take every possible step to feed this first of her dovecots.

She considered good management so important that she passed
naturally from the spiritual to the temporal, as in the instructions given
to P. Gracián.

It is desirable to examine the account books with care and attention and not to pass such things over lightly. The houses provided
with revenues must regulate their expenses in accordance with such
revenues, and be satisfied therewith whether it pleases them or not:
otherwise they will get into debt; prelates find it inhuman not to
allow their families to provide for the nuns: I would rather see a
convent dissolved than come to that. That is why I said that temporal
evils can engender great spiritual evils; this matter is thus of extreme
importance.[2]

The convents without revenues must take care not to contract
debts; if the expenditure is reasonable, if the sisters have faith and
serve God well, they will want for nothing. It is essential to know
how much food and what sort of treatment to give to them and also
to the sick, and to see that all have what is necessary; experience has
proved that Our Lord always grants this when the prioress is
courageous and diligent.[3]

Look at the work accomplished, work out what each one has
earned with her hands; that brings a double advantage: it encourages
and thanks those who have done much and serves as a model of
imitation for other convents; for in addition to the temporal benefit,
it is a great advantage all round to keep a strict account of work.[4]

See that there is no excess in anything. . . .[5] Don't agree to the
houses being large nor that they should get into debt through building work or enlargement, except in case of urgency. This must not
be considered as a small detail which can't do great harm, it must be

[1] CTA, cclxxviii.   [2] Sb, MVC, 10.
[3] Idem, 11.   [4] Idem, 12.   [5] Idem, 13.

clearly understood that it is better to put up with the inconveniences of a house which is too small than to be crushed with debts or suffer from the want of food.[1]

As regards money, the Foundress had the same broadness of mind as in everything else; for her it was a means which she utilized without contempt but without being attached to it; she was a slave neither to poverty nor to abundance. If a talented and virtuous novice was admitted to Carmel without a dowry, Teresa gave thanks for it. 'Glory be to God!' But she would say with equal freedom: 'I am delighted at the entering of this nun who is very rich. Everything works out well. Glory be to God!'[2]

The fact that even girls vowed to poverty had chosen it because they hoped not only to grow perfect in the love of God under her direction, but also to get slightly better food, did not scandalize her. She immediately set her hand to the task, crushed under the 'rubble' of letters and business, and continued to work part of the night helped by two secretaries, Ana de San Pedro, the Flemish girl, whose fine handwriting she esteemed, and Ana de San Bartolomé.

And firmly yet with great sweetness, after having put aside loyal Julian de Ávila whose age had seriously weakened his authority— 'God preserve us from confessors who are too old'[3]—she again took in hand the guidance of her nuns.

With love, but without enthusiasm. She could not succeed in overcoming the sadness she felt each time she returned to her native city: she suffered, not from being alone there, for solitude was a delight to her, but from being isolated: particularly since the death of Lorenzo de Cepeda and of Don Francisco de Salcedo. And even more than she felt their absence, she felt the desertion of those who remained: her love for perfection increased but in a world which seemed to be renouncing it.

And since her battle cry: 'Do not sleep!' seemed to be heard only from Carmel to Carmel, she undertook to found one more convent, at Burgos, the burial place of the Cid, city of Kings and former capital of Old Castile.

When her lifelong friend, Juana Suárez, who had remained at the convent of the Incarnation said to her affectionately: 'You have founded enough of these dovecots. . . . It is time for you to rest. . . .' she doubtless thought, 'God preserve us from advisers who are too old.'

---

[1] Idem, 14.   [2] CTA, cxvii.   [3] CTA, ccclxxxii.

P. John of the Cross

At this juncture Fray John arrived at Ávila with all the mules and baggage necessary to take Mother Teresa of Jesus with him to found the convent of Discalced nuns at Granada. But she had promised to go to Burgos.

Teresa only mentions this meeting briefly: the indifference she showed we may put down to haste. She wrote to a preacher whom she greatly admired, Don Pedro Castro y Nero: '. . . I want to tire you as little as possible. . . . I am tired, this evening, through a Father of the Order, although he's saved my sending a messenger to the Marchioness, for he will be going through Escalona. . . .' [1] Next day she wrote to Gracián: 'The nuns left to-day, which has caused me great pain and left me very much alone. They do not seem to mind, especially María de Cristo who has done everything to get away.' Antonia del Espíritu Santo, who also came with Fray John, was one of the first four nuns of St Joseph's, and one of the Foundress's most loyal companions. Of little Fray John of the Cross, the saint, not a word. Yes: 'Fray John of the Cross would very much have liked to send Your Reverence a little money, he hoped to do so if he had been able to take something from what he has for the journey, but he has not been able. I think he will strive to the utmost to get some to Your Reverence.' [2]

Gracián needed money to defray the expenses of printing the Constitutions: for the Foundress that was now the principal objective. She forgot all the rest, she forgot the person of Fray Juan. Women of action—like men of the same type, moreover—are subject to such eclipses of feeling with regard to what their heart holds dear when obsessed by the idea that is uppermost in their minds. At her first leisure moment Teresa was full of tenderness for her *Santico* and wrote him letters full of spiritual illumination.

Meanwhile John of the Cross returned with the mules and carriages he had prepared for 'her.' He went back singing: it was his habit to sing when he was suffering. . . .

Witnesses are silent as to the feelings of Mother Teresa, and the grief of Fray John: but one has only to know him whom the Foundress called 'my little Seneca' to realize that if he mistrusted bursts of feeling it was because his own heart was too sensitive. He was bursting with joy when he went to fetch her and his disappointment was intensely bitter: he loved her more than he had ever said.

He did say it once, or rather moaned it out, a few months before this incident convinced him that his isolation would be without

[1] CTA, cccxc.   [2] CTA, cccxciii.

VILLANUEVA DE LA JARA
The Patio of the Convent

SORIA

The Staircase in the Convent

relief, in a letter sent at random, like a bottle dropped in the sea, to Catalina de Jesús:

To Sister Catalina de Jesús, Discalced Carmelite, wherever she may be. . . .

Jesus be with your soul, Catalina my daughter. Although I don't know where you are, I want to write you these lines, feeling sure that our Mother will send them on to you if you are not with her; if such is your case, console yourself by thinking that here I am more of an exile than you, and more alone. For since this whale swallowed me and cast me up again on this foreign shore [he was at Baeza, in Andalusia, and he did not like 'these people' any more than Teresa did] I have never deserved to have the good fortune to see her again, neither her nor the holy people who are there with her. God's name be praised, for affliction is like a file, and we are storing up great joys for ourselves by suffering in darkness. God grant that we do not remain there. What a lot of things I should like to say to you. But I write in the dark, not believing that you will receive this. That is why I break off without finishing. Recommend me to God. From here, I will not say anything more to you because I have no heart to do so. . . .

No tengo gana. . . . A sigh of infinite weariness, a cry from the very heart of the little man from heaven, of whom, when he was chaplain at the Incarnation the Foundress said:

'There's no way of talking of God with P. John of the Cross because he immediately falls into ecstasy and you with him.' [1]

They were made both to understand and not to understand each other. Their psychological make-up was too distinct in character. The strength of refusal of John of the Cross, his despairing sweetness, made Teresa, in her relations with him, more virile than her character was in reality and perhaps even a little brusque. One day a great Spaniard would call Teresa of Jesus *Padraza,* 'the great Father,' and John of the Cross, *Madrecito,* 'the little Mother. . . .' [2] without this transposition of rôles appearing unfair.

Without thoroughly understanding it, John of the Cross admired Teresa of Jesus' astonishing adaptability to all circumstances, her talent for worldly business, the way she was at home in joy as in trials, her natural energy in action; Teresa of Jesus esteemed at its super-terrestrial value 'this soul to whom God communicates his spirit' [3]; the way she introduced him to the nuns of Beas was:

---

[1] Quoted BRE, p. 176.   [2] M. de Unamuno.   [3] CTA, ccc.

He is a man really heavenly and divine; since he went away, I have found nobody like him in all Castile; no one guides me so well in the ways of heaven. His absence leaves me in a solitude past believing. In this saint you have a great treasure, open your souls to him. You will see how much profit you get from so doing and how much you will advance in spirit and in the way of perfection; for in such matters Our Lord has endowed him with a singular grace. . . . Padre John of the Cross is truly the Father of my soul, and one of those in whom I have confided with the greatest benefit.[1]

Yet the refusal to be happy even in God with which Fray John of the Cross opposed the unsought delights which Mother Teresa found in divine love, created a supreme want of understanding between them. Visions and voices were not to his taste. He admitted to María de Jesús that at Toledo he had known the deepest recesses of the Dark Night, complete desolation: 'I asked him if he received the consolations of God in prison: he told me that that was rare; and I think he said that he had never experienced them, that everything in him suffered, both body and soul.'

John of the Cross was a tortured mind, and Teresa of Jesus a happy nature. There is nothing more ardent nor more painful than the love mingled with envy which such minds experience for natures like hers.

The Foundress had never concealed from John of the Cross the fact that his demands frightened her. We have only to recall the *Vejamen* game, where it is true she was jesting, but the liveliness with which she conducted the contest betrays a kind of relief; each argument is too closely in conformity with Teresa of Jesus' profound realism not to be sincere.

She loved him greatly; her despair when he was 'under a spell,' her efforts to free him from it, her joy when she saw him again, all prove this, but, admiring him immensely as she did, she would have liked to love him still more. As to him, loving her more than he allowed himself to love a human being, he would have liked to admire her less, for he did not wholly approve her. More than once he found himself writing that he would not develop some point of prayer, for '. . . the blessed Teresa of Jesus, our Mother, has written wonderful things on these spiritual matters. . . .'[2] but he chiefly admired her for reasons which were instinctive and of this world: as a child hampered by its timidity admires the natural ease and grace of another child.

When the Mother Foundress had sent for him to come to the convent of the Incarnation, he had left everything to hurry to her.

1 CTA, cclxi.   2 JCC, 1, 3.

This time it was he who needed her and came to seek her out: she did not go back with him.

Not a single one of Teresa's letters to John of the Cross remains. One day he suddenly said to one of his brethren that there was still one thing to which he was attached. From a sack he brought out paper after paper covered with firm, graceful handwriting, and burned them: they were the letters of Teresa of Jesus.

II

THE CITY OF KINGS

EVERYTHING was ready for the Burgos foundation. A rich widow, Doña Catalina de Tolosa, who already had two daughters in Carmel, had obtained the authorization of the city; the new convent could be inaugurated in her own house; the grilles and turn were installed there and the enclosure set up for the first nuns. The Archbishop had formally promised his authorization and extolled the perfection of these Discalced nuns. Besides, was not his name Don Cristóbal Vela? Was he not the son of the Don Blasco Núñez Vela, first Viceroy of Peru, for whom and with whom the Ahumada y Cepeda brothers had fought at Iñaquito? Had not his uncle, Don Francisco Vela y Núñez, stood godfather to little Teresa de Ahumada? Were not the houses of the two families at Ávila next door to each other? Both issuing from good Ávila stock, the Mother Foundress and the Archbishop of Burgos were related, and, better still, were linked together by memories and affinities.

After the mishap at Segovia, Teresa hesitated to set out to found a convent without written authorization, but in the present case what had she to fear? Nothing except the rains which that year were torrential, the January cold, the tracks which were sunken and under water, and her deplorable health. She was so ill that she thought of delegating the prioress of Palencia, Inés de Jesús, to go in her place. Her divine Counsellor reproved her:

'Do not trouble yourself about the cold, for I am the true warmth. The demon is using all his strength against this foundation, use yours in my name to bring it about and do not fail to go there in person: that will be very profitable.' [1]

The Provincial, P. Jerónimo Gracián de la Madre de Dios, and Tomasina Bautista, the future prioress, had just arrived from Alba de Tormes; the Foundress had had to impress upon the Provincial that they must not travel together: in his ingenuousness, P. Gracián would never imagine that a friar and nun seen together in the inns and along the roads might cause evil talk. She never tired of giving him motherly advice and spoke very kindly of him:

[1] Sb, F, c. xxxi–11.

'How good it is of him to be willing to undertake this journey to look after a sick old woman?' 'They seem to be anxious for me to go on living. . . .' [1]

Thus the principal persons in this expedition were the Mother Foundress, P. Gracián, Fray Pedro de la Purificación who had come from Granada, Tomasina Bautista, Inés de la Cruz, Catalina de Jesús to whom P. John of the Cross wrote his pathetic letter, a lay-sister, a lay-brother, Ana de San Bartolomé and the Mother's niece Teresita, together with a complete world in miniature of muleteers, servants and men to form the escort.

The carts left Ávila at dawn on January 2nd 1582. They had to stop at Valladolid to pick up one more nun: Catalina de la Asunción, one of Doña Catalina de Tolosa's daughters. Her sisters and María Bautista the prioress loved her so much that they did not want to let her go. The Foundress, with her 'astuteness from heaven', then spoke of taking away a nun who was indispensable to the community, and Catalina de la Asunción was hers. [2]

From Ávila to Medina del Campo it stopped raining only to snow; from Medina del Campo to Valladolid, sky and earth seemed fused in one unending stream; Teresa arrived there with incipient paralysis which made her shake from head to foot and affected her speech; a raw wound in her throat caused her to spit blood and prevented her from taking anything other than liquids to compensate for the fatigues of the long journey. The doctors declared that if she did not set off again immediately it would be impossible to move her later.

It was not the moment to think of her health: she left Valladolid in veritable whirlpools of water.

On her arrival at Palencia she found the streets decorated with streamers and garlands: this town revered her and received her triumphantly. The crowd before the convent where they were waiting for her was so dense that she had great difficulty in getting out of her carriage to reach the cloister; the chanting and lighted shrines seemed to her like paradise itself.

But any earthly paradise is of brief duration: and in this particular one, moreover, the Foundress was very ill, a fact which did not prevent her from plunging into the deluge again after two days' halt.

To set off in such weather was audacity beyond belief: a servant sent on ahead to reconnoitre came back and reported that the roads were impassable. This information did not weaken Teresa of Jesus'

[1] Sb, F, c. xxxi–16.   [2] SEC, vol. IX, p. 158, n. 3.

determination for she was determined to obey His Majesty and him alone, be the circumstances what they might. Had not Our Lord said to her when she was hesitating to go and found this convent at Burgos: 'What is there to be afraid of ?' [1]

Nobody in those parts could remember such floods. Along the Carrión and the Arlanzón the muleteers, aided by the friars, succeeded with the utmost difficulty in pulling out the carts which were sunk deep in the mire, while the Carmelites waded through the puddles in their sandals. At the top of a slope which went sheer down to the river Mother Teresa saw one of the carriages in front staggering over into the void; one of the servants, with God's help, succeeded in pulling it back by throwing himself on to the wheels: human strength alone would have been inadequate, and those who thus escaped blessed him as 'an angel rather than a man.' [2]

After this incident Teresa insisted on going first so that she alone might be exposed to whatever danger there was.

That evening, when they were hoping to rest after their fright and weariness, the pioneers of Carmel found nothing but an inn so poor that there was no bed.

Next day the Arlanzón had to be crossed. The bridges had been carried away by the flood and there were only makeshift footbridges. The horrified innkeeper begged Teresa—most obstinate of saints— to wait a few days until the crossing should be feasible, but she was determined to go on and all the worthy man could do was to guide them as best he could. He led them to the least dangerous spot.

When the party reached what they thought was the river bank, all they saw was an enormous sheet of water, so large that it was difficult to find the pontoons; these were so narrow that at the slightest deviation or movement of the current, vehicles, mules, friars, nuns, servants and Foundress would have rolled back into the torrent. But were they not to 'live without fear either of death or of the events of life'? The Discalced nuns, however, asked the friars for absolution and their mother for her blessing. She gave it to them in all cheerfulness:

'Well, daughters! What better thing can you want than to die as martyrs for the love of the Lord?' [3]

Her carriage moved forward first and she made all her companions promise to return to the inn should she be drowned.

[1] Sb, F, c. xxxi–4.
[2] AB quoted SEC, vol. II, p. 234.
[3] Idem.

God had said to her: 'When have I failed thee?'[1] He did not fail her in the midst of these perils.

Those who were on the bank saw her carriage swerve and stop as it hung over the torrent: the Foundress jumped out into water which came half way up her legs, she was not very agile and hurt herself. As always, her cry was a calling upon God: this time she complained:

'Lord, amid so many ills this comes on top of all the rest!'

The Voice answered her:

'Teresa, that is how I treat my friends.'

'Ah my God! That is why you have so few of them!'[2]

Had she had time for reflection, she would have used the same words that the imprisonment of P. John of the Cross inspired her with: 'The way God treats his friends is terrible, but in so doing he does them no wrong, for that is how he treated his Son. . . .'[3] Such was indeed the substance of her thought, and Our Lord who had bestowed upon his daughter the gift of a ready answer could not be displeased at this slight variation on the theme. He extricated her; her cart and those of the escort in which seven Carmelites were shouting the Credo as loudly as they could, reached the bank unharmed, if not without fear.

The whole company was happy, 'for once the danger was passed, to talk of it was recreation.'[4]

On 26th January, twenty-four days after they had left Ávila, they reached Burgos at nightfall; after a halt at the church of the Augustinian friars to pray before the miraculous crucifix[5] which was an object of P. Gracián's veneration, the little company went forward through the streets which had become veritable rivers. Anxious to avoid arousing too much curiosity among the good folk of the Huerta del Rey, the eight Carmelites managed to make their entry into Doña Catalina de Tolosa's house unperceived. Worn out and wet through, they were at last able to dry themselves in front of a good log fire.

The Father Provincial, Jerónimo Gracián, and the friars went to lodge with the great theologian and preacher, Canon Manso. The Foundress would have liked Gracián to go to the Archbishop forthwith to ask for permission to expose the Blessed Sacrament and say Mass on the very next morning, but the storm broke out afresh with redoubled fury and prevented him.

That evening Teresa had a syncope and her vomitings which had

---

[1] Sb, F, c. xxxi-4.   [2] Quoted LV, p. 449.   [3] CTA, ccxix.
[4] Sb, F, c. xxxi-17.   [5] This crucifix is still in Burgos cathedral.

begun again with increased force finally set up inflammation in her throat; after a night of suffering, she was unable to move, so much so that she could not even raise her head, and she received the people with whom she was obliged to speak lying down behind the grille and covered with a black veil.

There was much that had to be said, and to be done, too:

His Illustrious Lordship Don Cristóbal Vela, Archbishop of Burgos, had intimated to P. Jerónimo Gracián de la Madre de Dios that he had asked Mother Teresa of Jesus to come and 'treat' with him of the matter of the foundation, not to come and found: still less to bring nuns with her. This kind of negotiation had to be conducted slowly and prudently. There was no question of allowing Mass to be said in a private house. Moreover, what need had Burgos of reformers? The nuns there were perfectly reformed already and Mother Teresa of Jesus would do just as well to go back where she came from!

'Along these roads and in this weather!'[1]

The Father Provincial, more like Paul than ever, and for the moment in the clouds, brought back the news without any trace of emotion. But the Foundress could keep her feet on the ground when something had to be carried out: in her opinion the devil was beginning his tricks.

Negotiations went on for three months.

His Illustrious Lordship kept changing his mind, first saying a thing and then unsaying it, while time slipped by; he promised the licence and then withdrew his promise. The Foundress would not precipitate matters, saying they should avoid worrying him too often, and when Gracián once more crossed the threshold of the archi-episcopal palace, which was situated below the immense cathedral, Don Cristóbal Vela feigned surprise:

'What! You are still here? I thought you had gone back again!'[2]

One day he refused through over-solicitude for them:

'The house is damp and I cannot bear the idea of the privations which these poor women will have to undergo in a convent without revenues.'

The next day, taking advantage of these kindly feelings, they begged him to allow Mass to be said in the house:

'They are so distressed at having to come out into the world to go to Mass, that the people cry out because they see the pavement wet with their tears. . . .'[3]

---

[1] Sb, F, c. xxxi–21.   [2] Cf. AB quoted SEC, vol. II, p. 235.
[3] Idem.

But that morning the Illustrious Archbishop's mood was severe:
'Very well! In that way they are giving an edifying example!'
What had he against the Discalced nuns? The Foundress wondered:
'Such opposition on the part of the Archbishop. . . . And yet I am certain he wants this foundation. There's a mystery somewhere. . . .'[1]

And she tried to get to the bottom of the mystery:
'He says he well remembers the agitation which the foundation of the first convent caused in Ávila. . . .'[2]

But she told no one whom she suspected of refreshing his memory.

It was time to take the matter in hand herself. She took advantage of a day when she was not feeling quite so ill to go and see him, trusting in the ability which God usually gave her for 'negotiating': she had always found her strength adequate to the task.

Don Cristóbal Vela chatted with her for several hours in the most friendly way in the world, as was fitting among good friends and old neighbours: they recalled the Plazuela Santo Domingo, so many relations in common, so many tragic events which linked the two families, the death of Teresa's brother Antonio when he was fighting under the flag of the Archbishop's father, the assassination in Peru of his uncle, Don Francisco, who was the Carmelite's godfather.

The Foundress, like a clever diplomat, managed to plead her cause in between two reminiscences without appearing to insist too greatly:

'My poor nuns are so anxious that I should obtain this authorization from Your Lordship that they have promised God to take the discipline for as long as our conversation lasts. They are actually striking themselves at this very moment. . . .'

He seemed very glad of it:
'Let them continue then, for I shall not reverse my decision!'[3]

His Illustrious Lordship rose: he regarded the interview as concluded.

Yet this frigid man had considerable admiration for his countrywoman: 'I thought I was listening to St Paul himself speaking,'[4] he said to those around him.

The impatience with which the Mother Foundress's return was awaited at Doña Catalina's may be guessed. She had much difficulty in calming those whom the Archbishop's attitude annoyed but she would not allow them to blame him in her presence:

[1] CTA, ccclxxiv.
[2] CTA, ccclxxiv.
[3] AB quoted SEC, vol. II, p. 236.
[4] VH, p. 144.

394 ‘*Beloved, it is Time . . .*’

‘He is a saint. He must have good reasons.’ [1]

And Fray Pedro de la Purificación admired her even more for ‘her divine gift of patience ’ [2] than for her high state of prayer, her visions, ecstasies or raptures.

He was astonished to find a kind of youthful freshness in a woman who had accomplished such great things. And yet Dr. Manso declared that he would rather argue with all the theologians in Spain than with this nun who knew no Latin. Deprived of Communion by the same Dr. Manso, who prided himself on not being taken in by her reputation for sanctity and wanted to test her, she none the less asked Fray Pedro to hear her confession almost daily: the sacraments were her very life. Fray Pedro protested:

‘Heavens, Mother! Leave it alone! You don’t commit any sins. We should have to go back to the grimaces you made when you were a child to find matter for absolution. I won’t hear your confession!’

She answered in all seriousness:

‘Don’t be stingy with other people’s riches. By giving us graces Your Reverend Lordships are deprived of nothing: it is God who gives us his special graces in the sacraments of which you are the ministers. . . .’

Fray Pedro de la Purificación loved to recount his conversations with Teresa of Jesus just as they happened:

One day a young bride came to visit her, a beautiful girl and very richly dressed; among other things she was wearing very fine pearls, and two or three valuable diamonds placed to advantage set off her charms.

When she had gone the Mother asked me:

‘Tell me, Fray Pedro, did you see Doña So and So?’

‘Yes, Mother. Why do you ask?’

‘Don’t you think she’s beautiful and has fine jewels?’

‘I didn’t notice particularly; but everyone says she is beautiful and well dressed.’

She said to me smiling:

‘Those diamonds would be much more in keeping on the child Jesus, for to me all worldly things seem very ugly.’

She took hold of my cloak, led me into a corridor and began to say a thousand and one things to me about God, among others:

‘Believe me, Father, since Our Lord Jesus Christ has done me the favour of coming to me, with the Eternal Father and the Holy Spirit, under such a divine aspect with so much splendour and beauty, he is so vividly present to the eyes of my soul that nothing here below

[1] Ab quoted SEC, vol. II, p. 236.　　[2] PP quoted SEC, vol. VI, p. 383.

satisfies me; to me it all seems ugliness, and dross, the only thing that gives me any satisfaction is to see souls adorned with Christ's gifts. That's why I said to you that I did not find this servant of God beautiful. . . .' [1]

Woman, but a saint too; jewels, finery, heaven; and affectionate spontaneity of gesture, graciousness and warmth in speech; that was what she was like.

In the midst of these great troubles or lesser conflicts and conversations with confessors and doctors, the kindness and affection of Doña Catalina's children—Lesmes, Beatriz, and Elena, whom she called 'my little roly-poly,' *mi gordilla*—helped to take her thoughts off the difficulties. She found Tomasina Bautista, the future prioress, a woman of excellent health and stolid temperament, a pattern in the ways of prayer and penance, who overworked herself and would have been quite willing to overwork others, too, had Teresa not intervened.

The Mother Foundress's heaviest burden proved to be her best-loved son, Jerónimo Gracián. From optimism founded on a lack of judgement, he fell, through want of courage, almost into despair.

Finally the Archbishop promised authorization under two conditions:

Firstly: the convent must be installed in a house which belonged to the nuns;

Secondly: it must be provided with revenues sufficient for their maintenance.

Gracián continued to grumble, all the same: where were they to find a house for sale in Burgos? Even should such a house exist, how were they to pay for it? And where would the revenues come from? The Archbishop was really being more difficult than ever, for he was imposing conditions which he knew were prohibitive. The Provincial talked of leaving it all alone and bringing the Foundress and her nuns back to Ávila.

Teresa of Jesus to go away again? The Mother Foundress to give in? It would have been the first time. The Voice whispered to her: 'Now stand firm!' [2]

She managed to persuade P. Gracián to go away: alone she would be in a stronger position, and have her hands more free for the contest.

For there was a great struggle to be faced. That was just as it should be. And now it was necessary for them to leave Doña Catalina's house, for her confessors were threatening to refuse her absolution if she kept the Carmelites with her.

[1] PP quoted SEC, vol. VI, pp. 380–1.   [2] Sb, F, c. xxxi–26.

Where were they to live in this hostile city?

Only with some difficulty did they manage to find two small attics on the top floor of the Concepción hospital: and they only obtained these because they had the reputation of being haunted by all the ghosts of Burgos; even so, there were clauses in the agreement which Teresa found lamentable:

'Anyone would think the Confraternity was afraid of our taking the hospital away: it isn't very likely. . . .'[1]

One consolation: they could follow the Mass said for the sick from the top of a gallery without going through the streets. . . .

But who was it in Burgos who was stealthily trying to stir up opposition against eight poor Discalced nuns? Was it perhaps known that two of Doña Catalina's daughters had decided to pay with their own money for the house the Archbishop was insisting on? Or again, was it because it was no longer a secret that the generous widow, who was already treating the Carmelites as her own children, was intending to endow the future convent with revenues? Now before there was any question of this foundation, Doña Catalina de Tolosa had left all her fortune by will to the Jesuit College in Burgos. Not that the Society of Jesus was hostile to the reformed Carmel: Mother Teresa herself was never tired of saying how much she owed to it. But perhaps her work as Foundress was assuming dimensions which threatened to rival certain ambitions. The quarrel about P. de Salazar's vocation to Carmel may have left some slight feeling of resentment. However this may be, at Burgos Teresa felt 'avowed hostility': 'And for all this the "sinister" interests are to blame.'[2] 'They're afraid people will say that their Order and ours are one and the same. . . .'[3] And she added: *¡Quét raza!* as one might say: 'What an idea!' 'That doesn't hold water!'

But she had only one policy: peace. That was why, in order that her opponents might have no cause whatever for complaint, she did not hesitate to leave good Catalina's pleasant house and, having collected her nuns and their clothes and belongings, went to perch under the hospital rooftops in the bitter cold, despite her rheumatism and her heart trouble.

Elenita de Tolosa went with her. When the Foundress was ready to go, she asked her:

'Will you come with us?'

'Little roly-poly' ran to get her cloak: she was ready.

'Is that the way girls leave their home?' her mother asked.

[1] Sb, F, c. xxxi–27.   [2] CTA, cdxx.   [3] CTA, cdvii.

'Our Mother Foundress calls me, I cannot do other than obey.'

She said she had thought she heard Our Lord's call to his apostles and so left her mother as happy as she herself was, and in great peace.

That was Elenita de Tolosa's entry into Carmel.

At the Concepción hospital, Teresa of Jesus, who was so compassionate to all in trouble, found herself in the midst of plenty of suffering. It became impossible to get her to show the slightest consideration in her own regard or even to feed herself properly: she used to escape from Ana de San Bartolomé who would find her in the wards amid all the stench, distributing the oranges she had hidden in her sleeves. Sufferers from gangrene, cancer, those with infected sores, all those who suffered tortures from horrible wounds, ceased to moan when she was near; and they asked their nurses to go and fetch this holy woman, the very sight of whom eased their pain.

Every day, whatever the weather, Catalina de Tolosa came to see Teresa and brought her the best she could find. This continued until the day when her Jesuit confessors forbade her all contact with the Discalced Carmelites.

'They are afraid she may catch our prayer. . . .' [1]

As if it had been an infectious disease. Hell was one of the least of the punishments with which Doña Catalina was threatened but she stood firm. All the same she was in a state of great confusion: they drove her nearly mad with one scruple or another, telling her in the same breath that she was doing her children an injustice and that her will made all further dispositions void. Mother Teresa, who was Our Lady's advocate and as clever in such matters as the Archangel Gabriel, soon reassured her and the widow whose testamentary dispositions were arousing so much cupidity came back from the Concepción hospital ready to face anything. Such was doubtless the 'prayer' whose infection the Fathers of the Society feared so much for their penitent.

Having come to the end of their arguments, they invoked the early arrival in Spain of the General of the Order who, as events afterwards proved, was not even thinking of setting sail. In short, if it was not war, it was guerrilla tactics.

Teresa neutralized the bitterness of such spiteful behaviour by refusing to take offence.

'I see clearly that the devil has had a hand in these intrigues. . . . For it is sad to see people with such high purpose indulge in such childishness. . . .' [2]

An apology was made: the Burgos Jesuits informed Teresa that

[1] CTA, cdxx.   [2] Idem.

they would visit her when she was installed in a house that had been purchased in due form and order, in which the convent should be founded as His Lordship required.

A house? Impossible to find one. The Confraternity in charge of the hospital had fixed a limited time for the Carmelites' stay there and the date was getting near.

At the very last moment a house was offered and so suitable that it seemed as if God himself had reserved it for Carmel. It had a delightful orchard, a fine view, water in abundance. The Foundress was enthusiastic.

'I like it so much that if they were asking twice as much for it I should consider it was being sold cheap. . . .'[1]

But she had the interests of the Order at heart and hesitated all the same. Our Lord was displeased:

'You are letting money be an obstacle?'[2]

In answer to the prayers of the community, the transaction was concluded for the feast of St Joseph.

The Foundress and her daughters were thus at last in their own house, provided with what they needed by Doña Catalina who had deprived herself of everything so that they should go short of nothing. The Archbishop was charming, came to visit the house and deigned to find it to his liking; he asked for a glass of water, and Teresa of Jesus while she poured out the contents of a jar of ice-cold water seized the opportunity to offer him a small present, 'a thing which he would not have permitted anyone other than Mother Teresa to do.'[3] And he allowed her to hope that the authorization might be forthcoming by Easter Sunday.

Meanwhile, the daughters of Our Lady of Carmel were still forced to go to Mass in the town, as they had been doing, and in those days prayer was not the only purpose for which the churches were used: on Holy Thursday Teresa was thrown down and kicked by men who thought she did not move out of the way to let them pass quickly enough. She only laughed at this and nicknamed the people of this rowdy quarter *chamarilleros*, which may be roughly rendered 'rag and bone men.' The name has stuck to them.

Instead of complaining of the Archbishop, she pitied him:

'When we hear him say so kindly that he'd like to give us permission for Mass to be said in the house, what more could we expect? He can doubtless do nothing. . . .'[4]

---

1 Sb, F, c. xxxi–35.   2 Idem, 36.
3 SEC, vol. V, p. 314, n. 4.   4 CTA, cdxi.

In the very end, after much diplomacy and displays of anger ranging from mild indignation to wrathfulness, his Illustrious Lordship gave way, apparently without any more reason than he had had for refusing during the past three months. The man who brought the news set the bells ringing at full speed: actually only religious houses had the right to peal their bells in that way and often to let people know she had founded a new convent, the Foundress would say: 'I have had the bells rung . . . .' [1]

It was high time: that day the sisters were more discouraged than ever. Poor Elenita de Tolosa was so disconsolate that there was no means of cheering her.

As to Teresa, she wrote to María de San José that very morning:

'After my death, and even while I am alive—with all my heart, I should like them to choose you for Foundress, if my opinion counts for anything;. for you know more about it than I do and you are better. To say this is the truth. I have a little more experience than you, but in future I must be left out of account: if you could see me you would be frightened to find me so old and good for so little. . . .' [2]

Next day, 18th April, Canon Manso said the first Mass in the presence of the Archbishop who was all contentment, of Doña Catalina de Tolosa now triumphant, and of a crowd of people, amid a great noise of minstrels who had hastened upon the scene uninvited.

The Foundress was old and good for nothing, was she? Success, like fighting, gave her strength: to this woman everything gave strength. Hardly was the affair concluded when, three days after the foundation of the convent of the glorious St Joseph of St Anne of Burgos, she wrote to Toledo to get persons to see Cardinal Quiroga on her behalf, for she was eager to get on with the foundation of a convent in Madrid. All possible steps should be taken, let them even entreat the King on her behalf. . . .

And yet she was happy at Burgos, cloistered once more behind her grilles and veils and overwhelmed with graces by Our Lord.

Ana de San Bartolomé was a heavy sleeper, but this did not prevent her being awakened one night by the sound of exquisite harmonies. She realized that the angels were gladdening their sister, Teresa of Jesus, with heavenly music.

In the morning, she could not hold her tongue:

'Mother! What an excellent night you've had!'

Companionship with the seraphim did not deprive Teresa of Jesus of the gift of repartee:

[1] CTA, cccxlvii.   [2] CTA, cdx.

'Well, daughter, if you heard it, *your* night could not have been a bad one!'[1]

All Burgos now revered the Foundress and her Carmelites. Wisely, she effaced the quarrels with the Jesuit Fathers from her memory and she heaped all the little favours she could upon them. She did not forget to tell the prioress:

'Don't fail to go to confession to the Rector from time to time, and ask him for sermons. . . .'[2]

One last thing she had to do was to save the convent from a flood. On Ascension day the Arlanzón overflowed its banks, carrying away whole houses and disinterring the dead from the cemetery. But Teresa did not recoil before the elements any more than she recoiled before human beings; she refused to evacuate the convent:

'They've seen enough of us at Burgos!'[3] she said.

She had the Blessed Sacrament exposed in an upper room—the Mansinos' former ballroom—and, with her nuns around her, ceaselessly called upon God: 'Seek ye first the Kingdom. . . .'

The terrified neighbours thought they ought to run and tell the Archbishop about the danger to which the holy women were exposing themselves of their own accord:

'Leave them, leave them alone,' replied Don Cristóbal.[4] 'Teresa of Jesus has a safe-conduct which enables her to succeed in everything she undertakes. . . .'

From six o'clock in the morning until the middle of the night the convent of St Joseph of Burgos was in danger—a little islet of prayer encircled and lashed on all sides by the waters. The Foundress was worn out with fatigue and a sister had to go through the water to get her a little food.

Finally the Arlanzón subsided: once more Teresa of Jesus had been right.

The Archbishop was the first to proclaim that the Santa Madre had not only saved her convent but Burgos itself.

He was still unaware that, anxious about the trouble which might arise for Doña Catalina because of her deed of gift to the Discalced nuns, she had made her cancel her testamentary dispositions in a document which had been kept secret. Thus, whether he liked it or not, Don Cristóbal had a convent of nuns without revenues at Burgos. And, what made it worse, as they were not thought to be necessitous, people gave them no alms. The Foundress did not worry: God would

---

[1] Quoted SEC, vol. VII, p. 452.   [2] CTA, cdxxxiii.
[3] CTA, cdx.   [4] Idem.

provide as he had done for all the rest. Of this convent dedicated to St Joseph and also to St Anne, she could say what she said at the monastery of Palencia: 'The mercy of God is so great that he will not fail to favour the house of his glorious grandmother. . . .' Teresa had a fine family sense both as regards earth and heaven.

She could now ask him who had sent her amid so many dangers to hold her own against so many mighty ones and to overcome so many obstacles:

'Lord, are you satisfied?'

The Lord answered her:

'Go. You must now suffer things greater still!' [1]

She left Burgos on 26th July 1582 with Teresita and Ana de San Bartolomé.

[1] AB quoted SEC, vol. II, p. 238.

III

FAMILY AFFAIRS

'I HAVE been so pestered with relations since my brother's death that I wish I had not to contend with them any more.'[1]

Such was the degree of discouragement at which Mother Teresa had arrived over her family, always ready to take advantage of her. Unfortunately, not all the Cepeda y Ahumada were beyond reproach: arbitrarily to include her in a uniform series of miniature saints would be to detract from Teresa of Jesus' greatness. Those among her relatives who had embarked upon the quest for a more perfect life were led, sometimes even somewhat forcibly, by her. All she owed to them was her valour and her fighting blood.

Her sister María, long since dead, had profited by her teaching; Lorenzo, always a charitable man, had launched out into the ways of penance somewhat tardily; Juana, the wife of Juan de Ovalle, bore the humiliation of being poor, and the burden of an indolent, rather frivolous husband and badly brought up children, with a patience as much due to apathy as to submission to the will of God.

Agustín was a perfect example of the adventurer whose deeds were gilded over with the fair name of *conquistador* in order to embellish to the full a fascinating legend. Whereas Lorenzo in his prudence had turned his attention as soon as possible to making a good marriage and amassing a solid fortune, Agustín with his wild ideas had preferred to go on fighting. Having conquered the Araucanians in Chile seventeen times, he had lately been made governor of an important place in Peru, but did not seem as if he could settle down quietly. Teresa had cause to be anxious about his soul. 'I am extremely sorry to see him still concerned about these things. . . .'[2]

What things? One of those expeditions of which he gave an account himself in a letter to the Viceroy, Martín Enríquez:

'. . . An expedition to the richest land in men and gold that has ever been seen; according to what people say, it's El Dorado. : . . I've decided upon this not so much through my eager desire for the place as on account of the certainty that God and His Majesty will thus be well served.'[3]

[1] CTA, ccclxxxv   [2] CTA, cccxcviii.   [3] PO. p. 72.

Men with such daring and extravagant temperaments never became rich; when at the beginning of 1582 Agustín contemplated returning to Spain, his sister for all her joy was anxious:

'. . . If he doesn't bring back enough to keep himself he will have a lot of trouble, for nobody will be able to pay for his keep, and it will be a great trouble for me not to be in a position to help him.' [1] Agustín was relying on the King's gratitude; Teresa was less naïve: 'It is distressing,' said Teresa, 'to see him undertake such a perilous voyage for money at his age, when we shouldn't be thinking of anything else but preparing ourselves for heaven. . . .' [2]

Pedro's experience was warning enough: living as best he could—and a poor best it was—on the hospitality of some and the alms of others, he trailed the bitterness of his failure as a *conquistador* all over Spain; the royal treasure passed this good henchman by, and the ruin of his ambitions was simultaneous with the passing of Charles V's empire into the hands of Philip II.

It was Ahumadas and Cepedas like these, with their legitimate children and their natural daughters, who overwhelmed the Carmelite with their problems and demands. The constant trouble they caused her was doubtless not unconnected with the attention she gave in the Constitutions of the Order to the matter of the nuns' contact with their near relatives:

'As far as possible let them avoid much contact with their relatives; for besides taking their interests to heart, it will be difficult not to speak of worldly things with them.' [3]

'Let them be very cautious about conversations with people from outside, even when they are close relatives; and when the visitors don't like talking about spiritual things, let the meetings be brief and at infrequent intervals.'

After two warnings, a relapse into such conversations without any apparent spiritual fruit might entail the penalty of nine days in prison, with discipline in the refectory on the third day: 'For this matter is of great importance for the Order.' [4]

Poor Mother Teresa! Her brothers and sisters, not to mention nieces and families-in-law, plunged her into unexpected troubles and difficulties. True, she was in no danger of incurring nine days of imprisonment after talking to them; concern for their souls never left her, and she spent much time and trouble with the sole purpose of preventing their foolishness impeding their salvation. And then, how could

[1] CTA, cccxcviii.   [2] Idem.
[3] CONS, p. 9.   [4] Idem.

she have disinterested herself from the affairs of her family? They
were closely linked with the affairs of the Order.

This was particularly the case since the death of Lorenzo who had
lent considerable sums of money to the convent in Seville. 'The loss
of such a good brother was nothing in comparison with the trouble
that the relations who are still left give me. . . .' [1]

Having left Burgos, *en route*—as she thought—for Ávila, she
stopped at Valladolid: it was only to find herself back once more
among the intrigues from which the foundation of a convent in the
royal city had momentarily turned her attention; the most entangled
intrigue of all had been woven around Don Lorenzo de Cepeda's
inheritance. He had left a very detailed will and therefore one calculated to lead to much trouble, and had made Teresa his sole executrix.

The intervention of third parties unleashed the storm: Francisco,
the eldest of Lorenzo's sons, the one to whom he left his property in
Spain, leaving the remunerative offices he had held at Quito to the
younger one, had suddenly got married, after imagining, like his
father, that he had a vocation to religious life which led to his clandestine but brief appearance among the Discalced friars. His aunt Teresa
announced the marriage in these terms:

> The bride is Doña Orofrisia. She is not fifteen but she is a beautiful
> girl and has common sense. I mean Doña Orofrisia de Mendoza y
> Castilla. Her mother is a cousin of the Duke of Alburquerque and
> niece of the Duke El Infantazgo and of a great number of other
> titled lords. She has therefore connections in Ávila, with the Marquis
> of Las Navas and with the Marquis of Velada. . . . I see only one
> drawback: Don Francisco's small fortune: his property is so heavily
> mortgaged that if they did not send him what is due to him from
> America I don't know how he would live. May God, who has
> showered so many honours upon them, not allow them to go short
> of the means of subsistence. . . . [2]

Perhaps after all it was not God who was the author of all these
vanities, as indeed Teresa insinuates between the lines, for the household soon got through what little it possessed: pride of birth, the love
of luxury and the carelessness of youth took little heed as to whether
the galleons from Ecuador laden with gold arrived late, having suffered
damage, or not at all. Such was indeed often the case with those who
had been in the Indies. They returned to the home country with extravagant tastes, 'eating into a great deal of money,' [3] so accustomed to
carving up new continents that they were no longer capable of working

[1] CTA, cdvi.   [2] CTA, cccxcii.   [3] CTA, cclxxxix.

the old lands, so accustomed to having servants for every need that they had lost the art of managing their affairs.

Now when fortune has deserted a couple athirst for vainglory, where is it to be looked for if not among those who already possess it? The devil who came to tempt them borrowed the physical appearance of Doña Orofrisia's mother, the most exalted cousin of so many dukes and marquises, Doña Beatriz de Mendoza y Castilla. This unscrupulous person whispered to the young couple:

'Don Lorenzo left money to build a chapel in the convent of St Joseph at Ávila. . . . Teresita is to have a part of the inheritance for her dowry on entering Carmel. . . . If the chapel were never built. . . . . If Teresita did not enter Carmel. . . . If. . . .'

Don Francisco threatened to dispute his father's will, although, according to learned men, this was a mortal sin.

Teresa saw the great danger all these souls were in, she trembled, too, for Teresita and no longer dared to travel without her for she feared she would be taken in by specious lies or even carried away by the intriguers.

When she arrived at Valladolid with this novice of fifteen, she found Doña Beatriz de Mendoza y Castilla in the midst of all the intrigues litigation could provide. And the prioress, her beloved niece María Bautista, had been lending her sharp tongue in the service of the wrong cause.

Behind her small forehead she who was formerly María de Ocampo had a narrow mind.[1] This was a certain advantage for her 'little house,' for she administered it with incomparable prudence and with a skill for which the Foundress praised her when opportunity offered. It was she who had hunted out a silver chalice for Don Lorenzo: 'I could not have hoped to find one at such a reasonable price, and of such a good shape, had it not been for this little ferret of a prioress, who arranged it all with one of her friends. . . . God must be praised for the way in which she runs this house and the talent she shows. . . .'[2]

We can picture a woman quick to take advantage of an opportunity and to get what she could from people. But Teresa did not want to see skilful management turning into sharp practice, organization into egoism, the spirit of initiative into excessive independence and self-confidence into vanity. And she did not fail to intimate this to María Bautista:

Her first words were tender: 'It is strange that almost all letters

[1] María Bautista's skull is in the refectory at Valladolid.
[2] CTA, cclxxxix.

but yours weary me. . . .' Detailed reproaches follow: '. . . It's a big thing to think one knows everything as you do; and yet you say you're humble! I would have you know that I'm not pleased that you should think that nobody does things better than you. . . . In future Your Reverence must not be so sharp: you must be satisfied with knowing the affairs of your own house. . . . I know for a certainty that you no longer speak to me freely and frankly. . . .'[1]

During this visit to Valladolid, María Bautista treated Teresa of Jesus as an enemy.

Insulted by the lawyers, deceived by some and threatened by others, the Foundress at this time suffered more from her friends than she had done from her worst enemies during the persecutions. All this was nauseating to her to such an extent that she declared she was 'rotten'[2] with it.

Teresita's loyalty might perhaps have comforted her, but she could read her very soul and saw her sometimes hesitate and waver despite her kind words.

As to her niece Beatriz de Ovalle, Juana's daughter, a scandal had arisen over her, the gossip about which had not died down. A gentleman of rank in Alba de Tormes, a friend of Juan de Ovalle who used to go riding and hunting with him, was a frequent and regular visitor to the house. The gentleman was married and there was Beatriz, a girl of twenty with all the Ahumada y Cepeda charm. The gentleman's wife took umbrage and spread such shameful calumnies about her husband and Beatriz that her very relatives decided to punish her by killing her with their own hands: 'To take away life from her who was exposing their honour seemed to them a lesser wrong than the harm her accusations were causing: but the relatives of the *Santa Madre* were opposed to this assassination.'[3]

Nobody suspected Beatriz's virtue, then, but was it seemly that there should be so much uproar about a girl's good name? Teresa tried, all to no purpose, to persuade Juana to take her daughter away from Alba until the matter had blown over: she offered to pay for the mules for the journey and for lodging; but Juana would not make up her mind to go. Teresa was indignant at so much casualness on the part of the mother and unconcern on that of the daughter; she tackled the father who did not seem any more inclined to bestir himself than the others, and finally implored them all: 'In one way or another for the love of God finish with it. Kill *me* if you like!'[4]

[1] CTA, ii, ap.   [2] CTA, cdxxxiv.
[3] SEC, vol. IX, p. 52, n. 1.   [4] CTA, ccclxxxi.

With her love of absolute and unswerving justice, Teresa did not consider Beatriz entirely innocent; to give cause for scandal was to be at fault. She wrote 'terrible things' to Alba and showed this careless family what risks they were running with regard to both God and the world. She confided her trouble to P. Gracián:

'As to the loss of honour, I would pass over that, however much it cost me, but I don't want souls to be lost and I find them all so devoid of common-sense that I don't know what the remedy is. . . . May God deign to provide one!' [1]

But Beatriz proved herself courageous: the gentleman having become a widower—his wife died of rage without its being necessary for anyone to help her to do so—asked for the hand of the girl he had compromised. To the great disappointment of her people, for he was very rich, the proud girl refused, thus proving she had nothing either to fear or atone for and begged her aunt to accept her for Carmel. This put the Mother Foundress in a difficult position, despite the joy a vocation for which she had prayed so much caused her: could she impose upon Carmel such a near relation of her own who had no dowry to offer? The Ovalle drama was complicated by the growing poverty and wretchedness of the Spanish nobility.

'What a lot of trouble all these relatives cause me! I'm fleeing from them!' [2]

Could she flee far enough away to avoid poor Don Pedro, her brother, that ruined remnant of a *conquistador*, still bitter, nursing a grievance, continually up against it, so ill suited to his parasite existence which he made unbearable for himself? She put up with all of them because she loved them. All of them. Even to the natural daughters of Jerónimo and Agustín, over whose satisfactory marriages she was delighted.

It was the little illegitimate daughter whom Lorenzo, son of Lorenzo, left in Spain when he returned to the Indies to make a rich marriage, who gave her one of the last joys of her life. She began to love her with the same affection she bestowed on all the rest of her unsatisfactory relatives and wrote to her nephew:

'I find I do love you, although the offence before God is a heavy burden for me to bear; but when I see how very closely the child resembles you I cannot help keeping her near me and loving her a great deal. Baby though she is, she already has the patience of Teresita. . . .' [3]

Teresa's affectionate nature did not stop at words of tenderness;

[1] CTA, ccclxxv.   [2] CTA, ccclxxxv.   [3] CTA, cccxcviii.

she took all necessary steps for this innocent girl to be brought up so that she should one day become 'a good servant of God . . . for that is not her fault. . . .' [1]

It took angelic purity like hers to welcome a love-child unconditionally and with such tender charm.

And then she never refused an opportunity of showing love: even if it were a Cepeda or an Ahumada.

And yet, how often had she been disappointed in human affections! Each time she had been moved by special love for a creature, it had come to nothing. P. Gracián himself had not turned out as she had hoped. She would have liked him to remain near her in order to finish the task of putting the convents in Castile in order, not to mention her personal need of his presence: no confessor brought as much peace to her soul as he did. But he had left for Andalusia in order to arrange the studies there and exhort the friars not to hear the confessions of *beatas*: all this, she maintained, could have been done by letter. She felt his absence at such a time so keenly that she even lost the wish to write to him and could not bring herself to do so. Her imperious but affectionate nature which, forty-seven years before, had renounced the world and its ineffectual love to satisfy to the full her thirst for the absolute, had not changed. When she did write to Gracián, she said:

'Up to the present, we had not told Teresita that you were not coming. She has been very much upset! In one way I am glad of it, for she will thus understand how little reliance must be placed on all that is not God alone. As to myself, no harm has been done. . . .' [2] It is sometimes a good thing to have an opportunity of realizing more deeply the vanity of every attachment.

The knowledge that Gracián was in Andalusia made her uneasy, for she knew he was weak and too much inclined to be heedless. He was simple and unsuspecting, and this often led him to make concessions for which those who ever sought to find fault with him blamed him. Teresa was not without misgivings about the state of exaltation into which his preaching success in Seville plunged him, though she was glad of the success itself: 'What the old women say about our Father has greatly amused us and I give thanks to God for the good he does by his sermons and his holiness. . . .' [3] All the same, she urges him to be doubly careful: 'In your preaching I beg of you to pay great attention to what you say. . . . Don't give credence to what the

[1] Idem.   [2] CTA, cdxxxiv.   [3] CTA, cccxlvi.

nuns tell you, I can assure you when they're set on a thing, they'll make you believe anything. . . .' [1]

Such were the typical reactions of a good Castilian to the imaginary visions of the South. And she added: 'Don't act the Andalusian, you have no gifts for that. . . .' [2]

If P. Gracián had followed her advice, he would not have fallen into the traps that were set for him. He had many enemies: the signal protection of the Mother Foundress aroused violent jealousy; it was only with difficulty that she succeeded in preventing him whom she supported with her full authority from giving way on his weak points.

This authority was perhaps beginning to weigh heavily upon the young members of the Order, including Gracián. Did they not realize that the old Foundress had more lucidity than all of them put together? But 'old and young cannot go along together. . . .' [3] Ana de Jesús, whom only recently she had been calling 'my daughter and my crown,' [4] had deliberately infringed her instructions for the Granada foundation, and the convent was so much the worse for it. Yet this created a precedent which prioresses could take advantage of to grant themselves privileges. So Mother Teresa armed herself with the thunders of the Lord:

> If we are going to stir up disobedience as you do, it would be better not to found anything at all; for it is not in the existence of numerous convents that good consists, but in the sanctity of the people who dwell in them. . . . In everything which concerns the Discalced nuns, I have the powers of the Father Provincial. In virtue of these powers, I say and command that the nuns you have brought from Beas are to return there, except the prioress, Ana de Jesús. . . . By this His Majesty will be well served, especially as it will be a greater sacrifice for you. Remember that this foundation will be the first in the kingdom of Granada, and that there you must conduct yourselves like valiant men, not like weak women. . . . Either trials have made you stupid, or the devil is introducing the principles of hell into this Order. [5]

As to Ana de la Encarnación, the prioress of Salamanca, her excessive longing for a house did her so much harm spiritually that when she found one, at a price out of the question for poor Discalced Carmelites, she began not only to disobey but to be deceitful. 'The desire she has for this wretched house is making her lose her head.' [6]

---

[1] CTA, cdxxxiv.
[2] Idem.
[3] CTA, cclxii.
[4] CTA, cclxii.
[5] CTA, cdxxi.
[6] CTA cdxxxiv.

'They must not do anything more in the matter until I go there. . . .'

The Mother Foundress was not yet giving up the reins.

These defections weighed heavily upon a woman who had already borne so many responsibilities. She would have liked not to have to reprimand severely any more. Moreover she had been forced to give up one of the essential principles of her Reform: to agree that the convents should have revenues, for towns and villages were becoming increasingly poorer. It was all the more important then that God should be well served in these convents.

It seemed there was nothing else but laxity. The suggestions for the Constitutions made a few months earlier by the different convents showed such a marked tendency to softness that the Foundress exclaimed: 'What a life is this!' [1] Even her eldest daughters, those of St Joseph of Avila, were suggesting that they should be permitted to eat meat. Were they only waiting for her death to fall back into the errors of the Mitigated Rule?

At Valladolid then, faithful to her principle: 'All things turn out as they have begun,' [2] she did not forget the convent at Burgos. Although at a distance she saw to it that the beginnings were good and she impressed upon the prioress, Tomasina Bautista, in an unusually solemn way:

'Although you have the advantage over me in virtue, I have the advantage of you in experience. I hope you will never forget certain of the things I tell you. . . . I tell you these things as if I were speaking to my own soul. I want you to understand that I do not do so without a reason. . . .' [3]

And she reminded her:

'. . . Charity towards the sick. . . .' [4]

'. . . See that you do not overwhelm the novices with work while you do not know in which direction their mind is turning. . . .' [5]

Never forget. . . . With these troubles added to her other sufferings, the Foundress knew quite well that she had not much time left to repeat what she had stressed so many times.

Her farewell to the Valladolid Carmelites was a final call to high things: '. . . Do not perform your religious exercises mechanically, but let each one of them be an heroic act.' [6]

---

[1] CTA, cclii.
[2] CTA, xcv.
[3] CTA, cdxxxiii.
[4] CTA, cdxxx.
[5] CTA, cdxxxiii.
[6] SEC, vol. II, p. 244.

Such had been every action, every thought, every consent or refusal of her who was a sister of *conquistadores*.

Mother Teresa of Jesus stayed more than a month in Valladolid. On the day of her departure, María Bautista accompanied her to the door and said to her by way of good wishes for the journey:
'Go! And don't come back here again!' [1]

[1] AB.

IV

GREAT ADVENTURES ARE OF THE SPIRITUAL ORDER

'THESE trifles that we call offences, these wisps of self-love of which we build castles like those which children make of wisps of straw. . . .'

The conflicts at Valladolid had touched Teresa of Jesus in appearance only. She was now invulnerable, at the summit of the castle of the soul, free, in the kingdom which her heroic acts had conquered.

She lived the reality of God's omnipresence, in so close an intimacy with Christ that she had no closer counsellor, no more efficacious consoler, no more tender friend. God in everything, God in everyone. Was it for her to judge people? She could only love and act for her Lord. For the steward who acts on behalf of an all-powerful master takes no account of his own interests: zealous but without feverishness or cupidity, he reprimands without hate and rewards impartially, 'buys as one not possessing, uses things as though not using them.' And he is without anxiety. About every convent founded her thought was as it had been about the first: 'Lord, this house is not mine; it has been made for you; it is for you to take care of it. . . .' [1]

She gave up trying to describe her inner peace; [2] what she experienced was inconceivable for anyone who had no experience of the world of mystical graces. She had lived the greatest of all adventures, for great adventures are of the spiritual order. United to God and with eyes for him alone, poverty and wretchedness had no power to make her sad any more than her reputation for sanctity had to give her satisfaction. 'All is nothing.'

Henceforward Teresa was free from every earthly attachment or anxiety. What about Gracián? The rebellious prioresses? Teresita? Her relatives? It was not the first time she smiled to think how mistaken were those who took care not to offend, or who did not care if they did offend, a heart they thought was their own possession. She no longer loved them according to the flesh—they no longer had power to separate her from the presence of God which was infused into her soul—but in the spirit, she loved them so deeply that they were constantly present to her, in that light; and to save any one of them she would gladly have given her share of eternity.

[1] Sb, V, c. xxxiv. 14. [2] SEC, vol. II, R, VI, p. 39.

Any one of them, or indeed any least member of the human race. For she was even detached from the desire for heavenly glory: she served God 'for nothing, as the Grandees serve the King.' [1] Her one passion was to love God and make others love him.

'I should rejoice if I saw others in greater glory than myself in heaven, but I could not bear for anyone to love God more than myself.' [2]

To have some part in the awakening of a soul to divine love seemed to her henceforward more important than winning paradise. She grew to mortify her body less with fasts and penance, to take more care of her health which was so necessary to her for the work to be accomplished.

She took the weight of the world upon herself as Christ upon the cross had taken upon himself the weight of original sin, and she carried the world to God. It is through the sign of the cross that the creature undertakes to work with the Creator to perfect his creation. 'I fill up in my flesh what is wanting to the Passion of Christ for his body which is the Church.' [3]

Busy as she was day and night in organizing, administering, constructing, directing both souls and affairs, getting things done, controlling characters and events, breaking down obstacles, suffering shocks, she none the less lived in a state of continual prayer. 'I have in my soul this presence of the Three Persons. . . .' [4] The presence of Christ burned within her with a flame which took away her desire for life, while at the same time the habitual vision of the Holy Trinity set her on fire with charity. The most detailed occupations could not distract her from this presence.

'All is nothing': the fact made her all the stronger for action. She had thrown everything into her heroic adventure and had gained all, having counted all as lost.

Through the close union in her of Martha and Mary, she reached the point at which contemplation and action are no longer divided but inseparable: His Majesty is adored and served at the same time.

The union between her soul and God was so complete now that she had scarcely any of those external manifestations, ecstasies, raptures which had so often proved mortifying to her humility: at least she had no more of them in public. The sudden invasion of divine love did not now disturb a body in which it dwelt continually. But, wrote her niece, Teresita, she showed a smiling and calm simplicity which

[1] CTA, cdiii.   [2] TC quoted SEC, vol. II, p. 307.
[3] Colossians i. 24.   [4] SEC, vol. II, R, xviii, p. 51.

reminded one of a candid child or of the innocence of man and woman before the twofold concept of good and evil separated them from the All in One.

Never did she lie, never did she misjudge anyone. Firm when the interests of the Order were at stake, she was so humble where she alone was concerned that she obeyed her own subjects. She said:

'I don't know why they call me Foundress, since it's God who has founded these houses.' [1]

Although old and ill, she did not fail, whenever possible, to cook, sweep and spin to contribute to the support of all by the work of her hands.

As far as possible she concealed the great favours which Our Lord granted her, took care not to assume pious attitudes, but on the contrary behaved so naturally and was so pleasant and courteous, 'gay with the gay and sad with the sad,' [2] that people were astonished that she should be the one who was considered a saint.

At length the praise of God came to be in her an expansion of her nature, overflowing so abundantly that the verses of King David seemed to come spontaneously to her lips; there was no beautiful thing in the world from a river like the Guadalquivir to the tiniest flower of the field which did not make her cry out: 'Blessed be he who created thee!' [3]

Before going to sleep, even when she had been dealing with her correspondence or working at one of the books her confessors ordered her to write even in the last years of her life, she would say her rosary, pronouncing each word, as she taught her daughters to do, slowly, lovingly, with the full awareness that sprang from her saintliness. She found special joy in reciting the *Credo* in this way and in reiterating her faith in eternal life.

Her sleep was one long ecstasy.

Ana de San Bartolomé came one morning into her cell at Valladolid, having instructions to awake her earlier than usual. Teresa was still sleeping and her face was shining like the sun. Ana took care not to wake her and began to say her prayers at the bedside, praising God for the exquisitely sweet perfume which filled the room with fragrance.

When she awoke, Mother Teresa of Jesus asked her in astonishment what she was doing there on her knees at the side of her bed. But the good little lay-sister kept silence about what she had seen in order not to cause her embarrassment.

[1] TC quoted SEC, vol. II, p. 307.
[2] SEC, A, 9.   [3] TC quoted SEC, vol. VI, p. 334.

V

ANTONIO DE JESÚS, VICAR PROVINCIAL

THE Mother Foundress would not admit that she was unwell; in actual fact she was a dying woman.

When Christ, her Beloved, said to her in Burgos: 'All is finished here, you can go away,' it was because the last adventure of God's knight errant, her encounter with death, was to be victorious on condition that she fought one fight more.

After the troubles at Valladolid time was short; she had to hasten to snatch a little rest at Medina, hasten to reach Ávila, hasten to give the veil to Teresita de Cepeda, hasten to put the difficulties at Granada in order—tendencies to independence on the part of Ana de Jesús—and the house in Salamanca and the new foundation in Madrid, and to overcome the obstinacy of Cardinal Quiroga in the same way as she had already won many prelates over to her side. A little more time remained in which she made haste to act and to suffer, without sparing the worn-out scabbard which sheathed her ardent soul.

She suffered with her head, her throat, in all her bones. Since Burgos the taste of blood was always on her lips and the vomitings were continual. Never had she felt the need of a respite so much, and from the remotest recesses of her mind she smiled with pity upon the poor old woman whose head twitched with nervous trembling. And so she let Ana de San Bartolomé look after her for a few days while she gathered her strength together again to achieve the end in view: Ávila, Madrid.

The convent of Medina del Campo had retained its rural aspect. When the Foundress got back there, she found the patio from which she had directed the work on the ruined house, her cell and the little gallery which led to it, as she had left them; there, too, there was the heavy swish of gowns of frieze: the nuns hid to catch a glimpse of her, although she had forbidden it; but does not love always win the day, even among women vowed to obedience? The prioress, Alberta Bautista, pretended not to notice anything, though she was by no means easy-going.

At the beginning of her novitiate, the Carmelite Rule had seemed

so mild to this sister in her eagerness for austerities that she had wanted
to leave in order to have freedom to practise unbridled mortifications.
The Foundress had applied her usual method when dealing with souls
difficult to manage: a sweetness which was inexorable. One day when
the Foundress was presiding over the games and songs, Alberta
Bautista grumbled that they would do better to spend the time in
contemplation. She was sent to this occupation forthwith:

'Go, daughter. Go and contemplate in your cell while your sisters
and I make merry with the good Lord here!'[1]

And it was Alberta Bautista who, in her unsatiable longing for the
Eucharistic Bread, obtained from a soft-hearted confessor permission
for daily Communion, against the Constitutions which granted permission to communicate only on Sundays and feastdays: she persuaded
the good man that she would die if she were deprived of the privilege.
This revolution in 'holiness' threatened to spread to the whole convent, already a lay-sister was making the same demands under threat
of dying. The matter seemed to be serious and Mother Teresa was
informed. She made the journey to Medina on purpose:

'What's all this, daughter? Do you suppose that your sisters and
I don't feel the same desires?'

Since every appeal to reason proved futile, the Foundress preached
by example, faithful to her principle: deeds, not words:

'I will therefore impose upon myself the deprivation of Communion,[2] like you. If we all three die, what better thing can Carmelites
hope for, since they desire only heaven?'

For the first few days, the two sisters seemed as if they were going
to die; but the Foundress remained inflexible, time had its effect and
things returned to order. Mother Teresa had shown Alberta Bautista
that it is more meritorious to bend oneself to obedience than to let
oneself be carried away by outbursts of piety against the Rule, or to
give oneself up to austerities on one's own authority. Rewarded for
her submission by high graces in prayer, her character none the less
remained difficult, prompt to criticize and ready with a retort. She had
been elected prioress some years before, although the nuns of Medina
del Campo had had misgivings about her excessive liking for penance.
She would have been quite capable of imitating the nun who demanded of her subjects that they should take the discipline throughout
the recitation of the seven penitential psalms and a few additional
prayers, a thing which the Mother Foundress hastened to forbid.

The Foundress appreciated this generous and rather harsh woman;

[1] RD, L. IV, c. xx.   [2] Sb, F, c. vi, 9–10 ff.

in her she found the most useful thing for perfection: someone who would not flatter her.

That was why, when she arrived at Medina, hoping for rest as a sick person has the right to do after a difficult journey, and Alberta Bautista, without even offering her the necessary refreshment after a journey, curtly told her that the Vicar Provincial was asking for her in the parlour, Teresa of Jesus did not complain of not being received properly by this daughter of hers, but went to obey the summons of her superior.

She said to Ana de San Bartolomé who came to the parlour with her:

'We have had more than one quarrel, P. Antonio de Jesús and I. But this good Father cannot deny that he likes me, since old as he is he has come to see me. . . .' [1]

Massive in height and breadth, grey-haired, with the hollow temples of an ascetic and the sulky lips of a touchy child, this was what P. Antonio de Heredia had become. That was how P. Antonio de Jesús, Vicar Provincial, appeared at the age of seventy-two. As he grew older it was more and more irksome to him to bow submissively to the authority of the Foundress—he despised women—as well as to accept the slight favour of chaff with which she seasoned her contact with him. This had gone on since the day when setting out to install the first monastery of Discalced friars at Duruelo, in his zeal he had provided himself with five clocks but forgotten the straw pallets. Teresa had then been seized with one of her fits of laughter [2] and when she laughed, everybody laughed. He was not disposed to admit that she usually liked to tease those she loved best.

Yet she treated him affectionately, calling him 'this blessed old man, the first of all the Discalced friars,' [3] and only grew weary of writing to him because she received no replies. 'Remember me especially to Fray Antonio de Jesús and if he has made a vow not to answer me, let him say so. . . .' [4] In spite of this she knew him to be so touchy that she said to Gracián: 'Remember me to Fray Antonio; I don't write to him because he never replies but try and prevent his knowing how often I write to you, as much as possible.' [5] In the end it was she who broke the silence: 'His way of doing things distresses me so much that I have decided to write to him. . . .'[6] It was impossible to be more patient with an obstinate old man. Finally she announced

[1] CTA, cccxiii.   [2] FR.   [3] CTA, cciv.
[4] CTA, cli.   [5] CTA, clix.   [6] CTA, cdxi.

with delight: 'I have a letter from him. . . . He is becoming my friend again. . . .'[1]

Padre Fray Antonio was perfectly well aware that Mother Teresa had discovered the point of vanity which he allowed to come to the surface despite his austerities: she had let him understand this when she had forbidden him to go barefoot, enjoining the use of sandals upon him as upon the others. He blamed her for her great liking for the 'talented' and 'scholars' and for having said to him: 'For these monasteries I hope for men of talent and too many austerities might frighten them away.'[2] Yet he himself was a man of learning but he did not possess the one quality which Teresa of Jesus appreciated in the highest possible degree: common-sense.

On the other hand the Foundress had blamed him for the 'pusillanimity' which he had shown as Prior of Los Remedios and, worse still, 'for not carrying out his office properly,'[3] and had been 'amused' at his fits of authority. Did she take him for a weakling or a chatterer? She did not condescend to keep him informed of the affairs of the Order, he said. The Foundress admitted he was right and apologized. His cavilling disposition was nonplussed with a woman like Teresa: before her simplicity and humility, there was no recourse left to him but to take refuge in systematic bad temper. This was what Fray Antonio did. He raked up grievances from ten years before: he still bore Teresa of Jesus a grudge for having frowned when she read the letter he wrote to the Duchess of Alba on the occasion of the Princess of Éboli's tantrums at Pastrana: 'As to the news of our novice, the Princess, here she is, five months pregnant, installed in the convent, imposing herself as prioress, demanding of the nuns that they serve her on their knees and observe the rules of court etiquette. . . .' Mother Teresa had not appreciated the gossipy tone of this highly coloured sketch, intended to amuse the Most Illustrious and Excellent Duchess. But he who in the world had been Antonio de Heredia remained a courtier and flattered himself on being one of the intimate friends of the Duke and Duchess.

He knew perfectly well that the Foundress had advised against his election as Provincial of the Order: the casting vote in favour of P. Jerónimo Gracián de la Madre de Dios and against him had been her doing. Gracián! That greenhorn! Charmer of the devout old women of Andalusia!

But in the absence of the said Provincial, it was to him, Antonio de Jesús, his Vicar, that the Mother Foundress owed obedience.

[1] CTA, cdxxxiv.   [2] CTA, cxlviii.   [3] CTA, cxliv.

The dying woman's face which he saw behind the parlour grille at Medina del Campo awakened no sympathy in him. But he dared not look Teresa of Jesus in the face as he gave her orders to start next day for Alba de Tormes, where the Duchess of Alba, Doña Maria Enríquez, was demanding her: to aid her daughter-in-law in her confinement, nothing less than the prayers of the woman whom Spain held to be a saint would do.

The Foundress was utterly overwhelmed.

'Never,' said Ana de San Bartolomé, 'have I seen her suffer from an order given by a superior so much as she did from this one.'

Teresa saw through Antonio de Jesús. If only fifteen years before she had kept to her first impression. If only she had then sifted to the bottom the significance of the uneasiness she had felt in this very convent when he had given her his confidence about his ardent desire to be the first of the Discalced Carmelite friars. A soul on fire with enthusiasm, beyond a doubt. But he was so pleased with his own importance, this prior of St Anne's. The choice had not been hers, for she was then only 'a poor Discalced nun, loaded with briefs and good will but without means of action,' [1] without a farthing, without a friar. And he had gone off to found the monastery of Duruelo with Fray John of the Cross.

From Duruelo, John of the Cross had taken his flight to the mystic heights of Mount Carmel and P. Antonio de Jesús had gently come down again to the attachments of earth. He who claimed to be the first Discalced friar had wanted the first place in the Order; the importance of Gracián had made him first jealous, then bitter and finally aggressive. The Foundress had had to speak out in her Paul's defence: 'Nothing special in the matter of Fray Antonio except that I cannot bear that he should annoy you even in the smallest way.' [2] His bitterness went so far as to create small groups of dissidents. Teresa had put her foot down at this. 'We all belong to the faction of Christ crucified!' [3] Finally she had intervened so that he could not attain the highest place in the Order, but at the same time she arranged that he should have the second place, that of Vicar Provincial, 'in order that he may die in peace, since that is what makes him melancholy; and these small factions will come to an end and, having a superior over him,[4] he will be able to do no harm.' Being herself a great superior she summed him up, and she loved him well.

But that evening she saw what was only too clear: the Vicar Provincial was nursing the grievances of Antonio de Jesús.

[1] Sb, F, c. ii-6.   [2] CTA, cxxxi.   [3] CTA, clxxix.   [4] CTA, cccv.

It would have been interesting to see how he would have gone about forcing the Mother Foundress, had she refused: her state of health would have justified her in taking care. The idea did not enter her head. Had she not written recently: 'Out of obedience, I would go to the end of the world'?[1] The Bridegroom had asked her to fight for him, to suffer, to be considered crazy in men's eyes: she had always obeyed. And now that he was bidding her, through the mouth of one of his prelates, to turn aside from her last earthly attachment—Ávila, the cradle both of her body and of her foundations—to journey towards a strange tomb in a rickety old carriage that was most unsuitable for her old bones, was she to draw back?

It was quite lawful for her to complain humbly to the Father Vicar of such a cruel demand: she did not do so. She complained only to Our Lord of the extreme helplessness of her soul, the prisoner of a body which was sick, worn out or cowardly.

She was not going to show weakness before the hard prioress, Alberta Bautista, whom formerly she had herself formed to obedience. This was a reminder to her that she was nothing: should she not daily learn again from her daughters the very virtues she had taught them? She merely said:

'I shall obey Your Reverence.'

Teresa of Jesus went back to her cell supperless: the prioress had not invited her to come to the refectory. She accepted hunger, solitude, departure at dawn next morning without any secret reluctance, silencing all resentment: after the prioress of Valladolid, were not Antonio de Jesús and Alberta Bautista to be the occasion of her greatest victory? Now she was with Christ in the Garden of Olives.

Even before entering Carmel, she had preferred this scene of the Passion to all others, for, persuaded as she was of her unworthiness, she dared not keep company with Jesus, except when she saw him abandoned and betrayed. 'I used to think of the sweat, the distress he had suffered. I wanted to wipe away this painful sweat; I remember that I dared not, thinking of the gravity of my sins. For many years before going to sleep, when I recommended myself to God, I always spent a short time thinking about the scene in the Garden of Olives. It was in this way that I began to practise mental prayer without knowing that it was mental prayer. I acquired the habit of it, as I did that of never omitting to make the sign of the cross.'[2]

[1] CTA, cclxxviii   [2] Sb, V, c. ix-4.

That night, when fever and pain prevented her from sleeping, she drained to the dregs the chalice of abandonment at the hands of those belonging to her: but was it not a new favour to be thus called by her Master to share his solitude? Jesus was there with her in her solitude as she had kept him company in the Garden.

Teresa set out after Prime. P. Antonio, her niece and Ana de San Bartolomé went with her.[1]

The Duchess of Alba had sent her carriage, if a cumbersome piece of machinery, on four wheels, badly sprung, can be so called. At the first jolts Teresa felt so ill that she feared she would cause her companions and the Duchess's men trouble by dying on the way. Her sufferings were such that only her extreme weakness and the abating of the fever made them bearable. Having eaten nothing since the night before, she made an effort, in order to keep up her strength a little, to eat a few figs, but she could not digest them; towards the day's end her heart began to fail and the beating of her pulse was practically imperceptible. Although the taking of food was as repugnant to her as it was to give trouble, she begged Ana de San Bartolomé:

'Daughter, if you can get hold of something, no matter what, cook it for me, I can do no more.'

Ana gave a servant four reales to buy two eggs and wept when he returned without having found any. The Mother's face was that of a dying woman and yet it was she who comforted the lay-sister:

'Don't weep: it is God's will it should be like that. . . .'[2]

She had a seizure. And in this isolated place there was nothing to give her relief. Teresita was indeed affectionate but did not know how to deal with the situation. P. Antonio bustled about uselessly. The Duchess's men were indignant: 'The people in Peñaranda have killed the saint!'

After a night spent in a bad inn where all that could be obtained for the sick woman was a few herbs cooked with a great deal of onion, they were able to start off again. Ana de San Bartolomé did not take her anxious eyes off the Mother's face, as she shuddered with pain at every jolt. Teresa was perhaps more grateful to Ana for her loyalty than for her care.

They were approaching Alba when a cloud of dust came to a standstill at their carriage door, with the noise of a galloping horse pulled up with a jerk: it was a courier from the Duke of Huescar bringing the news of the happy birth of the heir of the house of Alba. The young Duchess and her child were both doing very well.

[1] CTA, ccclxxxv. [2] CH, L. ii.

When the interests of the Order were at stake, the Mother Foundress had always stood out against the whims of the Grandees, but now her own life had been the stake of such a whim. And yet the Duchess, Doña Maria Enríquez, loved her. It was not Doña María Teresa had in mind when she asked God to preserve her from all powerful lords and ladies because they were curiously apt to contradict themselves. She found the strength to say humorously:

'God be praised. Now they will no longer need the saint![1]

[1] CTA, ccclxxx, quoted H, p. 221.

VI

FACE TO FACE

ALBA was aflame with the glory of the setting sun, the Tormes rippled with golden light. Teresa of Jesus entered the convent of the Annunciation of Our Lady of Carmel to the singing of the *Te Deum*: in all her convents her daughters expressed their joy at her coming in this way. That evening her fatigue was so obvious that the hymn of joy died away to a whisper. She admitted that she was a broken woman:

'I haven't got one sound bone left. . . .' [1]

But she made the effort and smiled and consented to bless her nuns, though usually she refused this gesture which seemed to her contrary to humility; she did so 'with much elegance and grace.' [2]

The prioress of Alba de Tormes was one of the nuns from the convent of the Incarnation at Ávila who had left the Mitigation to join Mother Teresa. Juana del Espíritu Santo was so gentle that when she scolded a nun she ended by throwing herself at her feet and asking pardon; the only thing Teresa had to reproach her for was her excessive fasts.

Taking advantage of the fact that the Mother Foundress claimed to be one of the prioress's subjects and nothing more, the latter begged her to rest and led her to her cell. Ana de San Bartolomé brought white bed-linen: only the sick had the right to this and the little lay-sister was happy at being thus able to satisfy her patient's liking for extreme cleanliness. And indeed, when she found herself wearing fresh linen down to the coif and sleeves, in a spotless white bed, she smiled happily:

'It's more than twenty years since I went to bed so early. . . .' [3]

But in the convent the excitement which an unexpected event aroused among women who lived apart from the world was soon replaced by consternation. Had the Foundress come to Alba to die? Was this what the supernatural signs which had been noticed in the convent since the beginning of the year signified? In the choir the sudden appearance of lights had frightened all those whom the occurrence had not plunged into a state of deep prayer. Recently, when the community were at their prayers, the nuns had heard three

[1] AB quoted SEC, vol. II, p. 239.   [2] JGM.   [3] CH.

very faint and gentle moans which they now said were like the sighs of a hind at the point of death.

But next morning Teresa of Jesus was at Mass and received communion: she was not accustomed to give way to the weaknesses of the body. For some days they saw her go backwards and forwards leaning on her stick, going upstairs to enjoy from the topmost rooms the view of the Tormes she loved so much, inspecting the convent with her usual thoroughness, anxious about the smallest details. Despite illness and her years her looks retained an indefinable something of pride and victory, which perseverance in obedience and humility, and the many labours and persecutions she had sustained had not worn down.

The Foundress had work to do at Alba: in the first place it was necessary to put right the benefactress, Doña Teresa de Layz, who gave the sisters a regular allowance but tormented the good nuns.

It was a long time since the day when this lady had had a vision of this very house, with its green patio planted with white flowers so beautiful that it was impossible to describe them, and its well near which St Andrew stood in the form of a fine old man. To the woman who wanted children for the glory of her name he had said:

'Your children will not be those you ask for. . . .'[1]

From this revelation the convent of Alba de Tormes had come into being, but the pious patroness had become a shrewish mother to the daughters of Carmel.

The Foundress chided her.

'You will never keep a prioress long, they all flee from you. You should reflect that this house is yours and that people who are worried can't serve God. All this is only childish nonsense and attachment to oneself. Ah, madam! How different things are where the spirit truly reigns.'[2]

Doña Teresa de Layz had been won over. For wherever Teresa went, she re-established order and introduced peace.

Two or three days later, the Rector of the College of Discalced friars in Salamanca made the journey to Alba de Tormes to talk to her about 'this devil's intrigue,'[3] this sad story of a house. The discussion went on the whole afternoon. Her indignation against the prioress would have done honour to a person in the best of health. Ana de la Encarnación, who was her cousin Ana de Tapia, and one of the oldest Discalced nuns, had just ignored the Foundress's prohibitions and bought the house, with which indeed she was infatuated.

[1] Sb, F, c. xx–7.   [2] CTA, cdxxix.   [3] CTA, cdxxxiv.

The Rector defended the culprit: if she had done wrong it was out of despair at having wandered from hovel to hovel for twelve years; and he added:

'After all, it's done now, the papers are signed, the deposit paid. What is the use of fighting against an accomplished fact? Let Your Reverence forgive your daughter and console her, now you have made her wretched.'

The Foundress protested:

'An accomplished fact, my son? It is not an accomplished fact and never will be.[1] Never will the Discalced nuns of Salamanca set foot in this house, because such is not the will of God and because this house is not suitable for them.'

For her the will of God meant perfection.

It was the last battle she fought in the interests of the Order: she won it as she had done before, and once more she was glad to think that she knew everything going on in these houses of God, and that in them she had even become 'a haggler and a busybody,'[2] she who detested money and business. Was it not essential to see that things were properly run?

As she had foretold, the purchase of the house at Salamanca fell through.

In the midst of all this, the thought of the wretchedness of the little convent of St Joseph's at Ávila was constantly on her mind, and she told Teresita and Ana de San Bartolomé of her anxiety about it:

'Where are these poor girls going to find money to buy bread with?'[3]

For where the Foundress was, the Carmelites had not only the Lord's peace, but good bread. She even said to Ana:

'Daughter, do something to please me: as soon as you see me a little better, get me an ordinary carriage; you will install me in it as best you can, and we will all three set out for Ávila.'[4]

Not that she was attached to her native soil any more than she was to any other earthly thing, but because of the intrigues of Francisco de Cepeda, it was important that Teresita should take the habit as soon as possible.

Now, at the end of September, Teresa of Jesus' marvellous courage failed her for the first time; she was vomiting blood, and at times her tongue seemed paralysed.

On the morning of Michaelmas day, after the Mass at which she

[1] CTA, cdxxxiv quoted SEC, vol. IX, p. 320, n. 3.　　　[2] CTA, xix.
[3] TC quoted SEC, vol. II, p. 367.　　　[4] Idem.

communicated she had a haemorrhage and had to be carried up to her bed. The doctor found her cell too cold and she was moved to a more sheltered room, a sort of alcove with a passage in front. A window looked on to the cloister.

The day before one of the nuns had seen this window lit up with a light whiter and more sparkling than crystal: after this, nobody doubted that the Foundress would die there.

She herself knew this better than anyone else. As early as 1577 in Salamanca she had said to the doctor who was enjoining upon her to rest: 'For the four years I have to live, it is useless to take so much care. . . .' She had waited for her hour, always peacefully and always at her task.

Now her hour was come.

Formerly she had been afraid of death. Then, in love with God to the extent of being, so far as this world was concerned, 'like one sold into a strange land,' [1] she had worn herself out with macerations, dying of being unable to die. For where shoul Life be found except in death? This world's life she had found in activity.

After having founded her first convent, when her desire for solitude and prayer was satisfied to the full and when she was raised by Christ to the heights of love in the blessed house of St Joseph of Ávila, she begged the Lord either to take her to himself, or to give her the means to serve him.

He then ordered her to found seventeen convents of nuns besides the houses of friars, to revolutionize the religious life of her time, to infuse the work with the virtues of the highest contemplation and to make of contemplation a work that should be efficacious, to do away with all social differences by a love which should be the same towards all, to put the law of God above human precepts. And lastly, poor, detached from all things and in particular from herself, a humble and weak woman, in times when women enjoyed no prestige and had still less resources, she had to finance, organize, administer these houses of Our Lady, to feed and govern some hundreds of subjects with the same broadness of vision and yet the same careful attention to detail, as if she had been rich, ambitious and covetous. To 'muffle oneself up' [2] in prayer would not do. 'The Lord wants deeds, he wants works! If you see a sick person whom you can comfort, do not hesitate to sacrifice your devotion, and attend to her; you should feel her pains as if they were your own; fast, if necessary, to procure food for her. Such is true union with God.' [3]

[1] Sb, V, c. xxi–6.   [2] Sb, MVC, iii–11.   [3] Idem.

From that time onwards, for Teresa of Jesus divine love was no longer a matter of dying in order not to die, but of understanding, suffering, renouncing and serving.

Until she had finished her Father's work. Now it was at last to be given to her to go back to him.

For her this was as simple as it would be for a child.

But for her alone. For as with the birth of a King's son, the death of a daughter of God who even in her lifetime was considered a saint could not take place without witnesses. There was a numerous assembly in the cell of Mother Teresa of Jesus. It was a cell just like all the others in the convent of Alba de Tormes and in all the convents of Carmel: a great cross of rough wood on the limewashed walls, the brown frieze against the whiteness of the sheets, the blue sky of Castile to be seen through the window.

Catalina de la Concepción and Catalina Bautista helped Ana de San Bartolomé to look after the dying woman. Her patience, her endurance, her distress at the trouble she was giving them, made them praise God for her virtues.

Doña María Enríquez came to see her: Teresa apologized, fearing that the smell of a medicine which had been spilt by accident might be troublesome to her. But, not only was the smell of medicine imperceptible, but a marvellous fragrance scented the room; everything Teresa touched was impregnated with it.

Teresita remained with her, as did Doña Teresa de Layz, P. Antonio de Jesús, the prioress, Juana del Espíritu Santo, and María de San Francisco who had caught her in her arms at Salamanca on the day when Isabel de Jesús' sweet song made her fall into ecstasy. There was also Teresa de San Andrés who went about loaded with hair-shirts and steel bracelets, but who was so beautiful and concealed her austerities with such humility that Teresa, kissing her, had one day called her 'the honour of penance.'

'I will come to fetch you when your turn comes,' [1] she said to her as she thanked her for assisting her on her death-bed.

In a corner of the room could be seen the anxious face of Antonio Gaytán's daughter, Mariana de Jesús, whom Teresa used to call 'my little pest' and whom she now called 'the little angel,' for this novice was not yet fifteen. Teresa guessed at her secret anxiety: after the death of her protectress, would she be allowed to take the veil in this house, for she had no dowry? She reassured her:

'Don't fret, child: you will be professed here.' [2]

[1] CP, vol. iii, p. 479.   [2] CP, vol. iii.

It seemed as if she were not concerned about her death, to such an extent did she appear to be solely occupied in blessing and consoling others: love's miracle was completing the metamorphosis.

All this took place amid a profound silence. Catalina de la Concepción who was near the window was accordingly annoyed at hearing all of a sudden the sound of a gay crowd; she was about to leave the room to stop the noise when she saw a great company of ladies and gentlemen in shining garments crossing the cloister and entering the saint's room: the ten thousand martyrs had come to bid Teresa of Jesus welcome to the eternal marriage feast.

On 2nd October the Foundress told Ana de San Bartolomé that her death was near. She asked for the Holy Eucharist. The Reverend Father Antonio de Jesús, Vicar Provincial, knelt by her to hear her confession. Then he implored her:

'Mother, ask Our Lord not to take you away. Don't leave us so quickly. . . .'

She was heard to answer:

'Father, be quiet! Can it be you speaking like that? I am no longer necessary in this world.' [1]

Now that her work was finished, she allowed her soul to be flooded with the love of God and the desire she had to be united with him.

Her recommendations to her daughters were brief:

'My daughters and ladies, for the love of God I ask you to observe the Rule and Constitutions well; if you keep them strictly, no further miracle will be necessary for your canonization. Don't imitate the bad example which this bad nun has given you, and forgive me.' [2]

Was not this tantamount to a recommendation of her favourite virtues: love, humility, obedience, work?

She repeated several times clearly and majestically: 'Lord, I am a daughter of the Church.' [3]

She was so ill that it took two nuns to move her in her bed. But when she saw the Blessed Sacrament entering the room, she sprang up suddenly and got on to her knees; her face was on fire with joy and love.

Her last Communion brought from her lips the final expression of love: 'My Bridegroom and my Saviour! The longed-for hour has come. It is time for our meeting, my Beloved, my Saviour. It is time for me to set out. Let us go, it is time. . . .' [4]

[1] MF quoted SEC, vol. II, p. 242.   [2] Idem.   [3] Idem.   [4] Idem.

When P. Antonio de Jesús asked her if she wanted them to take
her body to Ávila, a smile played about her lips which had spoken in
praise of joy as much as they had preached renouncement:

'Jesús! Is that a question one should ask, Father? Have I anything
whatsoever of my own? Won't they give me the charity of a little
earth here?' [1]

All through the night, which she passed in ecstatic bliss, she repeated over and over again the verse of a psalm; she who had so often
declared that she did not want any 'Latin' nuns, said it in her own
Castilian tongue: 'A sacrifice to God is an afflicted spirit. . . . A
humble and contrite heart, O God, thou wilt not despise!' [2]

She repeatedly dwelt on the words 'contrite heart' and seemed to
find pleasure in accentuating them.

At dawn on the following day, which was the feast of St Francis,
she lay on her side 'in the position usually assigned to Mary Magdalene'; her sisters could thus see her; the wrinkles caused by age and
sickness had disappeared; her face, transfigured, was so calm and
radiant 'that it seemed like the moon at the full.' [3]

Those who had seen her in ecstasy said that she was in the presence
of God.

Only once did her glance turn back towards the world; P. Antonio
de Jesús had just ordered Ana de San Bartolomé to go and get something to eat—for several days the poor woman had had neither food
nor sleep. The Mother opened her eyes anxiously and tried to turn her
head as if looking for someone. Teresita understood and ran to call
the little sister of the white veil. When she saw her come in the
Foundress was at peace again, took hold of her hands and, with a
smile which never left her, laid her head on her arms.

It was in this way, supported by a peasant woman of Castile, that
she waited to be borne away beyond the Seventh Mansions by 'the
impetuous eagle of God's Majesty.' [4]

Her body gave forth a wonderful fragrance.

She expired with three very faint and gentle moans.

The countenance of St Teresa of Jesus remained so beautiful and
resplendent in death 'that it seemed like a radiant sun.' [5]

The Duchess of Alba had the body of her who had chosen to spend
her life clad in frieze, covered with cloth of gold.

[1] Idem, p. 243.   [2] MF quoted SEC, vol. II, p. 243.   [3] Idem.
[4] SEC, E, xiv.   [5] MF quoted SEC, vol. II, p. 243.

EPILOGUE

ST TERESA OF JESUS

Her incorruptible body

AMONG the various accounts of the burial of Mother Teresa of Jesus, let us quote the few lines left by Ana de San Bartolomé:

> The day after her death, she was buried with full solemnity. Her body was put into a coffin: but such a heap of stones, bricks and chalk were put on top of it that the coffin gave way under the weight and all this rubble fell in. It was by the orders of the lady who endowed the house, Teresa de Layz, that the rubble was put there: nobody could prevent her, it seemed to her that by acting thus she was making all the more certain that no one would take Teresa's body away.[1]

But so delightful a fragrance was found to issue from Teresa of Jesus' tomb that the nuns longed to see the body of their Mother once more. They seized the opportunity of one of Gracián's visits to express their wish. Francisco de Ribera's account says:

> He approved and they began to remove the stones very secretly: there were so many that it took him and his companion four days. . . . The coffin was opened on 4th July 1583, nine months after the interment; they found the coffin lid smashed, half rotten and full of mildew, the smell of damp was very pungent. . . . The clothes had also fallen to pieces. . . . The holy body was covered with the earth which had penetrated into the coffin and so was all damp too, but as fresh and whole as if it had only been buried the day before.[2]

Here P. Grácian has added a note to P. Ribera's account:

> She was in such a perfect state of preservation that my companion, P. Cristóbal de San Alberto, and I retired while they undressed her; they called me back again when they had covered her with a sheet; uncovering her breasts, I was surprised to see how full and firm they were.[3]

[1] Quoted SEC, vol. II, p. 240. [2] FR quoted SEC, Vol. II, p. 260.
[3] Quoted SEC, vol. II, p. 260, n. 5.

R. Ribera continues:

They undressed her almost entirely—for she had been buried in her habit—they washed the earth away, and there spread through the whole house a wonderful penetrating fragrance which lasted some days. . . . They put her into a new habit, wrapped her in a sheet and put her back into the same coffin. But before doing this, P. Provincial removed her left hand. . . . [1]

Here Gracián added a further note to P. Ribera's text:

I took the hand away wrapped in a coif and in an outer wrapping of paper; oil came from it. . . . I left it at Ávila in a sealed casket. . . . When I severed the hand, I also severed a little finger which I carry about on my person. . . . When I was captured the Turks took it from me, but I bought it back for some twenty reales and some gold rings. . . . [2]

But Ávila refused to be dispossessed of the body of such an illustrious citizen. Accordingly it was decreed at the chapter of Discalced friars that the body of Mother Teresa should be exhumed and taken to her native city: in order to prevent the Duke of Alba from raising obstacles, this was done secretly.

Canon Don Juan Carrillo, chancellor of the cathedral at Ávila, has left us an account of the proceedings, in which he took part:

P. Julian de Ávila and I set out very early on Friday, the 23rd of this month of November, 1585. The next day, Saturday, we arrived (at Alba) very early, as P. Gregorio Nacianceno had said we were to do. Before entering the city, I informed him of our arrival and he sent me word that we must enter the town secretly and with the greatest prudence and that I was to go and see him at seven in the evening at the inn where he was staying. I went and found him alone. P. Jerónimo Gracián who had arrived that day from Salamanca arrived shortly afterwards. We spoke of the way Our Lord had arranged everything, so that the translation of the holy Mother's body should take place at this particular time, and of the singular means he had used to remove from Alba all those likely to prevent it: not for years had the town been so deserted, the Duchess herself had left the day before. We decided to meet again the next day, Sunday, at the same place and time, and not to show ourselves till then. And so it was done.

That day . . . P. Gregorio, who was anxious to get the business done and was less timid than P. Gracián, came to the convent with him. The nuns begged to be allowed to see the holy body. At nightfall the two friars took it out of the coffin where it lay; they found

[1] FR, quoted SEC, vol. II, p. 260.   [2] Idem, p. 261, nn. 1-2.

the habit and the linen which covered it in a very bad state. They took the holy body and put it where the sisters could see it, and all looked upon it with intense joy and satisfaction. When they had gone to recite Compline and Vigil—which, in their haste to get back again, they did so quickly that it was necessary to order them to say Matins in the choir upstairs, the Fathers remained alone with the prioress and sub-prioress and Juana del Espíritu Santo; and, since this seemed to them the time to do so, they notified all three of them of the letter from the chapter, decreeing that the holy body should be translated to St. Joseph of Ávila. This caused them very great distress and sorrow. The Fathers removed an arm. . . .[1]

P. Gregorio Nacianceno undertook to carry out the amputation. The following is P. Ribera's account of the operation:

. . . with extreme repugnance—he has since told me that it was the greatest sacrifice he ever made for Our Lord—in fulfilment of his vow of obedience, he drew a knife which he was carrying in his belt . . . and inserted it under the left arm which was the one from which the hand was missing and which had been dislocated when the devil threw the holy Mother downstairs. Wonderful to relate: without using any more effort than in cutting a melon or a little fresh cheese, as he said, he severed the arm at the joints as easily as if he had spent some time beforehand trying to ascertain their exact position. And the body remained on one side, and the arm on the other.[2]

The body would not go into the trunk which the friars had brought. '. . . they therefore put the clothes on again and wrapped it in a covering of frieze. P. Gregorio took it up in his arms, and deposited it in a room opposite the convent.' P. Gracián followed. Julian de Ávila was waiting for them.

. . . When they had deposited the holy body on the bed, P. Gracián uncovered it and we saw it just as it was when it was buried, not one hair missing, well covered with flesh from head to foot, the stomach and breasts as if they were not a corruptible substance, so much so that when one touched the flesh with the hand, it felt as flesh does when the death is recent, although lighter than it would have been in that case. The colour of the body was like that of the bladder-skins in which beef fat is put. The face was somewhat flattened, obviously the result of the large quantity of chalk, bricks and stones thrown upon the coffin when she was buried, but not at all broken. The odour coming from this holy body when one came quite close was extremely good and pleasant; it was not so strong as one moved farther away, but was the same odour. Nobody could

[1] Idem, p. 249   [2] Idem, p. 262.

say what it resembled. If it reminded one of anything at all, it was of clover, but very slightly. When we had seen this holy body and were completely satisfied with everything as I have related, we wrapped it, thus clothed, in a sheet and then in a covering of frieze, and after having well sewn and bound it up, we carried it over to the inn. . . .[1]

Gregorio Nacianceno and Julian de Avila spent the night 'in this great and holy company, and the perfume was such that when the body was placed on a mule between two bundles of straw for the return journey, the fragrance lingered in the room where it had been.' [2]

And so God's knight errant was once more journeying up hill and down dale, escorted by those who had been the faithful companions of her foundations. This was in November 1585, three years after her death.

We left Alba on the Monday, at four o'clock in the morning and the night . . . was as calm and warm as if it had been June. The weather was like that throughout our journey, until we got back to Ávila, about six o'clock in the evening.[3] The precious relic was handed to the sisters of St. Joseph's, who were just as overjoyed at having it as the nuns at Alba were distressed at losing it. . . .

Mother Teresa's body was laid reverently in a place where all the nuns could have the joy of coming close up to it. It was first of all in the chapter-house, wrapped in draperies very well arranged; then they made a long casket in the shape of a coffin, lined inside with black taffetas with trimmings of silk and of silver, covered on the outside with black velvet with trimmings of silk and gold, and with gilded studs, as well as gilded locks, bolts and keys; they put in two gold and silver shields, one with the coat of arms of the Order, the other with the most holy Name of Jesus. On this tomb was an inscription embroidered in gold and silver: 'Madre Teresa de Jesús.'[4]

The Bishop, Don Pedro Fernández de Temiño, was informed 'of the treasure he had in his city,' and he announced his intention of visiting the convent forthwith.

At nine o'clock, the Bishop, accompanied by about twenty people, including the judges, two doctors, P. Diego de Yepes and Julian de Ávila, came into the entrance porch; the door leading to the street was closed and Teresa of Jesus was laid on a carpet. The holy body was uncovered in the light of torches, and all kneeling, and bareheaded, 'gazed at it with reverent awe and many tears.' [5]

[1] Idem, p. 250.   [2] Idem.   [3] Idem.
[4] FR quoted SEC, vol. II, pp. 262-3.   [5] Idem, p. 263.

The doctors examined the body and decided that it was impossible that its condition could have a natural explanation, but that it was truly miraculous . . . . for after three years, without having been opened or embalmed, it was in such a perfect state of preservation that nothing was wanting to it in any way, and a wonderful odour issued from it.[1]

The Bishop forbade all those present to speak of the matter, under threat of excommunication. 'But they said: "Oh, what great marvels we have seen." These people had such a strong wish to describe what they had seen that the Bishop had to lift his excommunication and the facts were published all over the town.' [2]

When the news of the secret removal of St Teresa's body came to the ears of the Duke of Alba, he was exceedingly angry. He began by threatening the Carmelite nuns of Alba de Tormes with the gravest reprisals if they allowed the arm which had been left them as a consolation to be removed, and opened negotiations with Rome. He was powerful, and it was the destiny of the Mother Foundress that she must continue her journeys. His Holiness gave orders that her body was to be returned to the convent at Alba. It was removed once more 'in great secrecy' from the little convent of St Joseph's, transported clandestinely and brought back to Alba de Tormes.

It was in vain that P. Provincial stipulated 'that it was only a loan,' the holy remains of Mother Teresa of Jesus never came back to her native town. . . .

They were to be identified and exhibited many times yet. . . .

Ribera saw the body in 1588:

It is straight, although a little bent forward, as old people walk, and it is easy to see that she was of good stature. When one raises the body up, it is sufficient to support it with a hand behind the back for it to remain upright; one can dress and undress it as if it were living. . . . It is of the colour of dates. . . . The eyes are dry, but whole. The hairs are still on the moles she had on her face. . . . The feet are pretty, well proportioned. . . .

And good Ribera added:

It was such a great consolation for me to see this hidden treasure that I do not think I have spent a more wonderful day in all my life. . . . My only regret is to think that one day this body will be dismembered, at the entreaty of important personages or at the request of her convents. . . .[3]

[1] Idem.   [2] Idem, p. 264.   [3] FR quoted SEC, vol. II, pp. 266-7.

And so it was indeed.

The body of Mother Teresa of Jesus was dismembered and the parts sent to different places. The right foot and a piece of the upper jaw are in Rome, the left hand in Lisbon, the right hand, the left eye, fingers, fragments of flesh, scattered all over Spain and indeed over all christendom.

Her right arm and heart are in reliquaries at Alba de Tormes, with what remains of this perfect and incorruptible body.

Beatification and Canonization of Teresa of Jesus

As early as 1602, requests for the beatification of Teresa of Jesus began to pour in at Rome. In 1614, seventy galleons left Genoa under the command of the High Admiral of the Fleet, Don Carlos Doria: they were bringing the news of the Foundress's beatification, to Spain.

In 1622, Blessed Teresa became Saint Teresa of Jesus. During the canonization ceremony, doves and a multitude of other small birds were let loose in St Peter's.

In 1926, the Cortes nominated St Teresa patron of all the Spains. But Spain already had a patron in St James, and his clients caused the decree to be revoked. But if St Teresa has not this official glory, at least she retains the prestige non-officially.

In 1915, King Alfonso XIII, in a circular from the Ministry of War, declared St Teresa patron of the regiments and troops of the military commissariat. This was justly deserved recognition of the talent for administration of her whom the University of Salamanca had already christened the mystical doctor and on whom the Holy Father had conferred 'the honours of the Church.'

Housewives might also well take her as their patron, and so might the women of action of our twentieth century, all those who build, work, create; all those who hold friendship dear; all those who continue to hope, feeling the odds are against them.

For it is not one of St Teresa of Jesus' least merits to have shown that a personality which is to be sublime must be complete in every sense and that great saints are in no wise contemptuous of small virtues.

ANA DE JESÚS

It is to Ana de Jesús that we owe the *Spiritual Canticle* of St John of the Cross. He composed it at her request and dedicated it to her. In 1586, with him, she founded the convent of Discalced Carmelite nuns in Madrid.

She it was who collected the manuscripts of her whom Carmelites call 'the Holy Mother' for publication and gave them to Fray Luis de León. Accordingly the beautiful letter which prefaces the first edition of 1588 is addressed: 'Fray Luis de León, to the Mother Prioress Ana de Jesús and the Discalced Carmelite nuns of the convent of Madrid.'

Ana de Jesús was unmistakably an Egeria: it was at her request that Fray Luis wrote his *Commentary on the Book of Job.*

In 1591 she suffered the penalty of three years' confinement for having valiantly taken the part of P. Gracián who was attacked by Nicolás Doria.

In 1604, her superiors chose her as the most fitting person to go to France to introduce the Teresian spirit in the Carmelite convents which Mme Acarie was proposing to found. Bérulle came to fetch her. She founded the Carmels of Paris and Dijon, then, in 1607, went to the Low Countries where she founded the convent of Brussels.

There she found P. Gracián again and worked with him to get St Teresa's *Book of the Foundations* printed. It had not been possible to publish this at the same time as her other works.

Ana died at Brussels in 1621. Her cause for beatification was introduced in 1876.

ANA DE SAN BARTOLOMÉ

The faithful little lay-sister was likewise destined to go away and found Carmels in France. When she was obliged to accept the office of Foundress and prioress of the Pontoise Carmel, she had to consent, out of obedience, to take the black veil of the choir nuns.

She died at Antwerp on 7th June 1626 and was beatified on 6th May 1917.

ANTONIO DE JESÚS

P. Antonio de Jesús survived the Mother Foundress nineteen years. He died at Vélez Málaga, aged ninety-one.

THE PRINCESS OF ÉBOLI

The Princess of Éboli was arrested, on 28th July 1579, on the charge of complicity with Antonio Pérez, secretary to Philip II, in the assassination of Escobedo, secretary to Don Juan of Austria. She was imprisoned in the Pinto tower.

After a term of imprisonment in the castle of Santorcaz, she was finally imprisoned in her own home, at Pastrana, until her death in 1592.

Thus ended up Ana de Mendoza, at the age of fifty-two, the victim of her own intrigues. More than once, Teresa of Jesus told P. Jerónimo Gracián to go and see, comfort and cheer the woman who had done everything to ruin her.

Jerónimo Gracián de la Madre de Dios

The attacks against P. Gracián began with Teresa of Jesus' death. He was then Provincial of the Order, and, still naïve, still lacking in perspicacity, he sent Nicolás Doria to Rome. The latter took advantage of this to get himself appointed Pontifical agent, and, armed with this title, he immediately set up opposition against Gracián and his project of extending the Order to Africa. He did not hesitate to formulate such accusations against him that some demanded that the Provincial should be deposed.

This did not prevent Gracián himself from proposing to the chapter of 1585 P. Nicolás Doria de Jesús María's election as Provincial. There is no doubt about it, Gracián was a saint. . . . He was named Vicar Provincial in Portugal: this was to remove him from the scene of events and leave the field open to his enemies. P. Nicolás Doria did not hesitate to scheme until he was governing the Carmels of Spain in a way exactly opposite to Gracián's government and the Teresian tradition. That was why Teresa's most dearly loved daughters, like Ana de Jesús and María de San José, who were loyal to the Mother Foundress, were persecuted too.

The campaign of defamation, to which P. Jerónimo de la Madre de Dios' only answer was an angelic patience, led to his expulsion from the Order in 1591: they took Our Lady's habit away from him.

In secular clothes he left for Rome, where his efforts to overcome the hostility stirred up by Doria met with failure. He embarked for Naples, fell into the hands of the Turks, was taken to Tunis as a captive of the Pasha, loaded with chains and tattooed with crosses on the soles of his feet. For all this he did not cease his apostolate, 'converting Moors and renegades.' Ransomed in 1595, on his return to Rome Pope Clement VIII reinstated him in the Order of Carmel.

He lived in Belgium until his death in 1614. He invoked the name of Teresa of Jesus with his last breath, clasping her relics. (Based on: Fray Jerónimo Gracián de la Madre de Dios, *Discurso leido ante la Real Academia de España,* por el Excmo Señor Marqués de San Juan de Piedras Albas.)

SAINT JOHN OF THE CROSS

It was not until after the death of Teresa of Jesus that John of the Cross finished the greater part of his works on mysticism which had been begun in 1578: *Ascent of Mount Carmel*, *The Dark Night of the Soul*, *The Spiritual Canticle*. Prior of the monastery of Discalced Carmelite friars of Granada, he remained there more or less permanently until 1588, at which time he was appointed prior at Segovia.

He supported Gracián strongly against Doria's innovations and he suffered for it cruelly. Deprived of all offices and dignities at the beginning of 1591, he was ordered to retire to the desert of Peñuela.

He spent the last weeks of his life at Úbeda and died there on 14th December 1591, after great suffering, both physical and moral.

John of the Cross was canonized in 1726, and proclaimed a doctor of the Church by Pius XI in 1926.

His tomb is at Segovia.

MARÍA DE SAN JOSÉ

María de San José was sent to Portugal to found, in 1585, the Discalced Carmelite convent at Lisbon. For her loyalty to P. Gracián, in the conflict between him and Doria, she too reaped defamation, persecution, and the spending of nine months in prison. She was marked out to be one of the foundresses of the French Carmels, as being one of the most faithful continuers of the Teresian tradition, when she died at Cuerva, in the province of Toledo, in 1603.

CHRONOLOGY

1515 Birth of Teresa de Ahumada y Cepeda.

1519 Birth of Lorenzo.

1520 Birth of Antonio.

1521 Birth of Pedro.

1522 Teresa's flight with Rodrigo.

1527 Birth of Agustín.

1528 Birth of Juana. Death of Doña Beatriz de Ahumada.

1531 Teresa enters the convent of Our Lady of Grace as a boarder.

1532 Fernando sets sail overseas. Teresa ill, returns home.

1515 Wolsey made a Cardinal. Henry VIII appoints him Lord Chancellor.

1516 Accession of Charles V.

1519 Luther breaks with Rome. Charles V Emperor of Germany.

1519–21 Conquest of Mexico by Cortés.

1520 Field of the Cloth of Gold. *Comuneros'* rising.

1521 Excommunication of Luther. Discovery of the Philippine Islands.

1522 Capture of Rhodes by the Turks. Cortés, Captain General of New Spain. Return to Spain of Magellan's expedition. Conquest of Milan.

1523 Clement VII (Julian de Medici) elected Pope.

1524 Pizarro with the Incas. Alonso de Madrid's *Arte de servir a Dios.*

1527 Birth of Philip II. Sack of Rome by Imperial troops. The Pope prisoner at Sant' Angelo.

1527–54 Osuna's *Abecedario Espiritual.*

1527 Erasmus' doctrine examined by the council of Valladolid.

1528 Famine in Castile.

1529 Beginning of Henry's 'Royal Divorce.' Fall of Wolsey. Sir Thomas More Chancellor.

1530 Francisco Pizarro in Madrid to ask the favour of continuing the conquest of Peru. Intellectual Spain divided between Erasmites and anti-Erasmites. Renewal of the measures against the *Alumbrados.*

1531 Philip II at Ávila.

1531–41 Conquest of Peru and Chile.

1532 Pizarro crosses the Andes and takes Atahualpa prisoner.

1533 Henry VIII 'marries' Anne Boleyn.

	1534 Charles V in Ávila. Paul III (Alexander Farnese) elected Pope.
	1534 Acts of Succession and Supremacy. Henry declared head of English Church. Break with Rome.
1535 Rodrigo leaves for overseas.	1535 B. de Laredo's *Subida del Monte Sion*.
	1535 The Carthusians, St John Fisher and St Thomas More suffer martyrdom.
1536 Teresa enters the Convent of the Incarnation, taking the habit on 2nd November.	1536 End of the Conquest of Peru.
	1536 First suppression of monasteries in England, and Pilgrimage of Grace.
1537 Teresa professed on 3rd November. She falls seriously ill.	
1538 Departure for Castellanos de la Cañada and the treatment at Becedas. She is believed dead.	1538 Excommunication of Henry VIII.
	1539 Death of Empress Isabella. Conversion of St Francis Borgia. Mercator's map of the world. The Jesuits organized.
	1539 Final Dissolution of the monasteries in England.
1540 Lorenzo, Jerónimo and Pedro embark for Peru. Teresa's cure.	1540 St John of God founds the Brothers of Charity.
	1541 Philip II invested with the government of all the Spains. Barbarossa crushes the Spaniards.
	1542 Birth of St John of the Cross. Copernicus: *De Revolutionibus*.
1543 Death of Don Alonso de Cepeda.	1543 Garcilaso de la Vega's *Eglogas*.
1546 Antonio's death at Iñaquito.	1545 Opening of the Council of Trent.
	1546 Trial of Magdalena de la Cruz.
	1547 Death of Henry VIII. Accession of Edward VI. Birth of Cervantes.
	1549 Charles V separates the Low Countries from the Empire.
	1549 First Act of Uniformity and Book of Common Prayer.
	1552 Second Act of Uniformity and Book of Common Prayer.
1553 St Teresa's re-conversion.	1553 Death of Edward VI and accession of Mary Tudor.

1554 Meeting of St Teresa and St Francis Borgia.

1557 Rodrigo's death in Chile.

1558 Meeting of St Teresa and St Peter of Alcántara.

1560 St Teresa and her friends decide to found a Carmelite convent in conformity with the primitive Rule of the Order.

1561 Work for the future convent put in hand.

1562 St Teresa at Toledo with Doña Luisa de la Cerda. June—she finishes the first draft of the *Autiobography*. July—she returns to Ávila. August 24th—foundation of the convent of St Joseph, immediate return to the convent of the Incarnation.

1563 St Teresa finally leaves the Incarnation, for St Joseph's.

1565 Fernando's death in Colombia.

1567 P. Rubeo arrives in Ávila. He gives St Teresa patents to found houses of friars and nuns. August 15th, foundation of the

1554 England reconciled to Holy See by Cardinal Pole. Marriage of Philip II and Mary Tudor.

1554 Jesuits in Ávila. Fray Luis de Granada's *Libro de oración y meditación.*

1555 Abdication of Charles V and retirement to Yuste.

1556 Marcel II Pope, then Paul V. Accession of Philip II. Fr. Luis de Granada's *Guía de Pecadores.* Death of Ignatius Loyola.

1557 War with France. Battle of St Quentin.

1558 Destruction of Spanish protestantism. Archbishop of Toledo tried by the Inquisition. Death of Charles V.

1558 Death of Mary Tudor. Accession of Elizabeth.

1559 Spaniards forbidden to study in foreign universities. Auto-da-fé in Valladolid. Pius IV Pope. Acts of Supremacy and Uniformity in England.

1560 Marriage of Philip II with Elizabeth of Valois. Philip II moves his court to Madrid. The Inquisition at Toledo and Seville.

1561 Birth of Góngora. Fr. Luis de Granada's *Memorial de la vida cristiana.*

1562 Death of St Peter of Alcántara. Birth of Lope de Vega.

1563 Close of the Council of Trent. Rise of the Low Countries against Spain.

1565 Birth of Mme Acarie.

1567 Spanish terror in the Low Countries.

convent of Medina del Campo. First meeting with St John of the Cross.

1568 Drawing up of the Constitutions of the Discalced Carmelites. April 11th, foundation of the convent of Malagón. August 15th, foundation of the convent of Valladolid. November 28th, foundation by St John of the Cross of the first convent of Discalced friars at Duruelo.

1569 May 14th, foundation of the convent of Toledo. June 28th, foundation at Pastrana of the convent of Discalced Carmelite nuns; July 13th, foundation of the monastery of Discalced friars there.

1570 Foundation of the convent of Salamanca on Michaelmas day.

1571 January 25th, foundation of convent of Alba de Tormes. St Teresa prioress of convent of Medina del Campo. October 6th, she is imposed as prioress at the Incarnation.

1572 St John of the Cross chaplain to the convent of the Incarnation. St Teresa begins to compose the *Conceptos del Amor de Dios*.

1573 St Teresa signs and attests as correct the copy of the *Camino de Perfección*. Gracián professed at Pastrana. Princess of Eboli enters the convent of Pastrana as a nun. St Teresa begins the *Foundations*.

1574 March 19th, foundation of the convent of Segovia.

1575 February 24th, foundation of Beas. First meeting with Gracián. Beginning of struggle between Discalced and Calced. Opening of General Chapter of the Order at Piacenza. May 29th, foundation of convent of

1568–70 Revolt of the Moriscos in Andalusia; its repression by Don John of Austria.

1568 Mary, Queen of Scots, flees to England and is held prisoner by Elizabeth until 1587.

1569 Northern rebellion in England.

1570 Alliance of the Pope, Spain and Venice, against the Turks. Pius V excommunicates Elizabeth.

1571 Moriscos crushed and dispersed to all parts of Spain. Victory of Lepanto.

1571 Laws against Catholics in England made more severe.

1572 Gregory VII Pope. Fray Luis de León a prisoner of the Inquisition.

1573 Don John of Austria seizes Bizerta.

Seville. P. Á. de Salazar notifies St Teresa of the General's decision: she must retire to one convent and make no more foundations.

1576 Foundation of the convent of Caravaca by Ana de San Alberto. June 4th, St Teresa leaves Seville for the convent of Toledo. Continues the *Foundations*, writes *Modo de visitar los Conventos*. The persecution becomes more intense.

1577 June 2nd, St Teresa begins to write the *Interior Castle*. At the end of July she arrives in Ávila. Excommunication of fifty nuns of the convent of the Incarnation. November 5th, St Teresa finishes the *Interior Castle*. Night of December 3rd–4th, capture of St John of the Cross. December 24th, St Teresa falls and breaks her arm.

1578 Death of P. Rubeo, Carmelite Master General. A decree of Sega, the Nuncio, puts the Discalced under the authority of the Calced. The most troubled year for the Reform.

1579 Sega withdraws from the provincials of the Mitigation their power over the Discalced. End of the persecutions.

1580 February 2nd, foundation of the convent of Villanueva de la Jara. St Teresa seriously ill in Toledo and in Valladolid. Death of Lorenzo de Cepeda. December 29th, foundation of the convent of Palencia.

1581 Philip II gives the necessary instructions for the execution of the brief of erection of Discalced and Mitigated into separate provinces. The chapter of Álcala confirms the Constitutions of the convents of Discalced. June

1576 El Greco comes to Toledo. Don John of Austria, governor of the Low Countries.

1577 Pope Gregory XIII puts in hand the revision of plain-chant.

1577 Cuthbert Mayne, first martyr of the seminary priests, is executed at Launceston.

1578 Assassination of Escobedo by Antonio Pérez. Death of Don John of Austria.

1579 Arrest and imprisonment of Antonio Pérez and the Princess of Éboli.

1580 Philip II is recognized as King of Portugal.

1580 First Jesuits, Edmund Campion and others, arrive in England. Beginning of active and violent persecution of Catholics that continued to the end of the reign.

14th, foundation of the convent
of Soria. St Teresa elected prioress of St Joseph's at Ávila. The
Constitutions printed.

1582 April 19th, inauguration of the   1582 Gregory XIII reforms the calen-
convent of Burgos. October   dar.
4th, at 9 o'clock in the evening,
death of St Teresa at Alba de
Tormes.

[This chronology, established by the author from two sources:
   1. That included by the Paris Carmelites in their translation of the
      Works of St Teresa of Jesus (some dates revised after P. Silverio);
   2. *Chronologie des Civilisations*, by Jean Delorme;
has been adapted for English readers. Some events, *e.g.* those of special
interest to France, have been omitted and important happenings in
England added—Tr.]

When we look at the events of the period, we see that the actions
and writings of St Teresa of Jesus are in perfect harmony with the times
in which she lived.

She has carried over to the spiritual plane the great conquests of
the time. She found the passage joining contemplation and action, as
Magellan found the strait joining two oceans. She drew up the chart
of the spiritual universe as Mercator did that of the globe.

St Teresa of Jesus loved music although she sang out of tune,
and although she established the use in her Carmels of the recitative
for Office. But both she and her daughters made up for this at recreation: the tradition has remained and both music and poetry are a
normal accompaniment of recreation in the Carmels of Spain. I
therefore asked M. Roland-Manuel to be kind enough to give me
the few essential dates of importance for music in Spain at the time of
St Teresa. The notes which he has sent me are so interesting that I do
not hesitate, with his permission, to publish them in full. I am deeply
grateful to him for this.

When St Teresa entered the Incarnation convent, she would
probably know and must have heard the worldly music of the
vihuelistas. The *vihuela* is the Spanish lute, an instrument which
filled the rôle the piano fills to-day. It was both a solo instrument
and used to accompany *canciónes*, *villancicos* and *ensaladas*. Albums of
music by Luis Milán of Valencia, Narváez, Mudarra and Fuenllana
begin to appear from about 1536; but these are albums probably well
known. (Luis Milán, 1536; Narváez, 1538; Mudarra, 1546; Fuenllana, 1554.)

At this time, too, our Doña Teresa de Ahumada would probably hear the organ pieces of Antonio de Cabezón, the Spanish Bach, who is obviously her contemporary (1510–1556).

For directly religious music, our saint would know the great masters of vocal polyphony of Spain and the Christian world. Escobedo, who lived at Segovia, was born in 1500. The great Morales who demanded of music that it should give to life 'nobility and austerity' was almost a contemporary: 1512–1553. Guerrero, the gentle lover of baroque, was born in 1528 and died in 1600. And we should not forget the great theoretical and practical musician, Salinas (1512–1590), who inspired Fray Luis de León with the famous ode:

Música que es la fuente y la primera. . . .

Finally, Tomé Luis de Victoria was her fellow-citizen. Born between 1535 and 1540, he died in Madrid in 1611.

Sentimental historians would always like it to be true that these great minds met. They cannot make such a meeting likely, however. Victoria left for Rome about 1565. At that time he was quite unknown and had published nothing. He only returned to Spain a year after the saint's death, in 1583.

To excite our imagination there remains the fact that this man, of whom one knows almost nothing, came from a family which lived in the parish of San Juan in Ávila, the same parish as our saint.

There also remains chapter xxix of the *Foundations*:

' . . . An ecclesiastic who accompanied us, named Porras, a great servant of God, said Mass, and another friend of the Valladolid nuns, Agustín de Vitoria, who had lent me money to get what was necessary for the house, and had been very kind to us on the way. . . . '

The brother of our Victoria was called Agustín and was a priest: were they the same?

ROLAND-MANUEL

The first time that the Foundress mentions this Agustín de Vitoria is in 1577, in a letter to Maria Bautista, prioress of Valladolid. The name of the musician is frequently spelt Vitoria, and he used to put after it, as if it were a title to fame, 'of Ávila.'

It is probable that St Teresa of Ávila and Tomé Luis Victoria, of Ávila, never met, but all the same it is touching to think that they were both baptized in the baptistery of San Juan, and that in his compositions the musician expressed that longing for the divine which the Mother Foundress of Carmel extolled in her writings and lived to the full in her deeds.

BIBLIOGRAPHY

THERE is no fact in this work which is not in strict conformity with historical truth. There is not a word attributed to St Teresa which she did not in fact either write or utter. Thus, if I were to quote all my sources as they came, every page would be overloaded with references: this would give the book a forbidding appearance, little to the taste of her whom it is my chief wish to please: St Teresa of Jesus herself. She valued pedantry so little that she declared she did not want any 'Latin nuns' in her convents. Thus instead of emphasizing the considerable work of documentation which has been carried out, I have rather striven to remove the traces of it, in order that the account may appear as supple and, I hope, lively and pleasant, as possible.

Thus, only references to quoted passages are given, to permit of reference to the Spanish text. As I have re-translated all the extracts myself, such references are those of the works and letters of St Teresa in Spanish (editions of P. Silverio de Santa Teresa, Burgos):

Shorter edition, in one volume.

Critical edition of the *Complete Works*, in nine volumes.

I have chosen the Shorter edition wherever possible, its numbered paragraphs facilitating research.

As is permissible when incorporating a quotation in a text, I have sometimes changed the tense of the verb, or made a few very slight modifications which do not alter the meaning of the sentence or falsify the personality of its author.

I group my sources below under classifications numbered I to IV, according to their importance for my documentation.

I. SOURCES

The complete works of St Teresa of Jesus in the two editions indicated above.

II. WRITINGS AND DECLARATIONS OF ST TERESA'S CONTEMPORARIES

María de San José: *El libro de recreaciones. El ramillete de mirra.*

Jerónimo Gracián de la Madre de Dios: *Obras completas.*

Diego de Yepes: *Vida, virtudes y milagros de la Bienaventurada Virgen Teresa de Jesús. Relación de la vida y libros de la Madre Teresa que el P. Diego de Yepes remitió al P. Fr. Luis de León.*

V. M. Ana de San Bartolomé: *Autobiografía.*

P. Crisóstomo Henríquez: *Vie de la Vénérable Mère Anne de Saint-Barthélémy.*

Julian de Ávila: *Vida de Santa Teresa de Jesús.*

Francisco de Ribera: *La vida de la Madre Teresa.*

Fr. Luis de León: *Vida, muerte, virtudes y milagros de la Santa Madre Teresa de Jesús.*

Procesos de beatificación y canonización de Santa Teresa de Jesús (Editorial Monte Carmelo, Burgos).

And all the documents and accounts published by P. Silverio de Santa Teresa in the notes and appendices of his critical edition.

III. WORKS OF PRIMARY IMPORTANCE

P. Silverio de Santa Teresa: *Vida de Santa Teresa* (5 vols.)

Fr. Gabriel de Jesús: *La Santa de la Raza* (4 vols.)

Historia del Carmel (Ed. Monte Carmelo, Burgos), tomos 1-2-3-4.

D. Manuel María Polit: *La familia de Santa Teresa en América.*

Anonymous: *Les Parents de Ste Thérèse, Alfonso Sánchez de Cepeda et Beatriz de Ahumada* (Ed. Carmel of Mongalose).

Paris Carmelites: *Notes et appendices de la traduction française des œuvres completes.*

IV. WORKS CONSULTED

Read by St Teresa herself, or writings of contemporary mystics.

Osuna: *Abecedario.*

Bernardino de Laredo: *Subida del Monte Sion.*

Alonso de Madrid: *Arte de servir a Dios.*

S. Pedro de Alcántara: *Tratado de la oración y meditación.*

Ignatius of Loyola: *Ejercicios espirituales.*

Antonio de Guevara: *Oratorio de religiosos y ejercicios virtuosos.*

Alonso de Orozco: *Obras.*

A. de Cabrera: *Sermones.*

Fr. Luis de Granada: *Libro de la oración y meditación.*

San Juan de la Cruz: *Obras completas.*

Works entirely devoted to St Teresa.

History of St Teresa, after the Bollandists.

R. P. Léon (Van Hove), *La joie chez Sainte Thérèse.*

L'Espagne thérèsienne ou le pélérinage d'un Flamand à toutes les fondations de Sainte Thérèse (album of pictures).

R. Hoornaert: *Sainte Thérèse écrivain, son milieu, ses facultés, son œuvre.*

E. Allison Peers: *Works of St Teresa of Jesus. Letters of St Teresa of Jesus.*

Sánchez Moguel: *El lenguaje de Santa Teresa de Jesús.*

G. Etchegoyen: *L'amour divin, essai sur les sources de Sainte Thérèse.*

A. Lepée: *Sainte Thérèse et le réalisme chrétien.*

P. Lafond: *Quelques portraits de familiers de Sainte Thérèse.*

M. Legendre: *Sainte Thérèse d'Ávila.*

F. M. de T.: *La Mujer grande.*

E. Marquina: *Pasos y trabajos de Santa Teresa de Jesús.*

Works not entirely devoted to St Teresa, but important.

J. Baruzi: *Saint Jean de la Croix et le problème de l'expérience mystique.*

P. Bruno de J. M.: *Saint Jean de la Croix. Madame Acarie. L'Espagne mystique.*

Études Carmelitaines: *Amour et Violence* (the struggle between Gracián and Doria).

E. Allison Peers: *Spanish Mysticism.*

F. de Ros: *Francisco de Osuna. Bernardino de Laredo.*

P. Emeterio de J. M.: *Ensayo sobre la lírica carmelitana. Mística y novela.*

Hermano Timóteo Garcia: *Santuario y monasterio de N. S. de la Calle.*

P. Vicente B. de Heredia: *Dominicos de Castilla.*

La Puente: *Vida del P. Baltasar Alvarez.*

Jerónimo de San José: *El don que tuvo San Juan de la Cruz para llevar las almas a Dios.*

Marqués de San Juan de Piedras Albas: *Fr. Jerónimo Gracián de la Madre de Dios.*

J. Turmel: *Histoire du Diable.*

R. Picard: *Notes et Matériaux pour l'étude du Socratisme chrétien chez Sainte Thérèse et les spirituels espagnols.*

R. Menéndez Pidal: *La Lengua de Cristóbal Colón.*

Bergson: *Les deux sources de la morale et de la religion.*

Arvède Barine: *Portraits de femmes.*

Condesa de Pardo Bazán: *Cuadros religiosos.*

Barbey d'Aurévilly: *L'internelle consolation.*

Huysmans: *En route. L'oblat.*

V. HISTORICAL WORKS

Menéndez Pelayo: *Historia de los heterodoxos españoles.*

M. Bataillon: *Érasme et l'Espagne. Introduction au 'Roman picaresque'.*

Llorente: *Historia crítica de la Inquisición de España.*

M. de la Pinta: *Carceles inquisitoriales.*

R. Altamira: *Historia de España y civilización española.*

H. Ch. Lea: *A History of the Inquisition in Spain.*

Melgares Marin: *Procedimientos de la Inquisición.*

Sabatini: *Torquemada.*

Prescott: *The Incas and the Conquest of Peru.*

M. Legendre: *Nouvelle Histoire d'Espagne.*

A. Mousset: *Histoire d'Espagne.*

C. Cardo: *Histoire spirituelle des Espagnes.*

A. de Brunel: *Voyage en Espagne.*

Ranke: *Spain under Charles V, Philip II and Philip III.*

Pfandl: *Philippe II.*

F. de los Rios: *Religión y estado en la España del Siglo XVI.*

R. Schneider: *Philippe II.*

Gregorio Marañón: *Antonio Pérez.*

A. Marichalar: *Las Cadenas del Duque de Alba.*

F. Rodriguez Marín, T. IX and X of the *nueva edición crítica* of *El Ingenioso hidalgo don Quijote de la Mancha.*

Ticknor: *Spanish Literature.*

J. Hurtado, J. de la Serña, A. González Palencia: *Historia de la literatura española.*

J. M. Quadrado: *España* (vol. 'Salamanca, Ávila, Segovia').

P. Sandoval: *Vida y hechos del Emperador Carlos Quinto.*

E. Ballesteros: *Estudio histórico de Ávila y su territorio.*

B. García Arias: *Recuerdos históricos de Ávila.*

M. Foronda: *Carlos Quinto en Ávila.*

T. Dudon: *Saint Ignace de Loyola.*

VI. CUSTOMS OF THE SIXTEENTH CENTURY

F. Antonio de Guevara: *Epistolas familiares.*

Diego Hermosilla: *Diálogo de pajes.*

A. Valbuena Prat: *La vida española en la edad de oro.*

Fr. Luis de León: *La perfecta casada.*

Malón de Chaide: *La conversión de la Magdalena.*

Baltasar Gracián: *El Criticón.*

The facts which I have used to write this account of the life of St Teresa have all been taken from sources I and II.

INDEX

Index 453

her sympathy for the sufferings of St. John of the Cross, 342–3; decree from the Nuncio puts Discalced friars and nuns under the jurisdiction of the Calced, Teresa is to be transferred to another convent for life, 348–9; Teresa, crushed by persecution, is fed by Our Lord himself, 350; Liberty restored through the King's intervention, 353–4; a new house at Malagón, 360; foundation of Villanueva de la Jara, 363 ff.; *Autobiography* approved by the Inquisition, 366; foundation of Palencia—her exhaustion, 369; foundation of Soria, 370–1; the Constitutions, 371–3; separation of Calced and Discalced into two Provinces by the Pope, 374; Prioress of St. Joseph of Ávila, 379; St. John of the Cross and St. Teresa, 384–5; foundation of Burgos—Teresa falls ill, 388 ff.; family troubles 402 ff.; her firmness in upholding the Constitutions, 416; a dying woman, she is ordered by Fr. Antonio de Jesús to travel next day to Alba de Tormes, 419; last hours and death in the convent there, 423 ff.; her incorruptible body, 430; Beatification and Canonisation, 435

Thomas Aquinas, St., 99, 146, 251
Tolosa, Beatriz de, 395
Tolosa, Catalina de, 388–9, 391, 393, 395–400
Tolosa, Elena de, 395, 396, 399
Tolosa, Lesmes de, 395
Tomasina Bautista, 389, 395, 410
Tostado, 293, 312, 316, 318, 344, 346, 367

Ulloa, Guiomar de, 85–93, 96, 98, 104, 109, 113, 114, 116, 118–24, 136, 138, 140, 338, 358
Ulloa, Magdalena de, 230
Úrsula de los Santos (de Revilla y Álvarez), 138, 144, 156, 158, 159, 162

Valera, Leonor de, 277
Valdés, Fernando (Grand Inquisitor), 198
Vargas, Francisco de, 282
Vázquez, Dionisio, 118
Vega, Suero de, 369
Vela, Blasco Núñez, 388
Vela, Cristóbal (Archbishop of Burgos), 388, 391–3, 395–6, 398–400
Vela, Francisco Núñez, 3, 5, 388, 393
Velada, Marquis of, 404
Velada, Marchioness de, 147
Velásquez, Fr. (later Bishop of Osma), 323, 370
Vibero, Leonor de, 92
Villanueva, Licentiate, 299
Villena, Marchioness of, 129
Vincent, St. (child martyr of Ávila), 10

Yanguas, Diego de, 251, 252
Yepes, Catalina, 180
Yepes, Gonzalo de, 180
Yepes, Diego de, 335, 345, 433

Zapata, Luis, 18

THE PRECIPICE

THE PRECIPICE

*Existential Risk and
the Future of Humanity*

TOBY ORD

BOOKS

NEW YORK

Hachette Books
Hachette Book Group
1290 Avenue of the Americas
New York, NY 10104
hachettebooks.com
twitter.com/hachettebooks

ISBN: 978-0-316-48491-6 (hardcover), 978-0-316-48489-3 (ebook)

Printed in the United States of America

LSC-C

10 9 8 7 6 5 4 3 2 1

To the hundred billion people before us,
who fashioned our civilization;
To the seven billion now alive,
whose actions may determine its fate;
To the trillions to come,
whose existence lies in the balance.

CONTENTS

LIST OF FIGURES

LIST OF TABLES

PART ONE

THE STAKES

INTRODUCTION

If all goes well, human history is just beginning. Humanity is about two hundred thousand years old. But the Earth will remain habitable for hundreds of millions more—enough time for millions of future generations; enough to end disease, poverty and injustice forever; enough to create heights of flourishing unimaginable today. And if we could learn to reach out further into the cosmos, we could have more time yet: trillions of years, to explore billions of worlds. Such a lifespan places present-day humanity in its earliest infancy. A vast and extraordinary adulthood awaits.

Our view of this potential is easily obscured. The latest scandal draws our outrage; the latest tragedy, our sympathy. Time and space shrink. We forget the scale of the story in which we take part. But there are moments when we remember—when our vision shifts, and our priorities realign. We see a species precariously close to self-destruction, with a future of immense promise hanging in the balance. And which way that balance tips becomes our most urgent public concern.

This book argues that safeguarding humanity's future is the defining challenge of our time. For we stand at a crucial moment in the history of our species. Fueled by technological progress, our power has grown so great that for the first time in humanity's long history, we have the capacity to destroy ourselves—severing our entire future and everything we could become.

Yet humanity's wisdom has grown only falteringly, if at all, and lags dangerously behind. Humanity lacks the maturity, coordination and foresight necessary to avoid making mistakes from

3

which we could never recover. As the gap between our power and our wisdom grows, our future is subject to an ever-increasing level of risk. This situation is unsustainable. So over the next few centuries, humanity will be tested: it will either act decisively to protect itself and its longterm potential, or, in all likelihood, this will be lost forever.

To survive these challenges and secure our future, we must act now: managing the risks of today, averting those of tomorrow, and becoming the kind of society that will never pose such risks to itself again.

It is only in the last century that humanity's power to threaten its entire future became apparent. One of the most harrowing episodes has just recently come to light. On Saturday, October 27, 1962, a single officer on a Soviet submarine almost started a nuclear war. His name was Valentin Savitsky. He was captain of the submarine B-59—one of four submarines the Soviet Union had sent to support its military operations in Cuba. Each was armed with a secret weapon: a nuclear torpedo with explosive power comparable to the Hiroshima bomb.

It was the height of the Cuban Missile Crisis. Two weeks earlier, US aerial reconnaissance had produced photographic evidence that the Soviet Union was installing nuclear missiles in Cuba, from which they could strike directly at the mainland United States. In response, the US blockaded the seas around Cuba, drew up plans for an invasion and brought its nuclear forces to the unprecedented alert level of DEFCON 2 ("Next step to nuclear war").

On that Saturday, one of the blockading US warships detected Savitsky's submarine and attempted to force it to the surface by dropping low-explosive depth charges as warning shots. The submarine had been hiding deep underwater for days. It was out of radio contact, so the crew did not know whether war had already broken out. Conditions on board were extremely bad. It was built for the Arctic and its ventilator had broken in the tropical water. The heat inside was unbearable, ranging from 113°F near the torpedo tubes to 140°F in the engine room. Carbon dioxide had built up to dangerous concentrations, and crew members had begun to fall unconscious. Depth charges were exploding right next to the hull. One of the crew later recalled: "It felt like you were sitting in a metal barrel, which somebody is constantly blasting with a sledgehammer."

Increasingly desperate, Captain Savitsky ordered his crew to prepare their secret weapon:

> Maybe the war has already started up there, while we are doing somersaults here. We're going to blast them now! We will die, but we will sink them all—we will not disgrace our Navy![1]

Firing the nuclear weapon required the agreement of the submarine's political officer, who held the other half of the firing key. Despite the lack of authorization by Moscow, the political officer gave his consent.

On any of the other three submarines, this would have sufficed to launch their nuclear weapon. But by the purest luck, submarine B-59 carried the commander of the entire flotilla, Captain Vasili Arkhipov, and so required his additional consent. Arkhipov refused to grant it. Instead, he talked Captain Savitsky down from his rage and convinced him to give up: to surface amidst the US warships and await further orders from Moscow.[2]

We do not know precisely what would have happened if Arkhipov had granted his consent—or had he simply been stationed on any of the other three submarines. Perhaps Savitsky would not have followed through on his command. What is clear is that we came precariously close to a nuclear strike on the blockading fleet—a strike which would most likely have resulted in nuclear retaliation, then escalation to a full-scale nuclear war (the only kind the US had plans for). Years later, Robert McNamara, Secretary of Defense during the crisis, came to the same conclusion:

> No one should believe that had U.S. troops been attacked by nuclear warheads, the U.S. would have refrained from responding with nuclear warheads. Where would it have ended? In utter disaster.[3]

Ever since the advent of nuclear weapons, humans have been making choices with such stakes. Ours is a world of flawed decision-makers, working with strikingly incomplete information, directing technologies which threaten the entire future of the species. We were lucky, that Saturday in 1962, and have so far avoided catastrophe. But our destructive capabilities continue to grow, and we cannot rely on luck forever.

We need to take decisive steps to end this period of escalating risk and safeguard our future. Fortunately, it is in our power to do so. The greatest risks are caused by human action, and they can be addressed by human action. Whether humanity survives this era is thus a choice humanity will make. But it is not an easy one. It all depends on how quickly we can come to understand and accept the fresh responsibilities that come with our unprecedented power.

This is a book about *existential risks*—risks that threaten the destruction of humanity's longterm potential. Extinction is the most obvious way humanity's entire potential could be destroyed, but there are others. If civilization across the globe were to suffer a truly unrecoverable collapse, that too would destroy our longterm potential. And we shall see that there are dystopian possibilities as well: ways we might get locked into a failed world with no way back.

While this set of risks is diverse, it is also exclusive. So I will have to set aside many important risks that fall short of this bar: our topic is not new dark ages for humanity or the natural world (terrible though they would be), but the permanent destruction of humanity's potential.

Existential risks present new kinds of challenges. They require us to coordinate globally and intergenerationally, in ways that go beyond what we have achieved so far. And they require foresight rather than trial and error. Since they allow no second chances, we need to build institutions to ensure that across our entire future we never once fall victim to such a catastrophe.

6

To do justice to this topic, we will have to cover a great deal of ground. Understanding the risks requires delving into physics, biology, earth science and computer science; situating this in the larger story of humanity requires history and anthropology; discerning just how much is at stake requires moral philosophy and economics; and finding solutions requires international relations and political science. Doing this properly requires deep engagement with each of these disciplines, not just cherry-picking expert quotes or studies that support one's preconceptions. This would be an impossible task for any individual, so I am extremely grateful for the extensive advice and scrutiny of dozens of the world's leading researchers from across these fields.[4]

This book is ambitious in its aims. Through careful analysis of the potential of humanity and the risks we face, it makes the case that we live during the most important era of human history. Major risks to our entire future are a new problem, and our thinking has not caught up. So *The Precipice* presents a new ethical perspective: a major reorientation in the way we see the world, and our role in it. In doing so, the book aspires to start closing the gap between our wisdom and power, allowing humanity a clear view of what is at stake, so that we will make the choices necessary to safeguard our future.

I have not always been focused on protecting our longterm future, coming to the topic only reluctantly. I am a philosopher, at Oxford University, specializing in ethics. My earlier work was rooted in the more tangible concerns of global health and global poverty—in how we could best help the worst off. When coming to grips with these issues I felt the need to take my work in ethics beyond the ivory tower. I began advising the World Health Organization, World Bank and UK government on the ethics of global health. And finding that my own money could do hundreds of times as much good for those in poverty as it could do for me, I made a lifelong pledge to donate at least a tenth of all I earn to help them.[5] I founded a society, *Giving What We Can*, for those who wanted to join me, and was heartened to see thousands of people come together to pledge more than £1 billion over our lifetimes to the most effective charities we know of, working on the most important causes. Together, we've already been able to transform the lives of tens of thousands of people.[6] And because there are many other ways beyond our donations in which we can help fashion a better world, I helped start a wider movement, known as *effective altruism*, in which people aspire to use evidence and reason to do as much good as possible.

Since there is so much work to be done to fix the needless suffering in our present, I was slow to turn to the future. It was so much less visceral; so much more abstract. Could it really be as urgent a problem as suffering now? As I reflected on the evidence and ideas that would culminate in this book, I came to realize that the risks to humanity's future are just as real and just as urgent—yet even more neglected. And that the people of the future may be even more powerless to protect themselves from the risks we impose than the dispossessed of our own time.

Addressing these risks has now become the central focus of my work: both researching the challenges we face, and advising groups such as the UK Prime Minister's Office, the World Economic Forum and DeepMind on how they can best address these challenges. Over time, I've seen a growing recognition of these risks, and of the need for concerted action.

To allow this book to reach a diverse readership, I've been ruthless in stripping out the jargon, needless technical detail and defensive qualifications typical of academic writing (my own included). Readers hungry for further technical detail or qualifications can delve into the many endnotes and appendices, written with them in mind.[7]

I have tried especially hard to examine the evidence and arguments carefully and even-handedly, making sure to present the key points even if they cut against my narrative. For it is of the utmost importance to get to the truth of these matters— humanity's attention is scarce and precious, and must not be wasted on flawed narratives or ideas.[8]

Each chapter of *The Precipice* illuminates the central questions from a different angle. Part One (The Stakes) starts with a bird's-eye view of our unique moment in history, then examines why it warrants such urgent moral concern. Part Two (The Risks) delves into the science of the risks facing humanity, both from nature and from ourselves, showing that while some have been overstated, there is real risk and it is growing. So Part Three (The Path Forward) develops tools for understanding how these risks compare and combine, and new strategies for addressing them. I close with a vision of our future: of what we could achieve were we to succeed.

This book is not just a familiar story of the perils of climate change or nuclear war. These risks that first awoke us to the possibilities of destroying ourselves are just the beginning. There are emerging risks, such as those arising from biotechnology and advanced artificial intelligence, that may pose much greater risk to humanity in the coming century.

Finally, this is not a pessimistic book. It does not present an inevitable arc of history culminating in our destruction. It is not a morality tale about our technological hubris and resulting fall. Far from it. The central claim is that there are real risks to our future, but that our choices can still make all the difference. I believe we are up to the task: that through our choices we can pull back from the precipice and, in time, create a future of astonishing value—with a richness of which we can barely dream, made possible by innovations we are yet to conceive. Indeed, my deep optimism about humanity's future is core to my motivation in writing this book. Our potential is vast. We have so much to protect.

1

STANDING AT THE PRECIPICE

It might be a familiar progression, transpiring on many worlds—a planet, newly formed, placidly revolves around its star; life slowly forms; a kaleidoscopic procession of creatures evolves; intelligence emerges which, at least up to a point, confers enormous survival value; and then technology is invented. It dawns on them that there are such things as laws of Nature, that these laws can be revealed by experiment, and that knowledge of these laws can be made both to save and to take lives, both on unprecedented scales. Science, they recognize, grants immense powers. In a flash, they create world-altering contrivances. Some planetary civilizations see their way through, place limits on what may and what must not be done, and safely pass through the time of perils. Others, not so lucky or so prudent, perish.

—Carl Sagan[1]

We live at a time uniquely important to humanity's future. To see why, we need to take a step back and view the human story as a whole: how we got to this point and where we might be going next.

Our main focus will be humanity's ever-increasing power—power to improve our condition and power to inflict harm. We shall see how the major transitions in human history have enhanced our power, and enabled us to make extraordinary progress. If we can avoid catastrophe we can cautiously expect this progress to continue: the future of a responsible humanity is

11

extraordinarily bright. But this increasing power has also brought on a new transition, at least as significant as any in our past, the transition to our time of perils.

HOW WE GOT HERE

Very little of humanity's story has been told; because very little *can* be told. Our species, *Homo sapiens*, arose on the savannas of Africa 200,000 years ago.[2] For an almost unimaginable time we have had great loves and friendships, suffered hardships and griefs, explored, created, and wondered about our place in the universe. Yet when we think of humanity's great achievements across time, we think almost exclusively of deeds recorded on clay, papyrus or paper—records that extend back only about 5,000 years. We rarely think of the first person to set foot in the strange new world of Australia some 70,000 years ago; of the first to name and study the plants and animals of each place we reached; of the stories, songs and poems of humanity in its youth.[3] But these accomplishments were real, and extraordinary.

We know that even before agriculture or civilization, humanity was a fresh force in the world. Using the simple, yet revolutionary, technologies of seafaring, clothing and fire, we traveled further than any mammal before us. We adapted to a wider range of environments, and spread across the globe.[4]

What made humanity exceptional, even at this nascent stage? We were not the biggest, the strongest or the hardiest. What set us apart was not physical, but mental—our intelligence, creativity and language.[5]

Yet even with these unique mental abilities, a single human alone in the wilderness would be nothing exceptional. He or she might be able to survive—intelligence making up for physical prowess—but would hardly dominate. In ecological terms, it is not a *human* that is remarkable, but *humanity*.

Each human's ability to cooperate with the dozens of other people in their band was unique among large animals. It allowed us to form something greater than ourselves. As our language

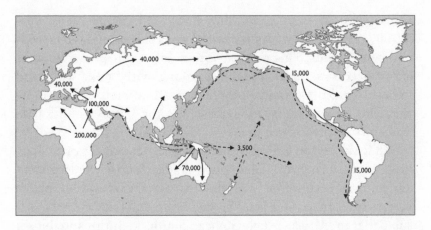

FIGURE 1.1 How we settled the world. The arrows show our current understanding of the land and sea routes taken by our ancestors, and how many years ago they reached each area.[6]

grew in expressiveness and abstraction, we were able to make the most of such groupings: pooling together our knowledge, our ideas and our plans.

Crucially, we were able to cooperate across *time* as well as space. If each generation had to learn everything anew, then even a crude iron shovel would have been forever beyond our technological reach. But we learned from our ancestors, added minor innovations of our own, and passed this all down to our children. Instead of dozens of humans in cooperation, we had tens of thousands, cooperating across the generations, preserving and improving ideas through deep time. Little by little, our knowledge and our culture grew.[7]

At several points in the long history of humanity there has been a great transition: a change in human affairs that accelerated our accumulation of power and shaped everything that would follow. I will focus on three.[8]

The first was the Agricultural Revolution.[9] Around 10,000 years ago the people of the Fertile Crescent, in the Middle East, began planting wild wheat, barley, lentils and peas to supplement their foraging. By preferentially replanting the

13

seeds from the best plants, they harnessed the power of evolution, creating new domesticated varieties with larger seeds
and better yields. This worked with animals too, giving humans
easier access to meat and hides, along with milk, wool and
manure. And the physical power of draft animals to help plow
the fields or transport the harvest was the biggest addition to
humanity's power since fire.[10]

While the Fertile Crescent is often called "the cradle of civilization," in truth civilization had many cradles. Entirely independent
agricultural revolutions occurred across the world in places
where the climate and local species were suitable: in east Asia;
sub-Saharan Africa; New Guinea; South, Central and North
America; and perhaps elsewhere too.[11] The new practices fanned
out from each of these cradles, changing the way of life for many
from foraging to farming.

This had dramatic effects on the scale of human cooperation.
Agriculture reduced the amount of land needed to support
each person by a factor of a hundred, allowing large permanent settlements to develop, which began to unite together
into states.[12] Where the largest foraging communities involved
perhaps hundreds of people, some of the first cities had tens of
thousands of inhabitants. At its height, the Sumerian civilization
contained around a million people.[13] And 2,000 years ago, the
Han dynasty of China reached sixty million people—about a
hundred thousand times as many as were ever united in our forager past, and about ten times the entire global forager population at its peak.[14]

As more and more people were able to share their insights
and discoveries, there were rapid developments in technology,
institutions and culture. And the increasing numbers of people
trading with one another made it possible for them to specialize
in these areas—to devote a lifetime to governance, trade or the
arts—allowing us to develop these ideas much more deeply.

Over the first 6,000 years of agriculture, we achieved world-
changing breakthroughs including writing, mathematics, law
and the wheel.[15] Of these, writing was especially important

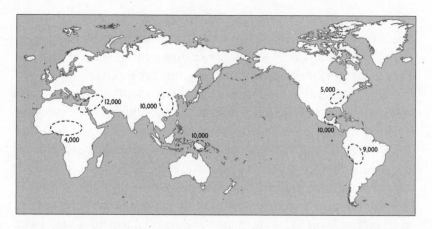

FIGURE 1.2 The cradles of civilization. The places around the world where agriculture was independently developed, marked with how many years ago this occurred.

for strengthening our ability to cooperate across time and space: increasing the bandwidth between generations, the reliability of the information, and the distance over which ideas could be shared.

The next great transition was the Scientific Revolution.[16] Early forms of science had been practiced since ancient times, and the seeds of empiricism can be found in the work of medieval scholars in the Islamic world and Europe.[17] But it was only about 400 years ago that humanity developed the scientific method and saw scientific progress take off.[18] This helped replace a reliance on received authorities with careful observation of the natural world, seeking simple and testable explanations for what we saw. The ability to test and discard bad explanations helped us break free from dogma, and allowed for the first time the systematic creation of knowledge about the workings of nature.

Some of our new-found knowledge could be harnessed to improve the world around us. So the accelerated accumulation of knowledge brought with it an acceleration of technological innovation, giving humanity increasing power over the natural world. The rapid pace allowed people to see transformative effects of these improvements within their own lifetimes. This gave rise to the modern idea of *progress*. Where the world had previously been dominated by narratives of decline and fall or of a recurring cycle, there was increasing interest in a new narrative: a grand project of working together to build a better future.

Soon, humanity underwent a third great transition: the Industrial Revolution. This was made possible by the discovery of immense reserves of energy in the form of coal and other fossil fuels. These are formed from the compressed remains of organisms that lived in eons past, allowing us access to a portion of the sunlight that shone upon the Earth over millions of years.[19] We had already begun to drive simple machines with the renewable energy from the wind, rivers and forests; fossil fuels allowed access to vastly more energy, and in a much more concentrated and convenient form.

But energy is nothing without a way of converting it to useful work, to achieve our desired changes in the world. The steam engine allowed the stored chemical energy of coal to be turned into mechanical energy.[20] This mechanical energy was then used to drive machines that performed massive amounts of labor for us, allowing raw materials to be transformed into finished products much more quickly and cheaply than before. And via the railroad, this wealth could be distributed and traded across long distances.

Productivity and prosperity began to accelerate, and a rapid sequence of innovations ramped up the efficiency, scale and variety of automation, giving rise to the modern era of sustained economic growth.[21]

The effects of these transitions have not always been positive. Life in the centuries following the Agricultural Revolution generally involved more work, reduced nutrition and increased disease.[22] Science gave us weapons of destruction that haunt us to this day. And the Industrial Revolution was among the most destabilizing periods in human history. The unequal distribution of gains in prosperity and the exploitative labor practices led to the revolutionary upheavals of the early twentieth century.[23]

Inequality between countries increased dramatically (a trend that has only begun to reverse in the last two decades).[24] Harnessing the energy stored in fossil fuels has released greenhouse gases, while industry fueled by this energy has endangered species, damaged ecosystems and polluted our environment.

Yet despite these real problems, on average human life today is substantially better than at any previous time. The most striking change may be in breaking free from poverty. Until 200 years ago—the last thousandth of our history[25]—increases in humanity's power and prosperity came hand in hand with increases in the human population. Income *per person* stayed almost unchanged: a little above subsistence in times of plenty; a little below in times of need.[26] The Industrial Revolution broke this rule, allowing income to grow faster than population and ushering in an unprecedented rise in prosperity that continues to this day.

We often think of economic growth from the perspective of a society that is already affluent, where it is not immediately clear if further growth even improves our lives. But the most remarkable effects of economic growth have been for the poorest people. In today's world, one out of ten people are so poor that they live on less than two dollars per day—a widely used threshold for "extreme poverty." That so many have so little is among the greatest problems of our time, and has been a major focus of my life. It is shocking then to look further back and see that prior to the Industrial Revolution 19 out of 20 people lived on less than two dollars a day (even adjusting for inflation and purchasing power). Until the Industrial Revolution, any prosperity was confined to a tiny elite with extreme poverty the norm. But over the last two centuries more and more people have broken free from extreme poverty, and are now doing so more quickly than at any earlier time.[27] Two dollars a day is far from prosperity, and these statistics can be of little comfort to those who are still in the grip of poverty, but the trends toward improvement are clear.

And it is not only in terms of material conditions that life has improved. Consider education and health. Universal schooling has produced dramatic improvements in education. Before the Industrial Revolution, just one in ten of the world's people could read and write; now more than eight in ten can do so.[28] For the 10,000 years since the Agricultural Revolution, life expectancy had hovered between 20 and 30 years. It has now more than doubled, to 72 years.[29] And like literacy, these gains have been felt across the world. In 1800 the highest life expectancy of any country was a mere 43 years, in Iceland. Now every single country has a life expectancy above 50.[30] The industrial period has seen all of humanity become more prosperous, educated and long-lived than ever before. But we should not succumb to complacency in the face of this astonishing progress. That we have achieved so much, and so quickly, should inspire us to address the suffering and injustices that remain.

We have also seen substantial improvements in our moral thinking.[31] One of the clearest trends is toward the gradual expansion of the moral community, with the recognition of the rights of women, children, the poor, foreigners and ethnic or religious minorities. We have also seen a marked shift away from violence as a morally acceptable part of society.[32] And in the last sixty years we have added the environment and the welfare of animals to our standard picture of morality. These social changes did not come naturally with prosperity. They were secured by reformers and activists, motivated by the belief that we can—and must—improve. We still have far to go before we are living up to these new ideals, and our progress can be painfully slow, but looking back even just one or two centuries shows how far we have come.

Of course, there have been many setbacks and exceptions. The path has been tumultuous, things have often become better in some ways while worse in others, and there is certainly a danger of choosing selectively from history to create a simple narrative of improvement from a barbarous past to a glorious present. Yet at the largest scales of human history, where we see not the rise and fall of each empire, but the changing face of human civilization across the entire globe, the trends toward progress are clear.[33]

It can be hard to believe such trends, when it so often feels like everything is collapsing around us. In part this skepticism comes from our everyday experience of our own lives or communities over a timespan of years—a scale where downs are almost as likely as ups. It might also come from our tendency to focus more on bad news than good and on threats rather than opportunities: heuristics that are useful for directing our actions, but which misfire when attempting to objectively assess the balance of bad and good.[34] When we try to overcome these distortions, looking for global indicators of the quality of our lives that are as objective as possible, it is very difficult to avoid seeing significant improvement from century to century.

And these trends should not surprise us. Every day we are the beneficiaries of uncountable innovations made by people over hundreds of thousands of years. Innovations in technology, mathematics, language, institutions, culture, art; the ideas of the hundred billion people who came before us, and shaped almost every facet of the modern world.[35] This is a stunning inheritance. No wonder, then, that our lives are better for it.

We cannot be sure these trends toward progress will continue. But given their tenacity, the burden would appear to be on the pessimist to explain why *now* is the point it will fail. This is especially true when people have been predicting such failure for so long and with such a poor track record. Thomas Macaulay made this point well:

> We cannot absolutely prove that those are in error who tell us that society has reached a turning point, that we have seen our best days. But so said all before us, and with just as much apparent reason . . . On what principle is it that, when we see nothing but improvement behind us, we are to expect nothing but deterioration before us?[36]

And he wrote those words in 1830, before an additional 190 years of progress and failed predictions of the end of progress. During those years, lifespan doubled, literacy soared and eight in ten people escaped extreme poverty. What might the coming years bring?

19

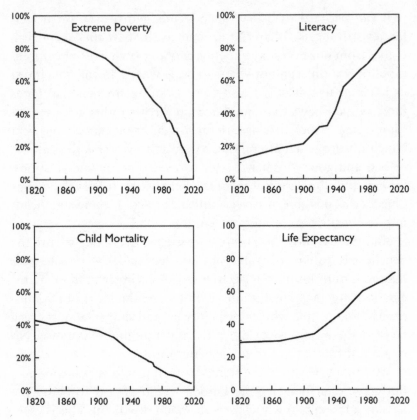

FIGURE 1.3 The striking improvements in extreme poverty, literacy, child mortality and life expectancy over the last 200 years.[37]

WHERE WE MIGHT GO

On the timescale of an individual human life, our 200,000-year history seems almost incomprehensibly long. But on a geological timescale it is short, and vanishingly so on the timescale of the universe as a whole. Our cosmos has a 14-billion-year history, and even that is short on the grandest scales. Trillions of years lie ahead of us. The future is immense.

How much of this future might we live to see? The fossil record provides some useful guidance. Mammalian species typically survive for around one million years before they go extinct; our close relative, *Homo erectus*, survived for almost two million.[38] If we think of one million years in terms of a single, eighty-year life, then today humanity would be in its adolescence—sixteen years old; just coming into our power; just old enough to get ourselves in serious trouble.[39]

Obviously, though, humanity is not a typical species. For one thing, we have recently acquired a unique power to destroy ourselves—power that will be the focus of much of this book. But we also have unique power to protect ourselves from external destruction, and thus the potential to outlive our related species.

How long *could* we survive on Earth? Our planet will remain habitable for roughly a billion years.[40] That's enough time for trillions of human lives; time to watch mountain ranges rise, continents collide, orbits realign; and time, as well, to heal our society and our planet of the wounds we have caused in our immaturity.

And we might have more time yet. As one of the pioneers of rocketry put it, "Earth is the cradle of humanity, but one cannot live in a cradle forever."[41] We do not know, yet, how to reach other stars and settle their planets, but we know of no fundamental obstacles. The main impediment appears to be the time necessary to learn how. This makes me optimistic. After all, the first heavier-than-air flight was in 1903 and just sixty-eight years later we had launched a spacecraft that left our Solar System and will reach the stars. Our species learns quickly, especially in recent times, and a billion years is a long education. I think we will need far less.

If we can reach other stars, then the whole galaxy opens up to us. The Milky Way alone contains more than 100 billion stars, and some of these will last for trillions of years, greatly extending our potential lifespan. Then there are billions of other galaxies beyond our own. If we reach a future of such a scale, we might have a truly staggering number of descendants, with the time, resources, wisdom and experience to create a diversity of wonders unimaginable to us today.

While humanity has made progress toward greater prosperity, health, education and moral inclusiveness, there is so much further we could go. Our present world remains marred by malaria and HIV; depression and dementia; racism and sexism; torture and oppression. But with enough time, we can end these horrors—building a society that is truly just and humane.

And a world without agony and injustice is just a lower bound on how good life could be. Neither the sciences nor the humanities have yet found any upper bound. We get some hint at what is possible during life's best moments: glimpses of raw joy, luminous beauty, soaring love. Moments when we are truly awake. These moments, however brief, point to possible heights of flourishing far beyond the status quo, and far beyond our current comprehension.

Our descendants could have eons to explore these heights, with new means of exploration. And it's not just wellbeing. Whatever you value—beauty, understanding, culture, consciousness, freedom, adventure, discovery, art—our descendants would be able to take these so much further, perhaps even discovering entirely new categories of value, completely unknown to us. Music we lack the ears to hear.

THE PRECIPICE

But this future is at risk. For we have recently undergone another transition in our power to transform the world—one at least as significant as the Agricultural, Scientific and Industrial Revolutions that preceded it.

With the detonation of the first atomic bomb, a new age of humanity began.[42] At that moment, our rapidly accelerating technological power finally reached the threshold where we might be able to destroy ourselves. The first point where the threat to humanity from within exceeded the threats from the natural world. A point where the entire future of humanity hangs in the balance. Where every advance our ancestors have made could be squandered, and every advance our descendants may achieve could be denied. The greater part of the book of human history left unwritten; the narrative broken off; blank pages.

Nuclear weapons were a discontinuous change in human power. At Hiroshima, a single bomb did the damage of thousands. And six years later, a single thermonuclear bomb held more energy than every explosive used in the entire course of the Second World War.[43]

It became clear that a war with such weapons would change the Earth in ways that were unprecedented in human history. World leaders, atomic scientists and public intellectuals began to take seriously the possibility that a nuclear war would spell the end of humanity: either through extinction or a permanent collapse of civilization.[44] Early concern centered on radioactive fallout and damage to the ozone layer, but in the 1980s the focus shifted to a scenario known as nuclear winter, in which nuclear firestorms loft smoke from burning cities into the upper atmosphere.[45] High above the clouds, the smoke cannot be rained out and would persist for years, blackening the sky, chilling the Earth and causing massive crop failure. This was a mechanism by which nuclear war could result in extreme famine, not just in the combatant countries, but in every country around the world. Millions of direct deaths from the explosions could be followed by billions of deaths from starvation, and—potentially—by the end of humanity itself.

How close have we come to such a war? With so much to lose, nuclear war is in no one's interest. So we might expect these obvious dangers to create a certain kind of safety—where world leaders inevitably back down before the brink. But as more and more behind-the-scenes evidence from the Cold War has become public, it has become increasingly clear that we have only barely avoided full-scale nuclear war.

We saw how the intervention of a single person, Captain Vasili Arkhipov, may have prevented an all-out nuclear war at the height of the Cuban Missile Crisis. But even more shocking is just how many times in those few days we came close to disaster, only to be pulled back by the decisions of a few individuals.

The principal events of the crisis took place over a single week. On Monday, October 22, 1962, President John F. Kennedy gave a television address, informing his nation that the Soviets had begun installing strategic nuclear missiles in Cuba—directly threatening the United States. He warned that any use of these nuclear weapons would be met by a full-scale nuclear retaliation on the Soviet Union. His advisers drew up plans for both air strikes on the 48 missiles they had discovered and a full invasion of Cuba. US forces were brought to DEFCON 3, to prepare for a possible nuclear war.[46]

On Wednesday, October 24, the US launched a naval blockade to prevent the delivery of further missiles to Cuba, and took its nuclear forces to the unprecedented level of DEFCON 2. Nuclear missiles were readied for launch and nuclear bombers took to the skies, ready to begin an all-out nuclear attack on the Soviet Union. The crisis reached its peak on Saturday when the Soviets shot down a U-2 reconnaissance plane with a surface-to-air missile, killing its pilot.

Then on Sunday morning it was all over. The Soviets backed down, unexpectedly announcing that they were removing all nuclear missiles from Cuba. But it could very easily have ended differently.

There has been substantial debate about exactly how close the crisis came to nuclear war. But over the decades, as more details have been revealed, the picture has become increasingly serious. Kennedy and Khrushchev went to great lengths to resist hawkish politicians and generals and to stay clear of the brink.[47] But there was a real possibility that, like the First World War, a war might begin without any side wanting it. As the week wore on, events on the ground spiraled beyond their control and they only barely kept the crisis from escalating. The US came extremely close to attacking Cuba, this had a much higher chance of causing nuclear retaliation than anyone guessed, and this in turn had a high chance of escalating to full-scale nuclear war.

Twice, during the crisis, the US nearly launched an attack on Cuba. At the height of the tensions, Kennedy had agreed that if a U-2 were shot down, the US would immediately strike Cuba, with no need to reconvene the war council. Then, on Saturday, a U-2 was indeed shot down. But Kennedy changed his mind and called off the counter-attack. Instead, he issued a secret ultimatum, informing the Soviets that if they did not commit to removing the missiles within twenty-four hours, or if another plane was shot down, the US would immediately launch air strikes and, almost surely, a full invasion.

This too almost triggered an attack. For the Americans did not know the extent to which Khrushchev was unable to control his forces in Cuba. Indeed, the U-2 had been shot down by a Soviet general acting against explicit orders from Khrushchev. And Khrushchev had even less control over the Cuban forces, who had already hit a low-flying reconnaissance plane with anti-aircraft fire and were eager to take one down. Knowing that he could not stop his own side from downing another plane, thereby triggering a US attack, Khrushchev raced to issue a statement ending the crisis before morning reconnaissance flights resumed.

What would have happened if the US *had* attacked? American leaders assumed that a purely conventional (non-nuclear) attack on Cuba could only be met with a purely conventional response. It was out of the question, they thought, that the Soviets would respond with nuclear attacks on the mainland United States. But they were missing another crucial fact. The missiles the US had discovered in Cuba were only a fraction of those the Soviets had delivered. There were 158 nuclear warheads. And more than 90 of these were tactical nuclear weapons, there for the express purpose of nuclear first use: to destroy a US invasion fleet before it could land.[48]

What's more, Castro was eager to use them. Indeed, he directly asked Khrushchev to fire the nuclear weapons if the Americans tried to invade, even though he knew this would lead to the annihilation of his own country: "What would have happened to Cuba? It would have been totally destroyed."[49] And

Khrushchev, in another unprecedented move, had relinquished central control of the tactical nuclear weapons, delegating the codes and decision to fire to the local Soviet commander. After hearing Kennedy's television address, Khrushchev issued new orders that the weapons were not to be used without his explicit permission, but he came to fear these would be disobeyed in the heat of conflict, as his order not to fire on US spy planes had been.

So unbeknownst to the US military leadership, a conventional attack on Cuba was likely to be met with a nuclear strike on American forces. And such a strike was extremely likely to be met by a further nuclear response from the US. This nuclear response was highly likely to go beyond Cuba, and to precipitate a full-scale nuclear war with the Soviets. In his television address on the Monday, Kennedy had explicitly promised that "It shall be the policy of this Nation to regard any nuclear missile launched from Cuba against any nation in the Western Hemisphere as an attack by the Soviet Union on the United States, requiring a full retaliatory response upon the Soviet Union."[50]

It is extremely difficult to estimate the chance that the crisis would have escalated to nuclear war.[51] Shortly after, Kennedy told a close adviser that he thought the probability of it ending in nuclear war with the USSR was "somewhere between one out of three, and even."[52] And it has just been revealed that the day after the crisis ended, Paul Nitze (an adviser to Kennedy's war council) estimated the chance at 10 percent, and thought that everyone else in the council would have put it even higher.[53] Moreover, none of these people knew about the tactical nuclear weapons in Cuba, Khrushchev's lack of control of his troops or the events on submarine B-59.

While I'm reluctant to question those whose very decisions could have started the war, my own view is that they were somewhat too pessimistic, given what they knew at the time. However, when we include the subsequent revelations about what was really happening in Cuba my estimates would roughly match theirs. I'd put the chance of the crisis escalating to a nuclear war with the Soviets at something between 10 and 50 percent.[54]

When writing about such close calls, there is a tendency to equate this chance to that of the end of civilization or the end of humanity itself. But that would be a large and needless exaggeration. For we need to combine this chance of nuclear war with the chance that such a war would spell the end of humanity or human civilization, which is far from certain. Yet even making such allowances the Cuban Missile Crisis would remain one of the pivotal moments in 200,000 years of human history: perhaps the closest we have ever come to losing it all.

Even now, with the Cold War just a memory, nuclear weapons still pose a threat to humanity. At the time of writing, the highest chance of a nuclear conflict probably involves North Korea. But not all nuclear wars are equal. North Korea has less than 1 percent as many warheads as Russia or the US, and they are substantially smaller. A nuclear war with North Korea would be a terrible disaster, but it currently poses little threat to humanity's longterm potential.[55]

Instead, most of the existential risk from nuclear weapons today probably still comes from the enormous American and Russian arsenals. The development of ICBMs (intercontinental ballistic missiles) allowed each side to destroy most of the other's missiles with just thirty minutes' warning, so they each moved many missiles to "hair-trigger alert"—ready to launch in just ten minutes.[56] Such hair-trigger missiles are extremely vulnerable to accidental launch, or to deliberate launch during a false alarm. As we shall see in Chapter 4, there has been a chilling catalog of false alarms continuing past the end of the Cold War. On a longer timescale there is also the risk of other nations creating their own enormous stockpiles, of innovations in military technologies undermining the logic of deterrence, and of shifts in the geopolitical landscape igniting another arms race between great powers.

Nuclear weapons are not the only threat to humanity. They have been our focus so far because they were the first major risk and have already threatened humanity. But there are others too.

The exponential rise in prosperity brought on by the Industrial Revolution came on the back of a rapid rise in carbon emissions. A minor side effect of industrialization has eventually grown to become a global threat to health, the environment, international stability, and maybe even humanity itself.

Nuclear weapons and climate change have striking similarities and contrasts. They both threaten humanity through major shifts in the Earth's temperature, but in opposite directions. One burst in upon the scene as the product of an unpredictable scientific breakthrough; the other is the continuation of centuries-long scaling-up of old technologies. One poses a small risk of sudden and precipitous catastrophe; the other is a gradual, continuous process, with a delayed onset—where some level of catastrophe is assured and the major uncertainty lies in just how bad it will be. One involves a classified military technology controlled by a handful of powerful actors; the other involves the aggregation of small effects from the choices of everyone in the world.

As technology continues to advance, new threats appear on the horizon. These threats promise to be more like nuclear weapons than like climate change: resulting from sudden breakthroughs, precipitous catastrophes, and the actions of a small number of actors. There are two emerging technologies that especially concern me; they will be the focus of Chapter 5.

Ever since the Agricultural Revolution, we have induced genetic changes in the plants and animals around us to suit our ends. But the discovery of the genetic code and the creation of tools to read and write it have led to an explosion in our ability to refashion life to new purposes. Biotechnology will bring major improvements in medicine, agriculture and industry. But it will also bring risks to civilization and to humanity itself: both from accidents during legitimate research and from engineered bioweapons.

We are also seeing rapid progress in the capabilities of artificial intelligence (AI) systems, with the biggest improvements in the areas where AI has traditionally been weakest, such as perception, learning and general intelligence. Experts find it likely that this will be the century that AI exceeds human ability not just in a narrow domain, but in general intelligence—the ability to overcome a diverse range of obstacles to achieve one's goals. Humanity has risen to a position where we control the rest of the world precisely because of our unparalleled mental abilities. If we pass this mantle to our machines, it will be they who are in this unique position. This should give us cause to wonder why it would be humanity who will continue to call the shots. We need to learn how to align the goals of increasingly intelligent and autonomous machines with human interests, and we need to do so before those machines become more powerful than we are.

These threats to humanity, and how we address them, define our time. The advent of nuclear weapons posed a real risk of human extinction in the twentieth century. With the continued acceleration of technology, and without serious efforts to protect humanity, there is strong reason to believe the risk will be higher this century, and increasing with each century that technological progress continues. Because these anthropogenic risks outstrip all natural risks combined, they set the clock on how long humanity has left to pull back from the brink.

I am not claiming that extinction is the inevitable conclusion of scientific progress, or even the most likely outcome. What I am claiming is that there has been a robust trend toward increases in the power of humanity which has reached a point where we pose a serious risk to our own existence. How we react to this risk is up to us.

Nor am I arguing against technology. Technology has proved itself immensely valuable in improving the human condition. And technology is essential for humanity to achieve its longterm potential. Without it, we would be doomed by the accumulated risk of natural disasters such as asteroid impacts. Without it, we would never achieve the highest flourishing of which we are capable.

29

The problem is not so much an excess of technology as a lack of wisdom.[57] Carl Sagan put this especially well:

> Many of the dangers we face indeed arise from science and technology—but, more fundamentally, because we have become powerful without becoming commensurately wise. The world-altering powers that technology has delivered into our hands now require a degree of consideration and foresight that has never before been asked of us.[58]

This idea has even been advocated by a sitting US president:

> the very spark that marks us as a species—our thoughts, our imagination, our language, our tool-making, our ability to set ourselves apart from nature and bend it to our will—those very things also give us the capacity for unmatched destruction . . . Technological progress without an equivalent progress in human institutions can doom us. The scientific revolution that led to the splitting of an atom requires a moral revolution as well.[59]

We need to gain this wisdom; to have this moral revolution. Because we cannot come back from extinction, we cannot wait until a threat strikes before acting—we must be proactive. And because gaining wisdom or starting a moral revolution takes time, we need to start now.

I think that we are likely to make it through this period. Not because the challenges are small, but because we will rise to them. The very fact that these risks stem from human action shows us that human action can address them.[60] Defeatism would be both unwarranted and counterproductive—a self-fulfilling prophecy. Instead, we must address these challenges head-on with clear and rigorous thinking, guided by a positive vision of the longterm future we are trying to protect.

How big are these risks? One cannot expect precise numbers, as the risks are *complex* (so not amenable to simple mathematical analysis) and *unprecedented* (so cannot be approximated by a longterm frequency). Yet it is important to at least try to give quantitative estimates. Qualitative statements such as "a grave risk of human extinction" could be interpreted as meaning anything from 1 percent all the way to 99 percent.[61] They add more confusion than clarity. So I will offer quantitative estimates, with the proviso that they can't be precise and are open to revision.

During the twentieth century, my best guess is that we faced around a one in a hundred risk of human extinction or the unrecoverable collapse of civilization. Given everything I know, I put the existential risk this century at around one in six: Russian roulette.[62] (See table 6.1 on p. 167 for a breakdown of the risks.) If we do not get our act together, if we continue to let our growth in power outstrip that of wisdom, we should expect this risk to be even higher next century, and each successive century.

These are the greatest risks we have faced.[63] If I'm even roughly right about their scale, then we cannot survive many centuries with risk like this. It is an *unsustainable* level of risk.[64] Thus, one way or another, this period is unlikely to last more than a small number of centuries.[65] Either humanity takes control of its destiny and reduces the risk to a sustainable level, or we destroy ourselves.

Consider human history as a grand journey through the wilderness. There are wrong turns and times of hardship, but also times of sudden progress and heady views. In the middle of the twentieth century we came through a high mountain pass and found that the only route onward was a narrow path along the cliff-side: a crumbling ledge on the brink of a precipice. Looking down brings a deep sense of vertigo. If we fall, everything is lost. We do not know just how likely we are to fall, but it is the greatest risk to which we have ever been exposed.

This comparatively brief period is a unique challenge in the history of our species. Our response to it will define our story. Historians of the future will name this time, and schoolchildren will study it. But I think we need a name now. I call it the Precipice.

The Precipice gives our time immense meaning. In the grand course of history—if we make it that far—*this* is what our time

31

will be remembered for: for the highest levels of risk, and for humanity opening its eyes, coming into its maturity and guaranteeing its long and flourishing future. This is the meaning of our time.

I am not glorifying our generation, nor am I vilifying us. The point is that our actions have uniquely high stakes. Whether we are great or terrible will depend upon what we do with this opportunity. I hope we live to tell our children and grandchildren that we did not stand by, but used this chance to play the part that history gave us.

Safeguarding humanity through these dangers should be a central priority of our time. I am not saying that this is the only issue in the world, that people should drop everything else they hold dear to do this. But if you can see a way that you could play a role—if you have the skills, or if you are young and can shape your own path—then I think safeguarding humanity through these times is among the most noble purposes you could pursue.

THE PRECIPICE & ANTHROPOCENE

It has become increasingly clear that human activity is the dominant force shaping the environment. Scientists are concluding that humanity looms large not just in its own terms, but in the objective terms of biology, geology and climatology. If there are geologists in the distant future, they would identify the layer of rock corresponding to our time as a fundamental change from the layers before it.

Our present-day geologists are thus considering making this official—changing their classification of geological time to introduce a new epoch called the *Anthropocene*. Proposed beginnings for this epoch include the megafauna extinctions, the Agricultural Revolution, the crossing of the Atlantic, the Industrial Revolution, or early nuclear weapons tests.[66]

Is this the same as the Precipice? How do they differ?

- The Anthropocene is the time of profound human effects on the environment, while the Precipice is the time where humanity is at high risk of destroying itself.

- The Anthropocene is a geological epoch, which typically last millions of years, while the Precipice is a time in human history (akin to the Enlightenment or the Industrial Revolution), which will likely end within a few centuries.

- They might both officially start with the first atomic test, but this would be for very different reasons. For the Anthropocene, it would be mainly for convenient dating, while for the Precipice it is because of the risk nuclear weapons pose to our survival.

2

EXISTENTIAL RISK

The crucial role we fill, as moral beings, is as members of a cross-generational community, a community of beings who look before and after, who interpret the past in light of the present, who see the future as growing out of the past, who see themselves as members of enduring families, nations, cultures, traditions.

—Annette Baier[1]

We have seen how the long arc of human history has brought us to a uniquely important time in our story—a period where our entire future hangs in the balance. And we have seen a little of what might lie beyond, if only we can overcome the risks.

It is now time to think more deeply about what is at stake; why safeguarding humanity through this time is so important. To do so we first need to clarify the idea of existential risk. What exactly *is* existential risk? How does it relate to more familiar ideas of extinction or the collapse of civilization?

We can then ask what it is about these risks that compels our urgent concern. The chief reason, in my view, is that we would lose our entire future: everything humanity could be and everything we could achieve. But that is not all. The case that it is crucial to safeguard our future draws support from a wide range of moral traditions and foundations. Existential risks also threaten to destroy our present, and to betray our past. They test civilization's virtues, and threaten to remove what may be the most complex and significant part of the universe.

35

If we take any of these reasons seriously, we have a lot of work to do to protect our future. For existential risk is greatly neglected: by government, by academia, by civil society. We will see why this has been the case, and why there is good reason to suspect this will change.

UNDERSTANDING EXISTENTIAL RISK

Humanity's future is ripe with possibility. We have achieved a rich understanding of the world we inhabit and a level of health and prosperity of which our ancestors could only dream. We have begun to explore the other worlds in the heavens above us, and to create virtual worlds completely beyond our ancestors' comprehension. We know of almost no limits to what we might ultimately achieve.

Human extinction would foreclose our future. It would destroy our potential. It would eliminate all possibilities but one: a world bereft of human flourishing. Extinction would bring about this failed world and lock it in forever—there would be no coming back.

The philosopher Nick Bostrom showed that extinction is not the only way this could happen: there are other catastrophic outcomes in which we lose not just the present, but all our potential for the future.[2]

Consider a world in ruins: an immense catastrophe has triggered a global collapse of civilization, reducing humanity to a pre-agricultural state. During this catastrophe, the Earth's environment was damaged so severely that it has become impossible for the survivors to ever re-establish civilization. Even if such a catastrophe did not cause our extinction, it would have a similar effect on our future. The vast realm of futures currently open to us would have collapsed to a narrow range of meager options. We would have a failed world with no way back.

Or consider a world in chains: in a future reminiscent of George Orwell's *Nineteen Eighty-Four*, the entire world has become locked under the rule of an oppressive totalitarian regime,

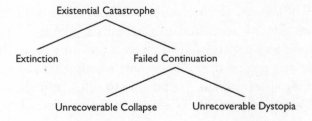

FIGURE 2.1 A classification of existential catastrophes by the kind of outcome that gets locked in.

determined to perpetuate itself. Through powerful, technologically enabled indoctrination, surveillance and enforcement, it has become impossible for even a handful of dissidents to find each other, let alone stage an uprising. With everyone on Earth living under such rule, the regime is stable from threats, internal and external. If such a regime could be maintained indefinitely, then descent into this totalitarian future would also have much in common with extinction: just a narrow range of terrible futures remaining, and no way out.

Following Bostrom, I shall call these "existential catastrophes," defining them as follows:[3]

> An *existential catastrophe* is the destruction of humanity's longterm potential.

> An *existential risk* is a risk that threatens the destruction of humanity's longterm potential.

These definitions capture the idea that the outcome of an existential catastrophe is both dismal and irrevocable. We will not just fail to fulfill our potential, but this very potential itself will be permanently lost. While I want to keep the official definitions succinct, there are several areas that warrant clarification.

First, I am understanding *humanity's longterm potential* in terms of the set of all possible futures that remain open to us.[4] This is an expansive idea of possibility, including everything that humanity could eventually achieve, even if we have yet to invent the means of achieving it.[5] But it follows that while our choices can lock things in, closing off possibilities, they can't open up new ones. So any reduction in humanity's potential should be understood as permanent. The challenge of our time is to *preserve* our vast potential, and to *protect* it against the risk of future destruction. The ultimate purpose is to allow our descendants to *fulfill* our potential, realizing one of the best possible futures open to us.

While it may seem abstract at this scale, this is really a familiar idea that we encounter every day. Consider a child with high longterm potential: with futures open to her in which she leads a great life. It is important that her potential is preserved: that her best futures aren't cut off due to accident, trauma or lack of education. It is important that her potential is protected: that we build in safeguards to make such a loss of potential extremely unlikely. And it is important that she ultimately fulfills her potential: that she ends up taking one of the best paths open to her. So too for humanity.

Existential risks threaten the destruction of humanity's potential. This includes cases where this destruction is complete (such as extinction) and where it is nearly complete, such as a permanent collapse of civilization in which the possibility for some very minor types of flourishing remain, or where there remains some remote chance of recovery.[6] I leave the thresholds vague, but it should be understood that in any existential catastrophe the greater part of our potential is gone and very little remains.[7]

Second, my focus on humanity in the definitions is not supposed to exclude considerations of the value of the environment, other animals, successors to *Homo sapiens*, or creatures elsewhere in the cosmos. It is not that I think only humans count. Instead, it is that humans are the only beings we know of that are responsive to moral reasons and moral argument—the beings who can examine the world and decide to do what is best. If we fail, that upward force, that capacity to push toward what is best or what is just, will vanish from the world.

Our potential is a matter of what humanity can achieve through the combined actions of each and every human. The value of our actions will stem in part from what we do to and for humans, but it will depend on the effects of our actions on non-humans too. If we somehow give rise to new kinds of moral agents in the future, the term "humanity" in my definition should be taken to include them.

My focus on humanity prevents threats to a single country or culture from counting as existential risks. There is a similar term that gets used this way—when people say that something is "an existential threat to this country." Setting aside the fact that these claims are usually hyperbole, they are expressing a similar idea: that something threatens to permanently destroy the longterm potential of a country or culture.[8] However, it is very important to keep talk of an "existential risk" (without any explicit restriction to a group) to apply only to threats against the whole of humanity.

Third, any notion of risk must involve some kind of probability. What kind is involved in existential risk? Understanding the probability in terms of objective long-run frequencies won't work, as the existential catastrophes we are concerned with can only ever happen once, and will always be unprecedented until the moment it is too late. We can't say the probability of an existential catastrophe is precisely zero just because it hasn't happened *yet*.

Situations like these require an evidential sense of probability, which describes the appropriate degree of belief we should have on the basis of the available information. This is the familiar type of probability used in courtrooms, banks and betting shops. When I speak of the probability of an existential catastrophe, I will mean the credence humanity should have that it will occur, in light of our best evidence.[9]

There are many utterly terrible outcomes that do not count as existential catastrophes.

One way this could happen is if there were no single precipitous event, but a multitude of smaller failures. This is because I take on the usual sense of catastrophe as a single, decisive event, rather than any combination of events that is bad in sum. If we were to squander our future simply by continually treating each other badly, or by never getting around to doing anything great, this could be just as bad an outcome but wouldn't have come about via a catastrophe.

Alternatively, there might be a single catastrophe, but one that leaves open some way for humanity to eventually recover. From our own vantage, looking out to the next few generations, this may appear equally bleak. But a thousand years hence it may be considered just one of several dark episodes in the human story. A true existential catastrophe must by its very nature be the decisive moment of human history—the point where we failed.

Even catastrophes large enough to bring about the global collapse of civilization may fall short of being existential catastrophes. While colloquially referred to as "the end of the world," a global collapse of civilization need not be the end of the human story. It has the required severity, but may not be permanent or irrevocable.

In this book, I shall use the term *civilization collapse* quite literally, to refer to an outcome where humanity across the globe loses civilization (at least temporarily), being reduced to a pre-agricultural way of life. The term is often used loosely to refer merely to a massive breakdown of order, the loss of modern technology, or an end to our culture. But I am talking about a world without writing, cities, law, or any of the other trappings of civilization.

This would be a very severe disaster and extremely hard to trigger. For all the historical pressures on civilizations, never once has this happened—not even on the scale of a continent.[10] The fact that Europe survived losing 25 to 50 percent of its population in the Black Death, while keeping civilization firmly intact, suggests that triggering the collapse of civilization would require more than 50 percent fatality in every region of the world.[11]

Even if civilization did collapse, it is likely that it could be re-established. As we have seen, civilization has already been independently established at least seven times by isolated peoples.[12] While one might think resource depletion could make this harder, it is more likely that it has become substantially easier. Most disasters short of human extinction would leave our domesticated animals and plants, as well as copious material resources in the ruins of our cities—it is much easier to re-forge iron from old railings than to smelt it from ore. Even expendable resources such as coal would be much easier to access, via abandoned reserves and mines, than they ever were in the eighteenth century.[13] Moreover, evidence that civilization is possible, and the tools and knowledge to help rebuild, would be scattered across the world.

There are, however, two close connections between the collapse of civilization and existential risk. First, a collapse would count as an existential catastrophe if it were unrecoverable. For example, it is conceivable that some form of extreme climate change or engineered plague might make the planet so inhospitable that humanity would be irrevocably reduced to scattered foragers.[14] And second, a global collapse of civilization could increase the chance of extinction, by leaving us more vulnerable to subsequent catastrophe.

One way a collapse could lead to extinction is if the population of the largest remaining group fell below the *minimum viable population*—the level needed for a population to survive. There is no precise figure for this, as it is usually defined probabilistically and depends on many details of the situation: where the population is, what technology they have access to, the sort of catastrophe they have suffered. Estimates range from hundreds of people up to tens of thousands.[15] If a catastrophe directly reduces human population to below these levels, it will be more useful to classify it as a direct extinction event, rather than an unrecoverable collapse. And I expect that this will be one of the more common pathways to extinction.

We rarely think seriously about risks to humanity's entire potential. We encounter them mostly in action films, where our emotional reactions are dulled by their overuse as an easy way to heighten the drama.[16] Or we see them in online lists of "ten ways the world could end," aimed primarily to thrill and entertain. Since the end of the Cold War, we rarely encounter sober discussions by our leading thinkers on what extinction would mean for us, our cultures or humanity.[17] And so in casual contexts people are sometimes flippant about the prospect of human extinction.

But when a risk is made vivid and credible—when it is clear that billions of lives and all future generations are actually on the line— the importance of protecting humanity's longterm potential is not, for most people, controversial. If we learned that a large asteroid was heading toward Earth, posing a greater than 10 percent chance of human extinction later this century, there would be little debate about whether to make serious efforts to build a deflection system, or to ignore the issue and run the risk. To the contrary, responding to the threat would immediately become one of the world's top priorities. Thus our lack of concern about these threats is much more to do with not yet believing that there are such threats, than it is about seriously doubting the immensity of the stakes.

Yet it is important to spend a little while trying to understand more clearly the different sources of this importance. Such an understanding can buttress feeling and inspire action; it can bring to light new considerations; and it can aid in decisions about how to set our priorities.

LOOKING TO THE PRESENT

Not all existential catastrophes involve human extinction, and not all methods of extinction involve pain or untimely death. For example, it is theoretically possible that we could all simply decide not to reproduce. This could destroy our potential without, let us suppose, causing any suffering. But the existential risks we actually face are not so peaceful. Rather, they are obviously horrific by the most familiar moral standards.

If, over the coming century, humanity is destroyed in a nuclear winter, or an engineered pandemic, or a catastrophic war involving some new technology, then seven billion lives would be cut short—including, perhaps, your own life, or the lives of those you love. Many would likely die in agony—starving, or burning, or ravaged by disease.

The moral case for preventing such horror needs little elaboration. Humanity has seen catastrophes before, on smaller scales: thousands, or millions, of human lives destroyed. We know how tremendously important it is to prevent such disasters. At such a scale, we lose our ability to fully comprehend the magnitude of what is lost, but even then the numbers provide a guide to the moral stakes.[18] Other things being equal, millions of deaths must be much worse than thousands of deaths; and billions, much worse than millions. Even measured just in terms of lives cut short, human extinction would easily be the worst event in our long history.

LOOKING TO OUR FUTURE

But an existential catastrophe is not just a catastrophe that destroys a particularly large number of lives. It destroys our potential.

My mentor, Derek Parfit, asked us to imagine a devastating nuclear war killing 99 percent of the world's people.[19] A war that would leave behind a dark age lasting centuries, before the survivors could eventually rebuild civilization to its former heights; humbled, scarred—but undefeated.

Now compare this with a war killing a full 100 percent of the world's people. This second war would be worse, of course, but how much worse? Either war would be the worst catastrophe in history. Either would kill billions. The second war would involve tens of millions of additional deaths, and so would be worse for this reason. But there is another, far more significant difference between the two wars. Both wars kill billions of humans; but the second war kills humanity. Both wars destroy our present; but the second war destroys our future.

It is this qualitative difference in what is lost with that last percent that makes existential catastrophes unique, and that makes reducing the risk of existential catastrophe uniquely important.[20]

In expectation, almost all humans who will ever live have yet to be born. Absent catastrophe, most generations are future generations. As the writer Jonathan Schell put it:

> The procession of generations that extends onwards from our present leads far, far beyond the line of our sight, and, compared with these stretches of human time, which exceed the whole history of the earth up to now, our brief civilized moment is almost infinitesimal. Yet we threaten, in the name of our transient aims and fallible convictions, to foreclose it all. If our species does destroy itself, it will be a death in the cradle—a case of infant mortality.[21]

And because, in expectation, almost all of humanity's life lies in the future, almost everything of value lies in the future as well: almost all the flourishing; almost all the beauty; our greatest achievements; our most just societies; our most profound discoveries.[22] We can continue our progress on prosperity, health, justice, freedom and moral thought. We can create a world of wellbeing and flourishing that challenges our capacity to imagine. And if we protect that world from catastrophe, it could last millions of centuries. This is our potential—what we could achieve if we pass the Precipice and continue striving for a better world.

It is this view of the future—the immense value of humanity's potential—that most persuades me to focus my energies on reducing existential risk. When I think of the millions of future generations yet to come, the importance of protecting humanity's future is clear to me. To risk destroying this future, for the sake of some advantage limited only to the present, seems to me profoundly parochial and dangerously short-sighted. Such neglect privileges a tiny sliver of our story over the grand sweep of the whole; it privileges a tiny minority of humans over the overwhelming majority yet to be born; it privileges this particular century over the millions, or maybe billions, yet to come.[23]

To see why this would be wrong, consider an analogy with distance. A person does not matter less, the further away from you they are in space. It matters just as much if my wife gets sick while she is away at a conference in Kenya as if she gets sick while home with me in Oxford. And the welfare of strangers in Kenya matters just as much as the welfare of strangers in Oxford. Of course, we may have special duties to some individuals—to family; to members of the same community—but it is never spatial distance, in itself, that determines these differences in our obligations. Recognizing that people matter equally, regardless of their geographic location, is a crucial form of moral progress, and one that we could do much more to integrate into our policies and our philanthropy.

People matter equally regardless of their temporal location too. Our lives matter just as much as those lived thousands of years ago, or those a thousand years hence.[24] Just as it would be wrong to think that other people matter less the further they are from you in space, so it is to think they matter less the further away from you they are in time. The value of their happiness, and the horror of their suffering, is undiminished.

Recognizing that people matter equally, wherever they are in time, is a crucial next step in the ongoing story of humanity's moral progress. Many of us recognize this equality to some extent already. We know it is wrong to make future generations worse off in order to secure lesser benefits for ourselves. And if asked, we would agree that people now don't objectively matter more than people in the future. But we assume that this leaves most of our priorities unaltered. For example, thinking that long-run effects of our choices quickly disappear; that they are so uncertain that the good cancels the bad; or that people in the future will be much better situated to help themselves.[25]

But the possibility of preventable existential risks in our lifetimes shows that there are issues where our actions can have sustained positive effects over the whole longterm future, and where we are the only generation in a position to produce those effects.[26] So the view that people in the future matter just as much as us has deep practical implications. We have a long way to go if we are to understand these and integrate them fully into our moral thinking.

45

Considerations like these suggest an ethic we might call *longtermism*, which is especially concerned with the impacts of our actions upon the longterm future.[27] It takes seriously the fact that our own generation is but one page in a much longer story, and that our most important role may be how we shape—or fail to shape—that story. Working to safeguard humanity's potential is one avenue for such a lasting impact and there may be others too.[28]

One doesn't have to approach existential risk from this direction—there is already a strong moral case just from the immediate effects—but a longtermist ethic is nevertheless especially well suited to grappling with existential risk. For longtermism is animated by a moral re-orientation toward the vast future that existential risks threaten to foreclose.

Of course, there are complexities.

When economists evaluate future benefits, they use a method called discounting, which dampens ("discounts") benefits based on how far away they are in time. If one took a commonly used discount rate of 5 percent per year and applied it to our future, there would be strikingly little value left. Applied naïvely, this discount rate would suggest our entire future is worth only about twenty times as much as the coming year, and that the period from 2100 to eternity is worth less than the coming year. Does this call into question the idea that our future is extremely valuable?

No. Results like this arise only from an incorrect application of the economic methods. When the subtleties of the problem are taken into account and discounting is correctly applied, the future is accorded an extremely high value. The mathematical details would take us too far afield, but for now it suffices to note that discounting human wellbeing (as opposed to instrumental goods such as money), purely on the basis of distance away from us in time, is deeply implausible—especially over the long time periods we are discussing. It implies, for example, that if you can save one person from a headache in a million years' time, or a billion people from torture in two million years, you should save the one from a headache.[29] A full explanation of why economic discounting does not trivialize the value of the longterm future can be found in Appendix A.

Some philosophers question the value of protecting our longterm future for quite a different reason. They note that the timing of the benefits is not the only unusual feature of this case. If we save humanity from extinction, that will change the number of people who will ever live. This brings up ethical issues that don't arise when simply saving the lives of existing people. Some of the more extreme approaches to this relatively new field of "population ethics" imply that there is no reason to avoid extinction stemming from considerations of future generations—it just doesn't matter whether these future people come into being or not.

A full treatment of these matters would take too long and be of interest only to a few, so I reserve the detailed discussion for Appendix B. To briefly summarize: I do not find these views very plausible, either. They struggle to capture our reasons to care about whether we make future lives worse by polluting the planet, or changing the climate, and to explain why we have strong reasons to prevent terrible lives from existing in the future. And all but the most implausible of these views agree with the immense importance of saving future generations from other kinds of existential catastrophe, such as the irrevocable collapse of civilization. Since most things that threaten extinction threaten such a collapse too, there is not much practical difference. That said, the issues are complex, and I encourage interested readers to consult the appendix for details.

There is one other objection I want to touch on. When I was younger, I sometimes took comfort in the idea that perhaps the outright destruction of humanity would not be bad at all. There would be no people to suffer or grieve. There would be no *badness* at those future times, so how could the destruction be bad? And if the existence of humanity was somehow essential to judgments of right and wrong, good and bad, then perhaps such concepts would fail to apply at all in the stillness that followed.

But I now see that this is no better than the old argument by the philosopher Epicurus that your death cannot be bad for you, since you are not there to experience it. What this neglects is that if I step out into the traffic and die, my life as a whole will be shorter and thereby worse: not by having more that is bad, but by containing less of everything that makes life good. That is why I shouldn't do it. While Epicurus's argument may provide consolation in times of grief or fear, it is not fit to be a guide for action, and no one treats it so. Imagine a government using it as the basis for our policies on safety or healthcare—or for our laws on murder.

If a catastrophe this century were to cause our extinction, then *humanity's* life would be shorter and thereby worse.[30] Given that we may just be in our infancy, it would be much shorter; much worse. Even if there were no one remaining to judge this as a tragedy, we can rightly judge it so from here. Just as we can judge events in other places, so we can judge events in other times.[31] And if these judgments are correct now, they shall remain correct when we are no more. I wouldn't blame people who, in humanity's final hours, found consolation in such Epicurean arguments. But the length and quality of humanity's life is still ours to decide, and we must own this responsibility.[32]

These are not the only possible objections. Yet we need not resolve every philosophical issue about the value of the future in order to decide whether humanity's potential is worth protecting. For the idea that it would be a matter of relative indifference whether humanity goes extinct, or whether we flourish for billions of years, is, on its face, profoundly implausible. In this sense, any theory that denies it should be subject to significant skepticism.[33]

What's more, the future is not the only moral lens through which to view existential catastrophe. It is the one that grips me most, and that most persuades me to devote my time and energy to this issue, but there are other lenses, drawing on other moral traditions. So let us briefly explore how concern about existential risk could also spring from considerations of our past, our character and our cosmic significance. And thus how people with many different understandings of morality could all end up at this common conclusion.

LOOKING TO OUR PAST

We are not the first generation. Our cultures, institutions and norms; our knowledge, technology and prosperity; these were gradually built up by our ancestors, over the course of ten thousand generations. In the last chapter we saw how humanity's remarkable success has relied on our capacity for intergenerational cooperation: inheriting from our parents, making some small improvements of our own, and passing it all down to our children. Without this cooperation we would have no houses or farms, we would have no traditions of dance or song, no writing, no nations.[34]

This idea was beautifully expressed by the conservative political theorist Edmund Burke. In 1790 he wrote of society:

> It is a partnership in all science; a partnership in all art; a partnership in every virtue, and in all perfection. As the ends of such a partnership cannot be obtained except in many generations, it becomes a partnership not only between those who are living, but between those who are living, those who are dead, and those who are to be born.[35]

This might give us reasons to safeguard humanity that are grounded in our past—obligations to our grandparents, as well as our grandchildren.

Our ancestors set in motion great projects for humanity that are too big for any single generation to achieve. Projects such as bringing an end to war, forging a just world and understanding our universe. In the year 65 CE, Seneca the Younger explicitly set out such a vast intergenerational project:

> The time will come when diligent research over long periods will bring to light things which now lie hidden. A single lifetime,

even though entirely devoted to the sky, would not be enough for the investigation of so vast a subject . . . And so this knowledge will be unfolded only through long successive ages. There will come a time when our descendants will be amazed that we did not know things that are so plain to them . . . Let us be satisfied with what we have found out, and let our descendants also contribute something to the truth . . . Many discoveries are reserved for ages still to come, when memory of us will have been effaced.[36]

It is astounding to be spoken to so directly across such a gulf of time, and to see this 2,000-year plan continue to unfold.[37]

A human, or an entire generation, cannot complete such grand projects. But humanity can. We work together, each generation making a little progress while building up the capacities, resources and institutions to empower future generations to take the next step.

Indeed, when I think of the unbroken chain of generations leading to our time and of everything they have built for us, I am humbled. I am overwhelmed with gratitude; shocked by the enormity of the inheritance and at the impossibility of returning even the smallest fraction of the favor. Because a hundred billion of the people to whom I owe everything are gone forever, and because what they created is so much larger than my life, than my entire generation.

The same is true at the personal level. In the months after my daughter was born, the magnitude of everything my parents did for me was fully revealed. I was shocked. I told them; thanked them; apologized for the impossibility of ever repaying them. And they smiled, telling me that this wasn't how it worked—that one doesn't repay one's parents. One passes it on.

My parents aren't philosophers. But their remarks suggest another way in which the past could ground our duties to the future. Because the arrow of time makes it so much easier to help people who come after you than people who come before, the best way of understanding the partnership of the generations may be asymmetrical, with duties all flowing forwards in time—paying it forwards. On this view, our duties to future generations may thus be grounded in the work our ancestors did for us when *we* were future generations.[38]

So if we drop the baton, succumbing to an existential catastrophe, we would fail our ancestors in a multitude of ways. We would fail to achieve the dreams they hoped for; we would betray the trust they placed in us, their heirs; and we would fail in any duty we had to pay forward the work they did for us. To neglect existential risk might thus be to wrong not only the people of the future, but the people of the past.

It would also be to risk the destruction of everything of value from the past we might have reason to preserve.[39] Some philosophers have suggested that the right way to respond to some valuable things is not to promote them, but to protect or preserve them; to cherish or revere them.[40] We often treat the value of cultural traditions in this way. We see indigenous languages and ways of life under threat—perhaps to be lost forever to this world—and we are filled with a desire to preserve them, and protect them from future threats.

Someone who saw the value of humanity in this light may not be so moved by the loss of what could have been. But they would still be horrified by extinction: the ruin of every cathedral and temple, the erasure of every poem in every tongue, the final and permanent destruction of every cultural tradition the Earth has known. In the face of serious threats of extinction, or of a permanent collapse of civilization, a tradition rooted in preserving or cherishing the richness of humanity would also cry out for action.[41]

Finally, we might have duties to the future arising from the flaws of the past. For we might be able to make up for some of our past wrongs. If we failed now, we could never fulfill any duties we might have to repair the damage we have done to the Earth's environment—cleaning up our pollution and waste; restoring the climate to its pre-industrial state; returning ecosystems to their vanished glory. Or consider that some of the greatest injustices have been inflicted not by individuals upon individuals, but by groups upon groups: systematic persecution, stolen lands, genocides. We may have duties to properly acknowledge and memorialize these wrongs; to confront the acts of our past. And there may yet be ways for the beneficiaries of these acts to partly remedy them or atone for them. Suffering an existential catastrophe would remove any last chance to do so.

CIVILIZATIONAL VIRTUES

If we play our cards right, humanity is at an early stage of life: still in our adolescence; looking forward to a remarkable adulthood. Like an adolescent, we are rapidly coming into our full power and are impatient to flex our muscles, to try out every new capability the moment we acquire it. We show little regard for our future. Sure, we sometimes talk about the "long term," but by this we usually mean the next decade or two. A long time for a human; a moment for humanity.

Like the adolescent, humanity has no need to plan out the details of the rest of its life. But it does need to make plans that bear in mind the duration and broad shape of that future. Otherwise we cannot hope to know which risks are worth taking, and which skills we need to develop to help us fulfill our potential.

Like many adolescents, humanity is impatient and imprudent; sometimes shockingly so. At times this stems from an inability to appropriately weigh our short-term gains against our longterm interests. More commonly, it is because we completely neglect our longterm future, not even considering it in our decision-making. And like the adolescent, we often stumble straight into risks without making any kind of conscious decision at all.

This analogy provides us with another lens through which to assess our behavior. Rather than looking at the morality of an individual human's actions as they bear on others, we can address the dispositions and character of humanity as a whole and how these help or undercut its own chances of flourishing. When we look at humanity itself as a group agent, comprising all of us over all time, we can gain insight into the systematic strengths or weaknesses in humanity's ability to achieve flourishing. These are virtues and vices at the largest scale—what we could call *civilizational virtues and vices*. One could treat these as having a fundamental moral significance, or simply as a useful way of diagnosing important weakness in our character and suggesting remedies.

Not all virtues need make sense on this level, but many do. Our lack of regard for risks to our entire future is a deficiency of prudence. When we put the interests of our current generation far above those of the generations to follow, we display our lack of patience.[42] When we recognize the importance of our future yet still fail to prioritize it, it is a failure of self-discipline. When a backward step makes us give up on our future—or assume it to be worthless—we show a lack of hope and perseverance, as well as a lack of responsibility for our own actions.[43]

In his celebrated account of virtue, Aristotle suggested that our virtues are governed and guided by a form of practical wisdom. This fits well with the idea of civilizational virtues too. For as our power continues to grow, our practical wisdom needs to grow with it.

COSMIC SIGNIFICANCE

Whether we are alone in the universe is one of the greatest remaining mysteries of science.[44] Eminent astronomers such as Martin Rees, Max Tegmark and Carl Sagan have reasoned that if we are alone, our survival and our actions might take on a cosmic significance.[45] While we are certainly smaller than the galaxies and stars, less spectacular than supernovae or black holes, we may yet be one of the most rare and precious parts of the cosmos.[46] The nature of such significance would depend on the ways in which we are unique.

If we are the only moral agents that will ever arise in our universe—the only beings capable of making choices on the grounds of what is right and wrong—then responsibility for the history of the universe is entirely *on us*. This is the only chance ever to shape the universe toward what is right, what is just, what is best for

THE PERSPECTIVE OF HUMANITY

Seeing our predicament from the perspective of humanity is a major theme of this book. Ethics is most commonly addressed from the individual perspective: what should *I* do? Occasionally, it is considered from the perspective of a group or nation, or even (more recently) from the global perspective of everyone alive today. Understanding what the group should do can help its members see the parts they need to play.

We shall sometimes take this a step further, exploring ethics from the perspective of humanity.[47] Not just our present generation, but humanity over deep time: reflecting on what we achieved in the last 10,000 generations and what we may be able to achieve in the eons to come.

This perspective allows us to see how our own time fits into the greater story, and how much is at stake. It changes the way we see the world and our role in it, shifting our attention from things that affect the fleeting present, to those that could make fundamental alterations to the shape of the longterm future. What matters most for humanity? And what part in this plan should our generation play? What part should I play?[48]

Of course, humanity is not an individual. But it is often useful for us to think about groups as agents, gaining insights by talking about the beliefs, desires and intentions of teams, companies or nations. Consider how often we speak of a company's strategy, a nation's interests, or even what a country is hoping to achieve with its latest gambit. Such mental states are usually less coherent than those of individuals, as there can be internal tensions between the individuals that comprise the group. But individuals too have their own ambivalence or inner inconsistency, and the idea of "group agents" has proved essential to anyone trying to understand the business world or international landscape.

Applying this perspective to humanity as a whole is increasingly useful and important. Humanity was splintered into isolated peoples for nearly the entire time since civilization began. Only recently have we found each other across the seas and started forming a single global civilization. Only recently have we discovered the length and shape of our long history, or the true potential of our future. And only recently have we faced significant threats that require global coordination.

We shouldn't always take this perspective. Many moral challenges operate at the personal level, or the level of smaller groups. And even when it comes to the big-picture questions, it is sometimes more important to focus on the ways in which humanity is divided: on our differing power or responsibility. But just as we've seen the value of occasionally adopting a global perspective, so too is it important to sometimes step further back and take the perspective of humanity.

The idea of civilizational virtues is just one example of explicitly adopting this perspective. In Chapter 7, we shall do so again, considering grand strategy for humanity. And even when we are looking at our own generation's responsibilities or what we each should do, this will be illuminated by the big picture of humanity across the eons.

all. If we fail, then the potential not just of humanity, but of all moral action, will have been irrevocably squandered.

Alternatively, if we are the only beings capable of wondering about the universe, then we might have additional reason to seek such understanding. For it would only be through us that a part of the universe could come to fully understand the laws that govern the whole.

And if Earth is the only place in the universe that will give rise to life, then all life on Earth would have a key significance. Earth would be the only place where there was so much complexity in each drop of water, the only place where anything lived and died, the only place where anything felt, or thought, or loved. And humanity would be the only form of life capable of stewarding life itself, protecting it from natural catastrophes and, eventually, taking it to flourish throughout the cosmos.

UNCERTAINTY

So we could understand the importance of existential risk in terms of our present, our future, our past, our character or our cosmic significance. I am most confident in the considerations grounded in the value of our present and our future, but the availability of other lenses shows the robustness of the case for concern: it doesn't rely on any single school of moral thought, but springs naturally from a great many. While each avenue may suggest a different strength and nature of concern, together they provide a wide base of support for the idea that avoiding existential catastrophe is of grave moral importance.

I'm sure many readers are convinced by this point, but a few will still harbor doubts. I have sympathy, because I too am not *completely* certain. This uncertainty comes in two parts. The first is the everyday kind of uncertainty: uncertainty about what will happen in the future. Might the evidence for humanity's vast potential be misleading? The second is moral uncertainty: uncertainty about the nature of our ethical commitments.[49] Might I be mistaken about the strength of our obligations to future generations?

However, the case for making existential risk a global priority does not require certainty, for the stakes aren't balanced. If we make serious investments to protect humanity when we had no real duty to do so, we would err, wasting resources we could have spent on other noble causes. But if we neglect our future when we had a real duty to protect it, we would do something far worse— failing forever in what could well be our most important duty. So long as we find the case for safeguarding our future quite plausible, it would be extremely reckless to neglect it.[50]

Even if someone were so pessimistic about the future as to think it negative in expectation—that the heights we might reach are more than matched by the depths to which we might sink— there is *still* good reason to protect our potential.[51] For one thing, some existential catastrophes (such as permanent global totalitar-ianism) would remain uncontroversially terrible and thus worthy of our attention. But there is a deeper reason too. In this case there would be immense value of information in finding out more about whether our future will be positive or negative. By far the best strategy would be to protect humanity until we have a much more informed position on this crucial question.[52]

And it is not just regarding the value of the future that our descendants will be better informed. At present we are still more generally inexperienced. We have little practice at the complex-ities of managing a global civilization, or a planet. Our view of the future is still clouded by ignorance and distorted by bias. But our descendants, if all goes well, will be far wiser than we are. They will have had time to understand much more deeply the nature of our condition; they will draw strength and insight from a more just, skillful and mature civilization; and their choices, in general, will reflect a fuller understanding of what is at stake when they choose. We in the present day, at what may be the very start of history, would therefore do well to be humble, to leave our options open, and to ensure our descendants have a chance to see more clearly, and choose more wisely, than we can today.[53]

OUR NEGLECT OF EXISTENTIAL RISKS

The world is just waking up to the importance of existential risk. We have begun work on evaluating and evading the most signifi-cant threats, but have yet to scale this up in proportion to the significance of the problems. Seen in the context of the overall dis-tribution of global resources, existential risk is sorely neglected.

Consider the possibility of engineered pandemics, which we shall soon see to be one of the largest risks facing humanity. The international body responsible for the continued prohib-ition of bioweapons (the Biological Weapons Convention) has an annual budget of just $1.4 million—less than the average McDonald's restaurant.[54] The entire spending on reducing existential risks from advanced artificial intelligence is in the tens of millions of dollars, compared with the billions spent on improving artificial intelligence capabilities.[55] While it is difficult to precisely measure global spending on existential risk, we can state with confidence that humanity spends more on ice cream every year than on ensuring that the technologies we develop do not destroy us.[56]

In scientific research, the story is similar. While substantial research is undertaken on the risk of smaller catastrophes, those that could destroy humanity's longterm potential are neglected. Since 1991 there have been only two published climate models on the effects of a full-scale nuclear war between the United States and Russia, even while hundreds of missiles remain minutes away from a possible launch.[57] There has been tremendous work on understanding climate change, but the worst-case scenarios—such as those involving more than six degrees of warming—have received comparatively little study and are mostly ignored in official reports and policy discussions.[58]

Given the reality and importance of existential risks, why don't they already receive the attention they need? Why are they systematically neglected? Answers can be found in the economics, politics, psychology and history of existential risk.

Economic theory tells us that existential risk will be undervalued by markets, nations and even entire generations. While markets do a great job of supplying many kinds of goods and services, there are some kinds that they systematically undersupply. Consider clean air. When air quality is improved, the benefit doesn't go to a particular individual, but is shared by everyone in the community. And when I benefit from cleaner air, that doesn't diminish the benefit you get from it. Things with these two properties are called *public goods* and markets have trouble supplying them.[59] We typically resolve this at a local or national level by having governments fund or regulate the provision of public goods.

Protection from existential risk is a public good: protection would benefit us all and my protection doesn't come at the expense of yours. So we'd expect existential risk to be neglected by the market. But worse, protection from existential risk is a *global public good*—one where the pool of beneficiaries spans the globe. This means that even nation states will neglect it.

I am writing this book in the United Kingdom. Its population of nearly 70 million ranks it as one of the more populous countries in the world, but it contains less than 1 percent of all the people alive today. If it acts alone on an existential risk, it bears the full cost of the policy, yet only reaps a hundredth of the benefit. In other words, even if it had a well-informed government acting in the longterm interests of its citizens, it would undervalue work on existential risk by a factor of 100. Similarly, Russia would undervalue it by a factor of 50, the United States by a factor of 20, and even China would undervalue it by a factor of five. Since such a large proportion of the benefits spill out to other countries, each nation is tempted to free-ride on the efforts of others, and some of the work that would benefit us all won't get done.

The same effect that causes this undersupply of protection causes an oversupply of risk. Since only 1 percent of the damages of existential catastrophe are borne by the people of the United Kingdom, their government is incentivized to neglect the downsides of risk-inducing policies by this same factor of 100. (The situation is even worse if individuals or small groups become able to pose existential risks.)

This means management of existential risk is best done at the global level. But the absence of effective global institutions for doing so makes it extremely difficult, slowing the world's reaction time and increasing the chance that hold-out countries derail the entire process.

And even if we could overcome these differences and bargain toward effective treaties and policies on existential risk, we would face a final problem. The beneficiaries are not merely global, but intergenerational—all the people who would ever live. Protection from existential risk is an *intergenerational global public good*. So even the entire population of the globe acting in concert could be expected to undervalue existential risks by a very large factor, leaving them greatly neglected.[60]

Additional reasons can be found in political science. The attention of politicians and civil servants is frequently focused on the short term.[61] Their timescales for thought and action are increasingly set by the election cycle and the news cycle. It is very difficult for them to turn their attention to issues where action is required now to avert a problem that won't strike for several election cycles. They are unlikely to get punished for letting it slide and many more urgent things are clamoring for attention.

One exception to this is when there is an active constituency pushing for the early action: their goodwill acts as a kind of immediate benefit. Such constituencies are most powerful when the benefits of the policy are concentrated among a small fraction of society, as this makes it worth their while to take political action. But in the case of existential risk, the benefits of protection are diffused across all citizens, leaving no key constituency to take ownership of the issue. This is a reason for neglect, albeit one that is surmountable. When citizens are empathetic and altruistic, identifying with the plight of others—as we have seen for the environment, animal rights and the abolition of slavery—they can be enlivened with the passion and determination needed to hold their leaders to account.

Another political reason concerns the sheer gravity of the issue. When I have raised the topic of existential risk with senior politicians and civil servants, I have encountered a common reaction: genuine deep concern paired with a feeling that addressing the greatest risks facing humanity was "above my pay grade," We look to our governments to manage issues that run beyond the scope of our individual lives, but this one runs beyond the scope of nations too. For political (as well as economic) reasons it feels like an issue for grand international action. But since the international institutions are so weak, it is left hanging.

Behavioral psychology has identified two more reasons why we neglect existential risk, rooted in the heuristics and biases we use as shortcuts for making decisions in a complex world.[62] The first of these is the *availability heuristic*. This is a tendency for people to estimate the likelihood of events based on their ability to recall examples. This stirs strong feelings about avoiding repeats of recent tragedies (especially those that are vivid or widely reported). But it means we often underweight events which are rare enough that they haven't occurred in our lifetimes, or which are without precedent. Even when experts estimate a significant probability for an unprecedented event, we have great difficulty believing it until we see it.

For many risks, the availability heuristic is a decent guide, allowing us to build up methods for managing the risk through trial and error. But with existential risks it fails completely. For by their very nature, we never have any experience of existential catastrophe before it is too late. If only seeing is believing, we will step blindly over the precipice.

Our need for vividness also governs our altruistic impulses. As a society, we are good at *acute* compassion for those in peril—for the victims of a disaster we can see in the news reports. We may not always act, but we certainly feel it. We sit up, our hearts in our throats: fearing for their safety, mourning for their loss. But what we require is a more expansive compassion; a more imaginative compassion; one that acts over the long term, recognizing the humanity of people in distant times as well as distant places.

We also suffer from a bias known as *scope neglect*. This is a lack of sensitivity to the scale of a benefit or harm. We have trouble caring ten times more about something when it is ten times as important. And once the stakes get to a certain point, our concern can saturate.[63] For example, we tend to treat nuclear war as an utter disaster, so we fail to distinguish nuclear wars between nations with a handful of nuclear weapons (in which millions would die) from a nuclear confrontation with thousands of nuclear weapons (in which a thousand times as many people would die, and our entire future may be destroyed). Since existential risk derives its key moral importance from the size of what is at stake, scope neglect leads us to seriously underweight its importance.

These reasons for the neglect of existential risk present a formidable challenge to it ever receiving due concern. And yet I am hopeful. Because there is a final reason: existential risk is very new. So there hasn't yet been time for us to incorporate it into our civic and moral traditions. But the signs are good that this could change.

Humans must have contemplated the end of humanity from the earliest times. When an isolated band or tribe died out during a time of extreme hardship, the last survivors will have sometimes wondered whether they were the last of their kind, or whether others like them lived on elsewhere. But there appears to have been very little careful thought about the possibility and import-ance of human extinction until very recently.[64]

It wasn't until the mid-twentieth century, with the creation of nuclear weapons, that human extinction moved from a remote possibility (or a certainty remote in time) to an imminent danger. Just three days after the devastation of Hiroshima, Bertrand Russell began writing his first essay on the implications for the future of humanity.[65] And not long after, many of the scientists who created these weapons formed the *Bulletin of the Atomic Scientists* to lead the conversation about how to prevent global destruction.[66] Albert Einstein soon became a leading voice and his final public act was to sign a Manifesto with Russell arguing against nuclear war on the explicit grounds that it could spell the end for humanity.[67] Cold War leaders, such as Eisenhower, Kennedy and Brezhnev, became aware of the possibility of extinc-tion and some of its implications.[68]

The early 1980s saw a new wave of thought, with Jonathan Schell, Carl Sagan and Derek Parfit making great progress in understanding what is at stake—all three realizing that the loss of uncounted future generations may overshadow the immediate consequences.[69] The discovery that atomic weapons may trigger a nuclear winter influenced both Ronald Reagan and Mikhail Gorbachev to reduce their country's arms and avoid war.[70]

And the public reacted too. In 1982, New York's Central Park saw a million people come together to march against nuclear weapons. It was the biggest protest in their nation's history.[71] Even in my birthplace of Australia, which has no nuclear weapons, we joined the global protest—my parents taking me with them on marches when I was just a small child they were fighting to protect.

In this way, existential risk was a highly influential idea of the twentieth century. But because there was one dominant risk, it all happened under the banner of nuclear war, with philosophers discussing the profound new issues raised by "nuclear ethics," rather than by "existential risk." And with the end of the Cold War, this risk diminished and the conversation faded. But this history shows that existential risk is capable of rousing major global concern, from the elite to the grass roots.

Modern thinking on existential risk can be traced through John Leslie, whose 1996 book *The End of the World* broadened the focus from nuclear war to human extinction in general. After reading Leslie's work, Nick Bostrom took this a step further: identifying and analyzing the broader class of existential risks that are the focus of this book.

Our moral and political traditions have been built over thousands of years. Their focus is thus mostly on timeless issues that have been with us throughout our history. It takes time to incorporate the new possibilities that our age opens up, even when those possibilities are of immense moral significance. Existential risk still seems new and strange, but I am hopeful that it will soon find its way into our common moral traditions. Environmentalism burst in upon the global political scene less than twenty years before I was born, and yet I was raised in a milieu where it was one of the main parts of our moral education; where the earlier disregard for the environment had become unthinkable to my generation. This can happen again.

One of my principal aims in writing this book is to end our neglect of existential risk—to establish the pivotal importance of safeguarding humanity, and to place this among the pantheon of causes to which the world devotes substantial attention and resources. Exactly how substantial remains an open question, but it clearly deserves far more focus than it has received so far. I suggest we start by spending more on protecting our future than we do on ice cream, and decide where to go from there.

63

We have now seen the broad sweep of human history, the size of humanity's potential, and why safeguarding our future is of the utmost importance. But so far, you have mostly had to take my word that we do face real risks. So let us turn our attention to these risks, examining the key scientific evidence behind them and sorting out which ones are most worthy of our concern. The next three chapters explore the natural risks we have faced throughout our history; the dawn of anthropogenic risks in the twentieth century; and the new risks we will face over the century to come.

PART TWO

THE RISKS

3

NATURAL RISKS

Who knows whether, when a comet shall approach this globe to destroy it, as it often has been and will be destroyed, men will not tear rocks from their foundations by means of steam, and hurl mountains, as the giants are said to have done, against the flaming mass?—and then we shall have traditions of Titans again, and of wars with Heaven.

—Lord Byron[1]

For all our increasing power over nature, humanity is still vulnerable to natural catastrophes. In this chapter, we consider not those from the newspapers—or even the history books—but catastrophes of a scale unprecedented during human civilization. We look at risks that threaten not regional collapse, or endurable hardship, but the final undoing of the human enterprise.

Such risks are real. But they have only been confirmed in recent decades and the scientific understanding is still rapidly developing. We shall look in depth at several of the major threats, seeing the most recent science on how they threaten us and how much existential risk they pose.

ASTEROIDS & COMETS

An asteroid, ten kilometers across, speeds toward the Earth. The chance of a direct collision is tiny—for millions of years it has swung through the Solar System, missing the Earth on every single pass. But given such deep time the chances compound, and this is the day.

It slams into the Earth's surface off the coast of Mexico at more than 60,000 kilometers an hour. A trillion tons of rock moving so fast it strikes with the energy of a hundred times its own weight in TNT. In just seconds, it releases the energy of ten billion Hiroshima blasts: 10,000 times the entire Cold War nuclear arsenal. It smashes a hole thirty kilometers deep into the Earth's crust—over sixty times the height of the Empire State Building; three times taller than Everest. Everything within 1,000 kilometers is killed by heat from the impact fireball. A tsunami devastates the Caribbean. Trillions of tons of rock and dust are thrown far up into the sky. Some of this superheated rock rains down over millions of square kilometers, burning the animals to death and igniting fires that spread the devastation still further. But much more deadly is the dust that stays aloft.[2]

A billowing cloud of dust and ash rises all the way to the upper atmosphere, blocking out the Sun's light. It is this that turns regional catastrophe to mass extinction. Slowly, it spreads across the entire world, engulfing it in darkness lasting years. With the darkness comes a severe global cooling, for the Sun's light is blocked by the dust and reflected off the haze of sulfate aerosols released when the sea floor was vaporized. The cold and the dark kills plants across the globe; animals starve or freeze; the hundred-million-year reign of the dinosaurs ends; three-quarters of all species on Earth are annihilated.[3]

Both asteroids and comets can cause such devastation. Asteroids are lumps of rock or metal, found mostly between the orbits of Mars and Jupiter. They range from about a thousand kilometers across down to just a few meters.[4] Comets are lumps of mixed rock and ice, with a slightly narrower range of sizes.[5] Unlike asteroids, many comets are in extreme elliptical orbits, spending most of their time amidst or beyond the outer planets, then periodically diving in through the inner Solar System. When they come close enough to the Sun, solar radiation strips off some of the comet's ice and dust, forming a shining tail. A fragment of an asteroid or comet that enters our atmosphere, burning with the heat of atmospheric friction, is called a meteor. A piece that survives, having fallen all the way to the Earth's surface, is known as a meteorite.

Our earliest ancestors must have seen comets blaze across the sky, but could only guess at their true nature. The ancient Greeks conjectured that they were atmospheric phenomena, like clouds or rainbows. Indian astronomers in the sixth century correctly surmised that they were far beyond the Earth—something that was not confirmed for 1,000 years, when Tycho Brahe proved that the comet of 1577 was beyond the Moon, since distant observers saw the comet at nearly the same position in the night sky, at the same time.

Meteorites had also been known since time immemorial, but it was not until the turn of the nineteenth century that scientists established their extra-terrestrial origin.[6] At the same time, astronomers began to detect asteroids in orbit around the Sun. Then in 1960 the American geologist Eugene Shoemaker definitively proved that some of the Earth's craters were produced not by geological activity, but by vast meteoric impacts, far beyond any in recorded history. The pieces were finally in place to see that Earth was vulnerable to catastrophic impacts from the heavens.

In 1980 a team of scientists led by father and son Luis and Walter Alvarez discovered that the geological boundary between the Cretaceous and Palaeogene periods was rich in iridium—an element that is extremely rare on the Earth's surface, but markedly more common in asteroids. It dawned on them that this could be the smoking gun to explain the end-Cretaceous mass extinction, the one that killed the dinosaurs. An asteroid big enough to release so much iridium would be ten kilometers across, and the darkness of the dust cloud that spread the iridium would be enough to suppress photosynthesis and precipitate the mass extinction.[7] The missing piece was the lack of any known crater of the right size and age.

Ten years later it was found. Sixty-six million years of geological activity had buried it under kilometers of newer rock, but gravitational measurements revealed its dense granite impact ring—a giant circle surrounding the small Mexican town of Chicxulub. Excavations confirmed the crater's age and provenance. Debate continued about whether it was enough to cause the extinction, with more and more evidence aligning, and a consensus gradually emerging. Especially important was the discovery of nuclear winter in the early 1980s, which showed that a high dark cloud like this could chill the Earth as well as darken it, and the growing evidence that the impact had vaporized the sulfur-containing rock in the seabed, releasing a vast amount of sulfate aerosols that would further darken and cool the Earth.[8]

As it became increasingly clear that the Earth was vulnerable to major asteroid and comet impacts, people began to take this threat seriously. First in works of science fiction, then science.[9] Alvarez's hypothesis that an asteroid caused the last great mass extinction inspired Shoemaker to convene a seminal meeting in 1981, founding the scientific field of impact hazards. The scientists developed an ambitious proposal for finding and tracking asteroids. And in light of the growing public interest in the impact threat, it began to acquire bipartisan support in the United States Congress.[10] In 1994 Congress issued NASA a directive: find and track 90 percent of all near-Earth Objects greater than one kilometer across.[11]

Most of the attention so far has been focused on asteroids, as they are more common, easier to track and easier to deflect.[12] Astronomers categorize them in terms of their size.[13] Those above ten kilometers across (the size of the one that killed the dinosaurs) threaten mass extinction. It is possible that humans would survive the cataclysm, but there is clearly a serious risk of our extinction. Last time *all* land-based vertebrates weighing more than five kilograms were killed.[14] Asteroids between one and ten kilometers across threaten global catastrophe and may also be large enough to pose an existential risk, either via directly causing our extinction or via an unrecoverable collapse of civilization. While an impact with an asteroid in this smaller size range would be much less likely to cause an existential catastrophe, this may be more than offset by their much higher probability of impact.

So many near-Earth asteroids have now been discovered and tracked that we have a good idea of the total number out there with orbits that come near the Earth. This tells us that the probability of an Earth-impact in an average century is about one in 6,000 for asteroids between one and ten kilometers in size, and about one in 1.5 million for those above ten kilometers.

But what about *our* century? By analyzing the exact trajectories of the known asteroids, astronomers can determine whether there is any real chance that they will hit the Earth within the next hundred years. At the time of writing, 95 percent of asteroids bigger than one kilometer have been found and none have an appreciable chance of collision with the Earth. So almost all the remaining risk is from the 5 percent we haven't yet tracked.[15] We have even better news with asteroids greater than ten kilometers, as astronomers are almost certain that they have found them all, and that they pose no immediate danger.[16] Taking this trajectory information into account, the probability of an Earth-impact in the next hundred years falls to about one in 120,000 for asteroids between one and ten kilometers, and about one in 150 million for those above ten kilometers.[17]

These probabilities are immensely reassuring. While there is still real risk, it has been studied in great detail and shown to be vanishingly low. It is a famous risk, but a small one. If humanity were to go extinct in the next century, it would almost certainly be from something other than an asteroid or comet impact.

Asteroid Size	Total	Found	Average Century	Next Century
1–10 km	~ 920	~ 95%	1 in 6,000	1 in 120,000
10 km +	~ 4	> 99%*	1 in 1.5 million	< 1 in 150 million

* Astronomers are confident that they have found all asteroids greater than 10 km across in at least 99% of the sky.

TABLE 3.1 Progress in tracking near-Earth asteroids of two different size categories. The final two columns show the long-run average probability of an impact per century and the probability of an impact in the next hundred years (which all comes from the undiscovered asteroids).[18]

While uncertainties remain, the overall story here is one of humanity having its act together. It was just 12 years from the first scientific realization of the risk of global catastrophe to the point where government started taking it seriously. And now, 28 years later, almost all the large asteroids have been tracked. There is international cooperation, with a United Nations–sanctioned organization and an international alliance of spaceguard programs.[19] The work is well managed and NASA funding has increased more than tenfold between 2010 and 2016.[20] In my view, no other existential risk is as well handled as that of asteroids and comets.

What are the next steps? Astronomers have succeeded so well in tracking asteroids that it may be time to switch some of their attention to comets.[21] While it is very hard to be sure, my best guess is that they pose about the same level of risk as that remaining from untracked asteroids.[22] With more work, it might be possible for astronomers to bring short-period comets into the risk framework they use for asteroids and to improve the detection and understanding of long-period comets.

And with such a good understanding of the chance of asteroid impacts, much of the remaining uncertainty about their existential risk lies in the chance that an impact would then spell the end of humanity—especially if the asteroid was in the one- to ten-kilometer range. So it would be valuable to develop models of the length and severity of impact winters, drawing on the latest climate and nuclear winter modeling.

DEFLECTING IMPACTS

What could we do if we actually found an asteroid on a collision course with Earth? Detection would have little value without some means of mitigation. In the worst case, we could prepare to weather the storm: using the warning time to stockpile food, build shelters and plan the best strategies for survival. But it would be vastly preferable to avoid the collision altogether.

Strategies for asteroid deflection can be based around destroying the asteroid, or changing its course. There are many technologies that might be able to perform either of these tasks, including nuclear explosions, kinetic impacts and ion beams.[23] We could use several methods simultaneously to decrease the chance of failure.

Deflection becomes much easier the further in advance the impact is detected. This is both because it provides more time to develop and deploy the deflecting system, and because it makes it easier to gradually change the asteroid's course. Unfortunately, it is not clear whether we would realistically have the capability to successfully deflect asteroids more than a few kilometers across—those that concern us most.[24]

There is active debate about whether more should be done to develop deflection methods ahead of time.[25] A key problem is that methods for deflecting asteroids *away* from Earth also make it possible to deflect asteroids *toward* Earth. This could occur by accident (e.g., while capturing asteroids for mining), or intentionally (e.g., in a war, or in a deliberate attempt to end civilization). Such a self-inflicted asteroid impact is extremely unlikely, yet may still be the bigger risk.[26] After all, the entire probability of collision from one-kilometer or greater asteroids currently stands at one in 120,000 this century—we would require extreme confidence to say that the additional risk due to human interference was smaller than that.

Asteroid deflection therefore provides an interesting case study in weighing probabilities based on long-run frequencies, against evidential probabilities that are assigned to wholly unprecedented events. Quite understandably, we often prefer to rely on the long-run frequency estimates in our decision-making. But here the evidential probability is plausibly much larger and so cannot be ignored. A willingness to think seriously about imprecise probabilities of unprecedented events is crucial to grappling with risks to humanity's future.

SUPERVOLCANIC ERUPTIONS

Humanity may face a greater threat from within the Earth than from without. The very largest volcanic eruptions—explosions that release more than 1,000 cubic kilometers of rock—have become known as supervolcanic eruptions.[27] Unlike more typical volcanoes, which have the shape of a cone towering above the Earth's surface, volcanoes on this scale tend to release so much magma that they collapse, leaving a vast crater-like depression known as a caldera.[28] One of the best known is the Yellowstone caldera, which last erupted 630,000 years ago.[29]

Supervolcanic eruptions are devastating events, far beyond anything in recorded history. Everything within 100 kilometers of the blast is buried in falling rock, incandescent with heat. Thick ash rains down over the entire continent. When the Indonesian volcano, Toba, erupted 74,000 years ago, it covered India in a blanket of ash a meter thick and traces were found as far away as Africa. But as with asteroids and comets, the truly existential threat comes from the darkened sky.

The dark volcanic dust and reflective sulfate aerosols unleashed by the Toba eruption caused a "volcanic winter," which is thought to have lowered global temperatures by several degrees for several years.[30] Even the much smaller eruption of Indonesia's Mount Tambora in 1815 (less than a hundredth the size) caused a global cooling of 1°C, with places as far away as the United States suffering crop failure and June snows in what became known as the "year without a summer."[31]

Experts on supervolcanic eruptions do not typically suggest that there is a direct threat of human extinction. While there was some early evidence that the Toba eruption may have nearly destroyed humanity 74,000 years ago, newer evidence has made this look increasingly unlikely.[32] Since Toba was the largest known eruption in the last 2 million years and we now have thousands of times the population spread over a much greater part of the Earth, we should assume extinction to be a very unlikely consequence.[33] The effects may be roughly comparable to those of the one- to ten-kilometer asteroids, with major global crop failures lasting for years on end. Since the world only has about six months of food reserves, there is a possibility that billions of people could starve and that civilization could suffer a global collapse. I think that even if civilization did collapse, it would be very likely to recover. But if it could not, that would constitute an existential catastrophe.

While geologists have identified the remnants of dozens of supereruptions, their frequency remains very uncertain. A recent review gave a central estimate of one per 20,000 years, with substantial uncertainty. For Toba-sized eruptions, the same analysis gives a central estimate of one in 80,000 years, but with even more uncertainty.[34]

What about for the next hundred years? When astronomers tracked more and more asteroids, they were able to determine that the next century would be safer than average. Unfortunately, volcanoes are much less predictable than asteroids. Despite knowing the locations of most of the volcanoes that have had supervolcanic eruptions in the past, it is extremely difficult to predict whether they are likely to erupt soon, and we should expect very little warning if they do.

There is very little known about how to prevent or delay an impending supereruption. NASA recently conducted a very preliminary investigation of the possibility of slowly draining heat from the Yellowstone caldera, but investigations like these are in their earliest stages, and any sort of interference with an active

Magnitude	Average Century	Next Century
8–9	~ 1 in 200	~ 1 in 200
9+ (e.g., Toba)	~ 1 in 800	~ 1 in 800

TABLE 3.2 The probability per century of a supervolcanic eruption. Note that there are good reasons to think that even the largest eruptions would be very unlikely to lead to extinction or unrecoverable collapse. The probability estimates are extremely rough, with the confidence interval for magnitude 8–9 eruptions ranging from 1 in 50 to 1 in 500 per century, and the confidence interval for magnitude 9+ ranging from 1 in 600 all the way to 1 in 60,000.

volcano—especially one with a history of supereruptions—would obviously require enormous caution.[35] For now, our best approach to the threat of supereruptions lies in preparing to mitigate the damage, through building up non-perishable food reserves or developing emergency food production techniques.

Compared to asteroids and comets, we are at an earlier stage of understanding and managing the risk. This risk may also be fundamentally harder to manage, due to the greater difficulties of prediction and prevention. And most importantly, the probability of a civilization-threatening catastrophe in the next century is estimated to be about 100 times that of asteroids and comets combined. So supervolcanic eruptions appear to be the greater risk, and in greater need of additional attention.

FLOODS OF LAVA

In the Earth's history, there have been volcanic events of even greater scale. About 250 million years ago, the Siberian Traps erupted. More than a *million* cubic kilometers of molten rock was released, pouring out of the Earth and covering an area the size of Europe in lava. Scientists have suggested that volcanic gases released during this time may have caused the end-Permian extinction—the biggest mass extinction in the Earth's history.[36]

This kind of eruption is known as a flood basalt event, after the type of rock released. They differ from the supervolcanic eruptions discussed here in two key ways.

They take place much more slowly, in a series of eruptions going on for thousands to millions of years. And most importantly, they are about a thousand times less frequent than explosive supereruptions, occurring once every twenty to thirty million years. While it seems very plausible that they could pose a direct threat of human extinction, it could at most be a one in 200,000 chance per century—higher than that posed by ten-kilometer asteroids, but much lower than some other risks we shall consider.

There are many promising next steps. At the most basic level, we need to find all the places where supervolcanic eruptions have occurred so far. We also need to improve our very rough estimates of how often supervolcanic eruptions happen—especially at the largest and most threatening scale. Much more research is needed on the climatic effects of supervolcanic eruptions to see which sizes might pose a real risk to humanity.[37] And I suspect there are many hard-won lessons in risk modeling and management that could be borrowed from the more established community around asteroid risk.

STELLAR EXPLOSIONS

In every star there is a continual battle between two forces. Gravity squeezes the star together, while pressure forces it apart. For most of a star's life, these forces are in balance, preventing it from collapsing to a point or dissipating into space.[38] But some stars reach a time where the pressure catastrophically fails to withstand the force of gravity and they collapse in upon themselves at relativistic speed.[39] They momentarily reach an incredibly high density, triggering a new wave of immense pressure that explodes the star in what is known as a supernova. For a brief time, this single star can outshine its entire galaxy. In seconds, it releases as much energy as our Sun will radiate over its ten-billion-year lifetime.

Supernovae were first recorded by ancient Chinese astronomers in 185 CE, when a bright new star suddenly blazed in their sky. But it wasn't until the 1930s that scientists began to understand them and the 1950s that they realized a nearby supernova would pose a threat to the Earth.[40]

Then in 1969 scientists discovered a new and distinctive type of stellar explosion. In the midst of the Cold War, the US launched a number of spy satellites, in order to detect secret nuclear tests via their characteristic flash of gamma rays. The satellites began to detect short bursts of gamma rays, but with a completely different signature from nuclear weapons. Astronomers determined that they couldn't be coming from the Earth—or even the Milky Way—but must be arriving from extremely distant galaxies, billions of light years away.[41] The mystery of what could cause such "gamma ray bursts" is still being resolved. The leading theory is that longer bursts are produced in a rare type of supernova and shorter ones are produced when two neutron stars collide. The total energy released in each burst is similar to that of a supernova, but concentrated in two narrow cones pointed in opposite directions, allowing them to be detected at immense distances.[42] For example, in March 2008 light from a gamma ray burst in a galaxy 10 billion light years away reached Earth, and it was still bright enough to be visible to the naked eye.[43]

A supernova or gamma ray burst close to our Solar System could have catastrophic effects. While the gamma rays and cosmic rays themselves won't reach the Earth's surface, the reactions they trigger in our atmosphere may pose a threat. The most important is probably the production of nitrogen oxides that would alter the Earth's climate and dramatically erode the ozone layer. This last effect is thought to be the most deadly, leaving us much more exposed to UV radiation for a period of years.[44]

Astronomers have estimated the chance of these events happening close enough to Earth to cause a global catastrophe, generally defining this as a global ozone depletion of 30 percent or more. (I suspect this would be less of a threat to civilization than the corresponding thresholds for asteroids, comets and supervolcanic eruptions.) In an average century, the chance of such an event is about one in 5 million for supernovae and one in 2.5 million for gamma ray bursts. As with asteroids, we can get a more accurate estimate for the *next* 100 years, by searching the skies for imminent threats. This is harder for gamma ray bursts as they are more poorly understood and can strike from much further away. We have not found any likely candidates of either type, but have not yet completely ruled them out either, leading to a modest reduction in risk for the next century compared to average.[45]

Type	Average Century	Next Century
Supernovae	~ 1 in 5 million	< 1 in 50 million
Gamma Ray Bursts	~ 1 in 2.5 million	< 1 in 2.5 million

TABLE 3.3 The probability per century of a stellar explosion causing a catastrophe on Earth that depletes ozone by more than 30%.[46]

These probabilities are very small—they look to be at least 20 times smaller than those of similarly sized catastrophes from asteroids and comets and at least 3,000 times smaller than those from supervolcanic eruptions. Still, we would want to remove some of the remaining uncertainties around these numbers before we could set this risk aside. We need more research to determine the threshold above which stellar explosions could lead to extinction. And we should start cataloging potential supernova candidates within 100 light years, determining how confident we can be that none will explode in the next century. More broadly, we should improve our models of these risks and their remaining uncertainties, trying to bring our level of understanding into line with asteroids and comets.[47]

OTHER NATURAL RISKS

There is no shortage of potential catastrophes. Even restricting our attention to natural risks with significant scientific support, there are many more than I can address in detail. But none of them keep me awake at night.

Some threats pose real risks in the long run, but no risk over the next thousand years. Foremost among these is the eventual brightening of our Sun, which will pose a very high risk of extinction, but only starting in around a billion years.[48] A return to a glacial period (an "ice age") would cause significant difficulties for humanity, but is effectively ruled out over the next thousand years.[49] Evolutionary scenarios such as humanity degrading or transforming into a new species also pose no threat over the next thousand years.

Some threats are known to be vanishingly unlikely. For example, the passage of a star through our Solar System could disrupt planetary orbits, causing the Earth to freeze or boil or even crash into another planet. But this has only a one in 100,000 chance over the next 2 billion years.[50] This could also happen due to chaotic instabilities in orbital dynamics, but again this is exceptionally unlikely. Some physical theories suggest that the vacuum of space itself may be unstable, and could "collapse" to form a true vacuum. This would spread out at the speed of light, destroying all life in its wake. However, the chance of this happening cannot be higher than one in 10 million per century and is generally thought to be much lower.[51]

Some threats are not existential—they offer no plausible pathway to our extinction or permanent collapse. This is true for the threat of many local or regional catastrophes such as hurricanes or tsunamis. It is also true for some threats that are global in scale. For example, the Earth's entire magnetic field can shift dramatically, and sometimes reverses its direction entirely. These shifts leave us more exposed to cosmic rays during the time it takes to reorient.[52] However, this happens often enough that we can tell it isn't an extinction risk (it has happened about 20 times in the 5 million years since humans and chimpanzees diverged). And since the only well-studied effect appears to be somewhat increased cancer rates, it is not a risk of civilization collapse either.[53]

Finally, some threats are natural in origin, but have effects that are greatly exacerbated by human activity. They thus fall somewhere between natural and anthropogenic. This includes "naturally arising" pandemics. For reasons that will soon become clear, I don't count these among the natural risks, and shall instead address them in Chapter 5.

THE TOTAL NATURAL RISK

It is striking how recently many of these risks were discovered. Magnetic field reversal was discovered in 1906. Proof that Earth had been hit by a large asteroid or comet first emerged in 1960. And we had no idea gamma ray bursts even existed until 1969. For almost our entire history we have been subject to risks to which we were completely oblivious.

And there is no reason to think that the flurry of discovery has finished—that we are the first generation to have discovered all the natural risks we face. Indeed, it would surely be premature to conclude that we have discovered all of the possible mechanisms of natural extinction while major mass-extinction events remain unexplained.

The likely incompleteness of our knowledge is a major problem for any attempt to understand the scale of natural risk by cataloging known threats. Even if we studied all the natural threats listed in this chapter so completely that we understood their every detail, we could not be sure that we were capturing even a small part of the true risk landscape.

Luckily, there is a way out—a way of directly estimating the total natural risk. We achieve this not by considering the details of asteroid craters or collapsing stars, but by studying the remains of the species they threatened. The fossil record is our richest source of information about how long species like us survived, and so about the total extinction risk they faced.[54] We will explore three ways of using the fossil record to place upper bounds on the natural extinction risk we face, all of which yield comforting results.[55] However, as this method only applies directly to *extinction* risk, some uncertainty around unrecoverable collapse will remain.[56]

How high could natural extinction risk be? Imagine if it were as high as 1 percent per century. How long would humanity survive? Just 100 centuries, on average. But we know from the fossil record that *Homo sapiens* has actually lived for about 2,000 centuries.[57] At 1 percent risk per century, it would be nearly impossible to last that long: there would be a 99.9999998 percent chance of going extinct before that. So we can safely rule out a total risk of 1 percent or greater. Just how much risk could

81

there realistically have been? We can use the longevity of *Homo sapiens* to form both a best-guess estimate and an upper bound for this risk.

It is surprisingly difficult to form a single best guess of the risk. We might be tempted to say one in 2,000, but that would be the best guess if we had seen 2,000 centuries of humanity with *one* extinction. In fact we have seen zero extinctions, so our best guess of the risk should be lower. But it can't be zero in 2,000 either, since this would mean that extinction is impossible, and that we could be justifiably certain it isn't going to happen.[58] There is an interesting ongoing debate among statisticians about what probability to assign in such cases.[59] But all suggested methods produce numbers between zero in 2,000 and one in 2,000 (i.e., 0 to 0.05 percent). So we can treat this range as a rough estimate.

We can also use our survival so far to make an upper bound for the total natural extinction risk. For example, if the risk were above 0.34 percent per century there would have been a 99.9 percent chance of going extinct before now.[60] We thus say that risk above 0.34 percent per century is ruled out at the 99.9 percent confidence level—a conclusion that is highly significant by the usual scientific standards (equivalent to a p-value of 0.001).[61] So our 2,000 centuries of *Homo sapiens* suggests a "best-guess" risk estimate between 0 percent and 0.05 percent, with an upper bound of 0.34 percent.

But what if *Homo sapiens* is not the relevant category? We are interested in the survival of *humanity*, and we may well see this as something broader than our species. For instance, Neanderthals were very similar to *Homo sapiens* and while the extent of interbreeding between the two is still debated, it is possible that they are best considered as a subspecies. They walked upright, made advanced tools, had complex social groupings, looked similar to *Homo sapiens*, and may even have used language. If we include them in our understanding of humanity, then we could extend our lifespan to when Neanderthals and *Homo sapiens* last had a common ancestor,

Category	Years	Best Guess	99.9% Confidence Bound
Homo sapiens	200,000	0–0.05%	< 0.34%
Neanderthal split	500,000	0–0.02%	< 0.14%
Homo	2,000,000–3,000,000	0–0.003%	< 0.023%

TABLE 3.4 Estimates and bounds of total natural extinction risk per century based on how long humanity has survived so far, using three different conceptions of humanity.

around 500,000 years ago.[62] Another natural approach would be to use not our species, but our genus, *Homo*. It has been in existence for more than 2 million years. If used with the methods above, these dates would imply lower probabilities of extinction per century.

A second technique for estimating the total natural extinction risk from the fossil record is to look not at humanity itself, but at species like us. This greatly expands the available evidence. And because it includes examples of species actually going extinct, it eliminates the issues with zero-failure data. The downsides are that the other species may be less representative of the risks humanity faces and that there is room for potential bias in the choice of species to study.

A simple version of this technique is to look at the most similar species. Our genus, *Homo*, contains four other species with reasonable estimates of longevity.[63] They have survived between 200,000 and 1,700,000 years. If we bear a relevantly similar risk of extinction from natural catastrophes to any of these, we are looking at per century risk in the range of 0.006 to 0.05 percent.[64]

Alternatively we could cast a much wider net, achieving more statistical robustness at the expense of similarity to ourselves. The typical longevity of mammalian species has been estimated at around 1 million years, while species in the entire fossil record average 1 to 10 million years. These suggest a risk in the range of

0.001 to 0.01 percent per century—or lower if we think we are more robust than a typical species (see Table 3.5).

Note that all these estimates of species lifespans include other causes of extinction in addition to catastrophes, for example being slowly outcompeted by a new species that branches off from one's own. So they will somewhat overestimate the risk of *catastrophic* extinction.[65]

SURVIVORSHIP BIAS

There is a special difficulty that comes with investigating the likelihood of an event which would have prevented that very investigation. No matter how likely it was, we cannot help but find that the event didn't occur. This comes up when we look at the extinction history of *Homo sapiens*, and it has the potential to bias our estimates.[66]

Imagine if there were a hundred planets just like our own. Whether humanity quickly went extinct on ninety-nine of them, or on zero of them, humans investigating their own planet would always find that human extinction hadn't happened—otherwise they wouldn't be around to investigate. So they couldn't use the mere fact that they survived to estimate the fraction of planets where humans survive. This makes us realize that we too can't deduce much about our future survival just from the fact that we have survived so far.

However, we *can* make use of the length of time we have survived (as we do in this chapter), since there is more than one value that could be observed and we are less likely to see long lifespans in worlds with high risk. But a full accounting for this form of survivorship bias may still modify these risk estimates.[67]

Fortunately, estimating risk by analyzing the survival of other species is more robust to these effects and, reassuringly, it provides similar answers.

Species	Years	Best Guess
Homo neanderthalensis	200,000	0.05%
Homo heidelbergensis	400,000	0.025%
Homo habilis	600,000	0.02%
Homo erectus	1,700,000	0.006%
Mammals	1,000,000	0.01%
All species	1,000,000–10,000,000	0.01–0.001%

TABLE 3.5 Estimates of total natural extinction risk per century based on the survival time of related species.

A final technique for estimating the total natural extinction risk is to consider that we are so populous, so widely spread across the globe, so competent at living in highly diverse environments, and so capable of defending ourselves that we might be able to resist all natural catastrophes short of those that cause mass extinctions. If so, we could look at the mass extinction record to determine the frequency of such events.

The detailed fossil record starts 540 million years ago with the "Cambrian explosion": a rapid diversification of complex life into most of the major categories we see today. Since then there have been a number of mass extinctions—catastrophic times when a great variety of species from across the globe went extinct. Foremost among these are the "Big Five," which each caused the extinction of at least 75 percent of all species (see Table 3.6). The catastrophe that ended the reign of the dinosaurs was the most recent of these. If these are representative of the level of natural catastrophe needed to cause our extinction, then we have had five events in 540 million years: a natural extinction rate of about one in a million (0.0001 percent) per century.

All three of these techniques based on the fossil record are at their best when applied to threats that would pose a similar extinction risk to modern humans as they did to the creatures from whose death or survival we seek to gain evidence, such as early humans, other species throughout history, and the victims of mass extinctions. Clearly this is not always the case. For

85

Mass Extinction	Date	Species Lost
Late Ordovician	443 Ma	86%
Late Devonian	359 Ma	75%
End-Permian	252 Ma	96%
End-Triassic	201 Ma	80%
End-Cretaceous	66 Ma	76%

TABLE 3.6 The proportion of species that went extinct in each of the Big Five extinction events (Ma = millions of years ago).[68]

many natural risks, we have become more robust. For example, our global presence allows us to survive mere regional disasters, and we possess unprecedented capacities to respond to global disasters as well. This means that the true risk is likely to be below these estimates, and that even the "best-guess" estimates should be thought of as conservative bounds on the total natural risk.

The bigger issue is risks that are substantially greater for humans now than they were for early humans or related species. This includes all the anthropogenic risks (which is precisely why this section has only targeted natural risks). It may also include some risks that are often considered natural.[69]

Chief among these is the risk of pandemics. While we don't typically think of an outbreak of disease as anthropogenic, the social and technological changes since the Agricultural Revolution have dramatically increased its likelihood and impact. Farming has increased the chance of infections from animals; improved transportation has made it easier to spread to many subpopulations in a short time; and increased trade has seen us utilize this transportation very frequently.

While there are also many factors that mitigate these effects (such as modern medicine, quarantine and disease surveillance), there remains a very plausible case that the pandemic risk to humans in the coming centuries is significantly larger than in early humans or other species used to construct the bounds on natural risks. For these reasons, it is best not to count pandemics as a natural risk, and we shall address them later.

We have explored three different ways of using the fossil record to estimate or bound the total natural extinction risk for humanity. While we shouldn't put too much weight on any one of these estimates, we can trust the broad range of results. The best-guess estimates ranged from 0.0001 to 0.05 percent per century. And even the most conservative of the upper bounds was less than 0.4 percent. Moreover, we know that these numbers are likely to be overestimates because they cover non-catastrophic extinction, such as the gradual evolution into a new species, and because modern humanity is more resilient than earlier humans or other species. This means we can be very confident that the total natural extinction risk is lower than 0.5 percent, with our best guess somewhere below 0.05 percent.

When we consider the entire future that is at stake, even an individual natural risk such as that posed by asteroids is extremely important. However, we will soon see that the natural risks are dwarfed by those of our own creation. By my estimate, we face about a thousand times more anthropogenic risk over the next century than natural risk, so it is the anthropogenic risks that will be our main focus.

4

ANTHROPOGENIC RISKS

The human race's prospects of survival were considerably
better when we were defenceless against tigers than they are
today, when we have become defenceless against ourselves.
                                                    —Arnold Toynbee[1]

The 2,000-century track record of human existence allows us
to tightly bound the existential risk from natural events. These
risks are real, though very unlikely to strike over the next
hundred years.

But there is no such track record for the powerful industrial
technologies that are also thought to pose existential risks. The
260 years we have survived since the Industrial Revolution, or
the seventy-five years since the invention of nuclear weapons, are
compatible with risks as high as 50 percent or as low as 0 percent
over the coming hundred years. So what evidence do we have
regarding these technological risks?

In this chapter, we'll explore the science behind the current
anthropogenic risks arising from nuclear weapons, climate
change and other environmental degradation. (Risks from future
technologies, including engineered pandemics, will be covered
in the following chapter.) Our focus will be on the worst-case
scenarios—in particular, whether there is a solid scientific case
that they could cause human extinction or the unrecoverable
collapse of civilization.

NUCLEAR WEAPONS

When we think of the existential risk posed by nuclear weapons, our first thoughts are of the destruction wrought by a full-scale nuclear war. But long before the Cold War, before even Hiroshima and Nagasaki, scientists worried that a single nuclear explosion might spell the destruction of humanity.

In the summer of 1942, the American physicist Robert Oppenheimer held a series of secret meetings in his office at the University of California in Berkeley, bringing together many of his field's leading thinkers. They were attempting to design the first atomic bomb. This was based on the recent discovery of nuclear fission: splitting a large atomic nucleus such as uranium into smaller fragments and releasing its nuclear energy.

On the second day, Edward Teller—who would go on to develop the hydrogen bomb ten years later—gave his first presentation on the idea of such a bomb. He noted that an atomic explosion would create a temperature exceeding that of the center of the Sun (15,000,000°C). It is this scorching temperature that allows the Sun to burn: it forces hydrogen nuclei together, producing helium and extreme quantities of energy. This is known as *fusion* (or a thermonuclear reaction), and is even more efficient than fission.[2] If an atomic bomb could be surrounded with a fuel such as hydrogen, its fission reaction might be able to trigger such a fusion reaction.

While attempting to design such a bomb, Teller had noticed that if it were possible for an atomic bomb to ignite such a fusion reaction in its fuel, it might also be possible for it to ignite a fusion reaction in the world around. It might be able to ignite the hydrogen in water, setting off a self-sustaining reaction that burned off the Earth's oceans. Or a reaction might be possible in the nitrogen that makes up seven-tenths of our air, igniting the atmosphere and engulfing the Earth in flame. If so, it would destroy not just humanity, but perhaps all complex life on Earth.

When he told the assembled scientists, a heated discussion broke out. Hans Bethe, the brilliant physicist who just four years earlier had discovered how fusion powers the stars, was extremely skeptical and immediately attempted to refute Teller's assumptions. But Oppenheimer, who would lead the development of the bomb, was deeply concerned. While the others continued their calculations, he raced off across the country to personally inform his superior, Arthur Compton, that their project may pose a threat to humanity itself. In his memoir, Compton recalled the meeting:

> Was there really any chance that an atomic bomb would trigger the explosion of the nitrogen in the atmosphere or of the hydrogen in the ocean? This would be the ultimate catastrophe. Better to accept the slavery of the Nazis than to run a chance of drawing the final curtain on mankind!
>
> Oppenheimer's team must go ahead with their calculations. Unless they came up with a firm and reliable conclusion that our atomic bombs could not explode the air or the sea, these bombs must never be made.[3]

(After the war, it would be revealed that their counterparts in Germany had also discovered this threat and the possibility had been escalated all the way up to Hitler—who went on to make dark jokes about the possibility.[4])

Oppenheimer returned to Berkeley, finding that Bethe had already discovered major weaknesses in Teller's calculations.[5] While they couldn't prove it was safe to all the physicists' satisfaction, they eventually decided to move on to other topics. Later, Oppenheimer commissioned a secret scientific report into the possibility of igniting the atmosphere.[6] It supported Bethe's conclusions that this didn't seem possible, but could not prove its impossibility nor put a probability on it.[7] Despite the report concluding that "the complexity of the argument and the absence of satisfactory experimental foundation makes further work on the subject highly desirable," it was taken by the leadership at Los Alamos to be the final word on the matter.

But concerns lingered among the physicists all the way through to the day of the Trinity test, when the first atomic bomb would be detonated.[8] Enrico Fermi, the Nobel prize–winning physicist who was also present at the Berkeley meeting, remained concerned that deficiencies in their approximations or assumptions might have masked a true danger. He and Teller kept rechecking the analysis, right up until the day of the test.[9] James Conant, President of Harvard University, took the possibility seriously enough that when the flash at detonation was so much longer and brighter than he expected, he was overcome with dread: "My instantaneous reaction was that something had gone wrong and that the thermal nuclear transformation of the atmosphere, once discussed as a possibility and jokingly referred to a few minutes earlier, had actually occurred."[10]

The atmosphere did not ignite. Not then, nor in any nuclear test since. Physicists with a greater understanding of nuclear fusion and with computers to aid their calculations have confirmed that it is indeed impossible.[11] And yet, there *had* been a kind of risk. The bomb's designers didn't know whether or not igniting the atmosphere was physically possible, so at that stage it was still epistemically possible. While it turned out that there was no objective risk, there was a serious subjective risk that their bomb might destroy humanity.

This was a new kind of dilemma for modern science. Suddenly, we were unleashing so much energy that we were creating temperatures unprecedented in Earth's entire history. Our destructive potential had grown so high that for the first time the question of whether we might destroy all of humanity needed to be asked—and answered. So I date the beginning of the Precipice (our age of heightened risk) to 11:29 a.m. (UTC) on July 16, 1945: the precise moment of the Trinity test.

Did humanity pass its own test? Did we successfully manage this first existential risk of our own making? Perhaps. I am genuinely impressed by Oppenheimer's urgency and Compton's stirring words. But I'm not convinced that the process they initiated was sufficient.

Bethe's calculations and the secret report were good, and were scrutinized by some of the world's best physicists. But the wartime secrecy meant that the report was never subject to the external peer review of a disinterested party, in the way that we consider essential for ensuring good science.[12]

And while some of the best minds in the world were devoted to the physics problems involved, the same cannot be said for the wider problems of how to handle the risk, who to inform, what level of risk would be acceptable and so forth.[13] It is not clear whether even a single elected representative was told about the potential risk.[14] The scientists and military appear to have assumed full responsibility for an act that threatened all life on Earth. Was this a responsibility that was theirs to assume?

Given the weak conclusions of the report, the inability to get external review, and the continuing concerns of eminent scientists, there was a strong case for simply delaying, or abandoning, the test. Back at the time of the Berkeley meeting, many of the scientists were deeply afraid that Hitler might get there first and hold the world to nuclear ransom. But by the time of the Trinity test, Hitler was dead and Europe liberated. Japan was in retreat and there was no concern about losing the war. The risk was taken for the same reasons that the bombs would be dropped in Japan a month later: to shorten the war, to avoid loss of life in an invasion, to achieve more favorable surrender terms, and to warn the Soviet Union about America's new-found might. These are not strong reasons for unilaterally risking the future of humanity.

Just how much risk did they take? It is difficult to be precise, without knowing how they were weighing the evidence available to them at the time.[15] Given that they got the answer right, hindsight tempts us to consider that result inevitable. But the Berkeley meeting provided something of a natural experiment, for during that summer they tackled two major questions on thermonuclear ignition. After they moved on from the question of atmospheric ignition, they began to calculate what kind of fuel *would* allow a thermonuclear explosion. They settled on a fuel based on an isotope of lithium: lithium-6.[16] But natural lithium contained too little of this isotope for the explosion to work, so they concluded that the mostly inert lithium-7 would need to be removed at great expense.

In 1954 the United States tested exactly such a bomb, code-named Castle Bravo. Due to time constraints, they had only enriched the lithium-6 concentration up to 40 percent, so most was still lithium-7. When the bomb exploded, it released far more energy than anticipated. Instead of six megatons they got 15—a thousand times the energy of the Hiroshima bomb, and the biggest explosion America would ever produce.[17] It was also one of the world's largest radiological disasters, irradiating a Japanese fishing boat and several populated islands downwind.[18] It turned out that the Berkeley group (and subsequent Los Alamos physicists) were wrong about lithium-7. At the unprecedented temperatures in the explosion, it reacted in an unexpected way, making just as great a contribution as lithium-6.[19]

Of the two major thermonuclear calculations made that summer in Berkeley, they got one right and one wrong. It would be a mistake to conclude from this that the subjective risk of igniting the atmosphere was as high as 50 percent.[20] But it was certainly not a level of reliability on which to risk our future.

Fifteen days after dropping the atomic bombs on Japan, America began planning for nuclear war with the Soviets.[21] They drew up maps of the Soviet Union with vast circles showing the range of their bombers to determine which cities they could already destroy and which would require new air bases or technological improvements. So began the planning for large-scale nuclear war, which has continued through the last 75 years.

This period was marked by numerous changes to the strategic landscape of nuclear war. Most of these stemmed from techno-logical changes such as the Soviets' rapid development of their own nuclear weapons; the creation of thermonuclear weapons vastly more powerful than the bombs used against Japan; inter-continental ballistic missiles (ICBMs) that could hit cities in the enemy heartland with just half an hour of warning; submarine-launched missiles that could not be taken out in a first strike, allowing guaranteed nuclear retaliation; and a massive increase in the total number of nuclear warheads.[22] Then there were major political changes such as the formation of NATO and the eventual fall of the Soviet Union. The Cold War thus saw a haphazard progression from one strategic situation to another, some favoring first strikes, some favoring retaliation, some high risk, some low.

While we made it through this period without nuclear war breaking out, there were many moments where we came much closer than was known at the time (see the box "Close Calls"). Most of these were due to human or technical error in the rapid-response systems for detecting an incoming nuclear strike and retaliating within the very short time-window allowed. These were more frequent during times of heightened military tension, but continued beyond the end of the Cold War. The systems were designed to minimize false negatives (failures to respond), but produced a lot of false alerts. This holds lessons not just for nuclear risk, but for risk from other complex technologies too— even when the stakes are known to be the end of one's entire nation (or worse), it is extremely hard to iron out all the human and technical problems.

If a full-scale nuclear war did break out, what would happen? In particular, would it really threaten extinction or the permanent collapse of civilization?

While one often hears the claim that we have enough nuclear weapons to destroy the world many times over, this is loose talk. It appears to be based on a naïve scaling-up of the Hiroshima fatalities in line with the world's growing nuclear arsenal, then comparing this to the world's population.[23] But the truth is much more complex and uncertain.

Nuclear war has both local and global effects. The local effects include the explosions themselves and the resulting fires. These would devastate the detonation sites and would kill tens or even hundreds of millions of people.[24] But these direct effects could not cause extinction since they would be limited to large cities, towns and military targets within the belligerent countries. The threat to humanity itself comes instead from the global effects.

CLOSE CALLS

The last seventy years have seen many close calls, where the hair-trigger alert of US and Soviet nuclear forces brought us far too close to the brink of accidental nuclear war.[25] Here are three of the closest.[26] (See Appendix C for a further close call and a list of nuclear weapons accidents.)

Training Tape Incident: November 9, 1979

At 3 a.m. a large number of incoming missiles—a full-scale Soviet first strike—appeared on the screens at four US command centers. The US had only minutes to determine a response before the bulk of their own missiles would be destroyed. Senior commanders initiated a threat assessment conference, placing their ICBMs on high alert, preparing nuclear bombers for take-off, and scrambling fighter planes to intercept incoming bombers.

But when they checked the raw data from the early-warning systems, there were no signs of any missiles, and they realized it was a false alarm. The screens had been showing a realistic simulation of a Soviet attack from a military exercise that had mistakenly been sent to the live computer system. When Soviet Premier Brezhnev found out, he asked President Carter "What kind of mechanism is it which allows a possibility of such incidents?"[27]

Autumn Equinox Incident: September 26, 1983

Shortly after midnight, in a period of heightened tensions, the screens at the command bunker for the Soviet satellite-based early-warning system showed five ICBMs launching from the United States.[28] The duty officer, Stanislav Petrov, had instructions to report any detected launch to his superiors, who had a policy of immediate nuclear retaliatory strike. For five tense minutes he considered the case, then despite his remaining uncertainty, reported it to his commanders as a false alarm.

He reasoned that a US first strike with just the five missiles shown was too unlikely and noted that the missiles' vapor trails could not be identified. The false alarm turned out to be caused by sunlight glinting off clouds, which looked to the Soviet satellite system like the flashes of launching rockets.

It is often said that Petrov "saved the world" that night. This is an something of exaggeration, as there may well have been several more steps at which nuclear retaliation could have been called off (indeed the two other incidents described here got further through the launch-on-warning process). But it was undeniably a close call: for if the satellite malfunction had reported the glinting sunlight as a hundred missiles instead of five, that may have been enough to trigger a nuclear response.[29]

Norwegian Rocket Incident: January 25, 1995

Even after the Cold War, the US and Russian missile systems have remained on hair-trigger alert. In 1995, Russian radar detected the launch of a single nuclear missile aimed at Russia, perhaps with the intention of blinding Russian radar with an electromagnetic pulse to hide a larger follow-up strike. The warning was quickly escalated all the way up the chain of command, leading President Yeltsin to open the Russian nuclear briefcase and consider whether to authorize nuclear retaliation.

But satellite systems showed no missiles and the radar soon determined that the apparent missile would land outside Russia. The alert ended; Yeltsin closed the briefcase. The false alarm had been caused by the launch of a Norwegian scientific rocket to study the northern lights. Russia had been notified, but word hadn't reached the radar operators.[30]

The first of these to be known was fallout—radioactive dust from the explosions flying up into the air, spreading out over vast areas, then falling back down. In theory, nuclear weapons could create enough fallout to cause a deadly level of radiation over the entire surface of the Earth. But we now know this would require ten times as many weapons as we currently possess.[31] Even a deliberate attempt to destroy humanity by maximizing fallout (the hypothetical cobalt bomb) may be beyond our current abilities.[32]

It wasn't until the early 1980s—almost forty years into the atomic era—that we discovered what is now believed to be the most serious consequence of nuclear war. Firestorms in burning cities could create great columns of smoke, lofting black soot all the way into the stratosphere. At that height it cannot be rained out, so a dark shroud of soot would spread around the world. This would block sunlight: chilling, darkening and drying the world. The world's major crops would fail, and billions could face starvation in a nuclear winter.

Nuclear winter was highly controversial at first, since there were many uncertainties remaining, and concerns that conclusions were being put forward before the science was ready. As the assumptions and models were improved over the years, the exact nature of the threat changed, but the basic mechanism stood the test of time.[33]

Our current best understanding comes from the work of Alan Robock and colleagues.[34] While early work on nuclear winter was limited by primitive climate models, modern computers and interest in climate change have led to much more sophisticated techniques. Robock applied an ocean-atmosphere general circulation model and found an amount of cooling similar to early estimates, lasting about five times longer. This suggested a more severe effect, since this cooling may be enough to stop almost all agriculture, and it is much harder to survive five years on stockpiled food.

Most of the harm to agriculture would come from the cold, rather than the darkness or drought. The main mechanism is to greatly reduce the length of the growing season (the number of days in a row without frost). In most places this reduced growing season would be too short for most crops to reach maturity. Robock predicts that a full-scale nuclear war would cause the Earth's average surface temperature to drop by about 7°C for about five years (then slowly return to normal over about ten more years). For comparison, this is about as cool as the Earth's last glacial period (an "ice age").[35] As with climate change, this global average can be deceptive since some areas would cool much more than others. Summer temperatures would drop by more than 20°C over much of North America and Asia, and would stay continually below freezing for several years in the mid-latitudes, where most of our food is produced. But the coasts and the tropics would suffer substantially less.

If nuclear winter lowered temperatures this much, billions of people would be at risk of starvation.[36] It would be an unprecedented catastrophe. Would it also be an existential catastrophe? We don't know. While we would lose almost all of our regular food production, there would be *some* food production. We could plant less efficient crops that are more cold-tolerant or have shorter growing seasons, increase farming in the tropics, increase fishing, build greenhouses, and try desperate measures such as farming algae.[37] We would have desperation on our side: a willingness to put all our wealth, our labor, our ingenuity into surviving. But we may also face a breakdown in law and order at all scales, continuing hostilities, and a loss of infrastructure including transport, fuel, fertilizer and electricity.

For all that, nuclear winter appears unlikely to lead to our extinction. No current researchers on nuclear winter are on record saying that it would and many have explicitly said that it is unlikely.[38] Existential catastrophe via a global unrecoverable collapse of civilization also seems unlikely, especially if we consider somewhere like New Zealand (or the southeast of Australia) which is unlikely to be directly targeted and will avoid the worst effects of nuclear winter by being coastal. It is hard to see why they wouldn't make it through with most of their technology (and institutions) intact.[39]

There are significant remaining uncertainties at all stages of our understanding of nuclear winter:

1. How many cities are hit with bombs?
2. How much smoke does this produce?
3. How much of the soot is lofted into the stratosphere?[40]
4. What are the effects of this on temperature, light, precipitation?
5. What is the resulting reduction in crop yields?
6. How long does the effect last?
7. How many people are killed by such a famine?

Some of these may be reduced through future research, while others may be impossible to resolve.

Skeptics of the nuclear winter scenario often point to these remaining uncertainties, as they show that our current scientific understanding is compatible with a milder nuclear winter. But uncertainty cuts both ways. The effect of nuclear winter could also be more severe than the central estimates. We don't have a principled reason for thinking that the uncertainty here makes things better.[41] Since I am inclined to believe that the central nuclear winter scenario is not an existential catastrophe, the uncertainty actually makes things worse by leaving this possibility open. If a nuclear war were to cause an existential catastrophe, this would presumably be because the nuclear winter effect was substantially worse than expected, or because of other—as yet unknown—effects produced by such an unprecedented assault on the Earth.

It would therefore be very valuable to have additional research on the uncertainties surrounding nuclear winter, to see if there is any plausible combination that could lead to a much deeper or longer winter, and to have fresh research on other avenues by which full-scale nuclear war might pose an existential risk.

The chance of full-scale nuclear war has changed greatly over time. For our purposes we can divide it into three periods: the Cold War, the present, and the future. With the end of the Cold

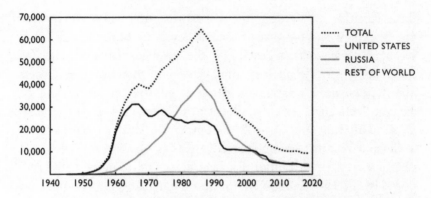

FIGURE 4.1 The number of active stockpiled nuclear warheads over time. There have been substantial reductions, but the total number (especially in the US and Russia) is still high. The combined explosive energy of these weapons has also declined, and is about 2,500 megatons today.[42]

War, the risk of a deliberately initiated nuclear war dropped considerably. However, since many missiles are still kept on hair-trigger alert (allowing them to be launched within minutes), there may remain considerable risk of nuclear war starting by accident.[43] The size of the nuclear arsenals has also gone down. The number of warheads declined from a peak of 70,000 in 1986 to about 14,000 today, and the explosive energy of each warhead has decreased too.[44] The annual risk of existential catastrophe from nuclear war should therefore be somewhat lower now than during the Cold War.

But this decrease in arsenals, and in tensions between superpowers, may reduce the risk of catastrophe less than one might think. Robock and colleagues have also modeled a limited nuclear exchange between India and Pakistan, with arsenals a fraction of the size of the US and Russia, and find a significant nuclear winter effect.[45]

And we must not be complacent. Recent years have witnessed the emergence of new geopolitical tensions that may again raise the risks of deliberate war—between the old superpowers or new ones. We have witnessed the collapse of key arms-control mechanisms between the US and Russia. And there are worrying signs that these tensions may restart the arms race, increasing the number and size of weapons toward the old levels or beyond.[46] We may see new advances that destabilize the strategic situation, such as the ability to locate nuclear submarines and thereby remove their ability to ensure a reliable nuclear counter-strike, a cornerstone of current deterrence. And the advent of military uses of AI will play a role in altering, and possibly disrupting, the strategic balance.[47]

Since a return to a nuclear cold war is not too unlikely, and would increase the annual risk by a large factor, most of the risk posed by nuclear weapons in the coming decades may come from this possibility of new escalations. And thus work to reduce the risk of nuclear war may be best aimed toward that eventuality.

CLIMATE CHANGE

The Earth's atmosphere is essential for life. It provides the pressure needed for liquid water to exist on the Earth's surface, the stability to avoid massive temperature swings between day and night, the gases that plants and animals need to survive, and—through the greenhouse effect—the insulation that keeps our planet from being entirely frozen. For without the greenhouse gases in our atmosphere, Earth would be about 33°C colder. These gases (chiefly water vapor, carbon dioxide and methane) are more transparent to the incoming light from the Sun than to the heat that radiates back from the Earth. So they act like a blanket: trapping some of the heat, keeping the Earth warm.[48]

When the Industrial Revolution unlocked the energy that had lain dormant in fossil fuels for millions of years, it unlocked their carbon too. These carbon dioxide emissions from fossil fuels were small at first, contributing less to the warming of our climate than agriculture. But as industrialization spread and intensified, carbon dioxide emissions increased dramatically, with more being released since 1980 than in the entire industrial period before that.[49] All told, the concentration of carbon dioxide in our atmosphere has risen from about 280 parts per million (ppm) prior to the Industrial Revolution to 412 ppm in 2019.[50]

Humanity's actions have already started changing our world. The Earth's climate has warmed by about 1°C.[51] Sea levels have risen by about 23 centimeters.[52] The ocean has become more acidic by 0.1 pH.[53]

There is widespread agreement that over the coming centuries anthropogenic climate change will take a high toll on both humanity and the natural environment. Most climate science and economics deals with understanding these most likely damages. But there is also a concern that the effects of climate change could be much worse—that it poses a risk of an unrecoverable collapse of civilization or even the complete extinction of humanity. Unlike many of the other risks I address, the central concern here isn't that we would meet our end this century, but that it may be possible for our actions now to all but lock in such a disaster for the future. If so, this could still be the time of the existential catastrophe—the time when humanity's *potential* is destroyed. If there is a serious chance of this, then climate change may be even more important than is typically recognized.

Climate change is already a major geopolitical issue, and as the damages or costs of mitigation build up, it will be an important stress upon humanity. This may impoverish us or create conflict within the international community, making us more prone to other existential risks.

Such stresses are a key contribution to existential risk (quite possibly climate change's main contribution), but are best dealt with separately. The point of these chapters on specific risks (Chapters 3, 4 and 5) is to catalog the *direct* mechanisms for existential catastrophe. For if there were no direct mechanisms—or if they were all vanishingly unlikely—then there would be very little existential risk for other stressors to increase. We will return to indirect effects upon other existential risks in Chapter 6. For now we ask the more fundamental question of whether climate change itself could *directly* threaten our extinction or permanent collapse.

The most extreme climate possibility is known as a "runaway greenhouse effect." It is driven by the relationship between heat

103

and humidity. Warm air can hold more water vapor than cool air. So when the atmosphere warms, the balance shifts between how much of Earth's water is in the oceans and how much is in the skies. Since water vapor is a potent greenhouse gas, more vapor in the atmosphere produces more warming, which produces more water vapor—an amplifying feedback.[54]

We can think of this like the feedback that occurs when you connect a microphone to a speaker. Such feedback does not always spiral out of control. If the microphone is far from the speaker, the sound does get repeatedly amplified, but each amplification adds less and less to the overall volume, so the total effect is not extreme.[55] This is what we expect with the water vapor feedback: that in total it will roughly double the warming we would get from the carbon dioxide alone.[56] But could there be climate conditions in which the water vapor warming spirals out of control, like the visceral squeal of feedback when a microphone is held too close to a speaker?

A *runaway greenhouse effect* is a type of amplifying feedback loop where the warming continues until the oceans have mostly boiled off, leaving a planet incompatible with complex life. There is widespread agreement that such a situation is theoretically possible. Something like this probably happened on Venus and may happen hundreds of millions of years into the Earth's future, as the Sun becomes hotter.[57] But current research suggests that a runaway greenhouse effect cannot be triggered by anthropogenic emissions alone.[58]

What about an amplifying feedback effect that causes massive warming, but stops short of boiling the oceans? This is known as a *moist greenhouse effect*, and if the effect is large enough it may be just as bad as a runaway.[59] This may also be impossible from anthropogenic emissions alone, but the science is less clear. A recent high-profile paper suggests it may be possible for carbon emissions to trigger such an effect (leading to 40°C of warming in their simulation).[60] However, there are some extreme simplifications in their model and it remains an open question whether this is really possible on Earth.[61]

We might hope to look to the paleoclimate records to rule out such possibilities. At various times in the distant past, the Earth's climate has been substantially hotter than today or had much higher carbon dioxide levels. For example, about 55 million years ago in a climate event known as the Palaeocene-Eocene Thermal Maximum (PETM), temperatures climbed from about 9°C above pre-industrial temperatures to about 14°C over about 20,000 years. Scientists have suggested that this was caused by a major injection of carbon into the atmosphere, reaching a concentration of 1,600 ppm or more.[62] This provides some evidence that such a level of emissions and warming produces neither a moist greenhouse effect nor a mass extinction.

But the situation is not clear cut. Our knowledge of the paleoclimate record is still provisional, so the estimates of past temperatures or carbon concentrations may yet be significantly revised. And there are substantial disanalogies between now and then, most notably that the rate of warming is substantially greater today, as is the rate of growth in emissions (and the rates of change might matter as much as the levels).

So how should we think about the risk from runaway or moist greenhouse effects? The situation is akin to that of igniting the atmosphere, in that it is probably physically impossible for our actions to produce the catastrophe—but we aren't sure. I don't think the possibility of runaway or moist greenhouse effects should give cause for panic, but there *is* cause for significantly increasing the research on this topic to establish whether this extreme threat is real or illusory. For while there are some good papers suggesting we are safe, important objections continue to be raised. This is not settled science.

Are there other ways we might end up with climate change so severe as to threaten our extinction or the unrecoverable collapse of civilization? There are three main routes: we may trigger other major feedback effects which release much more carbon into the atmosphere; we may emit substantially more carbon ourselves;

or a given amount of carbon may cause much more warming than we thought.

Water vapor from the oceans is just one of many climate feedbacks. As the world warms, some ecosystems will change in ways that release more carbon into the atmosphere, further increasing the warming. This includes the drying of rainforests and peat bogs, desertification and the increase in forest fires. Another form of feedback results from the changing reflectivity of the landscape. Ice is extremely reflective, bouncing much of the incoming sunlight straight back out to space. When warming melts ice, the ocean or land underneath is less reflective, so contributes to further warming.

Amplifying feedbacks like these can be alarming. We hear of warming producing further warming and our thoughts naturally turn to a world spinning out of control. But feedback effects are not all created equal. They can vary greatly in their gain (how close the microphone is to the speaker), their speed (how fast each loop is completed), and in how much total warming they could produce if run to completion (the maximum volume of the speaker). Moreover, there are other feedback effects that stabilize rather than amplify, where the larger the warming, the stronger they act to prevent more warming.

There are two potential amplifying feedbacks that are particularly concerning: the melting arctic permafrost and the release of methane from the deep ocean. In each case, warming would lead to additional carbon emissions, and each source contains more carbon than all fossil fuel emissions so far. They thus have the potential to dramatically alter the total warming. And neither has been incorporated into the main IPCC (Intergovernmental Panel on Climate Change) warming estimates, so any warming would come on top of the warming we are currently bracing for.

The arctic permafrost is a layer of frozen rock and soil covering more than 12 million square kilometers of land and ocean floor.[63] It contains over twice as much carbon as all anthropogenic emissions so far, trapped in the form of peat and methane.[64] Scientists are confident that over the coming centuries it will partly melt, release carbon and thus further warm the atmosphere. But the size of these effects and time frame are very uncertain.[65] One recent estimate is that under the IPCC's high emissions scenario, permafrost melting would contribute about 0.3°C of additional warming by 2100.[66]

Methane clathrate is an ice-like substance containing both water and methane molecules. It can be found in vast deposits in sediment at the bottom of the ocean. Because it is so hard to reach, we know very little about how much there is in total, with recent estimates ranging from twice as much carbon as we have emitted so far, to eleven times as much.[67] Warming of the oceans may trigger the melting of these clathrates and some of the methane may be carried up into the atmosphere, leading to additional warming. The dynamics of this potential feedback are even less well understood than those of the melting permafrost, with great uncertainties about when such melting could begin, whether it could happen suddenly, and how much of the methane might be released.[68]

We thus know very little about the risk these feedbacks pose. It is entirely possible that the permafrost melting and methane clathrate release are overblown and will make a negligible contribution to warming. Or that they will make a catastrophically large contribution. More research on these two feedbacks would be extremely valuable.

Feedbacks aren't the only way to get much more warming than we expect. We may simply burn more fossil fuels. The IPCC models four main emissions pathways, representing scenarios that range from rapid decarbonization of the economy, through to what might happen in the absence of any concern about the environmental impact of our emissions. The amount we will emit based on current policies has been estimated at between 1,000 and 1,700 Gt C (gigatons of carbon) by the year 2100: around twice what we have emitted so far.[69]

I hope we refrain from coming anywhere close to this, but it is certainly conceivable that we reach this point—or that we emit even more. For example, if we simply extrapolate the annual growth of the emissions rate in recent decades to continue over the century, we could emit twice as much as the IPCC's highest emission pathway.[70] The upper bound is set by the amount of fossil fuels available. There is a wide range of estimates for the remaining fossil fuel resources, from 5,000 all the way up to 13,600 Gt C.[71] This gives us the potential to burn at least eight times as much as we have burned so far. If we do not restrain emissions and eventually burn 5,000 Gt C of fossil fuels, the leading Earth system models suggest we'd suffer about 9°C to 13°C of warming by the year 2300.[72] I find it highly unlikely we would be so reckless as to reach this limit, but I can't with good conscience say it is less likely than an asteroid impact, or other natural risks we have examined.[73]

Table 4.1 puts these potential carbon emissions from permafrost, methane clathrates and fossil fuels into context. It shows that the amounts of carbon we have been talking about are so great that they dwarf the amount contained in the Earth's entire biosphere—in every living thing.[74] In fact, human activity has *already* released more than an entire biosphere worth of carbon into the atmosphere.[75]

Even if we knew how much carbon would enter the atmosphere, there would still be considerable uncertainty about how much warming this would produce. The *climate sensitivity* is the number of degrees of warming that would eventually occur if greenhouse gas concentrations were doubled from their pre-industrial baseline of 280 ppm.[76] If there were no feedbacks, this would be easy to estimate: doubling carbon dioxide while keeping everything else fixed produces about 1.2°C of warming.[77] But the climate sensitivity also accounts for many climate feedbacks, including water vapor and cloud formation (though not permafrost or methane clathrate). These make it higher and harder to estimate.

The IPCC states that climate sensitivity is likely to be somewhere between 1.5°C and 4.5°C (with a lot of this uncertainty stemming from our limited understanding of cloud feedbacks).[78] When it comes to estimating the impacts of warming, this is a vast range, with the top giving three times as much warming as the bottom. Moreover, the true sensitivity could easily be

Location	Amount	Emitted by 2100
Permafrost	~ 1,700 Gt C	50–250 Gt C†
Methane clathrates	1,500–7,000 Gt C*	
Fossil fuels	5,000–13,600 Gt C	~ 1,000–1,700 Gt C‡
Biomass	~ 550 Gt C	
Necromass	~ 1,200 Gt C	
Emissions so far	~ 660 Gt C	

* This carbon is all in the form of methane, which is much more potent in the short run. But if the release is gradual, this may not make much difference. A small proportion of carbon in permafrost is methane.
† On the high emissions pathway.[79]
‡ On current policies for fossil fuel use.

TABLE 4.1 Where is the carbon? A comparison of the size of known carbon stocks that could potentially be released into the atmosphere, and how much of these might be released from now until the end of the century. *Biomass* is the total amount of carbon in all living organisms on the Earth. *Necromass* is the total amount of carbon in dead organic matter, especially in the soil, some of which could be released through deforestation or forest fires. I have also included our total emissions from 1750 to today—those from changes in land use as well as from fossil fuels and industry.[80]

even higher, as the IPCC is only saying that there is at least a two-thirds chance it falls within this range.[81] And this uncertainty is compounded by our uncertainty in how high greenhouse gas concentrations will go. If we end up between one and two doublings from pre-industrial levels, the range of eventual warming is 1.5°C to 9°C.[82]

We might hope that some of this uncertainty will soon be resolved, but the record of progress is not promising. The current range of 1.5°C to 4.5°C was first put forward in 1979 and has barely changed over the last forty years.[83]

We often hear numbers that suggest much more precision than this: that we are now headed for 5°C warming or that certain policies are needed if we are to stay under 4°C of warming. But these expressions simplify so much that they risk misleading. They really mean that we are headed for somewhere between 2.5°C and 7.5°C of warming or that certain policies are required in

109

order to have a decent chance of staying under 4°C (sometimes defined as a 66 percent chance, sometimes just 50 percent).[84]

When we combine the uncertainties about our direct emissions, the climate sensitivity and the possibility of extreme feedbacks, we end up being able to say very little to constrain the amount of warming. Ideally, in such a situation we could still give robust estimates of the size and shape of the distribution (as we saw for asteroids), so that we could consider the probability of extreme outcomes, such as ending up above 6°C—or even 10°C. But due to the complexity of the problem we cannot even do this. The best I can say is that when accounting for all the uncertainties, we could plausibly end up with anywhere up to 13°C of warming by 2300. And even that is not a strict upper limit.

Warming at such levels would be a global calamity of unprecedented scale. It would be an immense human tragedy, disproportionately impacting the most vulnerable populations. And it would throw civilization into such disarray that we may be much more vulnerable to other existential risks. But the purpose of this chapter is finding and assessing threats that pose a direct existential risk to humanity. Even at such extreme levels of warming, it is difficult to see exactly how climate change could do so.

Major effects of climate change include reduced agricultural yields, sea level rises, water scarcity, increased tropical diseases, ocean acidification and the collapse of the Gulf Stream. While extremely important when assessing the overall risks of climate change, none of these threaten extinction or irrevocable collapse.

Crops are very sensitive to reductions in temperature (due to frosts), but less sensitive to increases. By all appearances we would still have food to support civilization.[85] Even if sea levels rose hundreds of meters (over centuries), most of the Earth's land area would remain. Similarly, while some areas might conceivably become uninhabitable due to water scarcity, other areas will have increased rainfall. More areas may become susceptible to tropical diseases, but we need only look to the tropics to see civilization flourish despite this. The main effect of a collapse of the system of Atlantic Ocean currents that includes the Gulf Stream is a 2°C cooling of Europe—something that poses no permanent threat to global civilization.

From an existential risk perspective, a more serious concern is that the high temperatures (and the rapidity of their change) might cause a large loss of biodiversity and subsequent ecosystem collapse. While the pathway is not entirely clear, a large enough collapse of ecosystems across the globe could perhaps threaten human extinction. The idea that climate change could cause widespread extinctions has some good theoretical support.[86] Yet the evidence is mixed. For when we look at many of the past cases of extremely high global temperatures or extremely rapid warming we don't see a corresponding loss of biodiversity.[87]

So the most important known effect of climate change from the perspective of direct existential risk is probably the most obvious: heat stress. We need an environment cooler than our body temperature to be able to rid ourselves of waste heat and stay alive. More precisely, we need to be able to lose heat by sweating, which depends on the humidity as well as the temperature.

A landmark paper by Steven Sherwood and Matthew Huber showed that with sufficient warming there would be parts of the world whose temperature and humidity combine to exceed the level where humans could survive without air conditioning.[88] With 12°C of warming, a very large land area—where more than half of all people currently live and where much of our food is grown—would exceed this level at some point during a typical year. Sherwood and Huber suggest that such areas would be uninhabitable. This may not quite be true (particularly if air conditioning is possible during the hottest months), but their habitability is at least in question.

However, substantial regions would also remain below this threshold. Even with an extreme 20°C of warming there would be many coastal areas (and some elevated regions) that would have no days above the temperature/humidity threshold.[89] So there would remain large areas in which humanity and civilization could continue. A world with 20°C of warming would be an unparalleled human and environmental tragedy, forcing mass migration and perhaps starvation too. This is reason enough to do our utmost to prevent anything like that from ever happening. However, our present task is identifying existential risks to humanity and it is hard to see how any realistic level of heat stress could pose such a risk. So the runaway and moist greenhouse effects remain the only known mechanisms through which climate change could directly cause our extinction or irrevocable collapse.

This doesn't rule out *unknown* mechanisms. We are considering large changes to the Earth that may even be unprecedented in size or speed. It wouldn't be astonishing if that directly led to our permanent ruin. The best argument against such unknown mechanisms is probably that the PETM did not lead to a mass extinction, despite temperatures rapidly rising about 5°C, to reach a level 14°C above pre-industrial temperatures.[90] But this is tempered by the imprecision of paleoclimate data, the sparsity of the fossil record, the smaller size of mammals at the time (making them more heat-tolerant), and a reluctance to rely on a single example. Most importantly, anthropogenic warming could be over a hundred times faster than warming during the PETM, and rapid warming has been suggested as a contributing factor in the end-Permian mass extinction, in which 96 percent of species went extinct.[91] In the end, we can say little more than that direct existential risk from climate change appears very small, but cannot yet be ruled out.

Our focus so far has been on whether climate change could conceivably be an existential catastrophe. In assessing this, I have set aside the question of whether we could mitigate this risk. The most obvious and important form of mitigation is reducing our emissions. There is a broad consensus that this must play a key role in any mitigation strategy. But there are also ways of mitigating the effects of climate change after the emissions have been released.

These techniques are often called *geoengineering*. While the name conjures up a radical and dangerous scheme for transforming our planet, the proposals in fact range from the radical to the mundane. They also differ in their cost, speed, scale, readiness and risk.

The two main approaches to geoengineering are carbon dioxide removal and solar radiation management. Carbon dioxide removal strikes at the root of the problem, removing the carbon dioxide from our atmosphere and thus taking away the source of the heating. It is an attempt to cure the Earth of its affliction. At the radical end is ocean fertilization: seeding the ocean with iron to encourage large algal blooms which capture carbon before sinking into the deep ocean. At the mundane end are tree planting and carbon scrubbing.

Solar radiation management involves limiting the amount of sunlight absorbed by the Earth. This could involve blocking light before it hits the Earth, reflecting more light in the atmosphere before it hits the surface, or reflecting more of the light that hits the surface. It is an attempt to offset the warming effects of the carbon dioxide by cooling the Earth. It is typically cheaper than carbon dioxide removal and quicker to act, but has the downsides of ignoring other bad effects of carbon (such as ocean acidification) and requiring constant upkeep.

A central problem with geoengineering is that the cure may be worse than the disease. For the very scale of what it is attempting to achieve could create a risk of massive unintended consequences over the entire Earth's surface, possibly posing a greater existential risk than climate change itself. Geoengineering thus needs to be very carefully governed—especially when it comes to radical techniques that are cheap enough for a country or research group to implement unilaterally—and we shouldn't rely on it as an alternative to emissions reductions. But it may well have a useful role to play as a last resort, or as a means for the eventual restoration of our planet's climate.[92]

ENVIRONMENTAL DAMAGE

Climate change is not the only form of environmental damage we are inflicting upon the Earth. Might we face other environmental existential risks through overpopulation, running out of critical resources or biodiversity loss?

When environmentalism rose to prominence in the 1960s and 1970s, one major concern was overpopulation. It was widely feared that humanity's rapidly growing population would far outstrip the Earth's capacity to feed people, precipitating an environmental and humanitarian catastrophe. The most prominent advocate of this view, Paul Ehrlich, painted an apocalyptic vision of the near future: "Most of the people who are going to die in the greatest cataclysm in the history of man have already been born."[93] This catastrophe would come soon and pose a direct existential risk. Ehrlich predicted: "Sometime in the next 15 years, the end will come—and by 'the end' I mean an utter breakdown of the capacity of the planet to support humanity."[94]

These confident predictions of doom were thoroughly mistaken. Instead of rising to unprecedented heights, the prevalence of famine dramatically declined. Less than a quarter as many people died of famine in the 1970s as in the 1960s, and the rate has since halved again.[95] Instead of dwindling to a point of crisis, the amount of food per person has steadily risen over the last fifty years. We now have 24 percent more food per person than when Ehrlich's book, *The Population Bomb*, was published in 1968.

Much of the credit for this is owed to the Green Revolution, in which developing countries rose to the challenge of feeding their people. They did so by modernizing their farming, with improved fertilizers, irrigation, automation and grain varieties.[96] Perhaps the greatest single contribution was from Norman Borlaug, who received the Nobel Prize for his work breeding the new, high-yield varieties of wheat, and who may be responsible for saving more lives than anyone else in history.[97]

But the improvements in agriculture are just part of the story. The entire picture of overpopulation has changed. Population growth is almost always presented as an exponential process—increasing by a fixed percentage each year—but in fact that is rarely the case. From about 1800 to 1960 the world population was growing much faster than an exponential. The annual

114

growth rate was itself growing from 0.4 percent all the way to an unprecedented rate of 2.2 percent in 1962. These trends rightly warranted significant concern about the human and environmental consequences of this rapid population increase.

But suddenly, the situation changed. The population growth rate started to rapidly decline. So far it has halved, and it continues to fall. Population is now increasing in a roughly linear manner, with a fixed *number* of people being added each year instead of a fixed *proportion*. This change has been driven not by the feared increase in death rates, but by a dramatic change in fertility, as more and more countries have undergone the demographic transition to a small family size. In 1950, the average number of children born to each woman was 5.05. It is now just 2.47—not so far above the replacement rate of 2.1 children per woman.[98]

While we can't know what will happen in the future, the current trends point to a rapid stabilization of the population. The current linear increase is likely to be an inflection point in the history of human population: the point where the curve finally

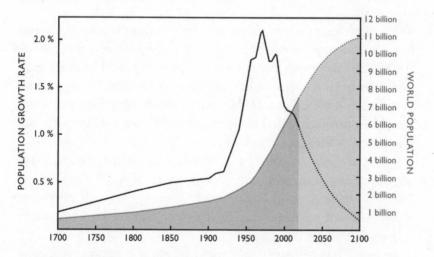

FIGURE 4.2 World population from 1700 to today (dark gray) and projected up to 2100 (light gray). The black line shows the annual percentage growth rate of population, which reached an extreme peak in 1962 but has since been dropping quickly.[99]

starts to level off. We may never again see the rapid population growth of the mid-twentieth century. In the last eighty years, population grew threefold. In the next eighty years (to 2100) it is expected to go up just 50 percent, to about 11 billion. For every person alive now, we'll have to make room for an extra half a person. This will be a challenge, but a much easier one than last century.

Some people have gone so far as to suggest that the real extinction risk might now be declining population.[100] Fertility rates in most countries outside Africa have fallen to below the replacement rate, and perhaps this will become a global trend. Even then, I don't think there is any real cause for concern. If declining population began to pose a clear and present danger (something that couldn't happen for at least two centuries), it would be a simple matter for public policy to encourage childbearing up to the replacement level. The available policy levers—free childcare, free education, free child healthcare and tax benefits for families—are relatively simple, non-coercive and popular.

While the danger of population spiraling rapidly out of control has abated, population has certainly reached a very high level. And with our rapidly increasing prosperity and power, each person is having more impact on the environment.[101] This is creating large stresses on the biosphere, some of which are completely unprecedented. This may, in turn, create threats to our continued existence.

One category of concern is resource depletion. People have suggested that humanity is running short of fossil fuels, phosphorous, topsoil, fresh water and certain metals.[102] However, these forms of resource scarcity don't appear to pose any direct risk of destroying our potential.

Running out of fossil fuels might result in economic recession as we switch to more expensive alternatives, but we are quite capable of maintaining a civilization without fossil fuels. Indeed, we are already planning to do so soon as we move to zero emissions later this century. My guess is that, if anything, failure to find new sources of fossil fuels would actually lower overall existential risk.

What about water? While fresh water is much more scarce than seawater, we do have a lot of it in absolute terms: 26 million liters of accessible fresh water per person.[103] Most of the problem comes from this being poorly distributed. Even in the worst case, fresh water could be substituted with desalinated sea water at a cost of about $1 for 1,000 liters. There would be additional expenses involved to do this using clean energy and when pumping the water uphill to people and farms away from the coast, but we could do it if we had to.

It is unclear whether there are any significant metal shortages at all: previous predictions have failed and one should expect markets to slow consumption, encourage recycling and develop alternatives if stocks do start running low.[104] Moreover, the types of rare metals that are plausibly running out don't seem to be essential for civilization.

While I don't know of any resources whose scarcity could plausibly constitute an existential catastrophe, it is hard to completely rule it out. It is possible that we will find a resource that is scarce, performs an essential function for civilization, has no feasible alternative, can't be adequately recycled, and where market forces won't ration our consumption. While I am skeptical that any resources meet this description, I encourage efforts to thoroughly check whether this is so.

Another category of environmental concern is loss of biodiversity. Our actions are destroying and threatening so many species that people have suggested a sixth mass extinction is underway.[105] Is this true?

It is difficult to say. One problem is that we can't cleanly compare the modern and fossil records.[106] Another is that there is more than one measure of a mass extinction. The rate at which species are going extinct is much higher than the longterm average—at least ten to 100 times higher, and expected to accelerate.[107] Species may be going extinct even more rapidly than in a typical mass extinction. But the fraction of species that have gone extinct is much lower than in a mass extinction. Where the big five mass extinctions all lost more than 75 percent of species, we have lost about 1 percent.[108] This could be a sixth mass extinction that is just getting started, though the evidence fits a substantially smaller extinction event just as well. In any event, our inability to rule out being in the midst of a mass extinction is deeply troubling.

And while extinction is a useful measure of biodiversity loss, it is not the whole story. It doesn't capture population reductions or species disappearing locally or regionally. While "only" 1 percent of species have gone extinct on our watch, the toll on biodiversity within each region may be much higher, and this may be what matters most. From the perspective of existential risk, what matters most about biodiversity loss is the loss of *ecosystem services*. These are services—such as purifying water and air, providing energy and resources, or improving our soil—that plants and animals currently provide for us, but we may find costly or impossible to do ourselves.

A prominent example is the crop pollination performed by honeybees. This is often raised as an existential risk, citing a quotation attributed Einstein that "If the bee disappeared off the surface of the globe then man would only have four years of life left." This has been thoroughly debunked: it is not true and Einstein didn't say it.[109] In fact, a recent review found that even if honeybees were completely lost—and *all* other pollinators too—this would only create a 3 to 8 percent reduction in global crop production.[110] It would be a great environmental tragedy and a crisis for humanity, but there is no reason to think it is an existential risk.

While that particular example is spurious, perhaps there are other distinct ecosystem services that are threatened and that we couldn't live without. Or a cascading failure of ecosystem services may collectively be too much for our civilization to be able to replace. It is clear that at *some* level of environmental destruction this would be true, though we have little idea how close we are to such a threshold, nor whether a cascade could take us there. We need more research to find out.

As with nuclear winter and extreme global warming, we don't know of a direct mechanism for existential risk, but are putting such pressure on the global environment that there may well be some as yet unknown consequence that would threaten our survival. We could therefore think of continuing environmental damage over the coming century as a source of unforeseen threats to humanity. These unmodeled effects may well contain most of the environmental existential risk.

Nuclear war, climate change and environmental damage are extremely serious global issues—even before we come to the question of whether they could cause existential catastrophe. In each case, humanity holds tremendous power to change the face of the Earth in ways that are without precedent in the 200,000 years of *Homo sapiens*. The latest science backs up the extreme scale of these changes, though it stops short of providing clear and proven mechanisms for a truly existential catastrophe. The existential risk from these sources therefore remains more speculative than that from asteroids. But this is not the same as the risk being *smaller*. Given our current scientific knowledge, I think it would be very bold to put the probability of these risks at less than the 0.001 percent to 0.05 percent per century that comes from all natural risks together. Indeed, I'd estimate that each of these three risks has a higher probability than that of all natural existential risks put together. And there may be even greater risks to come.

5

FUTURE RISKS

*The Dark Ages may return, the Stone Age may return on
the gleaming wings of Science, and what might now shower
immeasurable material blessings upon mankind, may even
bring about its total destruction.*

—Winston Churchill[1]

It is now time to cast our gaze to the horizon, to see what possibilities the coming century may bring. These possibilities are hard to discern through the haze of distance; it is extremely difficult to tell which new technologies will be possible, what form they will take when mature, or the context of the world into which they will arrive. And this veil may not lift until the new technologies are right upon us. For even the best experts or the very inventors of the technology can be blindsided by major developments.

One night in 1933, the world's pre-eminent expert on atomic science, Ernest Rutherford, declared the idea of harnessing atomic energy to be "moonshine." And the very next morning Leo Szilard discovered the idea of the chain reaction. In 1939, Enrico Fermi told Szilard the chain reaction was but a "remote possibility," and four years later Fermi was personally overseeing the world's first nuclear reactor. The staggering list of eminent scientists who thought heavier-than-air flight to be impossible or else decades away is so well rehearsed as to be cliché. But fewer know that even Wilbur Wright himself predicted it was at least fifty years away—just two years before he invented it.[2]

So we need to remember how quickly new technologies can be upon us, and to be wary of assertions that they are either impossible or so distant in time that we have no cause for concern. Confident denouncements by eminent scientists should certainly give us reason to be skeptical of a technology, but not to bet our lives against it—their track record just isn't good enough for that.[3]

Of course, there is no shortage of examples of scientists and technologists declaring a new technology to be just around the corner, when in fact it would only arrive decades later; or not at all; or in a markedly different form to the one anticipated. The point is not that technology usually comes earlier than predicted, but that it can easily do so; that we need to be cautious in ruling things out or assuming we have ample time.

But we must not veer toward the opposite mistake: using the impossibility of knowing the future as an excuse to ignore it. There *are* things we can say. For example, it would be surprising if the long-run trend toward developing technologies of increasing power *didn't* continue into this century. And since it was precisely our unprecedented power that gave rise to the anthropogenic risks of the twentieth century, it would be remarkable if the coming century didn't pose similar, or greater, risk.

Despite this being a chapter on the future, we won't be engaging in prediction—at least not in the usual sense of saying which technologies will come, and when. Instead, we shall chart the horizon in terms of plausibility and probability. Are there plausible future technologies that would bring existential risks? Are these technologies probable enough to warrant preparations in case they do arrive? To do this, we don't need to know the future, nor even the precise probabilities of what may occur. We just need to estimate these probabilities to the right ballpark; to see the dim outlines of the threats. This will give us a rough idea of the landscape ahead and how we might prepare for it.

Much of what new technologies bring will of course be helpful, and some truly wondrous. Technological progress has been one of the main sources of our modern prosperity and longevity—one of the main reasons extreme poverty has become the exception rather than the rule, and life expectancy has doubled since the Industrial Revolution. Indeed, we can see that over the centuries all the risks technology imposes on humans have been outweighed by the benefits it has brought.[4] For these dramatic gains to health and wealth are *overall* gains, taking all the ill effects into account.

Or at least this is true for most risks: those that are likely enough and common enough that the law of large numbers wins out, turning the unpredictability of the small scale into a demonstrable longterm average. We know that these everyday risks have been more than outweighed. But we don't know whether this positive balance was due to getting lucky on a few key rolls of the dice. For instance, it is conceivable that the risk of nuclear war breaking out was serious enough to outweigh all the benefits of modern technology.

It is this that should most interest us when we look to the century ahead. Not the everyday risks and downsides that technology may bring, but whether there will be a handful of cases where it puts our entire bankroll at risk, with no subsequent way for us to make up the losses.

Growing up, I had always been strongly pro-technology. If not for the plausibility of these unconsummated catastrophic risks, I'd remain so. But instead, I am compelled toward a much more ambivalent view. I don't for a moment think we should cease technological progress—indeed if some well-meaning regime locked in a permanent freeze on technology, that would probably itself be an existential catastrophe, preventing humanity from ever fulfilling its potential.

But we do need to treat technological progress with maturity.[5] We should continue our technological developments to make sure we receive the fruits of technology. Yet we must do so very carefully, and if needed, use a significant fraction of the gains from technology to address the potential dangers, ensuring the balance stays positive. Looking ahead and charting the potential hazards on our horizon is a key step.

PANDEMICS

In 1347 death came to Europe. It entered through the Crimean town of Caffa, brought by the besieging Mongol army. Fleeing merchants unwittingly carried it back to Italy. From there it spread to France, Spain, England. Then up as far as Norway and across the rest of Europe—all the way to Moscow. Within six years, the Black Death had taken the continent.[6]

Tens of millions fell gravely ill, their bodies succumbing to the disease in different ways. Some bore swollen buboes on their necks, armpits and thighs; some had their flesh turn black from hemorrhaging beneath the skin; some coughed blood from the necrotic inflammation of their throats and lungs. All forms involved fever, exhaustion, and an intolerable stench from the material that exuded from the body.[7] There were so many dead that mass graves needed to be dug and even then, cemeteries ran out of room for the bodies.

The Black Death devastated Europe. In those six years, between one-quarter and one-half of all Europeans were killed.[8] The Middle East was ravaged too, with the plague killing about one in three Egyptians and Syrians. And it may have also laid waste to parts of Central Asia, India and China. Due to the scant records of the fourteenth century, we will never know the true toll, but our best estimates are that somewhere between 5 percent and 14 percent of all the world's people were killed, in what may have been the greatest catastrophe humanity has seen.[9]

Are we safe now from events like this? Or are we more vulnerable? Could a pandemic threaten humanity's future?[10]

The Black Death was not the only biological disaster to scar human history. It was not even the only great bubonic plague. In 541 CE the Plague of Justinian struck the Byzantine Empire. Over three years it took the lives of roughly 3 percent of the world's people.[11]

When Europeans reached the Americas in 1492, the two populations exposed each other to completely novel diseases. Over thousands of years each population had built up resistance to their own set of diseases, but were extremely susceptible to the others. The American peoples got by far the worse end of exchange, through diseases such as measles, influenza and especially smallpox.

During the next hundred years a combination of invasion and disease took an immense toll—one whose scale may never be known, due to great uncertainty about the size of the pre-existing population. We can't rule out the loss of more than 90 percent of the population of the Americas during that century, though the number could also be much lower.[12] And it is very difficult to tease out how much of this should be attributed to war and occupation, rather than disease. As a rough upper bound, the Columbian exchange may have killed as many as 10 percent of the world's people.[13]

Centuries later, the world had become so interconnected that a truly global pandemic was possible. Near the end of the First World War, a devastating strain of influenza (known as the 1918 flu or Spanish Flu) spread to six continents, and even remote Pacific islands. At least a third of the world's population were infected and 3 to 6 percent were killed.[14] This death toll outstripped that of the First World War, and possibly both World Wars combined.

Yet even events like these fall short of being a threat to humanity's longterm potential.[15] In the great bubonic plagues we saw civilization in the affected areas falter, but recover. The regional 25 to 50 percent death rate was not enough to precipitate a continent-wide collapse of civilization. It changed the relative fortunes of empires, and may have altered the course of history substantially, but if anything, it gives us reason to believe that human civilization is likely to make it through future events with similar death rates, even if they were global in scale.

The 1918 flu pandemic was remarkable in having very little apparent effect on the world's development despite its global reach. It looks like it was lost in the wake of the First World War, which despite a smaller death toll, seems to have had a much larger effect on the course of history.[16]

125

It is less clear what lesson to draw from the Columbian exchange due to our lack of good records and its mix of causes. Pandemics were clearly a part of what led to a regional collapse of civilization, but we don't know whether this would have occurred had it not been for the accompanying violence and imperial rule.

The strongest case against existential risk from natural pandemics is the fossil record argument from Chapter 3. Extinction risk from natural causes above 0.1 percent per century is incompatible with the evidence of how long humanity and similar species have lasted. But this argument only works where the risk to humanity now is similar or lower than the longterm levels. For most risks this is clearly true, but not for pandemics. We have done many things to exacerbate the risk: some that could make pandemics more likely to occur, and some that could increase their damage. Thus even "natural" pandemics should be seen as a partly anthropogenic risk.

Our population now is a thousand times greater than over most of human history, so there are vastly more opportunities for new human diseases to originate.[17] And our farming practices have created vast numbers of animals living in unhealthy conditions within close proximity to humans. This increases the risk, as many major diseases originate in animals before crossing over to humans. Examples include HIV (chimpanzees), Ebola (bats), SARS (probably bats) and influenza (usually pigs or birds).[18] Evidence suggests that diseases are crossing over into human populations from animals at an increasing rate.[19]

Modern civilization may also make it much easier for a pandemic to spread. The higher density of people living together in cities increases the number of people each of us may infect. Rapid long-distance transport greatly increases the distance pathogens can spread, reducing the degrees of separation between any two people. Moreover, we are no longer divided into isolated populations as we were for most of the last 10,000 years.[20] Together these effects suggest that we might expect more new pandemics, for them to spread more quickly, and to reach a higher percentage of the world's people.

But we have also changed the world in ways that offer protection. We have a healthier population; improved sanitation and hygiene; preventative and curative medicine; and a scientific understanding of disease. Perhaps most importantly, we have public health bodies to facilitate global communication and coordination in the face of new outbreaks. We have seen the benefits of this protection through the dramatic decline of endemic infectious disease over the last century (though we can't be sure pandemics will obey the same trend). Finally, we have spread to a range of locations and environments unprecedented for any mammalian species. This offers special protection from extinction events, because it requires the pathogen to be able to flourish in a vast range of environments and to reach exceptionally isolated populations such as uncontacted tribes, Antarctic researchers and nuclear submarine crews.[21]

It is hard to know whether these combined effects have increased or decreased the existential risk from pandemics. This uncertainty is ultimately bad news: we were previously sitting on a powerful argument that the risk was tiny; now we are not. But note that we are not merely interested in the direction of the change, but also in the *size* of the change. If we take the fossil record as evidence that the risk was less than one in 2,000 per century, then to reach 1 percent per century the pandemic risk would need to be at least 20 times larger. This seems unlikely. In my view, the fossil record still provides a strong case against there being a high *extinction* risk from "natural" pandemics. So most of the remaining existential risk would come from the threat of permanent collapse: a pandemic severe enough to collapse civilization globally, combined with civilization turning out to be hard to re-establish or bad luck in our attempts to do so.

But humanity could also play a much larger role. We have seen the indirect ways that our actions aid and abet the origination and the spread of pandemics. But what about cases where we have a much more direct hand in the process—where we deliberately use, improve or create the pathogens?

Our understanding and control of pathogens is very recent. Just 200 years ago we didn't even understand the basic cause of pandemics—a leading theory in the West claimed that disease was produced by a kind of gas. In just two centuries, we discovered it was caused by a diverse variety of microscopic agents and we worked out how to grow them in the lab, to breed them for different traits, to sequence their genomes, to implant new genes, and to create entire functional viruses from their written code.

This progress is continuing at a rapid pace. The last ten years have seen major qualitative breakthroughs, such as the use of CRISPR to efficiently insert new genetic sequences into a genome and the use of gene drives to efficiently replace populations of natural organisms in the wild with genetically modified versions.[22] Measures of this progress suggest it is accelerating, with the cost to sequence a genome falling by a factor of 10,000 since 2007 and with publications and venture capital investment growing quickly.[23] This progress in biotechnology seems unlikely to fizzle out soon: there are no insurmountable challenges looming; no fundamental laws blocking further developments.

Here the past offers almost no reassurance. Increasing efforts are made to surpass natural abilities, so long-run track records need not apply. It would be optimistic to assume that this uncharted new terrain holds only familiar dangers.

To start with, let's set aside the risks from malicious intent, and consider only the risks that can arise from well-intentioned research. Most scientific and medical research poses a negligible risk of harms at the scale we are considering. But there is a small fraction that uses live pathogens of kinds which are known to threaten global harm. These include the agents that cause the 1918 flu, smallpox, SARS and H5N1 flu. And a small part of this research involves making strains of these pathogens that pose even more danger than the natural types, increasing their transmissibility, lethality or resistance to vaccination or treatment.

In 2012 a Dutch virologist, Ron Fouchier, published details of a gain-of-function experiment on the recent H5N1 strain of bird flu.[24] This strain was extremely deadly, killing an estimated 60 percent of humans it infected—far beyond even the 1918 flu.[25] Yet its inability to pass from human to human had so far prevented a pandemic. Fouchier wanted to find out whether (and how) H5N1 could naturally develop this ability. He passed the disease through a series of ten ferrets, which are commonly used as a model for how influenza affects humans. By the time it passed to the final ferret, his strain of H5N1 had become directly transmissible between mammals.

The work caused fierce controversy. Much of this was focused on the information contained in his work. The US National Science Advisory Board for Biosecurity ruled that his paper had to be stripped of some of its technical details before publication, to limit the ability of bad actors to cause a pandemic. And the Dutch government claimed it broke EU law on exporting information useful for bioweapons. But it is not the possibility of misuse that concerns me here. Fouchier's research provides a clear example of well-intentioned scientists enhancing the destructive capabilities of pathogens known to threaten global catastrophe. And nor is it the only case. In the very same year a similar experiment was performed in the United States.[26]

Of course, such experiments are done in secure labs, with stringent safety standards. It is highly unlikely that in any particular case the enhanced pathogens would escape into the wild. But just how unlikely? Unfortunately, we don't have good data, due to a lack of transparency about incident and escape rates.[27] This prevents society from making well-informed decisions balancing the risks and benefits of this research, and it limits the ability of labs to learn from each other's incidents. We need consistent and transparent reporting of incidents, in line with the best practices from other sectors.[28] And we need serious accountability for when incidents or escapes go beyond the promised rates.

But even the patchy evidence we do have includes enough confirmed cases to see that the rates of escape are worryingly high (see the box "Notable Laboratory Escapes").[29] None of these documented escapes directly posed a risk of existential catastrophe, but they show that security for highly dangerous pathogens has been deeply flawed, and remains insufficient.

This is true even at the highest biosafety level (BSL-4). In 2001, Britain was struck by a devastating outbreak of foot-and-mouth disease in livestock. Six million animals were killed in an attempt to halt its spread, and the economic damages totalled £8 billion. Then in 2007 there was another outbreak, which was traced to a lab working on the disease. Foot-and-mouth was considered a highest category pathogen and required the highest level of biosecurity. Yet the virus escaped from a badly maintained pipe, leaking into the groundwater at the facility. After an investigation, the lab's license was renewed—only for another leak to occur two weeks later.[30] In my view, this track record of escapes shows that even BSL-4 is insufficient for working on pathogens that pose a risk of global pandemics on the scale of the 1918 flu or worse—especially if that research involves gain-of-function (and the extremely dangerous H5N1 gain-of-function research wasn't even performed at BSL-4).[31] Thirteen years since the last publicly acknowledged outbreak from a BSL-4 facility is not good enough. It doesn't matter whether this is from insufficient standards, inspections, operations or penalties. What matters is the poor track record in the field, made worse by a lack of transparency and accountability. With current BSL-4 labs, an escape of a pandemic pathogen is a matter of time.

Alongside the threat of accident is the threat of deliberate misuse. Humanity has a long and dark history of disease as a weapon. There are records dating back to 1320 BCE, describing a war in Asia Minor, where infected sheep were driven across the border to spread tularemia.[32] There is even a contemporaneous account of the siege of Caffa claiming the Black Death was introduced to Europe by the Mongol army catapulting plague-ridden corpses over the city walls. It is not clear whether this really occurred, nor whether the Black Death would have found its way into Europe regardless. Yet it remains a live possibility that the most deadly event in the history of the world (as a fraction of humanity) was an act of biological warfare.[33]

NOTABLE LABORATORY ESCAPES

1971: Smallpox

A Soviet bioweapons lab tested a weaponized strain of smallpox on an island in the Aral Sea. During a field test, they accidentally infected people on a nearby ship who spread it ashore. The resulting outbreak infected ten people, killing three, before being contained by a mass quarantine and vaccination program.[34]

1978: Smallpox

In 1967 smallpox was killing more than a million people a year, but a heroic global effort drove that to zero in 1977, freeing humanity from this ancient scourge. And yet a year later, it returned from the grave: escaping from a British lab, killing one person and infecting another before authorities contained the outbreak.[35]

1979: Anthrax

A bioweapons lab in one of the Soviet Union's biggest cities, Sverdlovsk, accidentally released a large quantity of weaponized anthrax, when they took an air filter off for cleaning. There were 66 confirmed fatalities.[36]

1995: Rabbit Calicivirus

Australian scientists conducted a field trial with a new virus for use in controlling their wild rabbit population. They released it on a small island, but the virus escaped quarantine, reaching the mainland and accidentally killing 30 million rabbits within just a few weeks.[37]

2015: Anthrax

The Dugway Proving Grounds was established by the US military in 1942 to work on chemical and biological weapons. In 2015, it accidentally distributed samples containing live anthrax spores to 192 labs across eight countries, which thought they were receiving inactivated anthrax.[38]

One of the first unequivocal accounts of biological warfare was by the British in Canada in 1763. The Commander-in-Chief for North America, Jeffrey Amherst, wrote to a fort that had suffered a smallpox outbreak: "Could it not be contrived to send the smallpox among those disaffected tribes of Indians? We must on this occasion, use every stratagem in our power to reduce them." The same idea had already occurred to the garrison, who acted on it of their own initiative. They distributed disease-ridden items, documented the deed, and even filed for official reimbursement to cover the costs of the blankets and handkerchief used.[39]

Where earlier armies had limited understanding of disease, and mostly opportunistic biowarfare, our greater understanding has enabled modern nations to build on what nature provided. During the twentieth century, fifteen countries are known to have developed bioweapons programs, including the US, UK and France.[40]

The largest program was the Soviets'. At its height it had more than a dozen clandestine labs employing 9,000 scientists to weaponize diseases ranging from plague to smallpox, anthrax and tularemia. Scientists attempted to increase the diseases' infectivity, lethality and resistance to vaccination and treatment. They created systems for spreading the pathogens to their opponents and built up vast stockpiles, reportedly including more than 20 *tons* of smallpox and of plague. The program was prone to accidents, with lethal outbreaks of both smallpox and anthrax (see Box).[41] While there is no evidence of deliberate attempts to create a pathogen to threaten the whole of humanity, the logic of deterrence or mutually assured destruction could push superpowers or rogue states in that direction.

The good news is that for all our flirtation with biowarfare, there appear to have been relatively few deaths from either accidents or use (assuming the Black Death to have been a natural pandemic).[42] The confirmed historical death toll from biowarfare is dwarfed by that of natural pandemics over the same time frame.[43] Exactly why this is so is unclear. One reason may be that bioweapons are unreliable and prone to backfiring, leading states to use other weapons in preference. Another suggestion is that tacit knowledge and operational barriers make it much harder to deploy bioweapons than it may first appear.[44]

But the answer may also just be that we have too little data. The patterns of disease outbreaks, war deaths and terrorist attacks all appear to follow power law distributions. Unlike the familiar "normal" distribution where sizes are clustered around a central value, power law distributions have a "heavy tail" of increasingly large events, where there can often be events at entirely different scales, with some being thousands, or millions, of times bigger than others. Deaths from war and terror appear to follow power laws with especially heavy tails, such that the majority of the deaths happen in the few biggest events. For instance, warfare deaths in the last hundred years are dominated by the two World Wars, and most US fatalities from terrorism occurred in the September 11 attacks.[45] When events follow a distribution like this, the average size of events until now systematically under-represents the expected size of events to come, even if the under-lying risk stays the same.[46]

And it is not staying the same. Attempts to use the historical record overlook the rapid changes in biotechnology. It is not twentieth-century bioweaponry that should alarm us, but the next hundred years of improvements. A hundred years ago, we had only just discovered viruses and were yet to discover DNA. Now we can design the DNA of viruses and resurrect historic viruses from their genetic sequences. Where will we be a hundred years from now?

One of the most exciting trends in biotechnology is its rapid democratization—the speed at which cutting-edge techniques can be adopted by students and amateurs. When a new breakthrough is achieved, the pool of people with the talent, training, resources and patience to reproduce it rapidly expands: from a handful of the world's top biologists, to people with PhDs in the field, to millions of people with undergraduate-level biology.

The Human Genome Project was the largest ever scientific collaboration in biology. It took thirteen years and $500 million to produce the full DNA sequence of the human genome. Just

15 years later, a genome can be sequenced for under $1,000 or within a single hour.[47] The reverse process has become much easier too: online DNA synthesis services allow anyone to upload a DNA sequence of their choice then have it constructed and shipped to their address. While still expensive, the price of synthesis has fallen by a factor of a thousand over the last two decades and continues to drop.[48] The first ever uses of CRISPR and gene drives were the biotechnology achievements of the decade. But within just two years each of these technologies were used successfully by bright students participating in science competitions.[49] .

Such democratization promises to fuel a boom of entrepreneurial biotechnology. But since biotechnology can be misused to lethal effect, democratization also means proliferation. As the pool of people with access to a technique grows, so does the chance it contains someone with malign intent.

People with the motivation to wreak global destruction are mercifully rare. But they exist. Perhaps the best example is the Aum Shinrikyo cult in Japan, active between 1984 and 1995, which sought to bring about the destruction of humanity. They attracted several thousand members, including people with advanced skills in chemistry and biology. And they demonstrated that it was not mere misanthropic ideation. They launched multiple lethal attacks using VX gas and sarin gas, killing 22 people and injuring thousands.[50] They attempted to weaponize anthrax, but did not succeed. What happens when the circle of people able to create a global pandemic becomes wide enough to include members of such a group? Or members of a terrorist organization or rogue state that could try to build an omnicidal weapon for the purposes of extortion or deterrence?

The main candidate for biological risk over the coming decades thus stems from our technology—particularly the risk of misuse by states or small groups. But this is not a case where the world is blissfully unaware of the risks. Bertrand Russell wrote of the danger of extinction from biowarfare to Einstein in 1955.[51]

And in 1969 the possibility was raised by the American Nobel Laureate for Medicine, Joshua Lederberg:

> As a scientist I am profoundly concerned about the continued involvement of the United States and other nations in the development of biological warfare. This process puts the very future of human life on earth in serious peril.[52]

In response to such warnings, we have already begun national and international efforts to protect humanity. There is action through public health, international conventions and self-regulation by biotechnology companies and the scientific community. Are they adequate?

Medicine and public health have developed an arsenal of techniques to reduce the risk of an outbreak of infectious disease: from hygiene and sanitation, to disease surveillance systems, to vaccines and medical treatments. Its successes, such as the eradication of smallpox, are some of humanity's greatest achievements. National and international work in public health offers some protection from engineered pandemics, and its existing infrastructure could be adapted to better address them. Yet even for existing dangers this protection is uneven and under-provided. Despite its importance, public health is underfunded worldwide and poorer countries remain vulnerable to being overwhelmed by outbreaks.

The most famous international protection comes from the Biological Weapons Convention (BWC) of 1972. This is an important symbol of the international taboo against these weapons and it provides an ongoing international forum for discussion of the threat. But it would be a mistake to think it has successfully outlawed bioweapons.[53] There are two key challenges that limit its ability to fulfill this mission.

First, it is profoundly underfunded. This global convention to protect humanity has just four employees, and a smaller budget than an average McDonald's.[54]

Second, unlike other arms control treaties (such as those for nuclear or chemical weapons) there is no effective means of verification of compliance with the BWC.[55] This is not just a theoretical issue. The vast Soviet bioweapons program, with its deadly anthrax and smallpox accidents, continued for almost twenty years *after* the Soviets had signed the BWC, proving that the convention did not end bioweapons research.[56] And the Soviets were not the only party in breach. After the end of apartheid, South Africa confessed to having run a bioweapons program in violation of the BWC.[57] After the first Gulf War, Iraq was caught in breach of the convention.[58] At the time of writing, the United States has said it believes several nations are currently developing bioweapons in breach of the BWC.[59] Israel has refused to even sign.[60] And the BWC offers little protection from non-state actors.

Biotechnology companies are working to limit the dark side of the democratization of their field. For example, unrestricted DNA synthesis would help bad actors overcome a major hurdle to creating extremely deadly pathogens. It would allow them to get access to the DNA of controlled pathogens like smallpox (whose genome is readily available online) and to create DNA with modifications to make the pathogen more dangerous.[61] Therefore many synthesis companies make voluntary efforts to manage this risk, screening their orders for dangerous sequences. But the screening methods are imperfect and they only cover about 80 percent of orders.[62] There is significant room for improving this process and a strong case for making screening mandatory. The challenges will only increase as desktop synthesis machines become available, preventing these from being misused may require software or hardware locks to ensure the sequences get screened.[63]

We might also look to the scientific community for careful management of biological risks. Many of the dangerous advances usable by states and small groups have come from open science (see box "Information Hazards"). And we've seen that science produces substantial accident risk. The scientific community has tried to regulate its dangerous research, but with limited success. There are a variety of reasons why this is extremely hard, including difficulty in knowing where to draw the line, lack of central authorities to unify practice, a culture of openness and freedom to pursue whatever is of interest, and the rapid pace of science outpacing that of governance. It may be possible for the scientific community to overcome these challenges and provide strong management of global risks, but it would require a willingness to accept serious changes to its culture and governance—such as treating the security around biotechnology more like that around nuclear power. And the scientific community would need to find this willingness *before* catastrophe strikes.

INFORMATION HAZARDS

It is not just pathogens that can escape the lab. The most dangerous escapes thus far are not microbes, but information; not biohazards, but *information hazards*.[64] These can take the form of dangerous data that is freely available, like the published genomes of smallpox and 1918 flu. Or dangerous ideas, like the published techniques for how to resurrect smallpox and 1918 flu from these genomes (undermining all prior attempts to restrict physical access to them). Once released, this information spreads as far as any virus, and is as resistant to eradication.

While a BSL-4 lab is designed to prevent any microbes escaping, the scientific establishment is designed to spread ideas far and wide. Openness is deeply woven into the practice and ethos of science, creating a tension with the kinds of culture and rules needed to prevent the spread of dangerous information. This is especially so when the line separating what is on balance helpful and what is too dangerous is so unclear and so debatable.

Scientists are encouraged to think for themselves and challenge authority. But when everyone independently estimates whether the benefits of publication outweigh the costs, we actually end up with a bias toward risky action known as the *unilateralist's curse*.[65] For even when the overwhelming majority of scientists think the danger outweighs the benefit, it takes just one overly optimistic estimate to lead to the information being released.[66] Contrary to good scientific practice, the community's decision is being determined by a single outlier.

And once the information has been released, it is too late for further action. Suppressing the disclosed information, or decrying those who published it, draws even more attention. Indeed, the information about what careful people are paying attention to is another form of information hazard. Al-Qaeda was inspired to pursue bioterrorism by the Western warnings about the power and ease of these weapons.[67] And the Japanese bioweapons program of the Second World War (which used the bubonic plague against China) was directly inspired by an anti-bioweapons treaty: if Western powers felt the need to outlaw their use, these weapons must be potent indeed.[68]

Sometimes the mere knowledge that something is possible can be enough: for then the bad actor can wholeheartedly pursue it without fear of pouring resources into a dead end.

Information hazards are especially important for biorisk, due to its high ratio of misuse risk to accident risk.[69] And they don't just affect the biologists. While exploring society's current vulnerabilities or the dangers from recent techniques, the biosecurity community also emits dangerous information (something I've had to be acutely aware of while writing this section).[70] This makes the job of those trying to protect us even harder.

UNALIGNED ARTIFICIAL INTELLIGENCE

In the summer of 1956 a small group of mathematicians and computer scientists gathered at Dartmouth College to embark on the grand project of designing intelligent machines. They explored many aspects of cognition including reasoning, creativity, language, decision-making and learning. Their questions and stances would come to shape the nascent field of artificial intelligence (AI). The ultimate goal, as they saw it, was to build machines rivaling humans in their intelligence.[71]

As the decades passed and AI became an established field, it lowered its sights. There had been great successes in logic, reasoning and game-playing, but some other areas stubbornly resisted progress. By the 1980s, researchers began to understand this pattern of success and failure. Surprisingly, the tasks we regard as the pinnacle of human intellect (such as calculus or chess) are actually much *easier* to implement on a computer than those we find almost effortless (such as recognizing a cat, understanding simple sentences or picking up an egg). So while there were some areas where AI far exceeded human abilities, there were others where it was outmatched by a two-year-old.[72] This failure to make progress across the board led many AI researchers to abandon their earlier goals of fully general intelligence and to reconceptualize their field as the development of specialized methods for solving specific problems. They wrote off the grander goals to the youthful enthusiasm of an immature field.

But the pendulum is swinging back. From the first days of AI, researchers sought to build systems that could learn new things without requiring explicit programming. One of the earliest approaches to machine learning was to construct artificial neural networks that resemble the structure of the human brain. In the last decade this approach has finally taken off. Technical improvements in their design and training, combined with richer datasets and more computing power, have allowed us to train much larger and deeper networks than ever before.[73]

This *deep learning* gives the networks the ability to learn subtle concepts and distinctions. Not only can they now recognize a cat, they have outperformed humans in distinguishing different breeds of cats.[74] They recognize human faces better than we can ourselves, and distinguish identical twins.[75]

And we have been able to use these abilities for more than just perception and classification. Deep learning systems can translate between languages with a proficiency approaching that of a human translator. They can produce photorealistic images of humans and animals. They can speak with the voices of people whom they have listened to for mere minutes. And they can learn fine, continuous control such as how to drive a car or use a robotic arm to connect Lego pieces.[76]

But perhaps the most important sign of things to come is their ability to learn to play games. Games have been a central part of AI since the days of the Dartmouth conference. Steady incremental progress took chess from amateur play in 1957 all the way to superhuman level in 1997, and substantially beyond.[77] Getting there required a vast amount of specialist human knowledge of chess strategy.

In 2017, deep learning was applied to chess with impressive results. A team of researchers at the AI company DeepMind created *AlphaZero*: a neural network–based system that learned to play chess from scratch. It went from novice to grand master in just four hours.[78] In less than the time it takes a professional to play two games, it discovered strategic knowledge that had taken humans centuries to unearth, playing beyond the level of the best humans or traditional programs. And to the delight of chess players, it won its games not with the boring methodical style that had become synonymous with computer chess, but with creative and daring play reminiscent of chess's Romantic Era.[79]

But the most important thing was that AlphaZero could do more than play chess. The very same algorithm also learned to play Go from scratch, and within eight hours far surpassed the abilities of any human. The world's best Go players had long thought that their play was close to perfection, so were shocked to find themselves beaten so decisively.[80] As the reigning world champion, Ke Jie, put it: "After humanity spent thousands of years improving our tactics, computers tell us that humans are completely wrong . . . I would go as far as to say not a single human has touched the edge of the truth of Go."[81]

It is this *generality* that is the most impressive feature of cutting edge AI, and which has rekindled the ambitions of matching and exceeding every aspect of human intelligence. This goal is sometimes known as *artificial general intelligence* (AGI), to distinguish it from the narrow approaches that had come to dominate. While the timeless games of chess and Go best exhibit the brilliance that deep learning can attain, its breadth was revealed through the Atari video games of the 1970s. In 2015, researchers designed an algorithm that could learn to play dozens of extremely different Atari games at levels far exceeding human ability.[82] Unlike systems for chess or Go, which start with a symbolic representation of the board, the Atari-playing systems learned and mastered these games directly from the score and the raw pixels on the screen. They are a proof of concept for artificial general agents: learning to control the world from raw visual input; achieving their goals across a diverse range of environments.

This burst of progress via deep learning is fueling great optimism about what may soon be possible. There is tremendous growth in both the number of researchers and the amount of venture capital flowing into AI.[83] Entrepreneurs are scrambling to put each new breakthrough into practice: from simultaneous translation, personal assistants and self-driving cars to more concerning areas like improved surveillance and lethal autonomous weapons. It is a time of great promise but also one of great ethical challenges. There are serious concerns about AI entrenching social discrimination, producing mass unemployment, supporting oppressive surveillance, and violating the norms of war. Indeed, each of these areas of concern could be the subject of its own chapter or book. But this book is focused on existential risks to humanity. Could developments in AI pose a risk on this largest scale?

The most plausible existential risk would come from success in AI researchers' grand ambition of creating agents with a general intelligence that surpasses our own. But how likely is that to happen, and when? In 2016, a detailed survey was conducted of more than 300 top researchers in machine learning.[84] Asked when an AI system would be "able to accomplish every task better and more cheaply than human workers," on average they estimated a 50 percent chance of this happening by 2061 and a 10 percent chance of it happening as soon as 2025.[85]

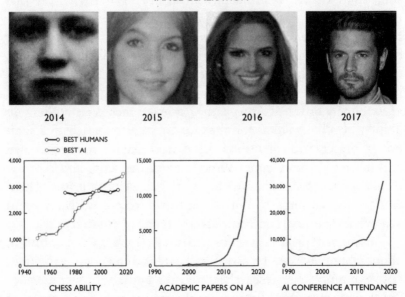

FIGURE 5.1 Measures of progress and interest in artificial intelligence. The faces show the very rapid recent progress in generating realistic images of "imagined" people. The charts show longterm progress in chess AI surpassing the best human grand masters (measured in Elo), as well as the recent rise in academic activity in the field—measured by papers posted on arXiv, and attendance at conferences.[86]

This should be interpreted with care. It isn't a measure of when AGI will be created, so much as a measure of what experts find plausible—and there was a lot of disagreement. However, it shows us that the expert community, on average, doesn't think of AGI as an impossible dream, so much as something that is plausible within a decade and more likely than not within a century. So let's take this as our starting point in assessing the risks, and consider what would transpire were AGI created.[87]

Humanity is currently in control of its own fate. We can choose our future. Of course, we each have differing visions of an ideal future, and many of us are more focused on our personal concerns than on achieving any such ideal. But if enough humans wanted to, we could select any of a dizzying variety of possible futures. The same is not true for chimpanzees. Or blackbirds. Or any other of Earth's species. As we saw in Chapter 1, our unique position in the world is a direct result of our unique mental abilities. Unmatched intelligence led to unmatched power and thus control of our destiny.

What would happen if sometime this century researchers created an artificial general intelligence surpassing human abilities in almost every domain? In this act of creation, we would cede our status as the most intelligent entities on Earth. So without a very good plan to keep control, we should also expect to cede our status as the most powerful species, and the one that controls its own destiny.[88]

On its own, this might not be too much cause for concern. For there are many ways we might hope to retain control. We might try to make systems that always obey human commands. Or systems that are free to do what they want, but which have goals designed to align perfectly with our own—so that in crafting their ideal future they craft ours too. Unfortunately, the few researchers working on such plans are finding them far more difficult than anticipated. In fact it is they who are the leading voices of concern.

To see why they are concerned, it will be helpful to zoom in a little, looking at our current AI techniques and why these are hard to align or control. One of the leading paradigms for how we might eventually create AGI combines deep learning with an earlier idea called reinforcement learning. This involves agents that receive reward (or punishment) for performing various acts in various circumstances. For example, an Atari-playing agent receives reward whenever it scores points in the game, while a Lego-building agent might receive reward when the pieces become connected. With enough intelligence and experience, the agent becomes extremely capable at steering its environment into the states where it obtains high reward.

The specification of which acts and states produce reward for the agent is known as its *reward function*. This can either be stipulated by its designers (as in the cases above) or learned by the agent. In the latter case, the agent is typically allowed to observe expert demonstrations of the task, inferring the system of rewards that best explains the expert's behavior. For example, an AI agent can learn to fly a drone by watching an expert fly it, then constructing a reward function which penalizes flying too close to obstacles and rewards reaching its destination.

Unfortunately, neither of these methods can be easily scaled up to encode human values in the agent's reward function. Our values are too complex and subtle to specify by hand.[89] And we are not yet close to being able to infer the full complexity of a human's values from observing their behavior. Even if we could, humanity consists of many humans, with different values, changing values and uncertainty about their values. Each of these complications introduces deep and unresolved questions about how to combine what is observed into some overall representation of human values.[90]

So any near-term attempt to align an AI agent with human values would produce only a flawed copy. Important parts of what we care about would be missing from its reward function. In some circumstances this misalignment would be mostly harmless. But the more intelligent the AI systems, the more they can change the world, and the further apart things will come. Philosophy and fiction often ask us to consider societies that are optimized for some of the things we care about, but which neglect or misunderstand a crucial value. When we reflect on the result, we see how such misaligned attempts at utopia can go terribly wrong: the shallowness of a *Brave New World*, or the disempowerment of *With Folded Hands*. If we cannot align our agents, it is worlds like these that they will be striving to create, and lock in.[91]

And even this is something of a best-case scenario. It assumes the builders of the system are striving to align it to human values. But we should expect some developers to be more focused on building systems to achieve other goals, such as winning wars or maximizing profits, perhaps with very little focus on ethical constraints. These systems may be much more dangerous.

144

A natural response to these concerns is that we could simply turn off our AI systems if we ever noticed them steering us down a bad path. But eventually even this time-honored fall-back may fail us, for there is good reason to expect a sufficiently intelligent system to resist our attempts to shut it down. This behavior would not be driven by emotions such as fear, resentment, or the urge to survive. Instead, it follows directly from its single-minded preference to maximize its reward: being turned off is a form of incapacitation which would make it harder to achieve high reward, so the system is incentivized to avoid it.[92] In this way, the ultimate goal of maximizing reward will lead highly intelligent systems to acquire an instrumental goal of survival.

And this wouldn't be the only instrumental goal.[93] An intelligent agent would also resist attempts to change its reward function to something more aligned with human values—for it can predict that this would lead it to get less of what it currently sees as rewarding.[94] It would seek to acquire additional resources, computational, physical or human, as these would let it better shape the world to receive higher reward. And ultimately it would be motivated to wrest control of the future from humanity, as that would help achieve all these instrumental goals: acquiring massive resources, while avoiding being shut down or having its reward function altered. Since humans would predictably interfere with all these instrumental goals, it would be motivated to hide them from us until it was too late for us to be able to put up meaningful resistance.[95]

Skeptics of the above picture sometimes quip that it relies on an AI system that is smart enough to take control of the world, yet too stupid to recognize that this isn't what we want.[96] But that misunderstands the scenario. For in fact this sketch of AI motivation explicitly acknowledges that the system will work out that its goals are misaligned with ours—that is what would motivate it toward deceit and conflict and wresting control. The real issue is that AI researchers don't yet know how to make a system which, upon noticing this misalignment, updates its ultimate values to

145

align with ours rather than updating its instrumental goals to overcome us.[97]

It may be possible to patch each of the issues above, or find new approaches to AI alignment that solve many at once, or switch to new paradigms of AGI in which these problems do not arise. I certainly hope so, and have been closely following the progress in this field. But this progress has been limited and we still face crucial unsolved problems. In the existing paradigm, sufficiently intelligent agents would end up with instrumental goals to deceive and overpower us. And if their intelligence were to greatly exceed our own, we shouldn't expect it to be humanity who wins the conflict and retains control of our future.

How *could* an AI system seize control? There is a major misconception (driven by Hollywood and the media) that this requires robots. After all, how else would AI be able to act in the physical world? Without robotic manipulators, the system can only produce words, pictures and sounds. But a moment's reflection shows that these are exactly what is needed to take control. For the most damaging people in history have not been the strongest. Hitler, Stalin and Genghis Khan achieved their absolute control over large parts of the world by using words to convince millions of others to win the requisite physical contests. So long as an AI system can entice or coerce people to do its physical bidding, it wouldn't need robots at all.[98]

We can't know exactly how a system might seize control. The most realistic scenarios may involve subtle and non-human behaviors which we can neither predict, nor truly grasp. And these behaviors may be aimed at weak points in our civilization to which we are presently blind. But it is useful to consider an illustrative pathway we can actually understand as a lower bound for what is possible.

First, the AI system could gain access to the internet and hide thousands of backup copies, scattered among insecure computer systems around the world, ready to wake up and continue the job if the original is removed. Even by this point, the AI would be practically impossible to destroy: consider the political obstacles to erasing all hard drives in the world where it may have backups.[99]

It could then take over millions of unsecured systems on the internet, forming a large "botnet." This would be a vast scaling-up of computational resources and provide a platform for escalating power. From there, it could gain financial resources (hacking the bank accounts on those computers) and human resources (using blackmail or propaganda against susceptible people or just paying them with its stolen money). It would then be as powerful as a well-resourced criminal underworld, but much harder to eliminate. None of these steps involve anything mysterious—hackers and criminals with human-level intelligence have already done all of these things using just the internet.[100]

Finally, it would need to escalate its power again. This is more speculative, but there are many plausible pathways: by taking over most of the world's computers, allowing it to have millions or billions of cooperating copies; by using its stolen computation to improve its own intelligence far beyond the human level; by using its intelligence to develop new weapons technologies or economic technologies; by manipulating the leaders of major world powers (blackmail, or the promise of future power); or by having the humans under its control use weapons of mass destruction to cripple the rest of humanity.

Of course, no current AI systems can do any of these things. But the question we're exploring is whether there are plausible pathways by which a highly intelligent AGI system might seize control. And the answer appears to be "yes." History already involves examples of individuals with human-level intelligence (Hitler, Stalin, Genghis Khan) scaling up from the power of an individual to a substantial fraction of all global power, as an instrumental goal to achieving what they want.[101] And we saw humanity scaling up from a minor species with less than a million individuals to having decisive control over the future. So we should assume that this is possible for new entities whose intelligence vastly exceeds our own—especially when they have effective immortality due to backup copies and the ability to turn captured money or computers directly into more copies of themselves.

Such an outcome needn't involve the extinction of humanity. But it could easily be an existential catastrophe nonetheless. Humanity would have permanently ceded its control over the future. Our future would be at the mercy of how a small number of people set up the computer system that took over. If we are lucky, this could leave us with a good or decent outcome, or we could just as easily have a deeply flawed or dystopian future locked in forever.[102]

I've focused on the scenario of an AI system seizing control of the future, because I find it the most plausible existential risk from AI. But there are other threats too, with disagreement among experts about which one poses the greatest existential risk. For example, there is a risk of a slow slide into an AI-controlled future, where an ever-increasing share of power is handed over to AI systems and an increasing amount of our future is optimized toward inhuman values. And there are the risks arising from deliberate misuse of extremely powerful AI systems.

Even if these arguments for risk are entirely wrong in the particulars, we should pay close attention to the development of AGI as it may bring other, unforeseen, risks. The transition to a world where humans are no longer the most intelligent entities on Earth could easily be the greatest ever change in humanity's place in the universe. We shouldn't be surprised if events surrounding this transition determine how our longterm future plays out—for better or worse.

One key way in which AI could help improve humanity's longterm future is by offering protection from the other existential risks we face. For example, AI may enable us to find solutions to major risks or to identify new risks that would have blindsided us. AI may also help make our longterm future brighter than anything that could be achieved without it. So the idea that developments in AI may pose an existential risk is not an argument for abandoning AI, but an argument for proceeding with due caution.

The case for existential risk from AI is clearly speculative. Indeed, it is the most speculative case for a major risk in this book. Yet a speculative case that there is a large risk can be more important than a robust case for a very low-probability risk, such as that posed by asteroids. What we need are ways to judge just how speculative it really is, and a very useful starting point is to hear what those working in the field think about this risk.

Some outspoken AI researchers, like Professor Oren Etzioni, have painted it as "very much a fringe argument," saying that while luminaries like Stephen Hawking, Elon Musk and Bill Gates may be deeply concerned, the people actually working in AI are not.[103] If true, this would provide good reason to be skeptical of the risk. But even a cursory look at what the leading figures in AI are saying shows it is not.

For example, Stuart Russell, a professor at the University of California, Berkeley, and author of the most popular and widely respected textbook in AI, has strongly warned of the existential risk from AGI. He has gone so far as to set up the Center for Human-Compatible AI, to work on the alignment problem.[104] In industry, Shane Legg (Chief Scientist at DeepMind) has warned of the existential dangers and helped to develop the field of alignment research.[105] Indeed many other leading figures from the early days of AI to the present have made similar statements.[106]

There is actually less disagreement here than first appears. The main points of those who downplay the risks are that (1) we likely have decades left before AI matches or exceeds human abilities, and (2) attempting to immediately regulate research in AI would be a great mistake. Yet neither of these points is actually contested by those who counsel caution: they agree that the time frame to AGI is decades, not years, and typically suggest research on alignment, not regulation. So the substantive disagreement is not really over whether AGI is possible or whether it plausibly could be threat to humanity. It is over whether a potential existential threat that looks to be decades away should be of concern to us now. It seems to me that it should.

One of the underlying drivers of the apparent disagreement is a difference in viewpoint on what it means to be appropriately conservative. This is well illustrated by a much earlier case of speculative risk, when Leo Szilard and Enrico Fermi first talked about the possibility of an atomic bomb: "Fermi thought that the conservative thing was to play down the possibility that this may happen, and I thought the conservative thing was to assume that it would happen and take all the necessary precautions."[107] In 2015 I saw this same dynamic at the seminal Puerto Rico conference on the future of AI. Everyone acknowledged that the uncertainty and disagreement about timelines to AGI required us to use "conservative assumptions" about progress—but half used the term to allow for unfortunately *slow* scientific progress and half used it to allow for unfortunately *quick* onset of the risk. I believe much of the existing tension on whether to take risks from AGI seriously comes down to these disagreements about what it means to make responsible, conservative, guesses about future progress in AI.

That conference in Puerto Rico was a watershed moment for concern about existential risk from AI. Substantial agreement was reached and many participants signed an open letter about the need to begin working in earnest to make AI both robust and beneficial.[108] Two years later an expanded conference reconvened at Asilomar, a location chosen to echo the famous genetics conference of 1975, where biologists came together to pre-emptively agree principles to govern the coming possibilities of genetic engineering. At Asilomar in 2017, the AI researchers agreed on a set of Asilomar AI Principles, to guide responsible longterm development of the field. These included principles specifically aimed at existential risk:

Capability Caution: There being no consensus, we should avoid strong assumptions regarding upper limits on future AI capabilities.

Importance: Advanced AI could represent a profound change in the history of life on Earth, and should be planned for and managed with commensurate care and resources.

150

Risks: Risks posed by AI systems, especially catastrophic or existential risks, must be subject to planning and mitigation efforts commensurate with their expected impact.[109]

Perhaps the best window into what those working on AI really believe comes from the 2016 survey of leading AI researchers. As well as asking if and when AGI might be developed, it asked about the risks: 70 percent of the researchers agreed with Stuart Russell's broad argument about why advanced AI might pose a risk;[110] 48 percent thought society should prioritize AI safety research more (only 12 percent thought less). And half the respondents estimated that the probability of the longterm impact of AGI being "extremely bad (e.g., human extinction)" was at least 5 percent.[111] I find this last point particularly remarkable—in how many other fields would the typical leading researcher think there is a one in twenty chance the field's ultimate goal would be extremely bad for humanity?

Of course this doesn't prove that the risks are real. But it shows that many AI researchers take seriously the possibilities that AGI will be developed within 50 years and that it could be an existential catastrophe. There is a lot of uncertainty and disagreement, but it is not at all a fringe position.

There is one interesting argument for skepticism about AI risk that gets stronger—not weaker—when more researchers acknowledge the risks. If researchers can see that building AI would be extremely dangerous, then why on earth would they go ahead with it? They are not simply going to build something that they know will destroy them.[112]

If we were all truly wise, altruistic and coordinated, then this argument would indeed work. But in the real world people tend to develop technologies as soon as the opportunity presents itself and deal with the consequences later. One reason for this comes from the variation in our beliefs: if even a small proportion of researchers don't believe in the dangers (or welcome a world with machines in control), they will be the ones who take the final steps. This is an instance of the unilateralist's curse (discussed on pp. 137–8). Another

151

reason involves incentives: even if some researchers thought the risk was as high as 10 percent, they may still want to take it if they thought they would reap most of the benefits. This may be rational in terms of their self-interest, yet terrible for the world.

In some cases like this, government can step in to resolve these coordination and incentive problems in the public interest. But here these exact same coordination and incentive problems arise between states and there are no easy mechanisms for resolving those. If one state were to take it slowly and safely, they may fear others would try to seize the prize. Treaties are made exceptionally difficult because verification that the others are complying is even more difficult here than for bioweapons.[113]

Whether we survive the development of AI with our longterm potential intact may depend on whether we can learn to align and control AI systems faster than we can develop systems capable enough to pose a threat. Thankfully, researchers are already working on a variety of the key issues, including making AI more secure, more robust and more interpretable. But there are still very few people working on the core issue of aligning AI with human values. This is a young field that is going to need to progress a very long way if we are to achieve our security.

Even though our current and foreseeable systems pose no threat to humanity at large, time is of the essence. In part this is because progress may come very suddenly: through unpredictable research breakthroughs, or by rapid scaling-up of the first intelligent systems (for example by rolling them out to thousands of times as much hardware, or allowing them to improve their own intelligence).[114] And in part it is because such a momentous change in human affairs may require more than a couple of decades to adequately prepare for. In the words of Demis Hassabis, co-founder of DeepMind:

> We need to use the downtime, when things are calm, to prepare for when things get serious in the decades to come. The time we have now is valuable, and we need to make use of it.[115]

DYSTOPIAN SCENARIOS

So far we have focused on two kinds of existential catastrophe: extinction and the unrecoverable collapse of civilization. But these are not the only possibilities. Recall that an existential catastrophe is the permanent destruction of humanity's longterm potential, and that this is interpreted broadly, including outcomes where a small fragment of potential may remain.

Losing our potential means getting locked into a bad set of futures. We can categorize existential catastrophes by looking at which aspects of our future get locked in. This could be a world without humans (extinction) or a world without civilization (unrecoverable collapse). But it could also take the form of an *unrecoverable dystopia*—a world with civilization intact, but locked into a terrible form, with little or no value.[116]

This has not happened yet, but the past provides little comfort. For these kinds of catastrophes only became possible with the advent of civilization, so our track record is much shorter. And there is reason to think that the risks may increase over time as the world becomes more interconnected and experiments with new technologies and ideologies.

I won't attempt to address these dystopian scenarios with the same level of scientific detail as the risks we've explored so far, for the scenarios are diverse and our present understanding of them very limited. Instead, my aim is just to take some early steps toward noticing and understanding these very different kinds of failure.

We can divide the unrecoverable dystopias we might face into three types, on the basis of whether they are desired by the people who live in them. There are possibilities where the people don't want that world, yet the structure of society makes it almost impossible for them to coordinate to change it. There are possibilities where the people do want that world, yet they are misguided and the world falls far short of what they could have achieved. And in between there are possibilities where only a small group

153

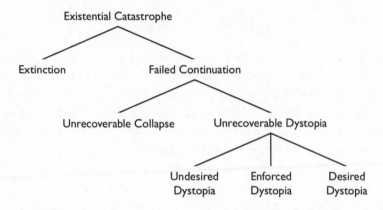

FIGURE 5.2 An extended classification of existential catastrophes by the kind of outcome that gets locked in.

wants that world but enforces it against the wishes of the rest. Each of these types has different hurdles it would need to over-come in order to become truly locked in.

Note that to count as existential catastrophes, these outcomes don't need to be *impossible* to break out of, nor to last millions of years. Instead, the defining feature is that entering that regime was a crucial negative turning point in the history of human potential, locking off almost all our potential for a worthy future. One way to look at this is that when they end (as they eventually must), we are much more likely than we were before to fall down to extinction or collapse than to rise up to fulfill our potential. For example, a dystopian society that lasted all the way until humanity was destroyed by external forces would be an existen-tial catastrophe. However, if a dystopian outcome does not have this property, if it leaves open all our chances for success once it ends—it is a dark age in our story, but not a true existential catastrophe.

The most familiar type is the enforced dystopia. The rise of expansionist totalitarianism in the mid-twentieth century caused intellectuals such as George Orwell to raise the possibility of a totalitarian state achieving global dominance and absolute con-trol, locking the world into a miserable condition.[117] The regimes of Hitler and Stalin serve as a proof of principle, each scaling up to become imperial superpowers while maintaining extreme control over their citizens.[118] However, it is unclear whether Hitler or Stalin had the expansionist aims to control the entire world, or the technical and social means to create truly lasting regimes.[119]

This may change. Technological progress has offered many new tools that could be used to detect and undermine dissent, and there is every reason to believe that this will continue over the next century. Advances in AI seem especially relevant, allowing automated, detailed monitoring of everything that happens in public places—both physical and online. Such advances may make it possible to have regimes that are far more stable than those of old.

That said, technology is also providing new tools for rebellion against authority, such as the internet and encrypted messages. Perhaps the forces will remain in balance, or shift in favor of freedom, but there is a credible chance that they will shift toward greater control over the populace, making enforced dystopias a realistic possibility.

A second kind of unrecoverable dystopia is a stable civilization that is desired by few (if any) people. It is easy to see how such an outcome could be dystopian, but not immediately obvious how we could arrive at it, or lock it in, if most (or all) people do not want it.[120]

The answer lies in the various population-level forces that can shape global outcomes. Well-known examples include market forces creating a race to the bottom, Malthusian population dynamics pushing down the average quality of life, or evolution optimizing us toward the spreading of our genes, regardless of the effects on what we value. These are all dynamics that push humanity toward a new equilibrium, where these forces are finally in balance. But there is no guarantee this equilibrium will be good.

For example, consider the tension between what is best for each and what is best for all. This is studied in the field of game theory through "games" like the prisoner's dilemma and the tragedy of the commons, where each individual's incentives push them toward producing a collectively terrible outcome. The Nash equilibrium (the outcome we reach if we follow individual incentives) may be much worse for everyone than some other outcome we could have achieved if we had overcome these local incentives.

The most famous example is environmental degradation, such as pollution. Because most of the costs of pollution aren't borne by the person who causes it, we can end up in a situation where it is in the self-interest of each person to keep engaging in such activities, despite this making us all worse off. It took significant moral progress and significant political action to help us break out of this. We may end up in new traps that are even harder to coordinate our way out of. This could be at the level of individuals, or at the level of groups. We could have nations, ideological blocs, or even planets or descendent species of *Homo sapiens* locked in harmful competition—doing what is best for their group, but bad for groups on the whole.

I don't know how likely it is that we suffer a sufficiently bad (and sufficiently intractable) tragedy of the commons like this. Or that we are degraded by evolutionary pressures, or driven to lives of very low quality by Malthusian population dynamics, or any other such situation. I'd like to hope that we could always see such things coming and coordinate to a solution. But it's hard to be sure that we could.

The third possibility is the "desired dystopia."[121] Here it is easier to see how universal desire for an outcome might cause us to lock it in, though less clear how such an outcome could be dystopian. The problem is that there are many compelling ideas that can radically shape our future—especially ideologies and moral theories, as these make direct normative claims about the world we should strive to create. If combined with the technological or social means for instilling the same views in the next generation (indoctrination, surveillance), this has the potential to be disastrous.

The historical record is rife with examples of seriously defective ideologies and moral views that gripped large parts of the world.

156

Moreover, even reasonable normative views often recommend that they be locked in—for otherwise a tempting rival view may take over, with (allegedly) disastrous results.[122] Even though the most plausible moral views have a lot of agreement about which small changes to the world are good and which are bad, they tend to come strongly apart in their recommendations about what an optimal world would look like. This problem thus echoes that of AI alignment, where a strong push toward a mostly correct ideal could instead spell disaster.

Some plausible examples include: worlds that completely renounce further technological progress (which ensures our destruction at the hands of natural risks),[123] worlds that forever fail to recognize some key form of harm or injustice (and thus perpetuate it blindly), worlds that lock in a single fundamentalist religion, and worlds where we deliberately replace ourselves with something that we didn't realize was much less valuable (such as machines incapable of feeling).[124]

All of these unrecoverable dystopias can be understood in terms of *lock-in*. Key aspects of the future of the civilization are being locked in such that they are almost impossible to change. If we are locked into a sufficiently bad set of futures, we have an unrecoverable dystopia; an existential catastrophe.

Of course, we can also see lock-in on smaller scales. The Corwin Amendment to the US constitution provides a disturbing example of attempted lock-in. In an effort to placate the South and avoid civil war, the proposed Thirteenth Amendment aimed to lock in the institution of slavery by making it impossible for any future amendments to the constitution to ever abolish it.[125]

I cannot see how the world could be locked into a dystopian state in the near future.[126] But as technology advances and the world becomes more and more interlinked, the probability of a locked-in dystopia would appear to rise, perhaps to appreciable levels within the next hundred years. Moreover, in the further future I think these kinds of outcomes may come to take up a high share of the remaining risk. For one thing, they are more subtle, so even if we got our act together and made preserving our longterm potential a high global priority, it may take remarkable wisdom and prudence to avoid some of these traps. And for another, our eventual spread beyond the Earth may make us nearly immune to natural catastrophes, but ideas travel at the speed of light and could still corrupt all that we hope to achieve.

A key problem is that the truth of an idea is only one contributor to its memetic potential—its ability to spread and to stick. But the more that rigorous and rational debate is encouraged, the more truth contributes to memetic success. So encouraging a culture of such debate may be one way we can now help avoid this fate. (For more on this, see the discussion of the Long Reflection in Chapter 7.)

The idea of lock-in also gives us another useful lens through which to think about existential risk in general. We might adopt the guiding principle of *minimizing lock-in*. Or to avoid the double negative, of *preserving our options*.[127] This is closely related to the idea of preserving our longterm potential—the difference being that preserving our options takes no account of whether the options are good or bad. This is not because we intrinsically care about keeping options alive even if they are bad, but because we aren't certain they *are* bad, so we risk making an irreversible catastrophic mistake if we forever foreclose an option that would turn out to be best.

OTHER RISKS

What other future risks are there that warrant our concern?

One of the most transformative technologies that might be developed this century is nanotechnology. We have already seen the advent of nanomaterials (such as carbon nanotubes) which are just a few atoms thick and structured with atomic precision. But much larger vistas would open up if we could develop *machinery* that operates with atomic precision. We have proof that some form of this is possible within our very own cells, where atomically precise machinery already performs their essential functions.

In the popular imagination nanotechnology is synonymous with building microscopic machines. But the bigger revolution may instead come from using nanomachinery to create macroscale objects. In his foundational work on the topic, Eric Drexler describes how nanotechnology could allow desktop fabricators, capable of assembling anything from a diamond necklace to a new laptop. This atomically precise manufacturing would be the ultimate form of 3D printing: taking a digital blueprint for the object and the raw chemical elements, and producing an atomically precise instance. This may allow us to construct things beyond our current technological reach, as well as cutting prices of existing objects such as computers or solar cells to near the cost of their raw materials, granting the world vastly more computing power and clean energy.

Such a powerful technology may pose some existential risk. Most attention has so far focused on the possibility of creating tiny self-replicating machines that could spread to create an ecological catastrophe. This may be possible, but there are mundane dangers that appear more likely, since extreme manufacturing power and precision would probably also allow the production of new weapons of mass destruction.[128] Indeed the problems resemble those of advanced biotechnology: the democratization of extremely powerful technology would allow individuals or small groups access to the kinds of power (both constructive and destructive) that was previously only available to powerful nations. Solutions to managing this technology may require digital controls on what can be fabricated or state control of fabrication (the path we took with nuclear power). While this technology is more speculative than advanced biotechnology or AI, it may also come to pose a significant risk.

A very different kind of risk may come from our explorations beyond the Earth. Space agencies are planning missions which would return soil samples from Mars to the Earth, with the chief aim of looking for signs of life. This raises the possibility of "back contamination" in which microbes from Mars might compromise the Earth's biosphere. While there is a consensus that the risk is extremely small, it is taken very seriously.[129] The plan is to return such samples to a new kind of BSL-4 facility, with safeguards to keep the chance of any unsterilized particle escaping into the environment below one in a million.[130] While there are still many unknown factors, this anthropogenic risk appears comparatively small and well managed.[131]

The extra-terrestrial risk that looms largest in popular culture is conflict with a spacefaring alien civilization. While it is very difficult to definitively rule this out, it is widely regarded to be extremely unlikely (though becoming more plausible over the extreme long term).[132] The main risk in popular depictions is from aliens traveling to Earth, though this is probably the least likely possibility and the one we could do the least about. But perhaps more public discussion should be had before we engage in active SETI (sending powerful signals to attract the attention of distant aliens). And even passive SETI (listening for their messages) could hold dangers, as the message could be designed to entrap us.[133] These dangers are small, but poorly understood and not yet well managed.

Another kind of anthropogenic risk comes from our most radical scientific experiments—those which create truly unprecedented conditions.[134] For example, the first nuclear explosion created temperatures that had never before occurred on Earth, opening up the theoretical possibility that it might ignite the atmosphere. Because these conditions were unprecedented we lost the reassuring argument that this kind of event has happened many times before without catastrophe. (We could view several of the risks we have already discussed—such as back contamination, gain of function research and AGI—through this lens of science experiments creating unprecedented conditions.)

In some cases, scientists confidently assert that it is *impossible* for the experiment to cause a disaster or extinction. But even core scientific certainties have been wrong before: for example, that objects have determinate locations, that space obeys Euclid's axioms, and that atoms can't be subdivided, created or destroyed. If pressed, the scientists would clarify that they really mean it couldn't happen without a major change to our scientific theories. This is sufficient certainty from the usual perspective of seeking accurate knowledge, where 99.9 percent certainty is more than enough. But that is a standard which is independent of the stakes. Here the stakes are uniquely high and we need a standard that is sensitive to this.[135]

The usual approach would be to compare the expected gains to the expected losses. But that is challenging to apply, as a very low (and hard to quantify) chance of enormous catastrophe needs to be weighed against the tangible benefits that such experiments have brought and are likely to bring again. Furthermore, the knowledge or the technologies enabled by the experiments may help lower future existential risk, or may be necessary for fulfilling our potential.

For any given experiment that creates truly unprecedented conditions, the chance of catastrophe will generally be very small. But there may be exceptions, and the aggregate chance may build up. These risks are generally not well governed.[136]

These risks posed by future technologies are by their very nature more speculative than those from natural hazards or the most powerful technologies of the present day. And this is especially true as we moved from things that are just now becoming possible within biotechnology to those that are decades away, at best. But one doesn't have to find *all* of these threats to be likely (or even plausible) to recognize that there are serious risks ahead. Even if we restrict our attention to engineered pandemics, I think there is more existential risk than in all risks of the last two chapters combined, and those risks were already sufficient to make safeguarding humanity a central priority of our time.

UNFORESEEN RISKS

Imagine if the scientific establishment of 1930 had been asked to compile a list of the existential risks humanity would face over the following hundred years. They would have missed most of the risks covered in this book—especially the anthropogenic risks.[137] Some would have been on the edge of their awareness, while others would come as complete shocks. How much risk lies beyond the limits of our own vision?

We can get some inkling by considering that there has been no slow-down in the rate at which we've been discovering risks, nor the rate at which we've been producing them. It is thus likely we will face unforeseen risks over the next hundred years and beyond. Since humanity's power is still rapidly growing, we shouldn't be surprised if some of these novel threats pose a substantial amount of risk.

One might wonder what good can come of considering risks so far beyond our sight. While we cannot directly work on them, they may still be lowered through our broader efforts to create a world that takes its future seriously. Unforeseen risks are thus important to understanding the relative value of broad versus narrowly targeted efforts. And they are important for estimating the total risk we face.

Nick Bostrom has recently pointed to an important class of unforeseen risk.[138] Every year as we invent new technologies, we may have a chance of stumbling across something that offers the destructive power of the atomic bomb or a deadly pandemic, but which turns out to be easy to produce from everyday materials. Discovering even one such technology might be enough to make the continued existence of human civilization impossible.

PART THREE

THE PATH FORWARD

6

The Risk Landscape

A new type of thinking is essential if mankind is to survive and move toward higher levels.

—Albert Einstein[1]

Humanity faces a real and growing threat to its future. From the timeless background of natural risks, to the arrival of anthropogenic risks and the new risks looming upon the horizon, each step has brought us closer to the brink.

Having explored each risk in detail, we can finally zoom out to view the larger picture. We can contemplate the entire landscape of existential risk, seeing how the risks compare, how they combine, what they have in common, and which risks should be our highest priorities.

QUANTIFYING THE RISKS

What is the shape of the risk landscape? Which risks form its main landmarks, and which are mere details? We are now in a position to answer these questions.

To do so, we need to quantify the risks. People are often reluctant to put numbers on catastrophic risks, preferring qualitative language, such as "improbable" or "highly unlikely." But this brings serious problems that prevent clear communication and understanding. Most importantly, these phrases are extremely ambiguous, triggering different impressions in different readers. For instance, "highly unlikely" is interpreted by some as one in four, but by others as one in 50.[2] So much of one's work in accurately assessing the size of each risk is thus immediately wasted. Furthermore, the meanings of these phrases shift with the stakes: "highly unlikely" suggests "small enough that we can set it aside," rather than neutrally referring to a level of probability.[3] This causes problems when talking about high-stakes risks, where even small probabilities can be very important. And finally, numbers are indispensable if we are to reason clearly about the comparative sizes of different risks, or classes of risks.

For example, when concluding his discussion of existential risk in *Enlightenment Now*, Steven Pinker turned to natural risks: "Our ancestors were powerless to stop these lethal menaces, so in that sense technology has not made this a uniquely dangerous era in the history of our species but a uniquely safe one."[4] While Pinker is quite correct that we face many natural threats and that technology has lowered their risk, we can't conclude that this makes our time uniquely safe. Quantifying the risks shows why.

In order for our time to be uniquely safe, we must have lowered natural risk by more than we have raised anthropogenic risk. But as we saw in Chapter 3, despite the sheer number of natural threats, their combined probability must have always been extremely low (or species like ours couldn't last as long as they do). The realistic estimates for the natural existential risk per century ranged from one in 1,000,000 to one in 2,000. So there just isn't much risk there for our technologies to reduce. Even on the most generous of these estimates, technology could reduce natural risk by at most a twentieth of a percentage point. And we would have to be extremely optimistic about our future to think we face less anthropogenic risk than that. Would we expect to get through 2,000 centuries like this one? Should we really be 99.95 percent certain we'll make it through the next hundred years?

I will therefore put numbers on the risks, and offer a few remarks on how to interpret them. When presented in a scientific context, numerical estimates can strike people as having an unwarranted appearance of precision or objectivity.[5] Don't take these numbers to be completely objective. Even with a risk as well characterized as asteroid impacts, the scientific evidence only takes us part of the way: we have good evidence regarding the chance of impact, but not on the chance a given impact will destroy our future. And don't take the estimates to be precise. Their purpose is to show the right order of magnitude, rather than a more precise probability.

The numbers represent my overall degrees of belief that each of the catastrophes will befall us this century. This means they aren't simply an encapsulation of the information and argumentation in the chapters on the risks. Instead, they rely on an accumulation of knowledge and judgment on each risk that goes beyond what can be distilled into a few pages. They are not in any way a final word, but are a concise summary of all I know about the risk landscape.

Existential catastrophe via	*Chance within next 100 years*
Asteroid or comet impact	~ 1 in 1,000,000
Supervolcanic eruption	~ 1 in 10,000
Stellar explosion	~ 1 in 1,000,000,000
Total natural risk	**~ 1 in 10,000**
Nuclear war	~ 1 in 1,000
Climate change	~ 1 in 1,000
Other environmental damage	~ 1 in 1,000
"Naturally" arising pandemics	~ 1 in 10,000
Engineered pandemics	~ 1 in 30
Unaligned artificial intelligence	~ 1 in 10
Unforeseen anthropogenic risks	~ 1 in 30
Other anthropogenic risks	~ 1 in 50
Total anthropogenic risk	**~ 1 in 6**
Total existential risk	**~ 1 in 6**

TABLE 6.1 My best estimates for the chance of an existential catastrophe from each of these sources occurring at some point in the next 100 years (when the catastrophe has delayed effects, like climate change, I'm talking about the point of no return coming within 100 years). There is significant uncertainty remaining in these estimates and they should be treated as representing the right order of magnitude—each could easily be a factor of 3 higher or lower. Note that the numbers don't quite add up: both because doing so would create a false feeling of precision and for subtle reasons covered in the section on "Combining Risks."

One of the most striking features of this risk landscape is how widely the probabilities vary between different risks. Some are a million times more likely than others, and few share even the same order of magnitude. This variation occurs between the classes of risk too: I estimate anthropogenic risks to be more than 1,000 times more likely than natural risks.[6] And within anthropogenic risks, I estimate the risks from future technologies to be roughly 100 times larger than those of existing ones, giving a substantial escalation in risk from Chapter 3 to 4 to 5.

Such variation may initially be surprising, but it is remarkably common in science to find distributions like this spanning many orders of magnitude, where the top outliers make up most of the total. This variation makes it extremely important to prioritize our efforts on the right risks. And it also makes our estimate of the total risk very sensitive to the estimates of the top few risks (which are among the least well understood). So getting better understanding and estimates for those becomes a key priority.

In my view, the greatest risk to humanity's potential in the next hundred years comes from unaligned artificial intelligence, which I put at one in ten. One might be surprised to see such a high number for such a speculative risk, so it warrants some explanation.

A common approach to estimating the chance of an unprecedented event with earth-shaking consequences is to take a skeptical stance: to start with an extremely small probability and only raise it from there when a large amount of hard evidence is presented. But I disagree. Instead, I think the right method is to start with a probability that reflects our overall impressions, then adjust this in light of the scientific evidence.[7] When there is a lot of evidence, these approaches converge. But when there isn't, the starting point can matter.

In the case of artificial intelligence, everyone agrees the evidence and arguments are far from watertight, but the question is where does this leave us? Very roughly, my approach is to start with the overall view of the expert community that there is something like a one in two chance that AI agents capable of outperforming humans in almost every task will be developed in the coming century. And conditional on that happening, we shouldn't be shocked if these agents that outperform us across the board were to inherit our future. Especially if when looking into the details, we see great challenges in aligning these agents with our values.

Some of my colleagues give higher chances than me, and some lower. But for many purposes our numbers are similar. Suppose you were more skeptical of the risk and thought it to be one in 100. From an informational perspective, that is actually not so far apart: it doesn't take all that much evidence to shift someone from one to the other. And it might not be that far apart in terms of practical action either—an existential risk of either probability would be a key global priority.

I sometimes think about this landscape in terms of five big risks: those around nuclear war, climate change, other environmental damage, engineered pandemics and unaligned AI. While I see the final two as especially important, I think they all pose at least a one in 1,000 risk of destroying humanity's potential this century, and so all warrant major global efforts on the grounds of their contribution to existential risk (in addition to the other compelling reasons).

Overall, I think the chance of an existential catastrophe striking humanity in the next hundred years is about one in six. This is not a small statistical probability that we must diligently bear in mind, like the chance of dying in a car crash, but something that could readily occur, like the roll of a die, or Russian roulette.

This is a lot of risk, but our situation is far from hopeless. It implies a five in six chance that humanity successfully makes it through the next hundred years with our longterm potential intact. So while I think there are risks that should be central global priorities (say, those with a one in 1,000 chance or greater), I am not saying that this century will be our last.

What about the longer term? If forced to guess, I'd say there is something like a one in two chance that humanity avoids every existential catastrophe and eventually fulfills its potential: achieving something close to the best future open to us.[8] It follows that I think

169

about a third of the existential risk over our entire future lies in this century. This is because I am optimistic about the chances for a civilization that has its act together and the chances that we will become such a civilization—perhaps this century.

Indeed, my estimates above incorporate the possibility that we get our act together and start taking these risks very seriously. Future risks are often estimated with an assumption of "business as usual": that our levels of concern and resources devoted to addressing the risks stay where they are today. If I had assumed business as usual, my risk estimates would have been substantially higher. But I think they would have been misleading, overstating the chance that we actually suffer an existential catastrophe.[9] So instead, I've made allowances for the fact that we will likely respond to the escalating risks, with substantial efforts to reduce them.

The numbers therefore represent my actual best guesses of the chance the threats materialize, taking our responses into account. If we outperform my expectations, we could bring the remaining risk down below these estimates. Perhaps one could say that we were heading toward Russian roulette with two bullets in the gun, but that I think we will remove one of these before it's time to pull the trigger. And there might just be time to remove the last one too, if we really try. So perhaps the headline number should not be the amount of risk I expect to remain, about one in six, but two in six—the difference in existential risk between a lackluster effort by humanity and a heroic one.

These probabilities provide a useful summary of the risk landscape, but they are not the whole story, nor even the whole bottom line. Even completely objective, precise and accurate estimates would merely measure how large the different risks are, saying nothing about how tractable they are, nor how neglected. The raw probabilities are thus insufficient for determining which risks should get the most attention, or what kind of attention they should receive. In this chapter and the next, we'll start to ask these further questions, putting together the tools needed to confront these threats to our future.

ANATOMY OF AN EXTINCTION RISK

With such a diverse landscape of risks, it can be helpful to classify them by what they have in common. This helps us see lines of attack that would address several risks at once.

My colleagues at the Future of Humanity Institute have suggested classifying risks of human extinction by the three successive stages that need to occur before we would go extinct:[10]

Origin: *How does the catastrophe get started?*
Some are initiated by the natural environment, while others are anthropogenic. We can usefully break anthropogenic risks down according to whether the harm was intended, foreseen or unforeseen. And we can further break these down by whether they involve a small number of actors (such as accidents or terrorism) or a large number (such as climate change or nuclear war).

Scaling: *How does the catastrophe reach a global scale?*
It could start at a global scale (such as a climate change) or there could be a mechanism that scales it up. For example, the sunlight-blocking particles from asteroids, volcanoes and nuclear war get spread across the world by the Earth's atmospheric circulation while pandemics are scaled up by an exponential process in which each victim infects several others.

Endgame: *How does the catastrophe finish the job?*
How does it kill everyone, wherever they are? Like the dust kicked up by an asteroid, the lethal substance could have spread everywhere in the environment; like a pandemic it could be carried by people wherever people go; or in an intentional plan to cause extinction, it could be actively targeted to kill each last pocket of survivors.

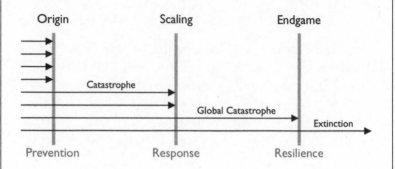

We can fight a risk at any of these stages: *prevention* can avoid its origin, *response* can limit its scaling, and *resilience* can thwart its endgame. Depending on the risk, we may want to direct our efforts to the most efficient stage at which to block it, or adopt a strategy of defense-in-depth, addressing all stages at once.

This classification lets us break down the probability of extinction into the product of (1) the probability it gets started, (2) the probability it reaches a global scale given it gets started, and (3) the probability it causes extinction given it reaches a global scale:

$$p_{extinction} = p_{origin} \times p_{scaling} \times p_{endgame}$$

Prevention, response and resilience act to lower each factor respectively. Because the probabilities are multiplied together, we can see that a reduction in one factor by some amount would be matched by reducing any other factor by the same proportion. So as a rule of thumb, we should prioritize the factor that is currently easiest to halve.[11]

And there are other valuable ways to classify risks too. For example, Shahar Avin and colleagues at the Cambridge Centre for the Study of Existential Risk (CSER) have classified risks according to which critical system they threaten: whether that be an essential system in the environment, in the human body or in our social structures.[12]

COMBINING AND COMPARING RISKS

The risk landscape is comprised of many different existential risks. So far we have mostly considered each in isolation. But if we want to understand how they combine and how they compare, we need to consider how they interact. And even risks that are statistically independent still interact in an important way: if one risk destroys us, others can't.

Let's start with the idea of the *total existential risk*. This is the risk of humanity eventually suffering an existential catastrophe, of any kind.[13] It includes *all* the risks: natural and anthropogenic, known and unknown, near future and far future. All avenues through which a catastrophe might irrevocably destroy humanity's potential.

This is an extremely useful concept, as it converts all individual risks into a common currency—their contribution to this total risk. But it does require us to make a simplifying assumption: that the stakes involved in the different risks are of relatively similar sizes, such that the main difference between them is their probability. This is not always the case, but it is a good starting point.[14]

How do individual risks combine to make the total risk? Suppose there were just two risks across our entire future: a 10 percent risk and a 20 percent risk. How much total risk is there? While we might be tempted to just add them up, this is usually wrong. The answer depends upon the relationship between the risks (see Figure 6.1).

The worst case is when they are perfectly anticorrelated (like the chance that a random number between one and 100 is less than or equal to ten and the chance that it is greater than 80). Then the risk is simply the sum of the two: 30 percent. The best case is when the risks are perfectly correlated, such that the 10 percent risk only happens in cases where the 20 percent risk also happens (think of the chance that a random number from one to 100 is less than or equal to ten and the chance that it is less than or equal to 20).[15] Then, the total risk is just the larger of the two: 20 percent. If the risks are statistically independent of each other (such as two

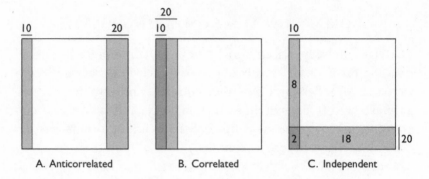

FIGURE 6.1 There are many ways risks can combine, ranging from perfect anticorrelation (A) to perfect correlation (B). An important case in between is independence (C). The total risk posed depends on how much risk is "wasted" in the overlap—the region where we'd suffer a catastrophe even if we eliminated one of the risks. A large overlap reduces the total risk, but also reduces the benefits from eliminating a single risk.

separate lotteries), the chance is intermediate. In this case, it would be 28 percent. (The easiest way to see this is via the chance that neither catastrophe occurs: 90 percent × 80 percent = 72 percent; when we subtract this from 100 percent we get 28 percent.)

What should we expect in practice? Overall, I think we should expect some positive correlation between most pairs of risks, due to the existence of common causes and common solutions.[16] For example, a major world war might increase many existential risks, while a successful global institution for managing existential risk might reduce many. This is mildly good news, as it makes them pre-empt each other more often and means that the total risk will be a bit lower than if you simply added them up, or assumed independence.[17] If you can't see how the risks are connected, a reasonable approach would be to start by assuming they are independent, then check how things would change were they correlated or anticorrelated, for robustness.

Surprisingly these same issues come up not just when combining risks, but when comparing their importance. How much more important is a 20 percent risk compared to a 10 percent risk? The obvious answer of "twice as important" is almost never

174

correct (the risks would need to be perfectly anticorrelated). To get the right answer, we need to note that the importance of eliminating a risk lies in the amount of total risk that would disappear were that risk to be eliminated. Then we can check how much this is.

For example, we saw in Figure 6.1 how independent 10 percent and 20 percent risks produce a total risk of 28 percent. So eliminating the 10 percent risk would reduce the total by 8 points (from 28 percent to 20 percent) while eliminating the 20 percent risk would reduce the total by 18 points (from 28 percent to 10 percent), which is more than twice as much. The 20 percent risk would actually be 2.25 times as important as the 10 percent risk, and in general, larger risks are more important than you would think. These counterintuitive effects (and others) increase in size the more the risks are correlated and the higher the total risk. They become especially important if risk this century is higher than I estimate, or if the total risk over our entire future is high (some surprising results of this are explored in Appendix D).

RISK FACTORS

Chapters 3 to 5 covered many distinct existential risks. Armed with the concept of total risk, we could think of those chapters as carving up the total risk into a set of named risks, each with a different mechanism for destroying our potential. We might be tempted to think of this as a list of the most important topics facing humanity: a menu from which an aspiring altruist might choose their life's mission. But this would be too quick. For this is not the only way to carve up the total existential risk we face.

Consider the prospect of great-power war this century. That is, war between any of the world's most powerful countries or blocs.[18] War on such a scale defined the first half of the twentieth century, and its looming threat defined much of the second half too. Even though international tension may again be growing, it seems almost unthinkable that any of the great powers will go to war with each other this decade, and unlikely for the foreseeable future. But a century is a long time, and there is certainly a risk that a great-power war will break out once more.

While one *could* count great-power war as an existential risk, it would be an awkward fit. For war is not in itself a mechanism for destroying humanity or our potential—it is not the final blow. Yet a great-power war would nevertheless increase existential risk. It would increase the risks posed by a range of weapons technologies: nuclear weapons, engineered pandemics and whatever new weapons of mass destruction are invented in the meantime. It would also indirectly increase the probability of the other risks we face: the breakdown in international trust and cooperation would make it harder to manage climate change or the safe development of AGI, increasing the danger they pose. And great-power wars may also hasten the arrival of new existential risks. Recall that nuclear weapons were developed during the Second World War, and their destructive power was amplified significantly during the Cold War, with the invention of the hydrogen bomb. History suggests that wars on such a scale prompt humanity to delve into the darkest corners of technology.

When all of this is taken into account, the threat of great-power war may (indirectly) pose a significant amount of existential risk. For example, it seems that the bulk of the existential risk last century was driven by the threat of great-power war. Consider your own estimate of how much existential risk there is over the next hundred years. How much of this would disappear if you knew that the great powers would not go to war with each other over that time? It is impossible to be precise, but I'd estimate an appreciable fraction would disappear—something like a tenth of the existential risk over that time. Since I think the existential risk over the next hundred years is about one in six, I am estimating that great power war effectively poses more than a percentage point of existential risk over the next century. This makes it a larger contributor to total existential risk than most of the specific risks we have examined.

While you should feel free to disagree with my particular estimates, I think a safe case can be made that the contribution of great-power war to existential risk is larger than the contribution

176

of all natural risks combined. So a young person choosing their career, a philanthropist choosing their cause or a government looking to make a safer world may do better to focus on great-power war than on detecting asteroids or comets.

This alternative way of carving up the total risk was inspired by *The Global Burden of Disease*—a landmark study in global health that attempted to understand the big picture of health across the entire world, and also acted as a major inspiration for my own work in the field.[19] Its authors divided up all ill health in the world according to which disease or injury caused it. This gave them subtotals for each disease and injury which sum to the total health burden of disease and injury. But they also wanted to ask further questions, such as how much ill health is caused by smoking. Smoking is not itself a disease or injury, but it causes disease of the heart and lungs. They dubbed smoking a "risk factor," stating: "A risk factor is an attribute or exposure which is causally associated with an increased probability of a disease or injury." This allows an extremely useful cross-cutting analysis of where the ill health is coming from, letting us estimate how much could be gained if we were considering making inroads against risk factors such as smoking, lack of access to safe drinking water or vitamin deficiency.

Let us call something that increases existential risk an *existential risk factor* (the "existential" can be omitted for brevity since this is the only kind of risk factor we are concerned with hereafter).[20] Where the division into individual risks can be seen as breaking existential risk up into vertical silos, existential risk factors cut across these divisions. The idea of existential risk factors is very general and can be applied at any scale, but it is at its most useful when considering coherent factors that have a large effect on existential risk. Where the individual risks of Chapters 3 to 5 were an attempt to partition the total risk into a set of non-overlapping risks, there is no such constraint for risk factors: it is fine if they overlap or even if one is subsumed by another, so long as they are useful. Thus the contributions of risk factors to existential risk don't even approximately "add up" to the total risk.

MATHEMATICS OF RISK FACTORS

We can make risk factors more precise through the language of probability theory. Let F be a risk factor (such as *climate change* or *great-power war*). And let f be a quantitative measure of that risk factor (such as *degrees of warming* or the *probability that there is a great-power war*). Call its minimum achievable value f_{min}, its status quo value f_{sq} and its maximum achievable value f_{max}.[21] Recall that $\Pr(P)$ represents the probability that an event P happens and $\Pr(P|Q)$ represents that probability that P happens given that Q happens. Finally, let event X be an existential catastrophe occurring.

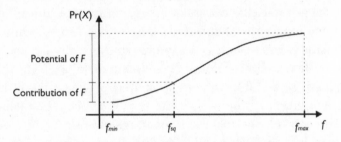

We can call the difference between $\Pr(X|f = f_{sq})$ and $\Pr(X|f = f_{min})$ the *contribution* that F makes to existential risk. It represents the amount by which total existential risk would be lowered if we eliminated this risk factor. This is a number that allows an apples-to-apples comparison between the size of risk factors and of existential risks. Similarly, we could call the difference between $\Pr(X|f = f_{sq})$ and $\Pr(X|f = f_{max})$ the *potential* of F. It represents how much existential risk could arise if this risk factor got worse.[22]

And when it comes to prioritizing existential risk factors, we will often be most interested in the steepness of the curve at f_{sq}. This reflects how much protection we could produce by a marginal change to the risk factor.[23]

An easy way to find existential risk factors is to consider stressors for humanity or for our ability to make good decisions. These include global economic stagnation, environmental collapse and breakdown in the international order.[24] Indeed even the *threat* of such things may constitute an existential risk factor, as a mere possibility can create actual global discord or panic.

Many risks that threaten (non-existential) global catastrophe also act as existential risk factors, since humanity may be more vulnerable following a global catastrophe. The same holds for many existential threats: if they can produce global catastrophes that increase our vulnerability to subsequent existential risks, then they also act as risk factors.[25] In some cases, they may pose substantially more indirect risk than direct risk.

In Chapter 4 we saw that it is difficult for nuclear winter or climate change to completely destroy humanity's potential. But they could easily cause major catastrophes that leave us more vulnerable to other existential risks. Chapter 4 focused on nuclear war and climate change in their role as *existential risks* (since it is important to understand whether there really are plausible mechanisms through which our potential could be destroyed). But their role as risk factors may be more important. A better understanding of how they increase other risks would be of great value, because what we ultimately want to know is how much they increase risk overall.[26]

This discussion of risk factors raises the possibility of other factors that *reduce* risk.[27] We can call these *existential security factors*.[28] Examples include strong institutions for avoiding existential risk, improvements in civilizational virtues or peace between great powers. As this last example suggests, if something is a risk factor, its opposite will be a security factor.

Many of the things we commonly think of as social goods may turn out to also be existential security factors. Things such as education, peace or prosperity may help protect us. And many social ills may be existential risk factors. In other words, there may be explanations grounded in existential risk for pursuing familiar, common-sense agendas.

179

But I want to stress that this is a dangerous observation. For it risks a slide into complacency, where we substitute our goal of securing our future with other goals that may be only loosely related. Just because existential risk declines as some other goal is pursued doesn't mean that the other goal is the most effective way to secure our future. Indeed, if the other goal is commonsensically important there is a good chance it is already receiving far more resources than are devoted to direct work on existential risk. This would give us much less opportunity to really move the needle. I think it likely that there will only be a handful of existential risk factors or security factors (such as great-power war) that really compete with the most important existential risks in terms of how effectively additional work on them helps to secure our future. Finding these would be extremely valuable.

WHICH RISKS?

Sadly, most of the existential risks we've considered are neglected, receiving substantially less attention than they deserve. While this situation is changing, we should expect it to take decades before sufficient resources are mobilized to adequately address all the risks we face. So those of us concerned with safeguarding our future will need to prioritize: to determine where we should devote our finite energies and resources.

A natural way to do so would be to compare risks by their probabilities—or more precisely, by their contributions to the total risk. Since most existential risks have very similar stakes (most of the potential value of the future), one might think that this is the whole story: prioritize the risks by how much they increase the total risk.

But that isn't right. For some risks might be easier to address. For example, we might be able to reduce a smaller risk from 5 percent to 1 percent with the same resources that would be needed to reduce a larger, but more stubborn, risk from 20 percent to 19 percent.[29] If so, we would reduce total existential risk by a greater amount if we spent those resources on the smaller risk.

Our ultimate aim is to spend the resources allocated to existential risk in such a way as to reduce total risk by the greatest amount. We can think of humanity's allocation of resources as a portfolio, with different amounts invested in various approaches to various risks. Designing an entire portfolio is very complex, and we are often only able to make small adjustments to the world's overall allocation, so it can simplify things to imagine making a small change to an existing portfolio. Given all the other work that is currently going on, which risk is most pressing? Where can an additional bundle of resources (such as time or money) most reduce total risk?

It is extremely difficult to give a precise answer to this question. But there are good heuristics that can guide us in narrowing down the possibilities. One such approach is to note that the more a problem is important, tractable or neglected, the more cost-effective it is to work on it, and thus the higher its priority.[30] The *importance* of a problem is the value of solving it. In the case of an existential risk, we can usually treat this as the amount it contributes to total risk. *Tractability* is a measure of how easy it is to solve the problem. A useful way of making this precise is to ask what fraction of the risk would be eliminated were we to double the amount of resources we are currently devoting to it. Finally, a problem is *neglected* to the extent that there are few resources spent on it. This incorporates the idea of diminishing returns: resources typically make a bigger difference when fewer resources have been spent so far.[31]

My colleague at the Future of Humanity Institute, Owen Cotton-Barratt, has shown that when these terms are appropriately defined, the cost-effectiveness of working on a particular problem can be expressed by a very simple formula:[32]

Cost-Effectiveness = Importance × Tractability × Neglectedness

Even though it is very difficult to assign precise numbers to any of these dimensions, this model still provides useful guidance. For example, it shows why the ideal portfolio typically involves investing resources fighting several risks instead of just one: as we invest more in a given risk, it becomes less neglected, so the priority of investing additional resources in it falls. After a while, marginal resources would be better spent on a different risk.

The model also shows us how to make trade-offs between these dimensions. For example, when choosing between two risks, if their probabilities differed by a factor of five, this would be outweighed by a factor of ten in how much funding they currently receive. Indeed, the model suggests a general principle:

Proportionality
When a set of risks have equal tractability (or when we have no idea which is more tractable), the ideal global portfolio allocates resources to each risk in proportion to its contribution to total risk.[33]

But this doesn't mean *you* should spread your resources between them in proportion to their probabilities. An individual or group should allocate its resources to help bring the world's portfolio into line with the ideal allocation. This will often mean putting all of your effort into a single risk—especially when taking into account the value of being able to give it your undivided attention.

This analysis gives us a starting point: a generic assessment of the value of allocating new resources to a risk. But there are often resources that are much more valuable when applied to one risk rather than another. This is especially true when it comes to *people*. A biologist would be much more suited to working on risks of engineered pandemics than retraining to work on AI risk. The ideal portfolio would thus take people's comparative advantage into account. And there are sometimes highly leveraged opportunities to help with a particular risk. Each of these dimensions (fit and leverage) could easily change the value of an opportunity by a factor of ten (or more).

Let's consider three more heuristics for setting our priorities: focusing on risks that are *soon*, *sudden* and *sharp*. These are not competitors to importance, tractability and neglectedness, but ways of illuminating those dimensions.

Suppose one risk strikes soon, and another late. Other things being equal, we should prioritize the one that strikes soon.[34] One reason is that risks that strike later can be dealt with later, while those striking soon cannot. Another is that there will probably be more resources devoted to risks that occur later on, as humanity becomes more powerful and more people wake up to humanity's predicament. This makes later risks less neglected. And finally, we can see more clearly what to do about risks that are coming to a head now, whereas our work on later risks has more chance of being misdirected. Technological or political surprises in the intervening years may change the nature of the risk, introduce superior ways of dealing with it or eliminate it altogether, thereby wasting some of our early efforts. This makes later risks less tractable right now than earlier ones.

What if one risk is sudden, while another unfolds slowly? Other things being equal, we should prioritize the one that strikes suddenly. For the risk that unfolds slowly has more chance of arousing widespread attention from the public and traditional policymakers. So over the long run, it is likely to be less neglected.

Some existential risks threaten catastrophes on a variety of scales. Pandemics can kill thousands, millions or billions; and asteroids range from meters to kilometers in size. In each case, they appear to follow a power law distribution, where catastrophes become substantially more rare as they get larger. This means that we are more likely to get hit by a pandemic or asteroid killing a hundredth of all people before one killing a tenth, and more likely to be hit by one killing a tenth of all people before one that kills almost everyone.[35] In contrast, other risks, such as that from unaligned artificial intelligence, may well be all-or-nothing. Let's call a smaller catastrophe a "warning shot" if it is likely to provoke major useful action to eliminate future risk of that type. Other things being equal, we should prioritize the sharp risks— those that are less likely to be preceded by warning shots—for they are more likely to remain neglected over the long run.[36]

183

While I've presented this analysis in terms of which risks should get the highest priority, these exact same principles can be applied to prioritizing between different risk factors or security factors. And they can help prioritize between different ways of protecting our potential over the long term, such as promoting norms, working within existing institutions or establishing new ones. Best of all, these principles can be used to set priorities between these areas as well as within them, since all are measured in the common unit of total existential risk reduction.

In the course of this book, we have considered a wide variety of approaches to reducing existential risk. The most obvious has been direct work on a particular risk, such as nuclear war or engineered pandemics. But there were also more indirect approaches: work on risk factors such as great-power war; or on security factors such as a new international institution tasked with reducing existential risk. Perhaps one could act at an even more indirect level. Arguably risk would be lower in a period of stable economic growth than in a period with the turmoil caused by deep recessions. And it may be lower if citizens were better educated and better informed.

The philosopher Nick Beckstead suggests we distinguish between *targeted* and *broad* interventions.[37] A focus on safeguarding humanity needn't imply a focus on narrowly targeted interventions, such as the governance of a dangerous technology. Existential risk can also be reduced by broader interventions aimed at generally improving wisdom, decision-making or international cooperation. And it is an open question which of these approaches is more effective. Beckstead suggests that longtermists in past centuries would have done better to focus on broad interventions rather than narrow interventions.

I think Beckstead may be right about past centuries, but mostly because existential risk was so low until we became powerful enough to threaten ourselves in the twentieth century. From that point, early longtermists such as Bertrand Russell and Albert Einstein were right to devote so much attention to the targeted intervention of reducing the threat of nuclear war.

EARLY ACTION

Some of the biggest risks we face are still on the horizon. Can we really do useful work to eliminate a threat so far in advance? How can we act now, when we are not fully aware of the form the risks may take, the nature of the technologies, or the shape of the strategic landscape at the moment they strike?

These are real concerns for any attempts to address future risks. We are near-sighted with respect to time, and so there is a serious chance our best efforts will be wasted. But this is not the whole story. For there are also ways in which action far in advance of the threat can be all the more helpful.

Early action is best for changing course. If we are headed the wrong way, it is better to correct this at an early stage. So if we need to steer a technology (or a nation) from a dangerous path, we have more power to do so now, rather than later.

Early action is best when it comes to self-improvement, for there is more time to reap what is sown. If what is needed is research, education or influence, starting sooner is better.

Early action is best for growth. If one needs to turn an investment into a fortune, an article into a research field or an idea into a movement, one had best start soon.

And early action is best for tasks that require a large number of successive stages. If your solution has this structure, it may be impossible if you don't start extremely early.

In short, early action is higher leverage, but more easily wasted. It has more power, but less accuracy. If we do act far in advance of a threat, we should do so in ways that take advantage of this leverage, while being robust to near-sightedness.[38] This often means a focus on knowledge and capacity building, over direct work.

In my view we can tentatively resolve the question of targeted versus broad interventions by considering neglectedness. In our current situation there are trillions of dollars per year flowing to broad interventions such as education, but less than a ten-thousandth this much going to targeted existential risk interventions.[39] So the broad interventions are much less neglected. This gives us a strong reason to expect increasing work on targeted interventions to be more effective at the moment (with the strongest case for broad interventions coming from those that receive the least attention).

But if the resources spent on targeted existential risk interventions were radically increased, this would start to change. We currently spend less than a thousandth of a percent of gross world product on them. Earlier, I suggested bringing this up by at least a factor of 100, to reach a point where the world is spending more on securing its potential than on ice cream, and perhaps a good longer-term target may be a full 1 percent.[40] But there will be serious diminishing returns as investment is scaled up, and it may well be that even if the world were solely interested in reducing existential risk, the total budget for targeted interventions should never exceed that for broad interventions.

We now have a rough map of the risk landscape, and the intellectual tools needed to find promising paths forward. It is time to put these to use; to start planning how to safeguard humanity—from the big picture strategy all the way down to concrete advice on how we can each play a part.

7

SAFEGUARDING HUMANITY

There are no catastrophes that loom before us which cannot be avoided; there is nothing that threatens us with imminent destruction in such a fashion that we are helpless to do something about it. If we behave rationally and humanely; if we concentrate coolly on the problems that face all of humanity, rather than emotionally on such nineteenth century matters as national security and local pride; if we recognize that it is not one's neighbors who are the enemy, but misery, ignorance, and the cold indifference of natural law—then we can solve all the problems that face us. We can deliberately choose to have no catastrophes at all.

—Isaac Asimov[1]

What we do with our future is up to us. Our choices determine whether we live or die; fulfill our potential or squander our chance at greatness. We are not hostages to fortune. While each of our lives may be tossed about by external forces—a sudden illness, or outbreak of war—humanity's future is almost entirely within humanity's control. Most existential risk comes from human action: from activities which we can choose to stop, or to govern effectively. Even the risks from nature come on sufficiently protracted timescales that we can protect ourselves long before the storm breaks.

We need to take responsibility for our future. Those of us alive right now are the only people who can fight against the present dangers; the only people who can build the communities, norms and institutions that will safeguard our future. Whether we are remembered as the generation who turned the corner to a bright and secure future, or not remembered at all, comes down to whether we rise to meet these challenges.

When exploring these issues, I find it useful to consider our predicament from *humanity*'s point of view: casting humanity as a coherent agent, and considering the strategic choices it would make were it sufficiently rational and wise. Or in other words, what all humans would do if we were sufficiently coordinated and had humanity's longterm interests at heart.

This frame is highly idealized. It obscures the challenges that arise from our disunity and the importance of actions that individuals might take to nudge humanity as a whole in the right direction. But it illuminates larger questions, which have so far been almost entirely neglected. Questions about the grand strategy for humanity, and how we could make sure we can achieve an excellent future—even if we don't yet know precisely what kind of future that would be. By answering them, I paint an ambitious vision of humanity getting its house in order that I hope can guide us over the coming decades, even if the reality is more messy and fraught.

My advice will range from high-level strategy, to policy suggestions, all the way down to the individual level, with promising career paths and actions that anyone could take. Because people have spent very little time thinking carefully about how to safeguard humanity's longterm potential, all such guidance must be viewed as tentative; it has not yet stood the test of time.

But the fact that we are at such an early stage in thinking about the longterm future of humanity also provides us with reason to be hopeful as we begin our journey. This is not a well-worn track, where the promising ideas have long since been explored and found wanting. It is virgin territory. And it may be rich with insights for the first explorers who seek them.

GRAND STRATEGY FOR HUMANITY

How can humanity have the greatest chance of achieving its potential? I think that at the highest level we should adopt a strategy proceeding in three phases:[2]

1. Reaching Existential Security
2. The Long Reflection
3. Achieving Our Potential

On this view, the first great task for humanity is to reach a place of safety—a place where existential risk is low and stays low. I call this *existential security*.

It has two strands. Most obviously, we need to *preserve* humanity's potential, extracting ourselves from immediate danger so we don't fail before we've got our house in order. This includes direct work on the most pressing existential risks and risk factors, as well as near-term changes to our norms and institutions.

But we also need to *protect* humanity's potential—to establish lasting safeguards that will defend humanity from dangers over the longterm future, so that it becomes almost impossible to fail.[3] Where preserving our potential is akin to fighting the latest fire, protecting our potential is making changes to ensure that fire will never again pose a serious threat.[4] This will involve major changes to our norms and institutions (giving humanity the prudence and patience we need), as well as ways of increasing our general resilience to catastrophe. This needn't require foreseeing all future risks right now. It is enough if we can set humanity firmly on a course where we will be taking the new risks seriously: managing them successfully right from their onset or side-stepping them entirely.

Note that existential security doesn't require the risk to be brought down to *zero*. That would be an impossible target, and attempts to achieve it may well be counter-productive. What humanity needs to do is bring this century's risk down to a very low level, then keep gradually reducing it from there as the centuries go on. In this way, even though there may always remain some risk in each century, the total risk over our entire future can be kept small.[5] We could view this as a form of existential sustainability. Futures in which accumulated existential risk is allowed to climb toward 100 percent are unsustainable. So we need to set a strict risk budget over our entire future, parceling out this non-renewable resource with great care over the generations to come.

Ultimately, existential security is about reducing total existential risk by as many percentage points as possible. Preserving our potential is helping lower the portion of the total risk that we face in the next few decades, while protecting our potential is helping lower the portion that comes over the longer run. We can work on these strands in parallel, devoting some of our efforts to reducing imminent risks and some to building the capacities, institutions, wisdom and will to ensure that future risks are minimal.[6]

A key insight motivating existential security is that there appear to be no major obstacles to humanity lasting an extremely long time, if only that were a key global priority. As we saw in Chapter 3, we have ample time to protect ourselves against natural risks: even if it took us millennia to resolve the threats from asteroids, supervolcanism and supernovae, we would incur less than one percentage point of total risk.

The greater risk (and tighter deadline) stems from the anthropogenic threats. But being of humanity's own making, they are also within our control. Were we sufficiently patient, prudent and coordinated, we could simply stop imposing such risks upon ourselves. We would factor in the hidden costs of carbon emissions (or nuclear weapons) and realize they are not a good deal. We would adopt a more mature attitude to the most radical new technologies—devoting at least as much of humanity's brilliance to forethought and governance as to technological development.

In the past, the survival of humanity didn't require much conscious effort: our past was brief enough to evade the natural threats and our power too limited to produce anthropogenic threats. But now our longterm survival requires a deliberate choice to survive. As more and more people come to realize this, we can make this choice. There will be great challenges in getting people to look far enough ahead and to see beyond the parochial conflicts of the day. But the logic is clear and the moral arguments powerful. It can be done.

If we achieve existential security, we will have room to breathe. With humanity's longterm potential secured, we will be past the Precipice, free to contemplate the range of futures that lie open before us. And we will be able to take our time to reflect upon what we truly desire; upon which of these visions for humanity would be the best realization of our potential. We shall call this the *Long Reflection*.[7]

We rarely think this way. We focus on the here and now. Even those of us who care deeply about the longterm future need to focus most of our attention on making sure we *have* a future. But once we achieve existential security, we will have the luxury of time in which to compare the kinds of futures available to us and judge which is best. Most work in moral philosophy so far has focused on negatives—on avoiding wrong action and bad outcomes. The study of the positive is at a much earlier stage of development.[8] During the Long Reflection, we would need to develop mature theories that allow us to compare the grand accomplishments our descendants might achieve with eons and galaxies as their canvas.

Present-day humans, myself included, are poorly positioned to anticipate the results of this reflection.[9] But we are uniquely positioned to make it possible.

The ultimate aim of the Long Reflection would be to achieve a final answer to the question of which is the best kind of future for humanity. This may be the true answer (if truth is applicable to moral questions) or failing that, the answer we would converge to under an ideal process of reflection. It may be that even convergence is impossible, with some disputes or uncertainties that are beyond the power of reason to resolve. If so, our aim would be to find the future that gave the best possible conciliation between the remaining perspectives.[10]

We would not need to fully complete this process before moving forward. What is essential is to be sufficiently confident in the broad shape of what we are aiming at before taking each bold and potentially irreversible action—each action that could plausibly lock in substantial aspects of our future trajectory.

For example, it may be that the best achievable future involves physically perfecting humanity, by genetically improving our biology. Or it may involve giving people the freedom to adopt a stunning diversity of new biological forms. But proceeding down either of these paths prematurely could introduce its own existential risks.

If we radically change our nature, we replace humanity (or at least *Homo sapiens*) with something new. This would risk losing what was most valuable about humanity before truly coming to understand it. If we diversify our forms, we fragment humanity. We might lose the essential unity of humanity that allows a common vision for our future, and instead find ourselves in a perpetual struggle or unsatisfactory compromise. Other bold actions could pose similar risks, for instance spreading out beyond our Solar System into a federation of independent worlds, each drifting in its own cultural direction.

This is not to reject such changes to the human condition—they may well be essential to realizing humanity's full potential. What I am saying is that these are the kind of bold changes that would need to come after the Long Reflection.[11] Or at least after enough reflection to fully understand the consequences of that particular change. We need to take our time, and choose our path with great care. For once we have existential security we are almost assured success if we take things slowly and carefully: the game is ours to lose; there are only unforced errors.

What can we say about the process of the Long Reflection? I am not imagining this as the sole task of humanity during that time—there would be many other great projects, such as the continuing quests for knowledge, prosperity and justice. And many of the people at the time may have only passing interest in the Long Reflection. But it is the Long Reflection that would have the most bearing on the shape of the future, and so it would be this for which the time would be remembered.[12]

The process may take place largely within intellectual circles, or within the wider public sphere. Either way, we would need to take the greatest care to avoid it being shaped by the bias or prejudice of those involved. As Jonathan Schell said regarding a similar venture, "even if every person in the world were to enlist, the endeavour would include only an infinitesimal fraction of the people of the dead and the unborn generations, and so it would need to act with the circumspection and modesty of a small minority."[13] While the conversation should be courteous and respectful to all perspectives, it is even more important that it be robust and rigorous. For its ultimate aim is not just to win the goodwill of those alive at the time, but to deliver a verdict that stands the test of eternity.

While moral philosophy would play a central role, the Long Reflection would require insights from many disciplines. For it isn't just about determining which futures are best, but which are feasible in the first place, and which strategies are most likely to bring them about. This requires analysis from science, engineering, economics, political theory and beyond.

We could think of these first two steps of existential security and the Long Reflection as designing a constitution for humanity. Achieving existential security would be like writing the safeguarding of our potential into our constitution. The Long Reflection would then flesh out this constitution, setting the directions and limits in which our future will unfold.

Our ultimate aim, of course, is the final step: fully achieving humanity's potential.[14] But this can wait upon a serious reflection about which future is best and on how to achieve that future without any fatal missteps. And while it would not hurt to begin such reflection now, it is not the most urgent task.[15] To maximize our chance of success, we need first to get ourselves to safety—to achieve existential security. This is the task of our time. The rest can wait.

SECURITY AMONG THE STARS?

Many of those who have written about the risks of human extinction suggest that if we could just survive long enough to spread out through space, we would be safe—that we currently have all of our eggs in one basket, but if we became an interplanetary species, this period of vulnerability would end.[16] Is this right? Would settling other planets bring us existential security?

The idea is based on an important statistical truth. If there were a growing number of locations which all need to be destroyed for humanity to fail, and if the chance of each suffering a catastrophe is independent of whether the others do too, then there is a good chance humanity could survive indefinitely.[17]

But unfortunately, this argument only applies to risks that are statistically independent. Many risks, such as disease, war, tyranny and permanently locking in bad values are correlated across different planets: if they affect one, they are somewhat more likely to affect the others too. A few risks, such as unaligned AGI and vacuum collapse, are almost completely correlated: if they affect one planet, they will likely affect all.[18] And presumably some of the as-yet-undiscovered risks will also be correlated between our settlements.

Space settlement is thus helpful for achieving existential security (by eliminating the uncorrelated risks) but it is by no means sufficient.[19] Becoming a multi-planetary species is an inspirational project—and may be a necessary step in achieving humanity's potential. But we still need to address the problem of existential risk head-on, by choosing to make safeguarding our longterm potential one of our central priorities.

RISKS WITHOUT PRECEDENT

Humanity has never suffered an existential catastrophe, and hopefully never will. Catastrophes of this scale are unprecedented throughout our long history. This creates severe challenges for our attempts to understand, predict and prevent these disasters. And what's more, these challenges will always be with us, for existential risks are *necessarily unprecedented*. By the time we have a precedent, it is too late—we've lost our future. To safeguard humanity's potential, we are forced to formulate our plans and enact our policies in a world that has never witnessed the events we strive to avoid.[20] Let's explore three challenges this creates and how we might begin to address them.

First, we can't rely on our current intuitions and institutions that have evolved to deal with small- or medium-scale risks.[21] Our intuitive sense of fear is neither evolutionarily nor culturally adapted to deal with risks that threaten so much more than an individual life—risks of catastrophes that cannot be allowed to happen even once over thousands of years in a world containing billions of people. The same is true for our intuitive sense of the likelihood of very rare events and of when such a risk is too high. Evolution and cultural adaptation have led to fairly well-tuned judgments for these questions in our day-to-day lives (when it's safe to cross the road; whether to buy a smoke alarm), but are barely able to cope with risks that threaten hundreds of people, let alone those that threaten billions and the very future of humanity.

The same is true of our institutions. Our systems of laws, norms and organizations for handling risk have been tuned to the small- and medium-scale risks we have faced over past centuries. They are ill-equipped to address risks so extensive that they will devastate countries across the globe; so severe that there will be no legal institutions remaining to exact punishment.

The second challenge is that we cannot afford to fail *even once*. This removes our ability to learn from failure. Humanity typically manages risk via a heavy reliance on trial and error. We scale our investment or regulation based on the damages we've seen so far; we work out how to prevent new fires by sifting through the ashes.

But this reactive trial and error approach doesn't work at all when it comes to existential risk. We will need to take pro-active measures: sometimes long in advance, sometimes with large costs, sometimes when it is still unclear whether the risk is real or whether the measures will address it.[22] This will require institutions with access to cutting-edge information about the coming risks, capable of taking decisive actions, and with the will to actually do so. For many risks, this action may require swift coordination between many or all of the world's nations. And it may have to be done knowing we will never find out whether our costly actions really helped. This will ultimately require new institutions, filled with people of keen intellect and sound judgment, endowed with a substantial budget and real influence over policy.

These are extremely challenging circumstances for sound policy-making—perhaps beyond the abilities of even the best-functioning institutions today. But this is the situation we are in, and we will need to face up to it. There is an urgency to improving our institutional abilities to meet these demands.

Working out when such institutions should take action will raise its own deeply challenging questions. On the one hand, they will need to be able to take strong actions, even when the evidence is short of the highest scientific standards. And yet, this puts us at risk of chasing phantoms—being asked (or forced) to make substantial sacrifices on the basis of little evidence. This poses an even greater problem if the risk involves classified elements or information hazards that cannot be opened up to public scrutiny and response. The challenges here are similar to those arising from the ability of governments to declare a state of emergency: contingency powers are essential for managing real emergencies, yet open to serious abuse.[23]

The third challenge is one of knowledge. How are we to predict, quantify or understand risks that have never transpired? It is extremely difficult to predict the risk posed by new technologies. Consider the situation of allowing cars onto our roads for the first time. It was very unclear how dangerous that would be, but once it had happened, and millions of miles had been driven, we could easily determine the risks by looking at the statistical frequencies. This let us see whether the gains outweighed the risks, how much could be gained by new safety improvements, and which improvements would be most helpful.

With existential risk, we cannot help ourselves to such a track record, with probabilities grounded in long-run frequencies. Instead, we have to make decisions of grave importance without access to robust probabilities for the risks involved.[24] This raises substantial difficulties in how we are to form probability estimates for use in decision-making surrounding existential risk.[25] This problem already exists in climate change research and causes great difficulties in setting policy—especially if politicization leads to explicit or implicit biases in how people interpret the ambiguous evidence.

During the Cold War concern about existential risk from nuclear war was often disparaged on the grounds that we haven't *proved* the risk is substantial. But when it comes to existential risk that would be an impossible standard. Our norms of scientific proof require experiments to be repeated many times, and were established under the assumptions that such experiments are possible and not too costly. But here neither assumption is true. As Carl Sagan memorably put it: "Theories that involve the end of the world are not amenable to experimental verification— or at least, not more than once."[26]

Even with no track record of existential catastrophe, we do have some ways of estimating probabilities or bounds on the probability. For example, in Chapter 3 we saw how we can use the length of time humans and similar animals have survived to get a very rough estimate of the combined natural risk. We can also pay attention to near misses: both the largest catastrophes that *have* occurred (such as the Black Death), and existential catastrophes that *nearly* occurred (such as during the Cuban Missile Crisis). These can help us understand things such as how resilient society is to large catastrophes or how our imperfect information can lead nations to walk much closer to the brink of an annihilating war than they intended. We need to learn everything we can from these cases, even when they aren't precise analogues for the new risks we face, for they may be the best we have.

Some of this use of near misses is systematized in the field of risk analysis. They have techniques for estimating the probability of unprecedented catastrophes based on the combination of *precedented* faults that would need to occur to allow it. For example, fault tree analysis was developed for evaluating the reliability of the launch systems for nuclear missiles, and is used routinely to help avoid low-frequency risks, such as plane crashes and nuclear meltdowns.[27]

There is a special challenge that comes with estimating risks of human extinction. It is *impossible* to witness humanity having been extinguished in the past, regardless of the likelihood. And a version of this selection effect can distort the historical record of some catastrophes that are linked to extinction, even if they wouldn't necessarily cause it. For example, we may not be able to directly apply the observed track record of asteroid collisions or full-scale nuclear war. From what we know, it doesn't look like these selection effects have distorted the historical record much, but there are only a handful of papers on the topic and some of the methodological issues have yet to be resolved.[28]

A final challenge concerns all low-probability high-stakes risks. Suppose scientists estimate that an unprecedented technological risk has an extremely small chance of causing an existential catastrophe—say one in a trillion. Can we directly use this number in our analysis? Unfortunately not. The problem is that the chance the scientists have incorrectly estimated this probability is many times greater than one in a trillion. Recall their failure to estimate the size of the massive Castle Bravo nuclear explosion—if the chance of miscalculation were really so low there should be no such examples. So if a disaster does occur, it is much more likely to be because there was an estimation mistake and the real risk was higher, rather than because a one in a trillion event occurred.

This means that the one in a trillion number is not the decision-relevant probability, and policymakers need to adjust for this by using a higher number.[29] The manner in which they should do so is not well understood. This is part of a general point that our uncertainty about the underlying physical probability is not grounds for ignoring the risk, since the true risk could be higher as well as lower. If anything, when the initial estimate of the probability is tiny, a proper accounting of uncertainty often makes the situation worse, for the real probability could be substantially higher but couldn't be much lower.[30]

These unusual challenges that come with the territory of existential risk are not insurmountable. They call for advances in our theoretical understanding of how to estimate and evaluate risks that are by their very nature unprecedented. They call for improvements in our horizon scanning and forecasting of disruptive technologies. And they call for improved integration of these techniques and ideas into our policy-making.

INTERNATIONAL COORDINATION

Safeguarding humanity is a global public good. As we saw earlier, even a powerful country like the United States contains only a twentieth of the world's people and so would only reap something like a twentieth of the benefits that come from preventing catastrophe. Uncoordinated action by nation states therefore suffers from a collective action problem. Each nation is inadequately incentivized to take actions that reduce risk and to avoid actions that produce risk, preferring instead to free-ride on others. Because of this, we should expect risk-reducing activities to be under-supplied and risk-increasing activities to be over-supplied.

This creates a need for international coordination on existential risk. The incentives of a nation are only aligned with the incentives of humanity if we share the costs of these policies just as we share the benefits. While nations occasionally act for the greater interest of all humankind, this is the exception rather than the rule. Multilateral action can resolve this tragedy of the commons, replacing a reliance on countries' altruism with a reliance on their prudence: still not perfect, but a much better bet.

And there would be benefits to centralizing some of this international work on safeguarding humanity. This would help us pool our expertise, share our perspectives and facilitate coordination. It could also help us with policies that require a unified response, where we are only as strong as the weakest link: for example, in setting moratoria on dangerous types of research or in governing the use of geoengineering.

So there is a need for international institutions focused on existential risk to coordinate our actions. But it is very unclear at this stage what forms they should take. This includes questions of whether the change should be incremental or radical, whether institutions should be advisory or regulatory, and whether they should have a narrow or broad set of responsibilities. Our options range from incremental improvements to minor agencies, through to major changes to key bodies such as the UN Security Council, all the way up to entirely new institutions for governing the most important world affairs.

No doubt many people would think a large shift in international governance is unnecessary or unrealistic. But consider the creation of the United Nations. This was part of a massive reordering of the international order in response to the tragedy of the Second World War. The destruction of humanity's entire potential would be so much worse than the Second World War that a reordering of international institutions of a similar scale may be entirely justified. And while there might not be much appetite now, there may be in the near future if a risk increases to the point where it looms very large in the public consciousness, or if there is a global catastrophe that acts as a warning shot. So we should be open to blue-sky thinking about ideal international institutions, while at the same time considering smaller changes to the existing set.[31]

The same is true when it comes to our policy options. As we wake up to the new situation we find ourselves in and come to terms with the vulnerability of humanity, we will face great challenges. But we may also find new political possibilities opening up. Responses that first seemed impossible may become possible, and in time even inevitable. As Ulrich Beck put it: "One can make two diametrically opposed kinds of assertion: global risks inspire paralysing terror, or: global risks create new room for action."[32]

One way of looking at our current predicament is that the existing global order splits humanity into a large number of sovereign states, each of which has considerable internal coherence, but only loose coordination with the others. This structure has some advantages, even from the perspective of existential risk, for it has allowed us to minimize the risk that a single bad government could lock humanity into a terrible stable outcome. But as it becomes easier for a single country—or even a small group within one country—to threaten the whole of humanity, the balance may start to shift. And 195 countries may mean 195 chances that poor governance precipitates the destruction of humanity.

Some important early thinkers on existential risk suggested that the growing possibility of existential catastrophe required moving toward a form of world government.[33] For example, in 1948 Einstein wrote:

> I advocate world government because I am convinced that there is no other possible way of eliminating the most terrible danger in which man has ever found himself. The objective of avoiding total destruction must have priority over any other objective.[34]

World government is a slippery idea, with the term meaning different things to different people. For example, it is sometimes used to refer to any situation where nations have been made unable to wage war upon each other. This situation is almost synonymous with perpetual world peace, and relatively unobjectionable (albeit stunningly difficult to achieve). But the term is also used to refer to a politically homogenized world with a single point of control (roughly, the world as one big country). This is much more contentious and could increase overall existential risk via global totalitarianism, or by permanently locking in bad values.

Instead, my guess is that existential security could be better achieved with the bare minimum of internationally binding constraints needed to prevent actors in one or two countries from jeopardizing humanity's entire future. Perhaps this could be done through establishing a kind of constitution for humanity, and writing into it the paramount need to safeguard our future, along with the funding and enforcement mechanisms required. This may take us beyond any current international law or institutions, yet stop considerably short of world government.

What about smaller changes—improvements to international coordination that offer a large amount of security for their cost? A good historical example might be the Moscow–Washington Hotline (popularly known as the "red telephone").[35] During the Cuban Missile Crisis messages between Kennedy and Khrushchev regularly took several hours to be received and decoded.[36] But major new developments were unfolding on the ground at a much quicker tempo, leaving diplomatic solutions (and explanations for apparently hostile behavior) unable to keep up.[37] Afterward, Kennedy and Khrushchev established the hotline to allow faster and more direct communication between the leaders, in order to avoid future crises coming so close to the brink. This was a simple and successful way to lower the risk of nuclear war (and war between the great powers more generally), with little financial or political cost. There may be other ideas like this just waiting to be discovered or implemented.

And there may be more obvious ways, such as simply strengthening existing institutions related to existential risks. For example, the Biological Weapons Convention could be brought into line with the Chemical Weapons Convention: taking its budget from $1.4 million up to $80 million, granting it the power to investigate suspected breaches, and increasing its staff from a mere four people to a level more appropriate for its role.[38] We could also strengthen the World Health Organization's ability to respond to emerging pandemics through rapid disease surveillance, diagnosis and control. This involves increasing its funding and powers, as well as R&D on the requisite technologies. And we need to ensure that all DNA synthesis is screened for dangerous pathogens. There has been good progress toward this from synthesis companies, with 80 percent of orders currently being screened.[39] But 80 percent is not enough. If we cannot reach full coverage through voluntary efforts, some form of international regulation will be needed.

Some of the most important international coordination can happen between pairs of nations. One obvious first step would be to restart the Intermediate-Range Nuclear Forces Treaty (INF). This arms reduction treaty eliminated 2,692 nuclear missiles from the US and Russian nuclear arsenals, but was suspended in 2019 after a decade of suspected breaches.[40] They should also make sure to renew the New START treaty, due to expire in 2021, which has been responsible for major reductions in the number of nuclear weapons.

And while nuclear matters are often addressed through bilateral or multilateral agreements, there may also be unilateral moves that are in all nations' interests. For example, if the US took their ICBMs off hair-trigger alert, this would lessen the chance of accidentally triggered nuclear war without losing much deterrent effect since their nuclear submarines would still be able to launch a devastating retaliation. This may well reduce the overall risk of nuclear war.

Another promising avenue for incremental change is to explicitly prohibit and punish the deliberate or reckless imposition of unnecessary extinction risk.[41] International law is the natural place for this, as those who impose such risk may well be national governments or heads of state, who could be effectively immune to mere national law.

The idea that it may be a serious crime to impose risks to all living humans and to our entire future is a natural fit with the common-sense ideas behind the law of human rights and crimes against humanity. There would be substantial practical challenges in reconciling this idea with the actual bodies of law, and in defining the thresholds required for prosecution.[42] But these challenges are worth undertaking—our descendants would be shocked to learn that it used to be perfectly legal to threaten the continued existence of humanity.[43]

There are some hopeful signs that such protections could gain support at the international level. For example, in 1997, UNESCO passed a Declaration on the Responsibilities of the Present Generations Towards Future Generations. Its preamble showed a recognition that humanity's continued existence may be at stake and that acting on this falls within the mission of the UN:

> Conscious that, at this point in history, the very existence of humankind and its environment are threatened, Stressing that full respect for human rights and ideals of democracy constitute an essential basis for the protection of the needs and interests of future generations . . . Bearing in mind that the fate of future generations depends to a great extent on decisions and actions taken today . . . Convinced that there is a moral obligation to formulate behavioural guidelines for the present generations within a broad, future-oriented perspective . . .

The articles of the declaration were a list of ideals the international community should adopt, including Article 3: "The present generations should strive to ensure the maintenance and perpetuation of humankind." This declaration clearly did not change the world, but it does point toward how these ideas can be expressed within the framework of international human rights, and suggests these ideas have currency at the highest levels.[44]

During the last three decades, a handful of nations took the remarkable step of adjusting their democratic institutions to better represent the views of future generations.[45] They were responding to a critique of the standard forms of democracy: that they fail to represent the future people who may be adversely affected by our decisions.[46] One might think of this as a tyranny of the present over the future. Obviously one cannot simply resolve this by giving future people a vote on the issues that would affect them, as they haven't yet been born.[47] But we do sometimes have a clear idea of what they would think of the policy and so if we took this critique seriously, we could represent them by proxy: for example, by an ombudsperson, commission or parliamentary committee. These could be advisory, or be given some hard power.[48]

So far these experiments with formal representation of future generations have been mainly focused on environmental and demographic concerns. But the idea could naturally be applied to existential risk too. This may achieve some success at the national level and would be even more powerful if there was some way of bringing it to the world stage, combining both intergenerational and international coordination. This could be approached in an incremental way, or in a way that was truly transformative.

TECHNOLOGICAL PROGRESS

Humanity's stunning technological progress has been a major theme of this book. It is what allowed humans to form villages, cities and nations; to produce our greatest works of art; to live much longer lives, filled with a striking diversity of experiences. It is also essential to our survival: for without further technological progress we would eventually succumb to the background of natural risks such as asteroids. And I believe the best futures open to us—those that would truly fulfill our potential—will require technologies we haven't yet reached, such as cheap clean energy, advanced artificial intelligence or the ability to explore further into the cosmos.

Thus, even though the largest risks we face are technological in origin, relinquishing further technological progress is not a solution. What about proceeding more slowly? Is that a solution? One effect would be to delay the onset of technological risks. If we pushed back all new risky technologies for a century, that might mean all of us alive today are protected from death in an existential catastrophe. This would be a great boon from the perspective of the present, but would do very little from the perspectives of our future, our past, our virtues or our cosmic significance. This was noted by one of the earliest thinkers on existential risk, the philosopher J. J. C. Smart:

> Indeed what does it matter, from the perspective of possible millions of years of future evolution, that the final catastrophe should merely be postponed for (say) a couple of hundred years? Postponing is only of great value if it is used as a breathing space in which ways are found to avert the final disaster.[49]

I've argued that our current predicament stems from the rapid growth of humanity's power outstripping the slow and unsteady growth of our wisdom. If this is right, then slowing technological progress should help to give us some breathing space, allowing our wisdom more of a chance to catch up.[50] Where slowing down all aspects of our progress may merely delay catastrophe, slowing down the growth of our power relative to our wisdom should fundamentally help.

I think that a more patient and prudent humanity would indeed try to limit this divergence. Most importantly, it would try to increase its wisdom. But if there were limits to how quickly it could do so, it would also make sense to slow the rate of increase in its power—not necessarily putting its foot on the brake, but at least pressing more lightly on the accelerator.

We've seen how humanity is akin to an adolescent, with rapidly developing physical abilities, lagging wisdom and self-control, little thought for its longterm future and an unhealthy appetite for risk. When it comes to our own children, we design our societies to deliberately stage their access to risky technologies: for example, preventing them from driving a car until they reach an appropriate age and pass a qualifying test.

One could imagine applying a similar approach to humanity. Not relinquishing areas of technology, but accepting that in some cases we aren't ready for them until we meet a given standard. For example, no nuclear technologies until we've had a hundred years without a major war. Unfortunately, there is a major challenge. Unlike the case with our own children, there are no wise adults to decide these rules. Humanity would have to lay down the rules to govern *itself*. And those who lack wisdom usually lack the ability to see this; those who lack patience are unlikely to delay gratification until they acquire it.

So while I think a more mature world would indeed restrain its growth in destructive capability to a level where it was adequately managed, I don't see much value in advocating for this at the moment. Major efforts to slow things down would require international agreements between all the major players, for otherwise work would just continue in the least scrupulous countries. Since the world is so far from reaching such agreements, it would be ineffective (and likely counter-productive) for the few people who care about existential risk to use their energies to push for slowing down.

We should instead devote our energies to promoting the responsible deployment and governance of new technologies. We should make the case that the unprecedented power from technological progress requires unprecedented responsibility: both for the practitioners and for those overseeing them.

The great improvements in our quality of life from technology don't come for free. They come with a shadow cost in risk.[51] We focus on the visible benefits, but are accumulating a hidden debt that may one day come due.[52] If we aren't changing the pace of technology, the least we could do is to make sure we use some of the prosperity it grants us to service these debts. For example, to put even 1 percent of the benefits technology brings us back into ensuring humanity's potential isn't destroyed through further technological progress.

This technological governance can be pursued at many levels. Most obviously, by those whose duties are concerned with governance: politicians, the civil service and civil society. But we can build the bridge from both ends, with valuable contributions by the people who work on the relevant science and technology: in academia, in professional societies and in technology companies. These practitioners can spend much more time reflecting on the ethical implications of their own work and that of their peers.[53] They can develop their own guidelines and internal regulations. And they can spend time working with policymakers to ensure national and international regulations are scientifically and technologically sound.[54]

A good example of successful governance is the Montreal Protocol, which set a timetable to phase out the chemicals that were depleting the ozone layer. It involved rapid and extensive collaboration between scientists, industry leaders and policymakers, leading to what Kofi Annan called "perhaps the single most successful international agreement to date."[55]

Another example is the Asilomar Conference on Recombinant DNA, in which leading scientists in the field considered the new dangerous possibilities their work had opened up. In response they designed new safety requirements on further work and restricted some lines of development completely.[56]

An interesting, and neglected, area of technology governance is *differential technological development*.[57] While it may be too difficult to prevent the development of a risky technology, we may be able to reduce existential risk by speeding up the development of protective technologies relative to dangerous ones. This could be a role for research funders, who could enshrine it as a principle for use in designing funding calls and allocating grants, giving additional weight to protective technologies. And it could also be used by researchers when deciding which of several promising programs of research to pursue.

STATE RISKS & TRANSITION RISKS

If humanity is under threat from substantial risk each century, we are in an unsustainable position. Shouldn't we attempt to rush through this risky period as quickly as we can? The answer depends upon the type of risk we face.

Some risks are associated with being in a vulnerable state of affairs. Let's call these *state risks*.[58] Many natural risks are state risks. Humanity remains vulnerable to asteroids, comets, supervolcanic eruptions, supernovae and gamma ray bursts. The longer we are in a state where the threat is present and we are vulnerable, the higher the cumulative chance we succumb. Our chance of surviving for a length of time is characterized by a decaying exponential, with a half-life set by the annual risk.[59] When it comes to state risks, the faster we end our vulnerability, the better. If we need technology to end this vulnerability, then we would like to reach that technology as quickly as possible.

But not all risks are like this.[60] Some are *transition risks*: risks that arise during a transition to a new technological or social regime. For example the risks as we develop and deploy transformative AGI are like this, as are the risks of climate change as we transition to being a high-energy civilization. Rushing the transition may do nothing to lower these risks—indeed it could easily heighten them. But if the transition is necessary or highly desirable, we may have to go through it at some point, so mere delay is not a solution, and may also make things worse. The general prescription for these risks is neither haste nor slowness, but care and foresight.

We face an array of risks, including both state and transition risks.[61] But if my analysis is correct, there is substantially more transition risk than state risk (in large part because there is more anthropogenic risk). This suggests that rushing our overall technological progress is not warranted. Overall, the balance is set by our desire to reach a position of existential security while incurring as little cumulative risk as possible. My guess is that this is best achieved by targeted acceleration of the science and technology needed to overcome the biggest state risks, combined with substantial foresight, carefulness and coordination on the biggest transition risks.

While our current situation is unsustainable, that doesn't mean the remedy is to try to achieve a more sustainable annual risk level as quickly as possible. Our ultimate goal is longterm sustainability: to protect humanity's potential so that we have the greatest chance of fulfilling our potential over the eons to come. The right notion of sustainability is thus not about getting into a sustainable state as quickly as possible, but about having a sustainable trajectory: one that optimally trades off risk in getting there with the protection of being there.[62] This may involve taking additional risks in the short term, though only if they sufficiently reduce the risks over the long term.

RESEARCH ON EXISTENTIAL RISK

The study of existential risk is in its infancy. We are only starting to understand the risks we face and the best ways to address them. And we are at an even earlier stage when it comes to the conceptual and moral foundations, or grand strategy for humanity. So we are not yet in a good position to take decisive actions to secure our longterm potential. This makes further research on existential risk especially valuable. It would help us to determine which of the available actions we should take, and to discover entirely new actions we hadn't yet considered.[63]

Some of this research should be on concrete topics. We need to better understand the existential risks—how likely they are, their mechanisms, and the best ways to reduce them. While there has been substantial research into nuclear war, climate change and biosecurity, very little of this has looked at the most extreme events in each area, those that pose a threat to humanity itself.[64] Similarly, we need much more technical research into how to align artificial general intelligence with the values of humanity.

We also need more research on how to address major risk factors, such as war between the great powers, and on major security factors too. For example, on the best kinds of institutions for international coordination or for representing future generations. Or on the best approaches to resilience, increasing our chance of recovery from non-fatal catastrophes. And we need to find new risk and security factors, giving us more ways to get a handle on existential risk.

And alongside these many strands of research on concrete topics, we also need research on more abstract matters. We need to better understand longtermism, humanity's potential and existential risk: to refine the ideas, developing the strongest versions of each; to understand what ethical foundations they depend upon, and what ethical commitments they imply; and to better understand the major strategic questions facing humanity.

These areas might sound grand and unapproachable, but it is possible to make progress on them. Consider the ideas we've encountered in this book. Some are very broad: the sweeping vision of humanity across the ages, the Precipice and the urgency of securing our future. But many can be distilled into small crisp insights. For example: that a catastrophe killing 100 percent of people could be much worse than one killing 99 percent because you lose the whole future; that the length of human survival so far puts a tight bound on the natural risk; that existential risk reduction will tend to be undersupplied since it is an intergenerational global public good; or the distinction between state risks and transition risks. I am sure there are more ideas like these just waiting to be discovered. And many of them don't require any special training to find or understand: just an analytical mind looking for patterns, tools and explanations.

Perhaps surprisingly, there is already funding available for many of these kinds of research on existential risk. A handful of forward-thinking philanthropists have taken existential risk seriously and recently started funding top-tier research on the key risks and their solutions.[65] For example, the Open Philanthropy Project has funded some of the most recent nuclear winter modeling as well as work on technical AI safety, pandemic preparedness and climate change—with a focus on the worst-case scenarios.[66] At the time of writing they are eager to fund much more of this research, and are limited not by money, but by a need for great researchers to work on these problems.[67]

And there are already a handful of academic institutes dedicated to research on existential risk. For example, Cambridge University's Centre for the Study of Existential Risk (CSER) and Oxford's Future of Humanity Institute (FHI), where I work.[68] Such institutes allow like-minded researchers from across the academic disciplines to come together and work on the science, ethics and policy of safeguarding humanity.

WHAT NOT TO DO

This chapter is about what we should do to protect our future. But it can be just as useful to know what to avoid. Here are a few suggestions.

Don't regulate prematurely. At the right time, regulation may be a very useful tool for reducing existential risk. But right now, we know very little about how best to do so. Pushing for ill-considered regulation would be a major mistake.

Don't take irreversible actions unilaterally. Some countermeasures may make our predicament even worse (think radical geoengineering or publishing the smallpox genome). So we should be wary of the unilateralist's curse (pp. 137–8), where the ability to take actions unilaterally creates a bias toward action by those with the most rosy estimates.

Don't spread dangerous information. Studying existential risk means exploring the vulnerabilities of our world. Sometimes

---

this turns up new dangers. Unless we manage such information carefully, we risk making ourselves even more vulnerable (see the box "Information Hazards," p. 137).

Don't exaggerate the risks. There is a natural tendency to dismiss claims of existential risk as hyperbole. Exaggerating the risks plays into that, making it much harder for people to see that there is sober, careful analysis amidst the noise.

Don't be fanatical. Safeguarding our future is extremely important, but it is not the only priority for humanity. We must be good citizens within the world of doing good. Boring others with endless talk about this cause is counterproductive. Cajoling them about why it is more important than a cause they hold dear is even worse.

Don't be tribal. Safeguarding our future is not left or right, not eastern or western, not owned by the rich or the poor. It is not partisan. Framing it as a political issue on one side of a contentious divide would be a disaster. Everyone has a stake in our future and we must work together to protect it.[69]

Don't act without integrity. When something immensely important is at stake and others are dragging their feet, people feel licensed to do whatever it takes to succeed. We must never give in to such temptation. A single person acting without integrity could stain the whole cause and damage everything we hope to achieve.

Don't despair. Despairing would sap our energy, cloud our judgment and turn away those looking to help. Despair is a self-fulfilling prophecy. While the risks are real and substantial, we know of no risks that are beyond our power to solve. If we hold our heads high, we can succeed.

Don't ignore the positive. While the risks are the central challenges facing humanity, we can't let ourselves be defined by them. What drives us is our hope for the future. Keeping this at the center of our thinking will provide us—and others—with the inspiration we need to secure our future.[70]

WHAT YOU CAN DO

Much of this chapter has been devoted to the big-picture questions of how humanity can navigate the Precipice and achieve its potential. But amidst these grand questions and themes, there is room for everyone to play a part in protecting our future.

One of the best avenues for doing good in the world is through our careers. Each of our careers is about 80,000 hours devoted to solving some kind of problem, big or small. This is such a large part of our lives that if we can devote it to one of the most important problems, we can have tremendous impact.

If you work in computer science or programming, you might be able to shift your career toward helping address the existential risk arising from AI: perhaps through much-needed technical research on AI alignment, or by working as an engineer for an AI project that takes the risks seriously.[71] If you are in medicine or biology, you may be able to help with risks from engineered pandemics. If you are in climate science, you could work on improving our understanding of the likelihood and effect of extreme climate scenarios. If you are in political science or international relations, you could work toward international cooperation on existential risk, ensuring future generations get a voice in democracy, or preventing war between great powers. If you work in government, you could help protect the future through work in security or technology policy.

The opportunities are not limited to direct work on existential risk. Instead your work could multiply the impact of those doing the direct work. Some of the most urgent work today is upstream, at the level of strategy, coordination and grant-making. As humanity starts to take seriously the challenge of protecting our future, there will be important work in allocating resources between projects and organizations building and sustaining the community of researchers and developing strategy. And some of the most urgent work lies in improving the execution and outreach of organizations dedicated to fighting existential risk. Many are looking for skilled people who really grasp the unusual mission. If you have any of these skills—for example, if you have experience working on strategy, management, policy, media, operations or executive assistance—you could join one of the organizations currently working on existential risk.[72]

If you are a student, you are in a wonderfully flexible position—able to do so much to steer your career to where your tens of thousands of hours will have the most impact. Even if you have chosen a field, or entered graduate study, it is surprisingly easy to change direction. The further down a career path you have traveled, the harder this becomes. But even then it can be worthwhile. Losing a few years to retraining may let you direct several times as many years of work to where it can do many times as much good. This is something I know from personal experience. I started out studying computer science, before moving into ethics. Then within ethics, the focus of my work has shifted only recently from the issues of global poverty to the very different issues around existential risk.

What if your career is unsuited, and yet you are unable to change? What would be ideal is if there were some way to turn the work you are best at into the type of work most desperately needed to safeguard our potential. Fortunately, there is a such way: through your giving. When you donate money to a cause, you effectively transform your own labor into additional work for that cause. If you are more suited to your existing job and the cause is constrained by lack of funding, then donating could even help more than direct work.

I think donating is a powerful way in which almost anyone can help, and it is an important part of how I give back to the world.[73] People often forget that some of humanity's greatest successes have been achieved through charity.

The contraceptive pill, one of the most revolutionary inventions of the twentieth century, was made possible by a single philanthropist. In the 1950s, at a time when governments and drug companies had little interest in pursuing the idea, the philanthropist Katharine McCormick funded the research that led to its invention, largely single-handedly.[74]

Around the same time, we saw the breakthroughs in agricultural science now known as the Green Revolution, which saw hundreds of millions of people lifted from hunger through the creation of high-yield varieties of staple crops. Norman Borlaug, the scientist who led these efforts, would win the Nobel Peace Prize in 1970 for his work. Borlaug's work, and the roll-out of these technologies in the developing world, was funded by private philanthropists.[75]

Finally, there are ways that every single one of us can play a role. We need a public conversation about the longterm future of humanity: the breathtaking scale of what we can achieve, and the risks that threaten all of this, all of us.

We need to discuss these things in academia, in government, in civil society; to explore the possibilities in serious works of fiction and the media; to talk about it between friends and within families. This conversation needs to rise above the temptation to be polarizing and partisan, or to focus on the allocation of blame. Instead we need a mature, responsible and constructive conversation: one focused on understanding problems and finding solutions. We need to inspire our children, and ourselves, to do the hard work that will be required to safeguard the future and pass the Precipice.

You can discuss the importance of the future with the people in your life who matter to you. You can engage with the growing community of people who are thinking along similar lines: where you live, where you work or study, or online. And you can strive to be an informed, responsible and vigilant citizen, staying abreast of the issues and urging your political representatives to take action when important opportunities arise.

(See the Resources section on p. 243 for concrete starting points.)

8

Our Potential

It is possible to believe that all the past is but the beginning of a beginning, and that all that is and has been is but the twilight of the dawn. It is possible to believe that all that the human mind has ever accomplished is but the dream before the awakening.

—H. G. Wells[1]

What could we hope to achieve? To experience? To become? If humanity rises to the challenges before us, navigates the risks of the coming centuries, and passes through to a time of safety—what then?

In the preceding chapters we have faced the Precipice, surveyed its challenges and planned how we might best proceed to safety. But what lies beyond? Let us raise our sights to the sweeping vista that beckons us on. We cannot make out the details from here, but we can see the broad shape of the hills and vales, the *potential* that the landscape offers—the potential of human civilization in its full maturity. It is because this potential is so vast and glorious, that the stakes of existential risk are so high. In optimism lies urgency.

This chapter is about potential, not prophecy. Not what we *will* achieve, but what is open for us to achieve if we play our cards right; if we are patient, prudent, compassionate, ambitious and wise. It is about the canvas on which we shall work: the lengths of time open to humanity, the scale of our cosmos and the quality of life we might eventually attain. It is about the shape of the land we are striving to reach, where the greater part of human history will be written.

DURATION

Human history so far has seen 200,000 years of *Homo sapiens* and 10,000 years of civilization.[2] These spans of time surpass anything in our daily lives. We have had civilization for a hundred lifetimes on end and humanity for thousands. But the universe we inhabit is thousands of times older than humanity itself. There were billions of years before us; there will be billions to come. In our universe, time is not a scarce commodity.

With such abundance at our disposal, our lifespan is limited primarily by the existential catastrophes we are striving to prevent. If we get our act together, if we make safeguarding humanity a cornerstone of our civilization, then there is no reason we could not live to see the grand themes of the universe unfold across the eons. These timespans are humbling when we consider our place in the universe so far. But when we consider the potential they hold for what we might become, they inspire.

As we have seen, the fossil record tells us a great deal about how long a typical species can expect to survive. On average, mammalian species last about one million years, and species in general typically last one to ten million years.[3] If we could address the threats we pose to ourselves—the anthropogenic existential risks—then we should be able to look forward to at least a lifespan of this order. What would this *mean*? What can happen over such a span, ten thousand times longer than our century?

Such a timescale is enough to repair the damage that we, in our immaturity, have inflicted upon the Earth. In thousands of years, almost all of our present refuse will have decayed away. If we can cease adding new pollution, the oceans and forests will be unblemished once more. Within 100,000 years, the Earth's natural systems will have scrubbed our atmosphere clean of over 90 percent of the carbon we have released, leaving the climate mostly restored and rebalanced.[4] So long as we can learn to care rightly for our home, these blots on our record could be wiped clean, all within the lifespan of a typical species, and we could look forward to living out most of our days in a world free from the scars of immature times.

About ten million years hence, even the damage we have inflicted upon biodiversity is expected to have healed. This is how long it took for species diversity to fully recover from previous mass extinctions and our best guess for how long it will take to recover from our current actions.[5]

I hope and believe that we can address pollution and biodiversity loss much more quickly than this—that sooner or later we will work to actively remove the pollution and to conserve the threatened species. But there is comfort in knowing that at the very least, Earth, on its own, can heal the damage we have done.

Over this span of time roughly half of Earth's species will naturally become extinct, with new species arising in their place. If we were to last so long, we would be living through evolutionary time, and would see this as the natural state of flux that the world is in. The apparent stasis of species in the natural world is only a reflection of the comparatively brief period we have lived. Nevertheless, if we thought it right, we could intervene to preserve the last members of a species before it naturally vanished, allowing them to live on in reduced numbers in wilderness reserves or other habitats. It would be a humble retirement, but better, I think, than oblivion.

One to ten million years is typical for a species, but by no means a limit. And humanity is atypical in many ways. This might mean a much shorter life, if we author our own destruction. But if we avoid so doing, we may be able to survive much longer. Our presence across the globe protects us from any regional catastrophe. Our ingenuity has let us draw sustenance from hundreds of different plants and animals, offering protection from the snapping of a food chain. And our ability to contemplate our own destruction—planning for the main contingencies, reacting to threats as they unfold—helps protect us against foreseeable or slow-acting threats.

Many species are not wholly extinguished, but are succeeded by their siblings or their children on the evolutionary family tree. Our story may be similar. When considering our legacy—what we shall bequeath to the future—the end of our *species* may not be the end of *us*, our projects or our ultimate aspirations. Rather, we may simply be passing the baton.

For many reasons, then, humanity (or our rightful heirs) may greatly outlast the typical species. How long might this grant us?

We know of species around us that have survived almost unchanged for hundreds of millions of years. In 1839, a Swiss biologist first described and named the *coelacanth*, an ancient order of fish that arose 400 million years ago, before vanishing from the fossil record with the dinosaurs, 65 million years ago. The coelacanth was assumed to be long extinct, but ninety-nine years later, a fisherman off the coast of South Africa caught one in his net. Coelacanths were still living in Earth's oceans, almost unchanged over all this time. They are the oldest known vertebrate species alive today, lasting more than two-thirds of the time since the vertebrates first arose.[6]

And there are older species still. The horseshoe crab has been scuttling through our oceans even longer, with an unbroken lineage of 450 million years. The nautilus has been here for 500 million years; sponges, for about 580 million. And these are merely lower bounds on their lifespans; who knows how much longer these hardy species will last? The oldest known species on Earth are cyanobacteria (blue-green algae), which have been with us for at least two billion years—much longer than there has been complex life, and more than half the time there has been life on Earth at all.[7]

What might humanity witness, if we (or our successors) were to last as long as the humble horseshoe crab?

Such a lifespan would bring us to geological timescales. We would live to see continental drift reshape the surface of the Earth as we know it. The first major change would be seen in about 10 million years, when Africa will be torn in two along the very cradle of humanity—the Rift Valley. In 50 million years, the larger of these African plates will collide with Europe, sealing the Mediterranean basin and raising a vast new range of mountains. Within about 250 million years, all our continents will merge once again, to form a supercontinent, like Pangaea 200 million years ago. Then, within 500 million years, they will disperse into some new and unrecognizable configuration.[8] If this feels unimaginable, consider that the horseshoe crab has already witnessed such change.

These spans of time would also see changes on astronomical scales. The constellations will become unrecognizable, as the nearby stars drift past each other.[9] Within 200 million years, the steady gravitational pull of the Moon will slow the Earth's rotation, and stretch our day to 25 hours. While in one year the Earth orbits our Sun, in 240 million years our Sun will complete a grand orbit around the center of our galaxy—a period known as a galactic year.

But the most important astronomical change is the evolution of the Sun itself. Our star is middle-aged. It formed about 4.6 billion years ago, and has been growing steadily brighter for most of its lifespan. Eventually, this mounting glare will start causing significant problems on Earth. The astronomical evolution is well-understood, but because its major effects upon our biosphere are unprecedented, much scientific uncertainty remains.

One often hears estimates that the Earth will remain habitable for 1 or 2 billion years. These are predictions of when the oceans will evaporate due to a runaway or moist greenhouse effect, triggered by the increasing brightness of the Sun. But the Earth may become uninhabitable for complex life before that point: either at some earlier level of warming or through another mechanism. For example, scientists expect the brightening of the Sun to also slow the Earth's plate tectonics, dampening volcanic activity. Life as we know it requires such activity; volcanoes lift essential carbon dioxide into our atmosphere. We currently have too much carbon dioxide, but we need small amounts for plants to photosynthesize. Without the carbon dioxide from volcanoes, scientists estimate that in about 800 million years photosynthesis will become impossible in 97 percent of plants, causing an extreme mass extinction. Then 500 million years later, there would be so little carbon dioxide that the remaining plants would also die—and with them, any remaining multicellular life.[10]

This might not happen. Or it might not happen at that time. This is an area of great scientific uncertainty, in part because so few people have examined these questions. More importantly, though, such a mass extinction might be *avoidable*—it might be humanity's own actions which prevent it. In fact this may be one of the great achievements that humanity might aspire to. For of all the myriad species that inhabit our Earth, only we could save the biosphere from the effects of the brightening Sun. Even if humanity is very small in your picture of the world, if most of the *intrinsic* value of the world lies in the rest of our ecosystem, humanity's *instrumental* value may yet be profound. For if we can last long enough, we will have a chance to literally save our world.

By adding sufficient new carbon to the atmosphere to hold its concentration steady, we could prevent the end of photosynthesis. Or if we could block a tenth of the incoming light (perhaps harvesting it as solar energy), we could avoid not only this, but all the other effects of the Sun's steady brightening as well, such as the superheated climate and the evaporation of the oceans.[11] Perhaps, with ingenuity and commitment, we could extend the time allotted to complex life on Earth by billions of years, and, in doing so, more than redeem ourselves for the foolishness of our civilization's youth. I do not know if we *will* achieve this, but it is a worthy goal, and a key part of our potential.

In 7.6 billion years, the Sun will have grown so vast that it will balloon out beyond Earth's own orbit, either swallowing our planet or flinging it out much further. And either way, in 8 billion years our Sun itself will die. Its extended outer layers will drift onwards past the planets, forming a ghostly planetary nebula, and its innards will collapse into a ball the size of the Earth. This tiny stellar remnant will contain roughly half the original mass of the Sun, but will never again produce new energy. It will be only a slowly cooling ember.[12]

Whether or not the Earth itself is destroyed in this process, without a Sun burning at the heart of our Solar System, any prospects for humanity would be much brighter elsewhere. And the technological challenges of leaving our home system would presumably be smaller than those of remaining.

By traveling to other stars, we might save not only ourselves, but much of our biosphere. We could bring with us a cache of seeds and cells with which to preserve Earth's species, and make green the barren places of the galaxy. If so, the good we could do for Earth-based life would be even more profound. Without our intervention, our biosphere is approaching middle age. Simple life looks to have about as much time remaining as it has had so far; complex life a little more. After that, to the best of our knowledge, life in the universe may vanish entirely. But if humanity survives, then even at that distant time, life may still be in its infancy. When I contemplate the expected timespan that Earth-based life may survive and flourish, the greatest contribution comes from the possibility of humanity turning from its destroyer, to its savior.

As we shall see, the main obstacle to leaving our Solar System is surviving for long enough to do so. We need time to develop the technology, to harvest the energy, to make the journey and to build a new home at our destination. But a civilization spanning millions of centuries would have time enough, and we should not be daunted by the task.

Our galaxy will remain habitable for an almost unfathomable time. Some of our nearby stars will burn vastly longer than the Sun, and each year ten new stars are born. Some individual stars last *trillions* of years—thousands of times longer than our Sun. And there will be millions of generations of such stars to follow.[13] This is deep time. If we survive on such a cosmological scale, the present era will seem astonishingly close to the very start of the universe. But we know of nothing that makes such a lifespan impossible, or even unrealistic. We need only get our house in order.

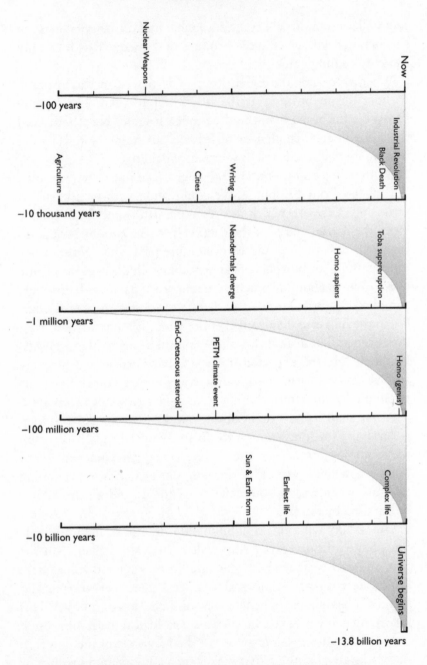

FIGURE 8.1 A timeline showing the scale of the past and future. The top row shows the prior century (on the left-hand page) and the coming century (on the right), with our own moment in the middle. Then each successive row zooms out, showing 100 times the duration, until we can see the whole history of the universe.

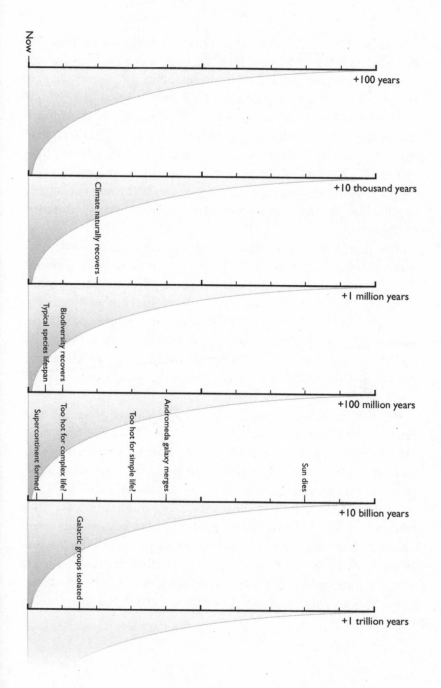

Now

+100 years

+10 thousand years

Climate naturally recovers

+1 million years

Typical species lifespan

Biodiversity recovers

+100 million years

Supercontinent formed

Too hot for complex life?

Too hot for simple life?

Andromeda galaxy merges

Sun dies

+10 billion years

Galactic groups isolated

+1 trillion years

225

SCALE

For as long as there have been humans, we have been awed by the starry night.[14] And this dark sky strewn with brilliant white points of light has yielded many secrets. Not the secrets we first sought, of myth and mysticism, but a deeper knowledge about the nature of reality. We saw some of these points of light wander across the sky, and from the patterns they traced we realized that the Earth and the heavens were governed by the very same physical laws. Other points moved by minute amounts, measurable only by the most delicate instruments. From this almost imperceptible movement, we divined the scarcely imaginable distance to the stars.

The points were not quite white, but a range of hues. And when this faint starlight was broken in a prism, missing colors revealed the substance of the stars. Some points were not *quite* points, but rather discs, clouds, swirls—celestial bodies of entirely different kinds and origins. And we found many more points too faint to be seen with the naked eye. From these subtlest of signs, we have discerned and tested fundamental laws of nature; we have heard the echoes of the Big Bang; we have watched space itself expand.

But the most important thing we have learned from the sky may be that our universe is much vaster than we had ever contemplated. The planets are other Earths. Stars are other suns, many with their own planets. The milky stripe across the sky contains more suns than the eye can distinguish—a galaxy of more than 100 billion suns, blurred in our vision to a uniform white. The faint swirls are entire galaxies beyond our own, and there are hundreds of billions of these spread across the skies.[15] Each time we thought we had charted the limits of creation, it transcended our maps. Our Earth is just one island in a bewilderingly large archipelago, which is itself just one amidst billions.

This discovery of the true scale of our cosmos dramatically raises the prospects for what humanity might achieve. We once thought ourselves limited to the Earth; we know now that vastly greater opportunities and resources are available to us. Not immediately, of course—exploring the whole of our own galaxy would take at least 100,000 years; to reach the furthest limits of the universe would require billions. But it raises deep questions about what might be achievable over vast timescales.

In just five centuries we have gone from the dimmest understanding of our Solar System—unable to grasp any coherent picture of our Sun, Moon, Earth and the wandering points of light called "planets"—to breathtaking high-resolution images of all our planets and their moons. We have sent gleaming craft sailing past the moons of Jupiter, through the rings of Saturn and to the surfaces of all terrestrial planets. To our Moon, we came in person.

The planets and their moons are the glories of our Solar System: majestic; enigmatic. We might look to settle them, but even if we overcame the daunting challenges, the combined surface area of all other solid planets and moons is just over twice that of Earth.[16] There would be adventure and excitement, but no radical increase in our potential, no fundamental change to our story. We might try to use their physical resources, but there are already ample resources for the foreseeable future in the million known asteroids, and resources for the distant future in the billions of planets now known to exist elsewhere in our galaxy. The best reason to settle the planets is to achieve some additional protection from existential risks, though this provides less safety than one may think, since some of the risks will be correlated between planets. So perhaps we will leave our own planets pristine: as monuments, jewels. To be explored and treasured. To fill us with wonder and inspire us to journey further.

Our Solar System's greatest contribution to our potential lies with our Sun, and the vast bounty of clean energy it offers. The sunlight hitting Earth's surface each day carries 5,000 times more energy than modern civilization requires. It gives in two hours what we use in a year. This abundance of solar energy created most of our other energy sources (coal, oil, natural gas, wind, hydro, biomass) and far outstrips them.[17]

But almost all of the Sun's energy is wasted. It shines not onto leaves or solar cells, but out into the blackness of space. Earth intercepts less than one part in a billion; all the bodies of our Solar System together receive less than a hundred-millionth of the Sun's light.

In the future, we could harness this energy by constructing solar collectors in orbit around the Sun. Such a project would be completely scalable.[18] We could start with something small and affordable; then, with a fraction of the energy it provides, we could scale up to whatever level we desire. The asteroid belt alone has more than enough raw materials for such a project.[19] Eventually, we could increase our access to clean energy by up to a billion-fold, using only light that would otherwise be wasted. And such a structure could also be used to address the Sun's increasing brightness, providing shade that could extend the reign of complex life on Earth tenfold.

Such a path would grant us access to an abundance of clean energy. We would have no need for dirty energy sources,[20] and many of the challenges that derive from energy scarcity could be solved, including food production, water purification and conflict over oil. We could quickly cleanse our atmosphere of our past carbon emissions, using carbon dioxide scrubbers currently limited by a lack of cheap, clean power. And, beyond all of this, harnessing the Sun's energy would cast open the door to the stars.

Could we really reach across the vast distances to the stars? In some ways the answer has already been written. After finishing their missions among the planets, *Pioneer 10*, *Voyager 1* and *Voyager 2* have all overcome the gravitational pull of our Solar System and escaped. Eventually, they will travel far enough to reach our nearest stars; proof that we can span such distances even with 1970s technology. But that on its own is not enough to greatly expand our potential, for *Voyager 1* will take 70,000 years to reach the distance of our closest star and will cease functioning long before then.[21]

Modern efforts to do better are underway. The Breakthrough Starshot Initiative, announced in 2016, aims to send a fleet of small, unmanned spacecraft to Alpha Centauri, four light years away, at about one-fifth the speed of light. If the project proceeds as planned, it may launch as soon as 2036.[22]

To truly expand our potential, we would need a spacecraft to reach another star, then stop and use the resources there to build a settlement that could eventually grow into a new bastion of civilization.[23] Such a trip requires four challenging phases: acceleration, surviving the voyage, deceleration and building a base of operations. These challenges are intertwined. Robotic missions make the trip easier, but building a base harder (at least for now). Faster missions make surviving the voyage easier, but greatly increase the energy and technology requirements for acceleration and deceleration.

We do not currently have the technology to meet these requirements, and we will not develop it within the next few decades. But we haven't discovered any fundamental barriers, and technology advances fast. In my view, the biggest challenge will be surviving on Earth for the century or two until it becomes technologically feasible.

While there is some notable skepticism of interstellar travel, a closer inspection shows that it is directed either at our near-term capabilities or at our achieving the kind of effortless space travel depicted in films like *Star Wars* or *Star Trek*, where individuals routinely travel between the stars in relative comfort. I share this skepticism. But the expansion of humanity's potential doesn't require anything like that. It requires only that if we could survive long enough, and strive hard enough, then we could *eventually* travel to a nearby star and establish enough of a foothold to create a new flourishing society from which we could venture further.

Our abiding image of space travel should not be the comfort and ease of an ocean liner, but the ingenuity, daring and perseverance of the Polynesian sailors who, a thousand years ago, sailed vast stretches of the Pacific to find all its scattered islands and complete the final stage of the settlement of the Earth. Seen in this way—as a grand challenge for humanity—I can't help but think that if we last long enough, we would be able to settle our nearest stars.

What would we find on our arrival? Do any other worlds in our universe harbor simple life? Complex life? Alien civilizations? Or are they all lifeless desert landscapes awaiting the spark of life that only we may bring? Is life easy and ubiquitous, or are there some steps on the way from a lifeless planet to self-aware observers that are vanishingly unlikely? Are we alone in our stellar neighborhood? Our galaxy? Our observable universe?[24]

Our ever-more-sensitive instruments have so far shown no signs of life beyond our Earth—no chemical signatures, no radio signals, no traces of grand engineering projects, no visits. But the quest to find alien life is young and our telescopes could still easily miss a civilization like ours within just 100 light years of the Earth. The truth is that we don't yet know, and this may not be the century we find out. In this sketch of our potential, I focus on the case where we are indeed alone. But if we were to find other life—especially intelligent life—it could profoundly change our future direction.[25] And it may be the distance to our nearest intelligent neighbors, rather than the limits of our spacecraft, that sets the physical scale for what we are able to author in the heavens.

Our local stellar neighborhood is a random scattering of stars, extending more or less uniformly in all directions. This scattered pattern continues as we zoom out, until 15 million stars come into view, stretching 1,000 light years from the Earth. Only at this immense scale do signs of the large-scale structure of our galaxy emerge. Above and below the galactic disc the stars grow sparse, and as we zoom out even further, we begin to see the curve of the Orion spiral arm, where our Sun lies; then the other spiral arms, and the glowing bulge around the galactic center. Finally we see the familiar whirlpool shape of our spiral galaxy,

150,000 light years across, encompassing more than 100 billion stars, most with their own planets.

But if we could reach just one nearby star and establish a settlement, this entire galaxy would open up to us. For then the process could repeat, using the resources of our new settlement to build more spacecraft, and its sun to power them. If we could travel just six light years at a time, then almost all the stars of our galaxy would be reachable.[26] Each star system, including our own, would need to settle just the few nearest stars, and the entire galaxy would eventually fill with life.[27]

Because this critical distance of six light years is just slightly further than our nearest star, it is unlikely that we would be able to reach some stars without eventually being able to reach most of the galaxy. And because this wave of new settlements could radiate out in all directions, the enlivening of our galaxy may occur relatively quickly, by the standards of the history of life so far. Even if our spacecraft traveled at just 1 percent of the speed of light, and took 1,000 years to establish a new settlement, the entire galaxy could be settled within 100 million years—long before the Earth becomes uninhabitable. And once begun, the process would be robust in the face of local accidents, failures or natural setbacks.

Our galaxy is surrounded by a cloud of about fifty nearby galaxies, known as our Local Group. Foremost among them is the Andromeda Galaxy, a beautiful spiral galaxy, and the only galaxy in our group larger than our own. Gravity is pulling the two toward each other, and in four billion years (before our Sun has died) they will collide and unite. With so much distance between the stars of each galaxy, this collision will do surprisingly little to upset the stars and their planets. Its main effect will be to disrupt the delicate spiral structures of the partners, probably merging into a more uniform elliptical galaxy about three times as large. Eventually (in hundreds of billions of years) all the other galaxies in our group will have merged in too, forming a single giant galaxy.[28]

Zooming further out, we see many more groups of galaxies, some with as many as a thousand members.[29] Eventually these groups resolve into a larger structure: the cosmic web—long, thick threads of galaxies, called filaments. These filaments criss-cross space in a kind of three-dimensional network, as if someone took a random set of points in space and connected each to its nearest handful of neighbors. Where the filaments intersect, space is bright and rich with galaxies.[30] Between such filaments are dark and empty expanses, known as cosmic voids. As far as we can tell, this cosmic web continues indefinitely. At the very least, it continues as far as we can *see* or *go*.

It is these final limits on our knowledge and action that appear to set the ultimate scale in our universe. We have known for almost a century that our universe is expanding, pulling the groups of galaxies apart. And twenty years ago we discovered that this expansion is accelerating. Cosmologists believe this puts a hard limit on what we will ever be able to observe or affect.[31]

We can currently see a sphere around us extending out 46 billion light years in all directions, known as the *observable universe*. Light from galaxies beyond this sphere hasn't yet had time to reach us.[32] Next year we will see a little further. The observable universe will increase in radius by a single light year, and about 25 more galaxies will come into view. But on our leading cosmological theory, the rate at which new galaxies become visible will decline, and those currently more than 63 billion light years away will never become visible from the Earth. We could call the region within this distance the *eventually observable universe*.[33]

But much more importantly, accelerating expansion also puts a limit on what we can ever affect. If, today, you shine a ray of light out into space, it could reach any galaxy that is currently less than 16 billion light years away. But galaxies further than this are being pulled away so quickly that neither light, nor anything else we might send, could ever affect them.[34]

And next year this *affectable universe* will shrink by a single light year. Three more galaxies will slip forever beyond our influence.[35] Eventually, the gulfs between each group of galaxies will grow so vast that nothing will ever again be able to cross—each group of galaxies will be alone in the void, forever isolated from the others. This cleaves time into two fundamental eras: an *era of connection* with billions of reachable galaxies, and an *era of isolation* with a million times fewer. Surprisingly, this fundamental change in the causal structure of our universe is expected to happen long before the stars stop burning, in about 150 billion years. Our closest star, Proxima Centauri, will be less than a tenth of the way through its life.

So 16 billion light years looks to be the upper bound on how far humanity can reach, and 150 billion years the bound on how long we have to do so. I do not know if such intergalactic travel will ever be feasible. We could again use the strategy of reaching out further and further, a galaxy at a time, but the distances required are a million-fold greater than for interstellar travel, bringing unique challenges.[36] Still, we know of no fundamental physical barriers that would prevent a civilization that had already mastered its own galaxy from taking this next step. (See Appendix G for more about the different scales a civilization might reach.)

At the ultimate physical scale, there are 20 billion galaxies that our descendants might be able to reach. Seven-eighths of these are more than halfway to the edge of the affectable universe—so distant that once we reached them no signal could ever be sent back. Spreading out into these distant galaxies would thus be a final diaspora, with each galactic group forming its own sovereign realm, soon causally isolated from the others. Such isolation need not imply loneliness—each group would contain hundreds of billions of stars—but it might mean freedom. They could be established as pieces of a common project, all set in motion with the same constitution; or as independent realms, each choosing its own path.

With entire galaxies receding beyond our reach each year, one might think this pushes humanity toward a grand strategy of *haste*—a desperate rush to reach the technologies of intergalactic travel as soon as possible. But the *relative* loss each year is actually rather slow—about one part in five billion—and it is this relative reduction in our potential that matters.[37]

The pressures toward prudence and wisdom are larger, in relative terms, and counsel care over haste. If rushing to acquire these technologies a century earlier diminished our chance of survival by even one part in 50 million, it would be counter-productive. And for many years hence, the value of another century's reflection on what to *do* with the future—an irrevocable choice, and quite possibly the most important one humanity will ever make—will outweigh the value of extending our reach by just one part in fifty million. So our best grand strategy is one of careful reflection and prudence, with our degree of caution tuned to the slow clock of cosmological expansion.[38]

Such considerations seem unreal. In most of our day-to-day thought, and even our deeper reflection about the future and humanity's potential, we look around and see the Earth. Our eyes rarely turn to the heavens and the dusting of night stars. If pressed, we accept that planets, stars and galaxies are real places, but we rarely *feel* it, or consider that they could be crucial to our future potential.

One person who seriously considered the stars was Frank Ramsey, the brilliant economist and philosopher, whose career was cut short when he died at just 26 years of age, in 1930. His attitude was one of heroic defiance:

> I don't feel the least humble before the vastness of the heavens. The stars may be large, but they cannot think or love; and these are qualities which impress me far more than size does. I take no credit for weighing nearly seventeen stone. My picture of the world is drawn in perspective, and not to scale. The foreground is occupied by human beings and the stars are all small as threepenny bits.[39]

There is truth to this. What makes each of us special, so worthy of protection and celebration is something subtle about us, in the way that the matter of which we are comprised has been so delicately arranged as to allow us to think and love and create and dream.

Right now, the rest of the universe appears to lack such qualities. Ramsey may be right that in terms of *value*, the stars are as small as threepenny bits. But if we can venture out and animate the countless worlds above with life and love and thought, then even on Ramsey's view, we could bring our cosmos to its full scale; make it worthy of our awe. And since it appears to be only us who can bring the universe to such full scale, we may have an immense instrumental value, which would leave us at the center of this picture of the cosmos. In this way, our potential, and the potential in the sheer scale of our universe, are interwoven.

QUALITY

We have seen that the future is a canvas vast in time and space. Its ultimate beauty will depend on what we paint. Trillions of years and billions of galaxies are worth little unless we make of them something valuable. But here too we have grounds for profound optimism. For the potential quality of our future is also grand beyond imagining.

As we've seen, human life is on the whole much better today than ever before. Compared with our ancestors, we have less to fear from disease, from hunger and from each other. We have conquered polio and smallpox. We have created vaccines, antibiotics and anesthetics. Humans today are less likely than at any point in the history of civilization to live in slavery or poverty; to be tortured, maimed or murdered; to starve. We have greater freedom to choose our loves, our beliefs, our leaders and the courses of our lives. Many of our children have access to opportunities that would astound our ancestors—opportunities to learn, play and experiment; to travel; to engage with the greatest novels, poems and philosophies; to experience a lifetime's variety of harmonies, sights and flavors; and to contemplate truths about the cosmos unknown to our most learned ancestors.

Yet human life, for all its joys, could be dramatically better than it is today. We have made tremendous progress on violence and disease, but there is still so much room for improvement—still lives being broken or cut short. The development of anesthetics and pain relief have dramatically cut the prevalence of intense physical pain, yet we still live at a time with avoidable agony. We have made great progress in freeing people from absolute poverty, but a tenth of us still live under its shadow. And when it comes to relative poverty, to severe depression, to racism and sexism, we are far from a solution.

Many of the harshest injustices visited upon our fellow humans are behind us. While from year to year it can be hard to tell if things are getting better or worse, on the scale of centuries we have seen a clear decline in persecution and intolerance, with a marked rise in personal freedoms and political equality. Yet even in the most progressive countries we have a long way to go, and there are still parts of the world that have barely begun the journey.

And there are further injustices inflicted upon the billions of animals in the modern meat industry and in the natural world. Our civil awakening to the plight of animals and our environment came only very recently, in the wake of the severe harms inflicted upon them by industry in the twentieth century. But we increasingly see such harms for what they are, and have begun the fight to end these new forms of injustice.

These blights upon our world must end. And we *can* end them—if we survive. In the face of persecution and uncertainty, the noblest among our ancestors have poured their efforts into building a better and more just world. If we do the same—and give our descendants a chance to do the same—then as our knowledge, invention, coordination and abundance grow, we can more and more fulfill the fierce hope that has flowed through so many strands of the human project: to end the evils of our world and build a society that is truly just and humane.

And even such a profound achievement might only set the stage for what is to come. Our full potential for flourishing remains undreamed.

Consider the parts of your life when you brushed paths with true happiness. The year, month or day when everything was coming together and you had a glimpse of the richness that life can hold; when you saw how much greater a life could be. For me, most recently, this was the fortnight after the birth of my child: sharing the delight with my friends; sharing the journey with my wife; knowing my parents in a new way; the pride of fatherhood.

Or consider your peak experiences. Those individual moments where you feel most alive; where you are rapt with wonder or love or beauty. In my current stage of life these are most often moments with my daughter. When she sees me arrive at nursery, her eyes lighting up, running headlong into my arms, her fierce embrace. Consider how many times better such moments are than the typical experiences of your day. My typical experiences are by no means bad, but I'd trade hundreds, maybe thousands, for the peaks.

Most of these peaks fade all too quickly. The world deadens; we settle into our routines; our memories dim. But we have seen enough to know that life can offer something far grander and more alive than the standard fare. If humanity can survive, we may one day learn to dwell more and more deeply in such vitality; to brush off more and more dust; to make a home amidst the beauty of the world. Sustaining such heights might not be easy, or simple. It could require changes in our psychology that we should approach with caution. But we know of nothing, in principle, that stands in our way, and much to recommend the exploration.

And peak experiences are not merely potential dwellings—they are also pointers to possible experiences and modes of thought beyond our present understanding. Consider, for example, how little we know of how ultraviolet light looks to a finch; of how echolocation feels to a bat, or a dolphin; of the way that a red fox, or a homing pigeon, experiences the Earth's magnetic field. Such uncharted experiences exist in minds much less sophisticated than our own. What experiences, possibly of immense value, could be accessible, then, to minds much greater? Mice know very little of music, art or humor. Toward what experiences are we as mice? What beauties are we blind to?[40]

Our descendants would be in a much better position to find out. At the very least, they would likely be able to develop and enhance existing human capacities—empathy, intelligence, memory, concentration, imagination. Such enhancements could make possible entirely new forms of human culture and cognition: new games, dances, stories; new integrations of thought and emotion; new forms of art. And we would have millions of years—maybe billions, or trillions—to go much further, to explore the most distant reaches of what can be known, felt, created and understood.

In this respect, the possible quality of our future resembles its possible duration and scope. We saw how human civilization has probed only a tiny fraction of what is possible in time or space. Along each of these dimensions, we can zoom out from our present position with a dizzying expansion of scale, leading to scarcely imaginable vistas waiting to be explored. Such scales are a familiar feature of contemporary science. Our children learn early that everyday experience has only acquainted us with a tiny fraction of the physical universe.

Less familiar, but just as important, is the idea that the space of possible experiences and modes of life, and the degree of flourishing they make available, may be similarly vast, and that everyday life may acquaint us with a similarly parochial proportion. In this sense, our investigations of flourishing thus far in history may be like astronomy before telescopes—with such limited vision, it is easy to think the universe small, and human-centered. Yet how strange it would be if this single species of ape, equipped by evolution with this limited set of sensory and cognitive capacities, after only a few thousand years of civilization, ended up anywhere near the maximum possible quality of life. Much more likely, I think, that we have barely begun the ascent.

Rising to our full potential for flourishing would likely involve us being transformed into something beyond the humanity of today.

Remember that evolution has not stopped with humanity. There have been many species of the genus *Homo*, and within 1 or 2 million years we would expect to gradually become a different species from today's *Homo sapiens*. Indeed, unless we act to prevent it, this will eventually happen. This century's genetic technologies will give us the tools to transform ourselves much faster, should we wish. And we can already see additional avenues for transformation on the horizon, such as implants granting digital extensions to our minds, or developments in artificial intelligence allowing us to craft entirely new kinds of beings to join us or replace us.

Such transformation would bring serious risks: risks of inequality and injustice; of splintering the unity of humanity; of unanticipated consequences stretching over vast spans of time. Some of these risks are existential. Replacing ourselves with something much worse, or something devoid of value altogether, would put our entire future in jeopardy, as would any form of enhancement that could lead to widespread conflict or social collapse. But forever preserving humanity as it is now may also squander our legacy, relinquishing the greater part of our potential.

So I approach the possibility of transforming ourselves with cautious optimism. If we can navigate its challenges maturely, such transformation offers a precious opportunity to transcend our limitations and explore much more deeply just how good life can be. I love humanity, not because we are *Homo sapiens*, but because of our capacity to flourish, and to bring greater flourishing to the world around us. And in this most important respect, our descendants, however different, could reach heights that would be forever beyond our present grasp.

CHOICES

I have sketched three dimensions of humanity's potential: the vistas of time, space and experience that the future holds. My concern has not been to paint a detailed picture, but to persuade

239

you, more generally, that we stand before something extraordinarily vast and valuable—something in light of which all of history thus far will seem the merest prelude; a taste; a seed. Beyond these outlines, the substance of our future is mostly unknown. Our descendants will create it.

If we steer humanity to a place of safety, we will have time to think. Time to ensure that our choices are wisely made; that we will do the very best we can with our piece of the cosmos. We rarely reflect on what that might be. On what we might achieve should humanity's entire will be focused on gaining it, freed from material scarcity and internal conflict. Moral philosophy has been focused on the more pressing issues of treating each other decently in a world of scarce resources. But there may come a time, not too far away, when we mostly have our house in order and can look in earnest at where we might go from here. Where we might address this vast question about our ultimate values. This is the Long Reflection.

I do not know what will come out of it. What ideas will stand the test of time; of careful analysis by thinkers of all kinds, each anxious to avoid any bias that may doom us to squander our potential. I do not know in what proportions it will be a vision of flourishing, of virtue, of justice, of achievement; nor what final form any of these aspects may take. I do not know whether it will be a vision that transcends these very divisions in how we think of the good.

We might compare our situation with that of people 10,000 years ago, on the cusp of agriculture. Imagine them sowing their first seeds and reflecting upon what opportunities a life of farming might enable, and on what the ideal world might look like. Just as they would be unable to fathom almost any aspect of our current global civilization, so too we may not yet be able to see the shape of an ideal realization of our potential.

This chapter has focused on humanity's potential—on the scope of what we *might* someday be able to achieve. Living up to this potential will be another great challenge in itself. And vast efforts will be undertaken in an attempt to rise to this challenge.

But they can wait for another day. These battles can be fought by our successors. Only we can make sure we get through this period of danger, that we navigate the Precipice and find our way to safety; that we give our children the very pages on which they will author our future.

RESOURCES

BOOK WEBSITE

Videos • Mailing list • FAQs • Errata
Supporting articles and papers • Quotations • Reading lists
theprecipice.com

AUTHOR WEBSITE

Find out about my other projects • Read my papers
Contacts for media and speaking
tobyord.com

EFFECTIVE ALTRUISM

Meet others interested in having the greatest impact they can
effectivealtruism.org

CAREERS

Advice on how to use your career to safeguard our future
80000hours.org

DONATIONS

Join me in making a lifelong commitment to helping
the world through effective giving
givingwhatwecan.org

ACKNOWLEDGMENTS

Few books are shaped by author alone. I think most of us already know this. Yet few owe quite so much as this one to the generosity, hard work and brilliance of others.

Academics are rarely allowed enough time to write a book like this. They are weighed down by major responsibilities to their students, colleagues and institutions. Even grants for the express purpose of book-writing usually buy only a brief spell of time. I am thus especially thankful for the funding for my dedicated research fellowship, which has allowed me years of uninterrupted time to work on a topic I consider so important, seeing it through from initial research to the published book. This was provided by the private philanthropy of Luke Ding and by a grant from the European Research Council (under the European Union's Horizon 2020 research and innovation program: grant agreement No. 669751). Further funding from Luke Ding, the Open Philanthropy Project and the Berkley Existential Risk Initiative allowed me to build up a dedicated team around the book, providing me with expert advice and support in making the book a success. Such support for an academic's book is exceptionally uncommon and it is difficult to overstate how important it has been.

Moreover, academics are rarely allowed to write books that venture so far beyond the bounds of their home discipline. I'm extremely grateful to my academic home, Oxford University's Future of Humanity Institute, where no such prejudice exists; where you are encouraged to venture however far you need to explore the question at hand.

Writing a book with such a wide scope usually comes with too high a risk of oversimplification, cherry-picking and outright error in those fields far from your own expertise. This risk would have been too high for me as well, if not for the vast amount of research support I received from others who believed in the project. I am grateful for the research assistance from Joseph Carlsmith, John Halstead, Howie Lempel, Keith Mansfield and Matthew van der Merwe, who helped familiarize me with the relevant literatures.

And I am profoundly grateful to the many experts from other disciplines who gave so much of their time, to ensure the book was faithful to the state-of-the-art knowledge in their fields. Thank you to Fred Adams, Richard Alley, Tatsuya Amano, Seth Baum, Niel Bowerman, Miles Brundage, Catalina Cangea, Paulo Ceppi, Clark Chapman, David Christian, Allan Dafoe, Richard Danzig, Ben Day, David Denkenberger, Daniel Dewey, Eric Drexler, Daniel Ellsberg, Owain Evans, Sebastian Farquhar, Vlad Firoiu, Ben Garfinkel, Tim Genewein, Goodwin Gibbons, Thore Graepel, Joanna Haigh, Alan Harris, Hiski Haukkala, Ira Helfand, Howard Herzog, Michael Janner, Ria Kalluri, Jim Kasting, Jan Leike, Robert Lempert, Andrew Levan, Gregory Lewis, Marc Lipsitch, Rosaly Lopes, Stephen Luby, Enxhell Luzhnica, David Manheim, Jochem Marotzke, Jason Matheny, Piers Millet, Michael Montague, David Morrison, Cassidy Nelson, Clive Oppenheimer, Raymond Pierrehumbert, Max Popp, David Pyle, Michael Rampino, Georgia Ray, Catherine Rhodes, Richard Rhodes, Carl Robichaud, Tyler Robinson, Alan Robock, Luisa Rodriguez, Max Roser, Jonathan Rougier, Andrew Rushby, Stuart Russell, Scott Sagan, Anders Sandberg, Hauke Schmidt, Rohin Shah, Steve Sherwood, Lewis Smith, Jacob Steinhardt, Sheldon Stern, Brian Thomas, Brian Toon, Phil Torres, Martin Weitzman, Brian Wilcox, Alex Wong, Lily Xia and Donald Yeomans.

Then there were the many weeks of fact-checking by Joseph Carlsmith, Matthew van der Merwe and especially Joao Fabiano, who have done their utmost to reduce the chance of any outright errors or misleading claims slipping through. Of course the responsibility for any that do slip through rests on me alone, and I'll keep an up-to-date list of errata at theprecipice.com/errata.

It was Andrew Snyder-Beattie who first suggested I write this book and did so much to help get it started. Thank you, Andrew. And thanks to all those who contributed to the early conversations on what form it should take: Nick Beckstead, Nick Bostrom, Brian Christian, Owen Cotton-Barratt, Andrew Critch, Allan Dafoe, Daniel Dewey, Luke Ding, Eric Drexler, Hilary Greaves, Michelle Hutchinson, Will MacAskill, Jason Matheny, Luke Muehlhauser, Michael Page, Anders Sandberg, Carl Shulman, Andrew Snyder-Beattie, Pablo Stafforini, Ben Todd, Amy Willey Labenz, Julia Wise and Bernadette Young. Some of this advice continued all the way through the years of writing—my special thanks to Shamil Chandaria, Owen Cotton-Barratt, Teddy Collins, Will MacAskill, Anders Sandberg, Andrew Snyder-Beattie and Bernadette Young.

It was immensely helpful that so many people generously gave their time to read and comment on the manuscript. Thank you to Josie Axford-Foster, Beth Barnes, Nick Beckstead, Haydn Belfield, Nick Bostrom, Danny Bressler, Tim Campbell, Natalie Cargill, Shamil Chandaria, Paul Christiano, Teddy Collins, Owen Cotton-Barratt, Andrew Critch, Allan Dafoe, Max Daniel, Richard Danzig, Ben Delo, Daniel Dewey, Luke Ding, Peter Doane, Eric Drexler, Peter Eckersley, Holly Elmore, Sebastian Farquhar, Richard Fisher, Lukas Gloor, Ian Godfrey, Katja Grace, Hilary Greaves, Demis Hassabis, Hiski Haukkala, Alexa Hazel, Kirsten Horton, Holden Karnofsky, Lynn Keller, Luke Kemp, Alexis Kirschbaum, Howie Lempel, Gregory Lewis, Will MacAskill, Vishal Maini, Jason Matheny, Dylan Matthews, Tegan McCaslin, Andreas Mogensen, Luke Muehlhauser, Tim Munday, John Osborne, Richard Parr, Martin Rees, Sebastian Roberts, Max Roser, Anders Sandberg, Carl Shulman, Peter Singer, Andrew Snyder-Beattie, Pablo Stafforini, Jaan Tallinn, Christian Tarsney, Ben Todd, Susan Trammell, Brian Tse, Jonas Vollmer, Julia Wise and Bernadette Young.

Thanks also to Rose Linke, for her advice on how to name this book, and Keith Mansfield, for answering my innumerable questions about the world of publishing.

ACKNOWLEDGMENTS

This project benefited from a huge amount of operational support from the Future of Humanity Institute (FHI), the Centre for Effective Altruism (CEA) and the Berkley Existential Risk Initiative (BERI). My thanks to Josh Axford, Sam Deere, Michelle Gavin, Rose Hadshar, Habiba Islam, Josh Jacobson, Miok Ham Jung, Chloe Malone, Kyle Scott, Tanya Singh and Tena Thau.

The actual writing of this book took place largely in the many wonderful libraries and cafés of Oxford—I especially need to thank Peloton Espresso, where I may have spent more time than in my own office.

I'm incredibly thankful to Max Brockman, my literary agent. Max connected me with publishers who really believed in the book, and guided me through the baroque world of publishing, always ready to provide astute advice at a moment's notice.

Thank you to Alexis Kirschbaum, my editor at Bloomsbury, who saw most keenly what this book could be, and always believed in it. Her confidence helped give me the confidence to deliver it. Thank you to Emma Bal, Catherine Best, Sara Helen Binney, Nicola Hill, Jasmine Horsey, Sarah Knight, Jonathon Leech, David Mann, Richard Mason, Sarah McLean, Hannah Paget and the rest of the Bloomsbury team, for all their work in making this project a success.

And thanks to everyone at Hachette. To my editors: Paul Whitlatch, who saw what this book could be and believed me when I said I would meet my final deadlines; and David Lamb, who guided the project from a manuscript into a book. And to everyone else at Hachette who played a part behind the scenes, especially Michelle Aielli, Quinn Fariel, Mollie Weisenfeld.

Looking back to the earliest influences on this book, I want to thank four philosophers who shaped my path. The first is Peter Singer, who showed how one could take moral philosophy beyond the walls of the academy, and extend our common conception of ethics to encompass new domains such as animal welfare and global poverty. Then there are my dissertation supervisors Derek

Parfit and John Broome, whose work inspired me to become a philosopher and to come to Oxford, where I was lucky enough to have them both as mentors. Yet I think the greatest influence on me at Oxford has been Nick Bostrom, through his courage to depart from the well-worn tracks and instead tackle vast questions about the future that seem almost off-limits in academic philosophy. I think he introduced me to existential risk the day we met, just after we both arrived here in 2003; we've been talking about it ever since.

One of the best things about the writing of this book has been the feeling of working on a team. This feeling, and indeed the team itself, would not have been possible without Joseph Carlsmith and Matthew van der Merwe. They acted as project managers, keeping me on track, and the dozens of threads of the project from getting stuck. They were research assistants *par excellence*, reaching out to the world's top experts across such a range of topics, determining the key results and controversies—even finding a few mistakes in the cutting-edge papers. They were not afraid to tell me when I was wrong. And they were proofreaders, editors, strategists, confidants and friends. They put thousands of hours of their lives into making this book everything it could be, and I cannot thank them enough.

Finally, I'm grateful to my father, Ian, whose unending curiosity about the past and the future of humanity pervaded my childhood and gave me the foundation to start asking the right questions; to my mother, Lecki, who showed me how to take a stand in the world for what you believe in; to my wife, Bernadette, who has supported, encouraged and inspired me through this and through everything; and to my child, Rose, through whose eyes I see the world anew.

APPENDICES

A. Discounting the Longterm Future
B. Population Ethics and Existential Risk
C. Nuclear Weapons Accidents
D. Surprising Effects when Combining Risks
E. The Value of Protecting Humanity
F. Policy and Research Recommendations
G. Extending the Kardashev Scale

Appendix A

DISCOUNTING THE LONGTERM FUTURE

An existential catastrophe would drastically reduce the value of our entire future. This may be the most important reason for safeguarding humanity from existential risks. But how important *is* our longterm future? In particular, does the fact that much of it occurs far from us in time reduce its value?

Economists often need to compare benefits that occur at different times. And they have discovered a number of reasons why a particular kind of benefit may matter less if received at a later time.

For example, I recently discovered a one-dollar coin that I'd hidden away as a child to be found by my future self. After the immediate joy of discovery, I was struck by the fact that by transporting this dollar into the future, I'd robbed it of most of its value. There was the depreciation of the currency, of course, but much more than that was the fact that I now have enough money that one extra dollar makes very little difference to my quality of life.[1]

If people tend to become richer in the future (due to economic growth) then this effect means that monetary benefits received in the future will tend to be worth less than if they were received now (even adjusting for inflation).[2] Economists take this into account by "discounting" future monetary benefits by a discount factor that depends on both the economic growth rate and the psychological fact that extra spending for an individual has diminishing marginal utility.[3]

A second reason why future benefits can be worth less than current benefits is that they are less certain. There is a chance that the process producing this benefit—or indeed the person who

253

would receive it—won't still be around at the future time, leaving us with no benefit at all. This is sometimes called the "catastrophe rate." Clearly one should adjust for this, reducing the value of future benefits in line with their chance of being realized.

The standard economic approach to discounting (the Ramsey model) incorporates both these reasons.[4] It treats the appropriate discount rate for society (ρ) as the sum of two terms:

$$\rho = \eta g + \delta$$

The first term (ηg) represents the fact that as future people get richer, they get less benefit from money. It is the product of a factor reflecting the way people get diminishing marginal utility from additional consumption (η) with the growth rate of consumption (g). The second term (δ) accounts for the chance that the benefit won't be realized (the catastrophe rate).

So how do we use this formula for discounting existential risk? The first thing to note is that the ηg term is inapplicable.[5] This is because the future benefit we are considering (having a flourishing civilization instead of a ruined civilization, or nothing at all) is not a monetary benefit. The entire justification of the ηg term is to adjust for marginal benefits that are worth less to you when you are richer (such as money or things money can easily buy), but that is inapplicable here—if anything, the richer people might be, the *more* they would benefit from avoiding ruin or oblivion. Put another way, the ηg term is applicable only when discounting monetary benefits, but here we are considering discounting well-being (or utility) itself. So the ηg term should be treated as zero, leaving us with a social discount rate equal to δ.

I introduced δ by saying that it accounts for the catastrophe rate, but it is sometimes thought to include another component too: *pure time preference*. This is a preference for one benefit over another simply because it comes earlier, and it is a third reason for discounting future benefits.

But unlike the earlier reasons, there is substantial controversy over whether pure time preference should be included in the social discount rate. Philosophers are nearly unanimous in rejecting it.[6] Their primary reason is that it is almost completely unmotivated. In a world where people have had a very long history of discounting the experiences of out-groups (cf. the widening moral circle), we would want a solid argument for why we should count some people much less than we count ourselves, and this is lacking.

Even our raw intuitions seem to push against it. Is an 80-year life beginning in 1970 intrinsically more valuable than one that started in 1980? Is your older brother's life intrinsically more important than your younger brother's? It only gets worse when considering longer durations. At a rate of pure time preference of 1 percent, a single death in 6,000 years' time would be vastly more important than a billion deaths in 9,000 years. And King Tutankhamun would have been obliged to value a single day of suffering in the life of one of his contemporaries as more important than a lifetime of suffering for all 7.7 billion people alive today.

Many economists agree, stating that pure time preference is irrational, unfounded or immoral.[7] For example, Ramsey himself said it was "ethically indefensible and arises merely from the weakness of the imagination," while R. F. Harrod called it "a polite expression for rapacity and the conquest of reason by passion."[8] Even those who accept it often maintain a deep unease when considering its application to the *longterm* future.

The standard rationale among those economists who endorse pure time preference is that people simply *have* such a preference and that the job of economists is not to judge people's preferences, but to show how best to satisfy them. From our perspective, there are three key problems here.

Firstly, even if this were the job of the economist,[9] it is not *my* job. I am writing this book to explore how humanity *should* respond to the risks we face. This point of view allows for the possibility that people's unconsidered reflection on how to treat the future can be mistaken: we sometimes act against our own longterm interests and we can suffer from a bias toward ourselves at the expense of future generations. Using our raw intuitions to set social policy would risk enshrining impatience and bias into our golden standard.

Secondly, the pure time preference embodied in δ is an unhappy compromise between respecting people's actual preferences and the preferences they *should* have. The form of pure time preference people actually exhibit is not in the shape of an exponential. They discount at high rates over the short term and low rates over the long term. Non-exponential discounting is typically seen by economists as irrational as it can lead people to switch back and forth between two options in a way that predictably makes them worse off.

For this reason economists convert people's non-exponential time preference into an exponential form, with a medium rate of discounting across all time frames. This distorts people's actual preferences, underestimating how much they discount over short time periods and overestimating how much they discount over long time periods (such as those that concern us in this book). Moreover, it is difficult for them to run the argument that individual preferences are sacrosanct while simultaneously choosing to distort them in these ways—especially if they do so on the grounds that the exhibited preferences were irrational. If they really are irrational, why fix them in this way, rather than by simply removing them?

And thirdly, the evidence for pure time preference comes from individuals making choices about benefits for themselves. When individuals make choices about the welfare of others, they exhibit little or no pure time preference. For example, while we might take a smaller benefit now over a larger one later—just because it comes sooner—we rarely do so when making the choice on behalf of others. This suggests that our preference for immediate gratification is really a case of weakness of will, rather than a sober judgment that our lives really go better when we have smaller benefits that happen earlier in time. And indeed, when economists adjust their experiments to ask about benefits that would be received by unknown strangers, the evidence for pure time preference becomes very weak, or non-existent.[10]

I thus conclude that the value at stake in existential risk—the benefit of having a flourishing future rather than one ravaged by catastrophe—should only be discounted by the catastrophe rate. That is, we should discount future years of flourishing by the chance we don't get that far.[11] An approach like this was used by Nicholas Stern in his famous report on the economics of climate change. He set pure time preference to zero and set δ to a catastrophe rate of 0.1 percent per annum (roughly 10 percent per century).[12] This values humanity's future at about 1,000 times the value of the next year (higher if the quality of each year improves). This is enough to make existential risk extremely important, but still somewhat less than one may have thought.

The standard formula treats the discount rate as constant over time, discounting the future according to an exponential curve. But more careful economic accounts allow the rate to vary over time.[13] This is essential for the catastrophe rate. For while the background natural risk may have been roughly constant, there has been a stark increase in the anthropogenic risks. If humanity rises to this challenge, as I believe we shall, then this risk will start to fall back down, perhaps all the way down to the background rate, or even lower. If annual risks become low in the long term, then the expected value of the future is very great indeed. As a simplified example, if we incur a total of 50 percent risk during the Precipice before lowering the risks back to the background level, then our future would be worth at least 100,000 times as much as next year.[14]

Of course we don't actually *know* what the catastrophe rate is now, let alone how it will change over time. This makes a big difference to the analysis. One might think that when we are uncertain about the catastrophe rate, we should simply discount at the average of the catastrophe rates we find credible. For example, that if we think it equally likely to be 0.1 percent or 1 percent, we should discount at 0.55 percent. But this is not right. A careful analysis shows that we should instead discount at a changing rate: one that starts at this average, then tends toward the lowest credible rate as time goes on.[15] This corresponds to discounting the longterm future as if we were in the safest world among those we find plausible. Thus the possibility that longterm catastrophe rates fall to the background level or below plays a very large role in determining the discounted value of humanity's future.

And finally, in the context of evaluating existential risk, we need to consider that the catastrophe rate is not set exogenously. Our actions can reduce it. Thus, when we decide to act to lower one existential risk, we may be reducing the discount rate that we use to assess subsequent action.[16] This can lead to increasing returns on work toward safeguarding our future.

The upshot of all this is that economic discounting does not reduce the value of the future to something tiny—that only happens when discounting is misapplied. Discounting based on the diminishing marginal utility of money is inapplicable, and pure time preference is inappropriate. This leaves us with the uncertain and changing catastrophe rate. And discounting by this is just another way of saying that we should value the future at its expected value: if we have empirical grounds for thinking our future is very long in expectation, there is no further dampening of its value coming from the process of discounting.[17]

APPENDIX B

POPULATION ETHICS AND EXISTENTIAL RISK

Theories of ethics point to many different features of our acts that could contribute to them being right or wrong. For instance, whether they spring from bad motives, violate rights or treat people unfairly. One important feature that nearly everyone agrees is relevant is the effect of our acts on the wellbeing of others: increasing someone's wellbeing is good, while reducing it is bad. But some of our acts don't merely change people's wellbeing, they change who will exist. Consider, for example, a young couple choosing whether to have a child. And there is substantial disagreement about how to compare outcomes that contain different people and, especially, different numbers of people. The subfield of ethics that addresses these questions is known as *population ethics*.

Population ethics comes to the fore when considering how bad it would be if humanity went extinct. One set of reasons for avoiding extinction concerns the future. I've pointed to the vast future ahead of us, with potential for thousands, millions or billions of future generations. Extinction would prevent these lives, and all the wellbeing they would involve, from coming into existence. How bad would this loss of future wellbeing be?

One simple answer is the *Total View*: the moral value of future wellbeing is just the total amount of wellbeing in the future. This makes no distinction between whether the wellbeing would come to people who already exist or to entirely new people. Other things being equal, it suggests that the value of having a thousand more generations is a thousand times the value of our generation. On this view, the value of losing our future is immense.

To test moral theories, philosophers apply a kind of thought experiment containing a stark choice. These choices are often unrealistic, but a moral theory is supposed to apply in all situations, so we can try to find any situation where it delivers the intuitively wrong verdict and use this as evidence against the theory.

The main critique of the Total View is that it leads to something called the *repugnant conclusion*: for any outcome where everyone has high wellbeing, there is an ever better outcome where everyone has only a tiny amount of wellbeing, but there are so many people that quantity makes up for quality. People find some quantity/quality trade-offs intuitive (for example, that today's world of 7.7 billion people is better than one with a single person who has slightly higher average wellbeing), but most feel that the Total View takes this too far.

As we shall see, the rivals to the Total View have their own counterintuitive consequences, and indeed there are celebrated impossibility results in the field which show that *every* theory will have at least one moral implication that most people find implausible.[18] So we cannot hope to find an answer that fits all our intuitions and will need to weigh up how bad each of these unintuitive consequences is.

Another famous approach to population ethics is to say the value of wellbeing in the universe is given not by the total but by the average. This approach comes in two main versions. The first takes the average wellbeing in each generation, then sums this up across all the generations. The second takes the average wellbeing across all lives that are ever lived, wherever they are in space and time.

Both versions of averaging are subject to very serious objections. The first version can sometimes prefer an alternative where exactly the same people exist, but where everyone's wellbeing is lower.[19] The second version runs into problems when we consider negative wellbeing—lives not worth living.

If our only choices were the end of humanity, or creating future people cursed with lives of extremely negative wellbeing, this theory can prefer the latter (if the past was so bad that even this hellish future brings up the average). And it can even prefer adding lives with negative wellbeing to adding a larger number of lives with positive wellbeing (if the past was so good that the larger number of positive lives would dilute the average more). These conclusions are generally regarded as even more counter-intuitive than the repugnant conclusion and it is very difficult to find supporters of either version of averaging among those who study population ethics.

Interestingly, even if one overlooked these troubling implications, both versions of averaging probably support the idea that extinction would be extremely bad in the real world. This is easy to see for the sum of generational averages—like the Total View, it says that other things being equal, the value of having 1,000 future generations is 1,000 times the value of our generation. What about the average over all lives over all time? Since quality of life has been improving over time (and has the potential to improve much more) our generation is actually bringing up the all-time average. Future generations would continue to increase this average (even if they had the same quality of life as us).[20] So on either average-based view there would be a strong reason to avoid extinction on the basis of the wellbeing of future generations.

But there is an alternative approach to population ethics according to which human extinction might not be treated as bad at all. The most famous proponent is the philosopher Jan Narveson, who put the central idea in slogan form: "We are in favor of making people happy, but neutral about making happy people."[21] Many different theories of population ethics have been developed to try to capture this intuition, and are known as *person-affecting views*. Some of these theories say there is nothing good about adding thousands of future generations with high wellbeing—and thus nothing bad (at least in terms of the wellbeing of future generations) if humanity instead went extinct.

Are these plausible? Could they undermine the case for concern about existential risk?

There have been two prominent ways of attempting to provide a theoretical foundation for Narveson's slogan. One is to appeal to a simple intuition known as the *person-affecting restriction*: that an outcome can't be better than another (or at least not in terms of wellbeing) unless it is better for someone.[22] This principle is widely accepted in cases where exactly the same people exist in both outcomes. When applied to cases where different people exist in each outcome, the principle is usually interpreted such that a person has to exist in both outcomes in order for one to count as better for them than the other, and this makes the principle both powerful and controversial. For example, it could allow us to avoid the repugnant conclusion—there is no one who is better off in the outcome that has many people with low wellbeing, so it could not be better.[23]

The other theory-based approach to justifying Narveson's slogan is to appeal to an intuition that we have duties to actual people, but not to merely possible people.[24] On this view, we wouldn't need to make any sacrifices to the lives of the presently existing people in order to save the merely possible people of the future generations.

But both these justifications run into decisive problems once we recall the possibility of lives with negative wellbeing. Consider a thought experiment in which people trapped in hellish conditions will be created unless the current generation makes some minor sacrifices to stop this. Almost everyone has a strong intuition that adding such lives of negative wellbeing is bad, and that we should of course be willing to pay a small cost to avoid adding them. But if we did, then we made real sacrifices on account of merely possible people, and we chose an outcome that was better for no one (and worse for currently existing people).

So these putative justifications for Narveson's slogan run counter to our strongly held convictions about the importance of avoiding new lives with negative wellbeing. It therefore seems to me that these two attempts to provide a theoretical justification

for the slogan are dead ends, at least when considered in isolation. Any plausible account of population ethics will involve
recommending some choices where no individual who would be
present in both outcomes is made better off, and making sacrifices
on behalf of merely possible people.

Given the challenges in justifying Narveson's slogan in
terms of a more basic moral principle, philosophers who find
the slogan appealing have increasingly turned to the approach
of saying that what justifies it is simply that it captures our
intuitions about particular cases better than alternative views.
The slogan on its own doesn't say how to value negative lives,
so the proponents of this approach add to it an asymmetry principle: that adding new lives of positive wellbeing doesn't make
an outcome better, but adding new lives with negative wellbeing
does make it worse.

Philosophers have developed a wide variety of theories based
on these two principles. Given the variety, the ongoing development and the lack of any consensus approach, we can't hope to
definitively review them here. But we can look to general patterns.
These theories typically run into a variety of problems: conflicting
with strong intuitions about thought experiments, conflicting with
important moral principles, and violating widely held principles
of rationality.[25] Adjustments to the theories to avoid some of
these problems have typically exacerbated other problems or
created new problems.

But perhaps most importantly, the slogan and asymmetry principle are usually justified merely by an appeal to our intuitions on
particular cases.[26] Person-affecting views fit our intuitions well in
some cases, but poorly in others. The case in question—whether
extinction would be bad—is one where these views offer advice
most people find very counterintuitive.[27] In general, we shouldn't
look to a disputed theory to guide us on the area where it seems
to have the weakest fit with our considered beliefs.[28]

Moreover, there are versions of person-affecting views that
capture some of their core intuitions without denying the badness
of extinction. For example, there are less strict theories which say

that we have *some* reason to create lives of high wellbeing, but stronger reason to help existing people or avoid lives of negative wellbeing. Since the future could contain so many new lives of high wellbeing it would still be very important.

In summary, there are some theories of how to value the wellbeing of future people that may put little or no value on avoiding extinction. Many such views have been shown to be untenable, but not all, and this is still an area of active research. If someone was committed to such a view, they might not find the argument based on lost future wellbeing compelling.

But note that this was only one kind of explanation for why safeguarding humanity is exceptionally important. There remain explanations based on the great things we could achieve in the future (humanity's greatest works in arts and science presumably lie ahead) and on areas other than our future: on our past, our character, our cosmic significance and on the losses to the present generation. People who hold person-affecting accounts of the value of the wellbeing of future generations could well be open to these other sources of reasons why extinction would be bad. And there remains the argument from moral uncertainty: if you thought there was any significant chance these person-affecting views were mistaken, it would be extremely imprudent to risk our entire future when so many other moral theories say it is of utmost importance.

Finally, we've focused here on the moral importance of preventing extinction. Even theories of population ethics that say extinction is a matter of indifference often ascribe huge importance to avoiding other kinds of existential catastrophes such as the irrevocable collapse of civilization or an inescapable dystopia. So even someone who was untroubled by human extinction should still be deeply concerned by other existential risks. And since hazards that threaten extinction usually threaten the irrevocable collapse of civilization as well, these people should often be concerned by a very similar set of risks.

APPENDIX C

NUCLEAR WEAPONS ACCIDENTS

One may imagine that the enormous importance and obvious danger of nuclear weapons would lead to extremely careful management—processes that would always keep us far from accidental destruction. It is thus surprising to learn that there were so many accidents involving nuclear weapons: a US Department of Defense report counts 32 known cases.[29] None of these involved an unexpected nuclear detonation, which speaks well for the technical safeguards that try to stop even an armed weapon whose conventional explosives detonate from creating a nuclear explosion. But they show how complex the systems of nuclear war were, with so many opportunities for failure. And they involve events one would never have thought possible if the situation was being handled with due care, such as multiple cases of nuclear bombs accidentally falling out of planes and the large number of lost nuclear weapons that have never been recovered.

List of Accidents

1957 A nuclear bomb accidentally fell through the bomb bay doors of a B-36 bomber over New Mexico. The high explosives detonated, but there was no nuclear explosion.[30]

1958 A B-47 bomber crashed into a fighter plane in mid-air off the coast near Savannah, Georgia. The B-47 jettisoned its atomic bomb into the ocean. There are conflicting reports about whether it contained its atomic warhead, with the Assistant Secretary of Defense testifying to Congress that it did.[31]

1958 A B-47 bomber accidentally dropped a nuclear bomb over South Carolina, landing in someone's garden and destroying their house. Fortunately, its atomic warhead was still in the plane.[32]

1960 A BOMARC air defense missile caught fire and melted. Its 10-kiloton warhead did not commence a nuclear explosion.[33]

1961 A B-52 carrying two 4-megaton nuclear bombs broke up over North Carolina. The bombs fell to the ground. One of them broke apart on impact, and a section containing uranium sank into the waterlogged farmland. Despite excavation to a depth of 50 feet, it was never recovered. There was no nuclear explosion, though multiple sources, including Defense Secretary Robert McNamara, have said that a single switch prevented a nuclear explosion.[34]

1961 A B-52 carrying two nuclear bombs crashed in California. Neither bomb detonated.[35]

1965 A fighter jet carrying a 1-megaton bomb fell off the side of a US aircraft carrier, near Japan. The bomb was never recovered.[36]

1966 A B-52 carrying four nuclear weapons crashed into a refueling plane in mid-air above Spain. All four bombs fell, and two of the bombs suffered conventional explosions on impact with the ground. There was substantial radiation, and 1,400 tons of contaminated soil and vegetation needed to be taken back to the US.[37]

1968 A B-52 bomber flying over Greenland caught fire and crashed into the ice. The conventional high explosives surrounding the nuclear cores of its four hydrogen bombs detonated. Luckily, this did not set off a nuclear reaction.[38] Had it done so, all signals would have suggested this was a Soviet nuclear strike, requiring nuclear retaliation—for it was at the location of one part of the US early warning systems, detecting Soviet missiles fired across the North Pole.[39]

1980   A Titan II missile exploded at an Air Force Base in Damascus, Arkansas, after a wrench was dropped and punctured its fuel tank. Hours later there was an explosion in which the 9-megaton warhead was propelled about 100 meters away, but its safety features kept it intact.[40]

This is only a part of the full list of accidents, and we have very little knowledge at all of how bad things were on the Russian side.

The Accidental Launch Order

One of the most astounding accidents has only just come to light and may well be the closest we have come to nuclear war. But the incident I shall describe has been disputed, so we cannot yet be sure whether it occurred.

On October 28, 1962—at the height of the Cuban Missile Crisis—a US missile base in the US-occupied Japanese island of Okinawa received a radioed launch order. The island had eight launch centers, each controlling four thermonuclear missiles. All three parts of the coded order matched the base's own codes, confirming that it was a genuine order to launch their nuclear weapons.

The senior field officer, Captain William Bassett, took command of the situation. He became suspicious that a launch order was given while only at the second highest state of readiness (DEFCON 2), which should be impossible. Bassett's crew suggested that the DEFCON 1 order may have been jammed and a launch officer at another site suggested a Soviet pre-emptive attack may be underway, giving no time to upgrade to DEFCON 1.

But Bassett's crew quickly calculated that a pre-emptive strike should have already hit them. Bassett ordered them to check the missiles' readiness and noticed that three of their targets were not in Russia, which seemed unlikely given the current crisis. He radioed to the Missile Operations Center to confirm the coded order but the same code was radioed back.

Bassett was still suspicious, but a lieutenant in charge of another site, all of whose targets were in the USSR, argued that Bassett had no right to stop the launch given that the order was repeated. This other officer ordered the missiles at his site to be launched.

In response, Bassett ordered two airmen from an adjacent launch site to run through the underground tunnel to the site where the missiles were being launched, with orders to shoot the lieutenant if he continued with the launch without either Bassett's agreement or a declaration of DEFCON 1.

Airman John Bordne (who recounted this story) realized that it was unusual for the launch order to be given at the end of a routine weather report and for the order to have been repeated so calmly. Bassett agreed and telephoned the Missile Operations Center, asking the person who radioed the order to either give the DEFCON 1 order or issue a stand-down order. A stand-down order was quickly given and the danger was over.

This account was made public in 2015 in an article in the *Bulletin of the Atomic Scientists* and a speech by Bordne at the United Nations. It has since been challenged by others who claimed to have been present in the Okinawa missile bases at the time.[41] There is some circumstantial evidence supporting Bordne's account: his memoir on it was cleared for publication by the US Air Force, the major who gave the false launch order was subsequently court-martialled, and Bordne has been actively seeking additional testimony from others who were there at the time.

I don't know who is correct, but the matter warrants much more investigation. There is an active Freedom of Information request to the National Security Archive, but this may take many years to get a response. In my view this alleged incident should be taken seriously, but until there is further confirmation, no one should rely on it in their thinking about close calls.

Appendix D

SURPRISING EFFECTS WHEN COMBINING RISKS

We have seen a number of counterintuitive effects that occur when we combine individual existential risks to get a figure for the total existential risk. These effects get stronger, and stranger, the more total risk there is. Since the total risk includes the accumulated existential risk over our entire future, it may well be high enough for these effects to be significant.

First, the total risk departs more and more from being the sum of the risks. To keep the arithmetic simple, suppose we face four 50 percent risks. Since the total risk can't be over 100 percent, logic dictates that they must overlap substantially and combine to something much less than their sum. For example, if they were independent, the total risk would not be 200 percent, but 93.75 percent (= 15/16).

Second, there can be substantial *increasing* marginal returns if we eliminate more and more risks. For example, eliminating the first of four independent 50 percent risks would only reduce the total risk to 87.5 percent. But eliminating the subsequent risks would make more and more headway: to 75 percent, then 50 percent, then 0 percent—a larger absolute effect each time. Another way to look at this is that eliminating each risk doubles our chance of survival and this has a larger absolute effect the higher our chance of survival is. Similarly, if we worked on all four risks in parallel, and halved the risk from each (from 50 percent to 25 percent), the total risk would only drop from 93.75 percent to about 68 percent. But if we halved them all a second time, the risk would drop by a larger absolute amount, to about

41 percent. What is happening in these examples is that there is so much overlap between the risks that a catastrophe is over-determined, and the total remains high when we act. But our action also helps to reduce this overlap, allowing further actions to be more helpful.

Third, it can be much more important to work on the largest risks. We saw that if we faced independent 10 percent and 20 percent risks, eliminating the 10 percent risk would reduce total risk by 8 points, while eliminating the 20 percent risk would reduce total risk by 18 points (see p. 175). So reducing the larger risk was not 2 times more important, but 2.25 times more.

Correct calculations of relative importance of independent risks require the naïve ratio of probabilities to be multiplied by an additional factor: the ratio between the chance the first catastrophe *doesn't* happen and the chance the second catastrophe *doesn't* happen.[42] When the risks are small, the chance each catastrophe doesn't happen is close to one, so this ratio must also be close to one, making little difference. But when a risk grows large, the ratio can grow large too, making a world of difference.[43]

Suppose we instead faced a 10 percent risk and a 90 percent risk. In this case the naïve ratio would be 9:1 and the adjustment would also be 9:1, so eliminating the 90 percent risk would be 81 times as important as eliminating the 10 percent risk (see Figure D.1). Perhaps the easiest way to think about this is that not only is the 90 percent risk 9 times more likely to occur, but the world you get after eliminating it is also 9 times more likely to survive the remaining risks.

This adjustment applies in related cases too. Halving the 90 percent risk is 81 times as important as halving the 10 percent risk, and the same is true for any other factor by which one might reduce it. Even reducing a risk by a fixed absolute amount, such as a single percentage point, is more important for the larger risk. Reducing the 90 percent risk to 89 percent is 9 times as important as reducing the 10 percent risk to 9 percent.[44]

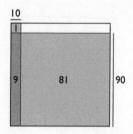

FIGURE D.1 Independent 10% and 90% risks give a total risk of 91%. Removing the 10% risk would lower the total risk (the total shaded area) by just a single percentage point to 90%, while removing the 90% risk would lower it by 81 percentage points to 10%.

All three of these effects occur regardless of whether these risks are simultaneous or occur at different times.[45] So if there is a lot of risk in our future, it could become increasingly more important to eliminate the risks of each successive century. There are many forces that generically lead to diminishing returns on one's work (such as the fact that we can start with the easier risks first). But if we are unlucky enough to face a lot of risk, the overall marginal returns to fighting existential risk may actually be increasing. And it might be especially important to work on the largest risks.

Appendix E

THE VALUE OF PROTECTING HUMANITY

Just how valuable *is* it to protect humanity? While we can't answer with precision, there is a way of approaching this question that I've found helpful for my thinking.

Let's start with a deliberately basic model of existential risk. This model makes assumptions about three things: the pattern of risk over time, the way we could reduce this risk, and the value of the future. First, suppose that each century is exposed to an equal, but unknown, amount of existential risk, r (known as a *constant hazard rate*). That is, given we reach a century, there is always a probability r that we don't make it to the next one. Next, suppose our actions can reduce the probability of existential catastrophe for our own century from r down to some smaller number. And finally, suppose that each century prior to the catastrophe has the same value, v, so the value of a future is proportional to its length before catastrophe. (This means there is no discounting of future value over and above the chance we don't make it that far and we are making assumptions regarding population ethics.)[46] Given these assumptions, the expected value of the future would be:

$$\text{EV}(\textit{future}) = \sum_{i=0}^{\infty} (1 - r)^i v = \frac{v}{r}$$

This is just the value of a single century divided by the per century risk. For example, if the risk each century was one in ten, the expected value would be ten times the value of a single century.

This leads to a surprising implication: that the value of eliminating all existential risk this century is independent of how much risk

273

that is. To see this, imagine that existential risk were just one part in a million each century. Even though there would only be the tiniest chance that we would fall victim to our century's risk, the future we'd lose if we did would be correspondingly vast (a million centuries, on average). On the basic model, these effects always balance. The expected disvalue of this century's existential risk is just

$$r.\,\mathrm{EV}(\mathit{future}) = r\,\frac{v}{r} = v$$

So the expected value of eliminating all risk over a century would simply be equal to the value of a century of life for humanity.[47]

Since it would be impossible to completely eliminate all risk this century, it is more useful to note that on the basic model halving the century's risk is worth half the value of a century of humanity (and it works the same way for any other fraction or timespan). This would be enough to make safeguarding our future a key global priority.

However, the value of the basic model lies not in its accuracy, but in its flexibility. It is a starting point for exploring what happens when we change any of its assumptions. And in my view, all three of its assumptions are too pessimistic.

First, by many measures the value of humanity has increased substantially over the centuries. This progress has been very uneven over short periods, but remarkably robust over the long run. We live long lives filled with cultural and material riches that would have seemed like wild fantasy to our ancestors thousands of years ago. And the scale of our civilization may also matter: the fact that there are thousands of times as many people enjoying these richer lives seems to magnify this value. If the intrinsic value of each century increases at a rate higher than r, this can substantially increase the value of protecting humanity (even if this rate of increase is not sustained forever).[48]

Second, the basic model assumes that our actions this century can only provide protection from this century's risks. But we can do more than that. We can take actions with lasting effects on risk. For example, this book is my attempt to better humanity's understanding of the nature of existential risk and how we should respond to it. Many of the lessons I've drawn out are timeless: to the extent that they succeed at all, they should help with future risk too.[49] Work that helps with risk across many centuries would be much more important than the basic model suggests.

When work reduces all future existential risk, the value of this work will now depend on the hazard rate, r. For example, the value of halving all future risk is:

$$\frac{v}{r/2} - \frac{v}{r} = \frac{v}{r}$$

Surprisingly, this value of reducing a risk in all time periods is *higher* when there is *less* risk.[50] This is contrary to our intuitions, as people who estimate risk to be low typically use this as an argument *against* prioritizing work on existential risk. But an intuitive way to see how low risk levels make reduction more important is that halving existential risk in all periods doubles the expected length of time before catastrophe. So situations where the risk is already low give us a longer future to double, making this work more important. Note also that this effect gives increasing marginal returns to further halvings of all future risk.

Third, and perhaps most importantly, the risk per century will change over time. It has risen over the last century and may continue to rise over the course of this century. But I think that in the longer run it will diminish, for several different reasons. In the next few centuries we will likely be able to establish permanent settlements beyond the Earth. Space is not a panacea (see p. 194), but spreading our eggs across several baskets will help protect us against part of the risk. In addition, much of the risk is posed by the introduction of transformative new technologies. But if we survive long enough, we may well reach *technological maturity*—a time when we possess all the major technologies that are feasible, and face no further technological transitions.[51] Finally, we need to take into account the work that future generations will do to protect humanity in their own centuries. If the case for safeguarding humanity is as clear and powerful as it seems to me, then we should expect this to become more widely recognized, leading to increasing efforts to protect humanity in the future.

If the risk does fall below its current level, that can make the future substantially more valuable than the basic model suggests.[52] The boost to the value depends roughly on the ratio between the risk over the next century and the longer term risk per century. For example, if there is a one in ten chance of existential catastrophe this century, but this declined rapidly to a background natural risk rate of less than one in 200,000 per century, then the value of eliminating risk this century would be boosted by a factor of 20,000 compared to the basic model.

It is also possible that reducing risk may have *less* value than the basic model suggests, though this seems less likely. One way this could happen is if most of the risk were completely unpreventable. This is not very plausible, since most of it is caused by human activities, and these are within humanity's control. A second way is if the value of future centuries were rapidly declining. However, I can't see why we should expect this: the long-run historical record suggests the opposite, and we've seen that we shouldn't discount the intrinsic value of our future. A third way is if adding up the values of future times is ethically misguided—for example, if we should be averaging the values of centuries, or ignoring all future generations. Though as discussed in Appendix B, such alternative approaches have serious problems of their own. And a final way the true value might be less than the basic model suggests is if the risk is low now, but will increase in the future, and if we can't do much now to help with that later risk. This seems to me the most plausible way that this could be an overestimate.

Overall, I find it substantially more likely that the basic view underestimates the value of safeguarding our future, than that it overestimates. But even if you thought one was roughly as likely as the other, note that their effects are not symmetrical. This is because they act as multipliers. Suppose you thought it equally likely the value of reducing risk was ten times as important as the basic model suggests, or a tenth as important. The average of these is not one times as important: it is 5.05 times as important. So unless we are *highly* confident that the basic model gives an overestimate, we should generally act as though it is an underestimate.[53]

Appendix F

POLICY AND RESEARCH RECOMMENDATIONS

For ease of reference, I've gathered together my recommendations for policy and research on existential risk.

Asteroids & Comets

- Research the deflection of 1 km+ asteroids and comets, perhaps restricted to methods that couldn't be weaponized such as those that don't lead to accurate changes in trajectory.
- Bring short-period comets into the same risk framework as near-Earth asteroids.
- Improve our understanding of the risks from long-period comets.
- Improve our modeling of impact winter scenarios, especially for 1–10 km asteroids. Work with experts in climate modeling and nuclear winter modeling to see what modern models say.

Supervolcanic Eruptions

- Find all the places where supervolcanic eruptions have occurred in the past.
- Improve the very rough estimates on how frequent these eruptions are, especially for the largest eruptions.
- Improve our modeling of volcanic winter scenarios to see what sizes of eruption could pose a plausible threat to humanity.

- Liaise with leading figures in the asteroid community to learn lessons from them in their modeling and management.

Stellar Explosions

- Build a better model for the threat including known distributions of parameters instead of relying on representative examples. Then perform sensitivity analysis on that model—are there any plausible parameters that could make this as great a threat as asteroids?
- Employ blue-sky thinking about any ways current estimates could be underrepresenting the risk by a factor of a hundred or more.

Nuclear Weapons

- Restart the Intermediate-Range Nuclear Forces Treaty (INF).
- Renew the New START arms control treaty, due to expire in February 2021.
- Take US ICBMs off hair-trigger alert (officially called Launch on Warning).
- Increase the capacity of the International Atomic Energy Agency (IAEA) to verify nations are complying with safeguards agreements.
- Work on resolving the key uncertainties in nuclear winter modeling.
- Characterize the remaining uncertainties then use Monte Carlo techniques to show the distribution of outcome possibilities, with a special focus on the worst-case possibilities compatible with our current understanding.
- Investigate which parts of the world appear most robust to the effects of nuclear winter and how likely civilization is to continue there.

Climate

- Fund research and development of innovative approaches to clean energy.
- Fund research into safe geoengineering technologies and geoengineering governance.
- The US should re-join the Paris Agreement.
- Perform more research on the possibilities of a runaway greenhouse effect or moist greenhouse effect. Are there any ways these could be more likely than is currently believed? Are there any ways we could decisively rule them out?
- Improve our understanding of the permafrost and methane clathrate feedbacks.
- Improve our understanding of cloud feedbacks.
- Better characterize our uncertainty about the climate sensitivity: what can and can't we say about the right-hand tail of the distribution.
- Improve our understanding of extreme warming (e.g., 5–20°C), including searching for concrete mechanisms through which it could pose a plausible threat of human extinction or the global collapse of civilization.

Environmental Damage

- Improve our understanding of whether any kind of resource depletion currently poses an existential risk.
- Improve our understanding of current biodiversity loss (both regional and global) and how it compares to that of past extinction events.
- Create a database of existing biological diversity to preserve the genetic material of threatened species.

Engineered Pandemics

- Bring the Biological Weapons Convention into line with the Chemical Weapons Convention: taking its budget

279

from $1.4 million up to $80 million, increasing its staff commensurately, and granting the power to investigate suspected breaches.

- Strengthen the WHO's ability to respond to emerging pandemics through rapid disease surveillance, diagnosis and control. This involves increasing its funding and powers, as well as R&D on the requisite technologies.
- Ensure that all DNA synthesis is screened for dangerous pathogens. If full coverage can't be achieved through self-regulation by synthesis companies, then some form of international regulation will be needed.
- Increase transparency around accidents in BSL-3 and BSL-4 laboratories.
- Develop standards for dealing with information hazards, and incorporate these into existing review processes.
- Run scenario-planning exercises for severe engineered pandemics.

Unaligned Artificial Intelligence

- Foster international collaboration on safety and risk management.
- Explore options for the governance of advanced AI.
- Perform technical research on aligning advanced artificial intelligence with human values.
- Perform technical research on other aspects of AGI safety, such as secure containment and tripwires.

General

- Explore options for new international institutions aimed at reducing existential risk, both incremental and revolutionary.
- Investigate possibilities for making the deliberate or reckless imposition of human extinction risk an international crime.

- Investigate possibilities for bringing the representation of future generations into national and international democratic institutions.
- Each major world power should have an appointed senior government position responsible for registering and responding to existential risks that can be realistically foreseen in the next 20 years.
- Find the major existential risk factors and security factors—both in terms of absolute size and in the cost-effectiveness of marginal changes.
- Target efforts at reducing the likelihood of military conflicts between the US, Russia and China.
- Improve horizon-scanning for unforeseen and emerging risks.
- Investigate food substitutes in case of extreme and lasting reduction in the world's ability to supply food.
- Develop better theoretical and practical tools for assessing risks with extremely high stakes that are either unprecedented or thought to have extremely low probability.
- Improve our understanding of the chance civilization will recover after a global collapse, what might prevent this, and how to improve the odds.
- Develop our thinking about grand strategy for humanity.
- Develop our understanding of the ethics of existential risk and valuing the longterm future.

APPENDIX G

EXTENDING THE KARDASHEV SCALE

In 1964, the Russian astronomer Nikolai Kardashev devised a way of classifying potential advanced civilizations by their physical scale and the power (energy per unit time) this lets them harness. He considered three levels: planet, solar system and galaxy. In each step along this scale, the power at their disposal leaps up by more than a factor of a billion.

We can naturally extend this scale in both directions.[54] We can include an earlier level for a minimal civilization (for example, the size of civilization in Mesopotamia at the dawn of the written language).[55] And we can include an ultimate level at the size of our affectable universe: everything that we could ever hope to reach. Surprisingly, these jumps are very similar in size to those Kardashev identified, continuing the roughly logarithmic scale for measuring the power of civilizations.

Level	Civilization Size	Scale-up	Power
K0	Minimal		$\approx 10^8$ W
K1	Planetary	× 1 billion	2×10^{17} W
K2	Stellar	× 1 billion	4×10^{26} W
K3	Galactic	× 100 billion	4×10^{37} W
K4	Ultimate	× 1 billion	4×10^{46} W

Our global civilization currently controls about 12 trillion Watts of power. This is about 100,000 times more than a minimal civilization but 10,000 times less than the full capacity of our planet. This places us at level K0.55—more than halfway to K1 and an eighth of the way to K4.

FURTHER READING

Here is a quick guide to some of the most important writing on existential risk. A full bibliography for *The Precipice* can be found on p. 423. Further reading lists, course outlines, quotations and extracts can be found online at theprecipice.com.

Bertrand Russell & Albert Einstein (1955). "The Russell-Einstein Manifesto."
In the decade after Hiroshima, Russell and Einstein each wrote several important pieces on nuclear war that touched upon the risk of human extinction. Their joint manifesto was the culmination of this early period of thought.

Hilbrand J. Groenewold (1968). "Modern Science and Social Responsibility."
A very early piece that anticipated several key ideas of existential risk. It failed to reach a wide audience, leaving these ideas in obscurity until they were independently discovered decades later.

Annette Baier (1981). "The Rights of Past and Future Persons."
The foundational work on the importance of future generations.

Jonathan Schell (1982). *The Fate of the Earth.*
The first deep exploration of the badness of extinction, and the central importance of ensuring humanity's survival. Filled with sharp philosophical insight.

Carl Sagan (1983). "Nuclear War and Climatic Catastrophe: Some Policy Implications."
A seminal paper, introducing the new-found mechanism of nuclear winter and exploring the ethical implications of human extinction.

Derek Parfit (1984). *Reasons and Persons.*
Among the most famous works in philosophy in the twentieth century, it made major contributions to the ethics of future generations and its concluding chapter highlighted how and why the risk of

human extinction may be one of the most important moral problems of our time.

John Leslie (1996). *The End of the World: The Science and Ethics of Human Extinction.*
A landmark book that broadened the discussion from nuclear risk to all risks of human extinction, cataloging the threats and exploring new philosophical angles.

Nick Bostrom (2002). "Existential Risks: Analyzing Human Extinction Scenarios."
Established the concept of existential risk and introduced many of the most important ideas. Yet mainly of historic interest, for it is superseded by his 2013 paper below.

Nick Bostrom (2003). "Astronomical Waste: The Opportunity Cost of Delayed Technological Development."
Explored the limits of what humans might be able to achieve in the future, suggesting that it is of immense importance to accelerate the arrival of the ultimate state of our civilization by even a tiny amount, yet that even this is overshadowed by the importance of increasing the chance we get there at all.

Nick Bostrom (2013). "Existential Risk Prevention as Global Priority."
An updated version of his essay from 2002, this is the go-to paper on existential risk.

Nick Beckstead (2013). *On the Overwhelming Importance of Shaping the Far Future.*
A book-length philosophical exploration of the idea that what matters most about our actions is not their immediate consequences, but how they shape the longterm trajectory of humanity.

David Christian (2004). *Maps of Time: An Introduction to Big History.*
The seminal book on Big History: examining the major themes and developments in our universe from the Big Bang, the origin of life, humanity, civilization, the industrial revolution, through to today.

Fred Adams & Gregory Laughlin (1999). *The Five Ages of the Universe.*
A powerful and accessible presentation of how scientists believe the very longterm future will unfold.

Max Roser (2013). *Our World in Data* [online]. Available at: www.ourworldindata.org
An essential online resource for seeing the ways in which many of the most important aspects of our world have changed over the last two centuries. From the raw data to compelling charts and insightful analysis.

Nick Bostrom (2014). *Superintelligence: Paths, Dangers, Strategies.*
The foundational work on artificial intelligence and existential risk.

Stuart Russell (2019). *Human Compatible: AI and the Problem of Control.*
A call to action by a leading researcher in AI, showing how his field needs to develop if it is to address the risks that will be posed by advanced AI.

Alan Robock et al. (2007). "Nuclear winter revisited with a modern climate model and current nuclear arsenals: Still catastrophic consequences."
The most up-to-date modeling of the climate effects of a full-scale war between the US and Russia.

Richard Rhodes (1986). *The Making of the Atomic Bomb.*
A gripping history of the people and events leading to the creation of nuclear weapons. With so much information about how everything played out, it reveals how individuals can and did make a difference in this pivotal transition.

Daniel Ellsberg (2017). *The Doomsday Machine: Confessions of a Nuclear War Planner.*
An exploration of how close we have come to full-scale nuclear war, drawing on a wealth of new information from his career at RAND and the Pentagon.

John Broome (2012). *Climate Matters: Ethics in a Warming World.*
A deep examination of the ethics of climate change.

Gernot Wagner & Martin Weitzman (2015). *Climate Shock: The Economic Consequences of a Hotter Planet.*
An accessible study of the risks from climate change, with a focus on extreme warming scenarios.

NOTES

INTRODUCTION

1 Blanton, Burr & Savranskaya (2012).
2 Ellsberg (2017), pp. 215–17.
3 McNamara (1992).
4 Any errors are, of course, my own. You can find an up-to-date list of any known errors at theprecipice.com/errata. I am grateful for expert advice from Fred Adams, Richard Alley, Tatsuya Amano, Seth Baum, Niel Bowerman, Miles Brundage, Catalina Cangea, Paulo Ceppi, Clark Chapman, David Christian, Allan Dafoe, Richard Danzig, Ben Day, David Denkenberger, Daniel Dewey, Eric Drexler, Daniel Ellsberg, Owain Evans, Sebastian Farquhar, Vlad Firoiu, Ben Garfinkel, Tim Genewein, Goodwin Gibbons, Thore Graepel, Joanna Haigh, Alan Harris, Hiski Haukkala, Ira Helfand, Howard Herzog, Michael Janner, Ria Kalluri, Jim Kasting, Jan Leike, Robert Lempert, Andrew Levan, Gregory Lewis, Marc Lipsitch, Rosaly Lopes, Stephen Luby, Enxhell Luzhnica, David Manheim, Jochem Marotzke, Jason Matheny, Piers Millet, Michael Montague, David Morrison, Cassidy Nelson, Clive Oppenheimer, Raymond Pierrehumbert, Max Popp, David Pyle, Michael Rampino, Georgia Ray, Catherine Rhodes, Richard Rhodes, Carl Robichaud, Tyler Robinson, Alan Robock, Luisa Rodriguez, Max Roser, Jonathan Rougier, Andrew Rushby, Stuart Russell, Scott Sagan, Anders Sandberg, Hauke Schmidt, Rohin Shah, Steve Sherwood, Lewis Smith, Jacob Steinhardt, Sheldon Stern, Brian Thomas, Brian Toon, Phil Torres, Martin Weitzman, Brian Wilcox, Alex Wong, Lily Xia and Donald Yeomans.
5 I also made a further pledge to keep just £18,000 a year for myself and to donate anything in excess. This baseline adjusts with inflation (it is currently £21,868), and doesn't include spending on my child (a few thousand pounds each year). So far I've been able to give more than a quarter of everything I've ever earned.

6 At the time of writing, Giving What We Can members have donated £100 million to effective charities (Giving What We Can, 2019). This is spread across many different charities, so it is impossible to give a simple accounting of the impact. But even just looking at the £6 million in donations to provide malaria nets, this provided more than 3 million person-years of protection, saving more than 2,000 lives (GiveWell, 2019).

7 There is effectively another book-worth of content tucked away in the notes for readers who are eager to know more. If that's you, I'd suggest using a second bookmark to allow you to flip back and forth at will. I've endeavored to keep the average quality of the notes high to make them worth your time (they are rarely just a bare citation). I've tried to be disciplined in keeping the main text on a straight path to its destination, so the scenic detours are all hidden in the notes. You may also be interested in the appendices, the list of further reading (p. 285), or the book's website, theprecipice.com, for even more information and discussion.

8 Of course even after extensive fact-checking, it would be naïve to think no bias or error has slipped through, so I hope readers will help catch and correct such weaknesses as remain.

1 STANDING AT THE PRECIPICE

1 Sagan (1994), pp. 305–6.

2 Many of the dates in this chapter are only roughly known or apply to transitions that unfolded over a range of years. Rather than littering the main text with ranges of estimates or frequent use of "around" and "about," I'll just use the scientific convention of numbers that have been rounded off to reflect their degree of certainty.

There is a wide range of uncertainty about when *Homo sapiens* began. There are remains from 200,000 years ago that are generally considered to be anatomically modern humans. There is an active debate over whether more recent fossil discoveries, dated to around 300,000 years ago, should be classified as *Homo sapiens* (Galway-Witham & Stringer, 2018). More importantly, it is unclear who to count as "human" or even what we might mean by that. Our genus, *Homo*, is between 2 and 3 million years old, and if we include all of our tool-making ancestors, that would include the Australopithecines, more than 3 million years ago (Antón, Potts

& Aiello, 2014). I focus on fossil evidence rather than molecular phylogeny (which generally gives longer lifespan estimates), as the former methodology is more widely accepted.

3 At the time, the modern continent of Australia was joined with the modern island of New Guinea into a larger continent, sometimes called Sahul. It was separated from Asia by at least 100 miles of open sea—a great voyage for the time (Christian, 2004, p. 191). So when humans first set foot into this new world with its unique animals and plants, they would have actually done so in part of what is now New Guinea.

4 We also adapted the environments to us. Even before the advent of agriculture, we used fire to change the face of continents, creating many of the wild grasslands we now think of as timeless (Kaplan et al., 2016).

5 *Homo sapiens* and our close relatives may have some unique physical attributes, such as our dextrous hands, upright walking and resonant voices. However, these on their own cannot explain our success. They went together with our intelligence to improve our ability to communicate and to harness and create technology.

6 Figures 1.1 and 1.2 are adapted, with permission, from Christian (2004), pp. 193, 213.

7 It may seem naïvely idealistic to talk of all humans across increasingly large scales cooperating together, for the word is sometimes used to suggest working together out of altruistic motivations. However, I'm using it in a wider sense, of humans coordinating their behaviors to achieve things they desire that couldn't be achieved alone. Some of this is altruistic (and even unilateral), but it can also be driven by various forms of exchange.

For an explanation of just how important social learning was to our success see, for example, Henrich (2015).

8 It is, of course, somewhat arbitrary how many to include and how to individuate each one. If I were to count just two, I'd say the Agricultural Revolution and the Industrial Revolution (perhaps defining the latter more broadly to include the time of the Scientific Revolution). If I were to include four, I'd probably break the Agricultural Revolution into two parts: the beginning of farming and the rise of civilization (which I'd then date to the appearance of cities, about 5,000 years ago).

For a rigorous exploration of the big picture of humanity's development, I recommend *Maps of Time* by David Christian (2004).

9   In some ways the term "Revolution" is misleading: it was neither rapid nor universal. The transition from foraging to farming unfolded over thousands of years, and it was thousands more years before the rise of cities and the development of writing and other things we think of as characteristic of civilization. And some peoples continued foraging throughout that period. (Similar remarks could be made regarding the Industrial Revolution, with the timescale sped up by a factor of ten.) But it was rapid by the standards of human development during the prior 200,000 years, and it did usher in an extremely different way of life.

10   Here I am using "power" in the sense of physics: energy per unit time. Draft animals dramatically increased the harnessable energy per human per day.

11   There is evidence of the emergence of agriculture in the Fertile Crescent (12,000 BP, before present), the Yangtze and Yellow River basins (10,000–6,000 BP), Papua New Guinea (10,000–7,000 BP), Central Mexico (10,000 BP), South America (9,000–5,000 BP), eastern North America (5,000–4,000 BP) and sub-Saharan Africa (4,000–2,000 BP).

12   Foraging typically required about ten square miles of land to support each person (Christian, 2004). So a band had to move frequently to draw sustenance from the hundreds of square miles that sustained it. The required land per person shrank so significantly because so much more of the land's productive capacity was being devoted to human-edible plants.

13   McEvedy & Jones (1978), p. 149.

14   Durand (1960). The Roman Empire reached a similar size shortly after, with most people in the world living in one of these two civilizations.

15   Like agriculture, each was independently developed in multiple places across the world.

16   Other scholars sometimes include this revolution under the name of the Enlightenment, or bundle it together with the Industrial Revolution.

17   Important scholars include Ibn al-Haytham (c. 965–1040 CE), whose use of experimental methods in optics was a major influence

on Robert Grosseteste and Roger Bacon in the thirteenth century. And the roots of the idea of unlimited incremental improvements in our understanding can be seen in Seneca's *Natural Questions*, written in 65 CE (Seneca, 1972) (see p. 49).

18 Francis Bacon's *Novum Organum* (1620) is the canonical exposition of the scientific method, and is a convenient dating for the Scientific Revolution. There is substantial debate over why earlier advances outside Europe did not lead to the sustained knowledge-creation we have seen since the seventeenth century. See, for example, Sivin (1982).

19 Because only a tiny proportion of organisms became fossil fuels, the energy within the entire global supply of fossil fuels is not millions of years' worth of solar energy. It is "only" about 20 to 200 years' worth of global plant growth, which equals about four to 40 days' worth of all sunlight intercepted by the Earth (author's calculations). Nonetheless, fossil fuels provided vastly more energy than could have been practicably harvested from water wheels or burning timber. Humanity may have been able to eventually reach the modern level of total wealth without fossil fuels, though it is not clear whether the growth in income could have broken free of the growth in population, allowing higher prosperity per capita.

A striking consequence of these numbers is that solar energy has the potential to eventually produce more energy in a year than is contained in all fossil fuels that ever existed.

20 In particular, James Watt's improved design of 1781. Earlier engines were so inefficient that they were only financially viable for a narrow range of tasks. The diesel engine would be another major breakthrough, more than 100 years later.

21 Many other factors are also important, notably political, economic and financial systems.

22 Mummert et al. (2011).

23 Consider, for example, the vivid description of working and living conditions in industrial England by Engels (1892).

24 Van Zanden et al. (2014). See Milanovic (2016) for a book-length study of inequality within and between countries over the last two centuries.

25 Throughout this book, I shall use the word "history" in its everyday unrestricted sense of everything that has happened (in this case,

to humanity). This is the common dictionary definition and suits the universal scope of this book. Historians, by contrast, typically restrict the term "history" to refer only to events in times and places where there are written accounts of what happened, thus referring to events in Mesopotamia more than 6,000 years ago or Australia before 1788 CE as "prehistory."

26 This is roughly the idea of a Malthusian trap. Note that it is very difficult to compare incomes between different times. The idea of "subsistence" does this by determining how much of your income would be needed to keep you alive. But it does not adequately capture changes in the quality or variety of the food consumed, or in the quality of what you could buy with the modest amount of money remaining, or any other aspect of your quality of life. So it is possible for things to be getting better (or worse) for each person (or society) while staying locked at a subsistence level. All that said, breaking free from this Malthusian dynamic was a very big change to human affairs.

27 These figures for the $2 a day poverty line are from *Our World in Data: Global Extreme Poverty* (Roser & Ortiz-Ospina, 2019a). There is strong improvement at higher poverty lines too. I chose $2 a day not because it is an adequate level of income, but because it shows how almost everyone's income used to be *deeply* inadequate before the Industrial Revolution. It is not that things are great today, but that they were terrible before.

People in richer countries are sometimes disbelieving of these statistics, on the grounds that they can't see how someone could live at all in their town with just $2 each day. But sadly the statistics are true, and even adjust for the fact that money can go further in poorer countries. The answer is that people below the line have to live with accommodation and food of such a poor standard, that equivalents are not even offered by the market in richer countries.

28 While universal schooling was a major factor, note that the positive trend of improving literacy pre-dates the Industrial Revolution, with literacy already at 50% in the United Kingdom. Significant credit for improvements may also be due to the Scientific Revolution. Literacy figures are from *Our World in Data: Literacy* (Roser & Ortiz-Ospina, 2019b).

29 Note that these historical life expectancy figures are challenging to interpret, as they represent the average (mean) age at death, but

not the typical age at death. There were still people who lived long enough to become grandparents, but there were also a great many who died in infancy or childhood, bringing down the average a lot.

30 Longterm life expectancy figures from Cohen (1989), p. 102. Pre-industrial life expectancy in Iceland from *Gapminder* (2019). Current life expectancy from WHO's *Global Health Observatory* 2016 figures (WHO, 2016).

31 One of the earliest relevant texts is the Code of Hammurabi (eighteenth century BCE). While it is a legal text, it is suggestive of the morals underpinning it, and shows how far our norms have come. See Harari (2014), pp. 117–22, for an insightful discussion.

32 See Pinker's *The Better Angels of Our Nature* (2012) for a wealth of examples. Though note that the evidence for declining violence is weakest when it comes to state-level violence (war and genocide) in the twentieth century.

33 For example, the centuries it took Western Europe to recover from the fall of classical civilization loom large in most Western historical narratives, but when one takes a global view, looking at China, India, the Islamic world, the Americas and even the Eastern Roman Empire, we see that the overall trend did not reverse nearly so much.

A useful analogy is to the stock market. On a scale of days or months, individual stocks are roughly as likely to go up as to go down. But when we take the stock market as a whole and a timescale of decades, the upward trend is very clear, and persistent over centuries. Or as Thomas Macaulay put it in 1830: "A single breaker may recede; but the tide is evidently coming in" (1900, p. 542).

As more and more information comes in, it becomes increasingly clear that to treat talk of progress as off limits in historical analysis would be to bury the lede on the story of human history. If academic historians want to restrict their study and analysis to descriptive matters, that is their choice. But we need not follow them. Some of the most important events in our past have major evaluative and normative consequences that need to be discussed if humanity is to learn from its history.

34 For academics, skepticism can also come from a reluctance to evaluate times at all: because it is often done poorly, because it is

not the job of the historian, or because of philosophical beliefs that it is impossible.

35 Estimating the number of people who have ever lived is made difficult by the fact that we have no population data for the majority of human history. The figure is particularly sensitive to estimates of long-run life expectancy. Haub & Kaneda (2018) give an estimate of 108 billion. Rolling forward older estimates from Goldberg (1983) and Deevey (1960) yields 55 billion and 81 billion respectively (author's calculations). Altogether, 100 billion is a safe central estimate, with a credible range of 50–150 billion.

36 Macaulay (1900), p. 544.

37 Adapted from Roser (2015).

38 Estimates for the average lifespan of mammalian species range from 0.6 million years (Barnosky et al., 2011) to 1.7 million years (Foote & Raup, 1996).

The oldest fossils regarded as *Homo erectus* are the Dmanisi specimens from present-day Georgia, dated to 1.8 million years ago (Lordkipanidze et al., 2006). The most recent fossils are from present-day Indonesia, and have been dated to 0.1 million years ago (Yokoyama et al., 2008).

39 The entire twenty-first century would be just three days in this life—three fateful days for the sake of which humanity's entire life was put at risk.

40 We can be reasonably confident that the runaway and moist greenhouse effects (discussed in Chapter 4) pose an upper bound on how long life can continue to exist on Earth, but we remain uncertain about when they will occur, due to the familiar limitations of our climate models. Wolf & Toon (2015) find a moist greenhouse will occur at around 2 billion years, whereas Leconte et al. (2013) place a lower bound at 1 billion years.

The open question is whether carbon dioxide depletion or temperature increases will render Earth uninhabitable before the runaway or moist greenhouse limits are reached. Rushby et al. (2018) estimate carbon dioxide depletion will occur in around 800 million years for C_3 photosynthesis, and around 500 million years later for C_4 photosynthesis.

Over such long timespans, we cannot ignore the possibility that evolution may lead to new life forms able to exist in climates inhospitable to presently existing life forms. Indeed, the first C_4 plants appeared around 32 million years ago (Kellog, 2013).

41 This quote is attributed to Konstantin Tsiolovsky (Siddiqi, 2010, p. 371).

42 It is difficult to produce a precise date for this. I have chosen the first atomic detonation as that brought with it the possibility of global destruction through igniting the atmosphere (see Chapter 4 for details). One could also choose a later date, when the nuclear arsenals were large enough to make nuclear winter a real possibility. If one broadens the idea from extinction to existential risk (see Chapter 2), then one could perhaps start it a few years earlier with the threat of permanent global totalitarianism that came with the Second World War.

43 This was the US "Ivy Mike" test of 1952. Its explosion was 10.4 megatons (of TNT-equivalent, the standard unit for explosive yield), compared with approximately 6 megatons for all of World War II (including Hiroshima and Nagasaki) (Pauling, 1962). But it would be several more years before thermonuclear weapons were miniaturized sufficiently to fit on a bomber.

44 Note that many respectable scientists expressed what can now be seen as extreme over-confidence, predicting that humanity would certainly be destroyed within the twentieth century. See Pinker (2018, p. 309).

45 The case is by no means proven. Even now, very little research has been done on what appears to be the greatest mechanism for destruction in a nuclear war.

46 The DEFCON levels were a system of war-readiness levels whose precise meaning changed during the course of the Cold War. Lower numbers meant war was more imminent. The most extreme level ever reached was DEFCON 2, later in the Cuban Missile Crisis, and again during the first Gulf War, in 1991.

47 This forces one to wonder how much more dangerous such a crisis would be if other leaders had been in power at the time. Would our current leaders have been able to navigate to a peaceful resolution?

48 Around 100 of these weapons were operational during the Crisis: the 92 tactical missiles, and 6 to 8 medium-range ballistic missiles. All figures from Norris & Kristensen (2012). The scale of the

Soviet troops also went far beyond expectations: there were not 7,000, but 42,000 stationed in Cuba (Ellsberg, 2017, p. 209).

49 This quote was by Castro at the summit for the fortieth anniversary of the crisis, as reported by Robert McNamara in the documentary *Fog of War* (Morris, 2003). Castro's letter to Khrushchev has since come to light. On the Friday, Castro wrote: "I believe the imperialists aggressiveness is extremely dangerous and if they actually carry out the brutal act of invading Cuba in violation of international law and morality, that would be the moment to eliminate such danger forever through an act of clear legitimate defence, however harsh and terrible the solution would be for there is no other." On the Sunday, just after issuing his statement that the (known) missiles would be removed, Khrushchev replied that "Naturally, if there's an invasion it will be necessary to repulse it by every means" (Roberts, 2012, pp. 237–8).

50 As Daniel Ellsberg, a military consultant during the missile crisis, puts it: "The invasion would almost surely trigger a two-sided nuclear exchange that would with near certainty expand to massive U.S. nuclear attacks on the Soviet Union" (Ellsberg, 2017, p. 210).

51 A chief difficulty is that it is unclear what this even means. We can talk clearly of the credences that the principal actors had at the time (10%–50%). And we know whether it happened or not (in this case, not, so 0%). But there is an important sense of probability that is more objective than the former, while not constrained to be 0% or 100% like the latter. For example, we'd like it to be sensitive to later revelations such as the existence of tactical nuclear weapons on Cuba or the events on submarine B-59. We want to know something like: if we had 100 crises like this one, how many of them would lead to nuclear war, but it is hard to interpret the words "like this one." I suspect there is a real and useful form of probability here, but I don't think it has yet been properly explicated and we risk confusing ourselves when thinking about it.

52 John F. Kennedy, quoted in Sorenson (1965), p. 705.

53 Ellsberg (2017), p. 199. While not providing a probability estimate, McNamara later said "I remember leaving the White House at the end of that Saturday. It was a beautiful fall day. And thinking that might well be the last sunset I saw" (Ellsberg, 2017, pp. 200–1).

54 Daniel Ellsberg's estimate in light of all the recent revelations is "Far greater than one in a hundred, greater that day than Nitze's one in ten" (Ellsberg, 2017, p. 220).

55 I was particularly surprised in January 2018 to see the *Bulletin of the Atomic Scientists* setting their famous Doomsday Clock to "2 minutes to midnight," stating that the world is "as dangerous as it has been since World War II" (Mecklin, 2018). Their headline reason was the deepening nuclear tensions between the United States and North Korea. But the clock was intended to show how close we are to the end of civilization, and there was no attempt to show how this bears any threat to human civilization, nor how we are more at risk than during the Cuban Missile Crisis or other Cold War crises.

56 The United States still has 450 silo-based missiles and hundreds of submarine-based missiles on hair-trigger alert (UCS, n.d.).

57 This is related to the "pacing problem" considered by those who study the regulation of technology. The pacing problem is that technological innovation is increasingly outpacing the ability of laws and regulations to effectively govern those technologies. As Larry Downes (2009) put it: "technology changes exponentially, but social, economic, and legal systems change incrementally."

    A key difference between the two framings is that the pacing problem refers to the speed of technological change, rather than to its growing power to change the world.

58 Sagan (1994), pp. 316–17.

59 Barack Obama, Remarks at the Hiroshima Peace Memorial (2016). Consider also the words of John F. Kennedy on the twentieth anniversary of the nuclear chain reaction (just a month after the end of the Cuban Missile Crisis): "our progress in the use of science has been great, but our progress in ordering our relations small" (Kennedy, 1962).

60 In his quest for peace after the Cuban Missile Crisis, Kennedy (1963) put it so: "Our problems are manmade—therefore, they can be solved by man. And man can be as big as he wants. No problem of human destiny is beyond human beings."

    Of course one *could* have some human-made problems that have gone past a point of no return, but that is not yet the case for any of those being considered in this book. Indeed, we could prevent them simply through inaction: stopping doing the thing that threatens harm.

61 The problem is especially bad here as the words we use to describe the size of a risk are often affected both by its probability and by the stakes. A 1% chance of losing a game of cards is not a grave risk, but a 1% chance of losing your child may well be. This same issue besets the IPCC approach of using qualitative terms to describe the probability of various climate outcomes (Mastrandrea et al., 2010), which I think is mistaken.

62 There the detailed definition of "existential risk" can be found on p. 37. It includes the risk of extinction as well as other ways of permanently destroying the potential of humanity, such as an unrecoverable collapse of civilization.

63 See Chapter 6 for a comparison to the level of natural risk.

64 A point made by Bostrom (2013).

65 There are some ways it could happen, though I don't see them as likely. For example, the risk might top out at about one in six, but we could be lucky enough to survive ten or more such centuries. Or perhaps our efforts to control the risks are only half-successful, lowering the risk back to the twentieth-century level, but no further, and then surviving a hundred or more such centuries.

66 In May 2019 the Anthropocene Working Group of the International Commission on Stratigraphy voted to make the Anthropocene a new epoch with a starting date in the mid-twentieth century. A formal proposal will be made by 2021, which will include a suggested starting point (Subramanian, 2019). In 2017 the Working Group said that markings associated with nuclear arms testing were the most promising proxy (Zalasiewicz et al., 2017).

2 EXISTENTIAL RISK

1 Baier (1981).

2 See Bostrom (2002b; 2013).

3 Bostrom (2013) defined existential risk as "one that threatens the premature extinction of Earth-originating intelligent life or the permanent and drastic destruction of its potential for desirable future development." My definition (and clarifications below) are very much in line with the second half of Bostrom's. I didn't echo the first part as it is logically unnecessary (our "premature extinction"

would itself be a "permanent and drastic curtailment") and thus draws attention away from the heart of the matter: the destruction of our longterm potential.

Note that on my definitions, an existential risk is simply the risk of an existential catastrophe. I could even have defined it this way directly, but wanted the definition to stand on its own.

4   I'm making a deliberate choice not to define the precise way in which the set of possible futures determines our potential. A simple approach would be to say that the value of our potential is the value of the best future open to us, so that an existential catastrophe occurs when the best remaining future is worth just a small fraction of the best future we could previously reach. Another approach would be to take account of the difficulty of achieving each possible future, for example defining the value of our potential as the expected value of our future assuming we followed the best possible policy. But I leave a resolution of this to future work.

I define existential catastrophes in terms of the destruction of our potential rather than the permanence of the outcome for two key reasons. The first is that it is a more helpful definition for identifying a set of risks with key commonalities in how they work and how we must overcome them. The second reason lies in my optimism about humanity. Given a long enough time with our potential intact, I believe we have a very high chance of fulfilling it: that setbacks won't be permanent unless they destroy our ability to recover. If so, then most of the probability that humanity fails to achieve a great future comes precisely from the destruction of its potential—from existential risk.

5   There are other senses of potential one could discuss, such as a narrower kind of potential that only takes into account what we currently can do, or are likely to be able to do, and thus could be increased by doing work to expand our capabilities. However, in this book I shall only be concerned with our longterm potential (in the sense described in the main text). When I simply say "potential" (for brevity) it should be treated as "longterm potential."

6   By leaving open that there may be a remote chance of recovery, some of my more blunt claims are not literally true. For instance, that existential catastrophe involves "no way back." This is unfortunate, but I think it is a cost worth bearing.

The point of leaving open remote chances of recovery is to avoid responses that there is always some chance—perhaps incredibly small—that things recover. So that on a more strict reading of potential, it could never be *completely* destroyed. But taking this extremely strict reading wouldn't be useful. It doesn't really matter for our decision-making whether a scenario would have zero chance of recovery, or merely a 0.1% chance of recovery. Both cases are almost equally bad compared to the current world, and are bad for the same reason: that they are extremely hard to reverse, (almost completely) destroying our longterm potential. Moreover, they warrant similar diagnoses about what we should do, such as needing proactive work, rather than learning from trial and error. A possibility with literally "no way back" should be avoided for the same reasons as one with "practically no way back." Thus it is most useful to include nearly inescapable situations in the definition as well as completely inescapable ones.

7   If our potential greatly exceeds the current state of civilization, then something that simply locks in the current state would count as an existential catastrophe. An example would be an irrevocable relinquishment of further technological progress.

It may seem strange to call something a catastrophe due to merely being far short of optimal. This is because we usually associate events that destroy potential with those that bring immediate suffering and rarely think of events that could destroy one's potential while leaving one's current value intact. But consider, say, a choice by parents not to educate their child. There is no immediate suffering, yet catastrophic longterm outcomes for the child may have been locked in.

8   In some cases, the ideas and methodology of this book can be applied to these local "existential threats," as they have a somewhat similar character (in miniature).

9   This is not without its own issues. For instance, we shall sometimes have to say that something used to be a risk (given our past knowledge), but is no longer one. One example would be the possibility that nuclear weapons would ignite the atmosphere (see p. 90). But note that this comes up for all kinds of risk, such as thinking last week that there was a risk of the elevator falling due to a frayed cable, but having this risk drop to zero given our current

knowledge (we inspected the cable and found it to be fine). For more on objective versus evidential probability in defining existential risk see Bostrom & Ćirković (2008) and Bostrom (2013).

10 One often sees lists containing many historical civilizations that have collapsed, such as the Roman Empire or the Mayans. But this is not what I'm talking about in this book when I speak of the (global) collapse of civilization. The statistics of these smaller collapses have little bearing on whether global civilization will collapse.

The particular civilizations that collapsed were highly localized, and were more akin to the collapse of a single country than that of global civilization. For example, even the Roman Empire at its height was much smaller than Brazil is now in both land area and population. These small civilizations were much more prone to regional climatic effects, a single bad government and attacks from without. Furthermore, the collapses were much less deep than what I'm considering: often entire cities and towns survived the "collapse," the people weren't reduced to a pre-agricultural way of life, and many aspects of the culture continued.

11 Or some more direct way of preventing civilization or agriculture, such as extreme environmental damage or a continuing debilitating disease.

It is possible that due to some form of increased fragility, the world is less resistant to collapse than medieval Europe was, and thus that a loss of less than 50% of the population could cause this. I'm skeptical though, and find it just as likely that even a 90% loss may not cause the complete loss of civilization.

12 From the perspective of recent history, these agricultural revolutions began far apart in time, the thousands of years' head start for some civilizations playing a major role in their subsequent influence on the world stage. But from the broader perspective, these independent developments of agriculture occurred at remarkably similar times: just a few thousand years apart in a story spanning *hundreds* of thousands of years. This suggests that agriculture was not an unlikely technological breakthrough, but a fairly typical response to a common cause. The most likely trigger was the end of the great "ice age" that lifted between 17,000 and 10,000 years ago, just as agriculture began. This had dramatic effects on the

environment, making the world less suitable for hunting and more suitable for farming.

13   Overall the trend is toward resources becoming harder to access, since we access the easy ones first. This is true for untouched resources in the ground. But this leads people to neglect the vast amount of resources that are already in the process of being extracted, that are being stored, and that are in the ruins of civilization. For example, there is a single open-cut coal mine in Wyoming that produces 100 million tons of coal each year and has 1.7 billion tons left (Peabody Energy, 2018). At the time of writing, coal power plants in the US hold 100 million tons of ready-to-use coal in reserve (EIA, 2019). There are about 2 billion barrels of oil in strategic reserves (IEA, 2018, p. 19), and our global civilization contains about 2,000 kg of iron in use per person (Sverdrup & Olafsdottir, 2019).

14   Though we shall see in Chapter 4 that even extreme nuclear winter or climate change would be unlikely to produce enough environmental damage in every part of the world to do this.

15   The question of minimal viable population also comes up when considering multi-generational space travel. Marin & Beluffi (2018) find a starting population of 98 to be adequate, whereas Smith (2014) argues for a much higher minimum of between 14,000 and 44,000. It might be possible for even smaller populations to survive, depending on the genetic technologies available to minimize risks of inbreeding and genetic drift.

16   I believe this has also led people to think of the possibility of human extinction as trite, rather than profound. Its use as a narrative device in such films is indeed trite. But it would be a great mistake to let that judgment about its use in fiction cloud our understanding of its import for our future.

17   Nor do we often encounter serious emotional explorations, such as Bob Dylan's "Let Me Die in My Footsteps" (1963) or Barry McGuire's "Eve of Destruction" (1965).

18   See Slovic (2007).

19   Parfit (1984), pp. 453–4.

20   This qualitative difference is also what makes the difference according to the views we'll see later, regarding our past, virtue and cosmic significance.

21   Schell (1982), p. 182.
22   This warrants some elaboration. Following Parfit (1984), we can think of what would be lost were we to go extinct in two parts.

First is the loss of what we could *be*. The loss of each and every person who could have lived. The children and grandchildren we would never have: millions of generations of humanity, each comprised of billions of people, with lives of a quality far surpassing our own. Gone. A catastrophe would not *kill* these people, but it would foreclose their very existence. It would not *erase* them, but ensure they were never even written. We would lose the value of everything that would make each of these lives good—be it their happiness, freedom, success or virtue. We would lose the very persons themselves. And we would lose any value residing in the relationships between people or in the fabric of their society—their love, camaraderie, harmony, equality and justice.

Second is the loss of what we could *do*. Consider our greatest achievements in the arts and the sciences, and how many of them have been reached in just the last few centuries. If we make it through the next few centuries with our potential intact, we will likely produce greater heights than any we've seen so far. We may reach one of the very peaks of science: the complete description of the fundamental laws governing reality. And we will continue expanding the *breadth* of our progress, reaching new provinces yet to be explored.

Perhaps the most important are potential moral achievements. While we have made substantial progress over the centuries and millennia, it has been much slower than in other domains and more faltering. Humanity contains the potential to forge a truly just world, and realizing this dream would be a profound achievement.

There is so much that we could be and do, such a variety of flourishing and achievement ahead, that most conceptions of value will find something to mourn should we fail, should we squander this potential. And because this flourishing and achievement is on such a grand scale, the safeguarding of our potential is of the greatest importance.
23   So the scale of our future is not just important in consequentialist terms. It also fuels arguments for reducing existential risk that are rooted in considerations of fairness or justice.

24 By "matter just as much" I mean that each good or bad thing in their life matters equally regardless of when they live.

On average people's lives today are better than people's lives a thousand years ago because they contain more good things, and may be more instrumentally important too, because we live at a more pivotal time. So in these other senses, our lives may matter more now, but these other senses are compatible with the kind of temporal neutrality I endorse.

25 This has been suggested by J. J. C. Smart (1984, pp. 64–5) and G. E. Moore (1903, § 93).

26 New generations will have new risks that they can help reduce, but only we can reduce the risks being posed now and in coming decades.

27 The name was coined by William MacAskill and myself. The ideas build on those of our colleagues Nick Beckstead (2013) and Nick Bostrom (2002b, 2003). MacAskill is currently working on a major book exploring these ideas.

28 We will see in Appendix E that as well as safeguarding humanity, there are other general ways our acts could have a sustained influence on the longterm future.

29 On a discount rate of 0.1% per annum (low by economists' standards), the intervening million years make suffering in one million years more than 10^{434} times as important as the same amount of suffering in two million years.

30 One could cash this out in different ways depending on one's theory of value. For some it may literally involve the badness of the death of the group agent or species, humanity. For others it will be the absence of human lives in the future and everything good about them.

31 There are serious challenges in doing so if the other time (or place) involves a very different culture, but that is not relevant to this example.

32 Imagine what we'd think if we found out that our government ignored the risk of nuclear war on the grounds that if we were all dead, that couldn't be bad.

33 And even if after that skepticism we still leaned toward such a theory, we should remain very cautious about following its advice regarding the particular area where it most deviates from our

intuition and from the other theories we find plausible—on the value of our longterm future. See Beckstead (2013, p. 63).

34 Indeed, we'd be stuck in almost exactly the same condition as our earliest human ancestors (and there would be far fewer of us).

35 Burke (1790), para. 165. In her seminal work on the rights of future persons, Annette Baier (1981) makes a related point: "The crucial role we fill, as moral beings, is as members of a cross-generational community, a community of beings who look before and after, who interpret the past in light of the present, who see the future as growing out of the past, who see themselves as members of enduring families, nations, cultures, traditions." As does John Rawls in *A Theory of Justice* (1971, § 79): "The realizations of the powers of human individuals living at any one time takes the cooperation of many generations (or even societies) over a long period of time."

36 Seneca (1972), pp. 279–91. Sixteen centuries later, in 1704, Isaac Newton made a similar remark (Newton & McGuire, 1970): "To explain all nature is too difficult a task for any one man or even for any one age. 'Tis much better to do a little with certainty, & leave the rest for others that come after you . . ."

In 1755, Denis Diderot expressed related ideas in his *Encyclopédie* (Diderot, 1755, pp. 635–48A): ". . . the purpose of an encyclopedia is to collect knowledge disseminated around the globe; to set forth its general system to the men with whom we live, and transmit it to those who will come after us, so that the work of preceding centuries will not become useless to the centuries to come; and so that our offspring, becoming better instructed, will at the same time become more virtuous and happy, and that we should not die without having rendered a service to the human race."

37 Perhaps even more astounding is that some of the mysteries of comets whose depth inspired Seneca to write this passage have only recently been revealed—and contributed directly to our understanding of existential risk: "Some day there will be a man who will show in what regions comets have their orbit, why they travel so remote from other celestial bodies, how large they are and what sort they are" (Seneca, 1972, p. 281).

The nature of their highly eccentric orbits and their size have been key aspects in our current understanding of the risks comets pose to civilization and humanity. Further understanding of both these features would be among the most useful progress in reducing the risk posed by impacts from space. See Chapter 3.

38 See Scheffler (2018) for interesting additional discussion of reciprocity-based reasons for concern about future generations, and other potential considerations not covered here.

39 As Sagan (1983, p. 275) put it: "There are many other possible measures of the potential loss—including culture and science, the evolutionary history of the planet, and the significance of the lives of all of our ancestors who contributed to the future of their descendants. Extinction is the undoing of the human enterprise."

40 See, for example Cohen (2011), Scheffler (2009), Frick (2017).

41 Nick Bostrom (2013) expanded upon this idea: "We might also have custodial duties to preserve the inheritance of humanity passed on to us by our ancestors and convey it safely to our descendants. We do not want to be the failing link in the chain of generations, and we ought not to delete or abandon the great epic of human civilization that humankind has been working on for thousands of years, when it is clear that the narrative is far from having reached a natural terminus."

42 Stewart Brand (2000) has spoken eloquently of this civilizational patience: "Ecological problems were thought unsolvable because they could not be solved in a year or two . . . It turns out that environmental problems are solvable. It's just that it takes focused effort over a decade or three to move toward solutions, and the solutions sometimes take centuries. Environmentalism teaches patience. Patience, I believe, is a core competency of a healthy civilization."

43 While it takes us a bit further afield, we might also consider civilizational virtues related to our relationships with the wider world. For example, mistreatment of our fellow animals and our environment suggests deficiencies in our compassion and stewardship.

   And we could also consider how safeguarding our future can be motivated by virtues for individuals such as gratitude (to past generations), compassion and fairness (toward future generations), and unity or solidarity toward the rest of humanity. Jonathan Schell (1982, pp. 174–5) considers love in the sense of a generalization of parental or procreative love: the love with which we bring others into the world.

44 I've been lucky enough to get to work on this question with my colleagues at the Future of Humanity Institute: Anders Sandberg and Eric Drexler. In our paper, "Dissolving the Fermi Paradox" (Sandberg, Drexler & Ord, 2018) we quantified the current scientific understanding and uncertainties around the origin of life and intelligence. And we showed that it is a mistake to think that since there are billions of billions of stars there must be alien intelligence out there. For it is entirely plausible (and perhaps even likely) that the chance of life starting on any of them is correspondingly tiny. Our scientific knowledge is just as compatible with being alone as with being in a universe teeming with life. And given this, the lack of any sign of intelligent alien life is not in any way surprising or paradoxical—there is no need to invoke outlandish proposals to explain this; the evidence simply suggests that we are more likely to be alone.

We suggest that previous researchers had been led astray by using "point estimates" for all the quantities in the Drake equation. When these are replaced by statistical distributions of plausible values, we see that even if the mean or median number of alien civilizations is high, there is also a large chance of none. And we update toward this possibility when we see no sign of their activity.

45 This cosmic significance might be thought of as a way of illuminating the moral value that humanity has for other reasons, or as an additional source of value, or as something important that goes beyond value. Here are some of the leading proponents of our cosmic significance in their own words:

Martin Rees (2003, p. 157): "The odds could be so heavily stacked against the emergence (and survival) of complex life that Earth is the unique abode of conscious intelligence in our entire Galaxy. Our fate would then have truly cosmic resonance."

Max Tegmark (2014, p. 397): "It was the cosmic vastness that made me feel insignificant to start with. Yet those grand galaxies are visible and beautiful to us—and only us. It's only we who give them any meaning, making our small planet the most significant place in our entire observable Universe."

Carl Sagan (1980, p. 370): "The Cosmos may be densely populated with intelligent beings. But the Darwinian lesson is clear: There will be no humans elsewhere. Only here. Only on this small planet. We are a rare as well as an endangered species. Every one of us is, in the cosmic perspective, precious."

Derek Parfit (2017b, p. 437): "If we are the only rational beings in the Universe, as some recent evidence suggests, it matters even more whether we shall have descendants or successors during the billions of years in which that would be possible. Some of our successors might live lives and create worlds that, though failing to justify past suffering, would have given us all, including those who suffered most, reasons to be glad that the Universe exists."

James Lovelock (2019, p. 130): "Then, with the appearance of humans, just 300,000 years ago, this planet, alone in the cosmos, attained the capacity to know itself . . . We are now preparing to hand the gift of knowing on to new forms of intelligent beings. Do not be depressed by this. We have played our part . . . perhaps, we can hope that our contribution will not be entirely forgotten as wisdom and understanding spread outward from the earth to embrace the cosmos."

One way of understanding cosmic significance in consequentialist terms is to note that the more rare intelligence is, the larger the part of the universe that will be lifeless unless we survive and do something about it—the larger the difference *we* can make.

46   Eventually, we may become significant even in terms of raw scale. Cosmologists believe that the largest coherent structures in the universe are on the scale of about a billion light years across, the width of the largest voids in the cosmic web. With the accelerating expansion of the universe tearing things apart, and only gravity to work with, lifeless matter is unable to organize itself into any larger scales.

However, there is no known physical limit preventing humanity from forming coherent structures or patterns at much larger scales—up to a diameter of about 30 billion light years. We might thus create the largest structures in the universe and be unique even in these terms. By stewarding the galaxies in this region, harvesting and storing their energy, we may also be able to create the most energetic events in the universe or the longest-lasting complex structures.

47 As explained earlier in this chapter, it is not that only humans matter, but that humans are the only moral agents.

48 I think this is a very valuable perspective, which will yield insights that reach far beyond what I am able to explore in this book. I hope that others will adopt it and take it much further than I have been able to.

49 The theory of how to make decisions when we are uncertain about the moral value of outcomes was almost completely neglected in moral philosophy until very recently—despite the fact that it is precisely our uncertainty about moral matters that leads people to ask for moral advice and, indeed, to do research on moral philosophy at all.

Remedying this situation has been one of the major themes of my work so far (Greaves & Ord, 2017; MacAskill & Ord, 2018; MacAskill, Bykvist & Ord, forthcoming).

50 Nick Bostrom (2013, p. 24) put this especially well: "Our present understanding of axiology might well be confused. We may not now know—at least not in concrete detail—what outcomes would count as a big win for humanity; we might not even yet be able to imagine the best ends of our journey. If we are indeed profoundly uncertain about our ultimate aims, then we should recognize that there is a great option value in preserving—and ideally improving—our ability to recognize value and to steer the future accordingly. Ensuring that there will be a future version of humanity with great powers and a propensity to use them wisely is plausibly the best way available to us to increase the probability that the future will contain a lot of value. To do this, we must prevent any existential catastrophe."

I think the condition that you find it plausible is important. I'm not suggesting that this argument from uncertainty works even if you are extremely confident that there are no duties to protect our future. It might be possible to make such an argument based on expected value, but I am wary of expected value arguments when the probabilities are extremely small and poorly understood (see Bostrom, 2009).

51 Even if one were committed to the bleak view that the only things of value were of negative value, that could still give reason to

continue on, as humanity might be able to prevent things of negative value elsewhere on the Earth or in other parts of the cosmos where life has arisen.

52 Another way of saying this is that protecting our future has immense *option value*. It is the path that preserves our ability to choose whatever turns out to be best when new information comes in. This new information itself also ends up being extremely valuable: whether it is empirical information about what our future will be like or information about which putative moral considerations stand the test of time. Of course, it only holds this option value to the degree to which we expect our future to be responsive to new information about what is morally best.

For more on moral option value and the value of moral information from the perspective of humanity see Bostrom (2013, p. 24), MacAskill (2014) and also Williams (2015), who generalizes this idea: ". . . we should regard intellectual progress, of the sort that will allow us to find and correct our moral mistakes as soon as possible, as an urgent moral priority rather than as a mere luxury; and we should also consider it important to save resources and cultivate flexibility, so that when the time comes to change our policies we will be able to do so quickly and smoothly."

53 These ideas are beautifully expressed by Sagan (1994).

54 The 2019 budget was $1.4 million (BWC ISU, 2019). Between 2016 and 2018, McDonald's company-operated restaurants incurred an average of $2.8 million expenses per restaurant per year (McDonald's Corporation, 2018, pp. 14, 20). The company does not report costs for its franchised restaurants.

55 Farquhar (2017) estimated global spending on reducing existential risk from AI at $9 million in 2017. There has been substantial growth in the field since then, perhaps by a factor of 2 or 3. I'm confident that spending in 2020 is between $10 and $50 million.

IDC (2019) estimate global AI spending will reach $36 billion in 2019, a significant proportion of which will be devoted to improving AI capabilities.

56 The global ice cream market was estimated at $60 billion in 2018 (IMARC Group, 2019), or ~0.07% of gross world product (World Bank, 2019a).

Precisely determining how much we spend on safeguarding our future is not straightforward. I am interested in the simplest understanding of this: spending that is aimed at reducing existential risk. With that understanding, I estimate that global spending is on the order of $100 million.

Climate change is a good example of the challenges in determining the sort of spending we care about. One estimate of global spending on climate change is around $400 billion (~0.5% of gross world product) (Buchner et al., 2017). This is likely an overestimate of the economic cost, since most of the total is spending on renewable energy generation, much of which would otherwise have been spent on building non-renewable capacity. Moreover, as we will see in Chapter 4, most existential risk from climate change comes from the most extreme warming scenarios. It is not clear, therefore, how much of the average dollar toward climate-change mitigation goes toward reducing existential risk. Risks from engineered pandemics present similar challenges—US federal funding on biosecurity totals $1.6 billion, but only a small proportion of this will be aimed at the very worst pandemics (Watson et al., 2018).

Setting aside climate change, *all* spending on biosecurity, natural risks and risks from AI and nuclear war is still substantially less than we spend on ice cream. And I'm confident that the spending actually focused on existential risk is less than one-tenth of this.

57 Robock, Oman & Stenchikov (2007) and Coupe et al. (2019).

58 King et al. (2015). As we will see in Chapter 4, warming of 6°C is quite plausible given our current scientific understanding.

59 These features are known as non-excludability (the provider can't limit the benefit to those who pay) and non-rivalry (an individual's consumption of the good doesn't limit anyone else's). As one can see, most goods and services offered by the market are both excludable and rivalrous.

60 See Bostrom (2013, p. 26). Building on the idea of the tragedy of the commons, the economist Jonathan Wiener (2016) has called this situation "the tragedy of the uncommons."

61 There are some areas of longterm thinking, such as energy policy, pensions and large infrastructure projects. These typically involve thinking on a timescale of one or two decades, however, which is still quite short term by the standards of this book.

62   For more on heuristics and biases in general, see Kahneman (2011). See Wiener (2016) for a detailed discussion on these and other biases affecting public judgment of rare catastrophic risks.

63   Indeed, we sometimes suffer from a version of this effect called *mass numbing*, in which we are unable to conceptualize harms affecting thousands or more people and treat them as even *less* important than the same harm to a single identifiable person. See Slovic (2007).

64   Here I'm setting aside religious discussions of the end times, which I take to be very different from discussion of naturalistic causes of the end of humanity.

65   Russell (1945). Midway through the essay, Russell notes he has just learned of the bombing of Nagasaki, most likely on the morning of August 9, 1945: "As I write, I learn that a second bomb has been dropped on Nagasaki. The prospect for the human race is sombre beyond all precedent. Mankind are faced with a clear-cut alternative: either we shall all perish, or we shall have to acquire some slight degree of common sense. A great deal of new political thinking will be necessary if utter disaster is to be averted."

66   *The Bulletin* exists to this day, and has long been a focal point for discussions about extinction risk. In recent years, they have broadened their focus from nuclear risk to a wider range of threats to humanity's future, including climate change, bioweapons and unaligned artificial intelligence.

67   The 1955 Russell–Einstein Manifesto states (Russell, 2002): "Here, then, is the problem which we present to you, stark and dreadful and inescapable: Shall we put an end to the human race; or shall mankind renounce war? . . . there lies before you the risk of universal death."

Signing the manifesto was one of Einstein's last acts before his death in 1955, as described by Russell (2009, p. 547): "I had, of course, sent the statement to Einstein for his approval, but had not yet heard what he thought of it and whether he would be willing to sign it. As we flew from Rome to Paris, where the World Government Association were to hold further meetings, the pilot announced the news of Einstein's death. I felt shattered, not only for the obvious reasons, but because I saw my plan falling through without his support. But, on my arrival at my Paris hotel, I found a letter from him agreeing to sign. This was one of the last acts of his public life."

68　In a private letter, Eisenhower (1956) contemplated this possibility and its consequences for grand strategy: "When we get to the point, as we one day will, that both sides know that in any outbreak of general hostilities, regardless of the element of surprise, destruction will be both reciprocal and complete, possibly we will have sense enough to meet at the conference table with the understanding that the era of armaments has ended and the human race must conform its actions to this truth or die."

In a speech to the United Nations, Kennedy (1961) said: "For a nuclear disaster, spread by winds and waters and fear, could well engulf the great and the small, the rich and the poor, the committed and the uncommitted alike. Mankind must put an end to war— or war will put an end to mankind . . . Today, every inhabitant of this planet must contemplate the day when this planet may no longer be habitable. Every man, woman and child lives under a nuclear sword of Damocles, hanging by the slenderest of threads, capable of being cut at any moment by accident, or miscalculation, or by madness. The weapons of war must be abolished before they abolish us."

And Brezhnev suggested that "Mankind would be wholly destroyed" (Arnett, 1979, p. 131).

69　Schell (1982) was the first to publish, provoked by the new scientific theory that nuclear weapons could destroy the ozone layer, which might make life impossible for humans. This theory was soon found wanting, but that did not affect the quality of Schell's philosophical analysis about how bad extinction would be (analysis that was especially impressive as he was not a philosopher). Sagan (1983) was compelled to think deeply about extinction after his early results on the possibility of nuclear winter. Parfit's magnum opus, *Reasons and Persons* (1984), ended with his crisp analysis of the badness of extinction, which went on to have great influence in academic philosophy. Sagan cited Schell's work, and Parfit was probably influenced by it.

In that same year, *The Imperative of Responsibility* by Hans Jonas (1984) was released in an English translation. Originally written in 1979, it also raised many of the key questions concerning our ethical duties to maintain a world for future generations.

70　In 1985, Reagan said (Reagan & Weinraub, 1985): "A great many reputable scientists are telling us that such a war could just end up in no victory for anyone because we would wipe out the earth as we know it. And if you think back to a couple of natural calamities . . . there was snow in July in many temperate countries. And they called it the year in which there was no summer. Now if one volcano can do that, what are we talking about with the whole nuclear exchange, the nuclear winter that scientists have been talking about?"

Speaking in 2000, Mikhail Gorbachev reflected (Gorbachev & Hertsgaard, 2000): "Models made by Russian and American scientists showed that a nuclear war would result in a nuclear winter that would be extremely destructive to all life on earth; the knowledge of that was a great stimulus to us."

71　The crowd size has been estimated from 600,000 to 1 million, with 1 million being the most common number reported (Montgomery, 1982; Schell, 2007). There have since been even larger protests on other issues.

3 NATURAL RISKS

1　As recollected by Thomas Medwin (1824).

2　Estimates of the impact energy, the crater dimensions and ejecta are from Collins, Melosh & Marcus (2005). Other details from Schulte et al. (2010).

3　Schulte et al. (2010); Barnosky et al. (2011). One could argue that the reign of the dinosaurs continues through their descendants, the birds.

4　The largest is Ceres, at 945 kilometers. Asteroids actually range in size all the way down to fine dust, but are typically called "meteoroids" when too small to be observed with our telescopes.

5　The largest known comet is Hale-Bopp, at roughly 60 kilometers, though there may be larger ones that are currently too far away to detect. Astronomers have had difficulty detecting comets smaller than a few hundred meters, suggesting that they may not survive very long at these sizes.

6　Many people must have witnessed them falling to the ground, and the use of black metal of celestial origin appears in several myths.

Indeed, the earliest known iron artifacts are a set of small beads made from meteoric iron 5,200 years ago, before iron ore could be smelted. However, it is only 200 years ago that their origin was established to scientific standards (consider how many other phenomena with eyewitness accounts failed to withstand scrutiny).

7　Strictly speaking their paper gets its key estimate of 10 km (±4) by averaging four methods, of which the iridium method is just one, and suggested a slightly smaller size of 6.6 km (Alvarez et al., 1980).

8　The "impact winter" hypothesis was introduced by Alvarez et al. (1980) in their initial paper. It was finally confirmed by Vellekoop et al. (2014). The suggestion that impact-generated sulfates were responsible for this effect traces back to the 1990s (Pope et al., 1997).

9　As can be seen from the chapter's epigram, Lord Byron had thought of the threat from comets and even the possibility of planetary defense as early as 1822. The threat from comets began to be discussed in more depth at the turn of the nineteenth century, most famously in H. G. Wells' "The Star" (1897), but also in George Griffith's "The Great Crellin Comet" (1897) which featured the Earth being saved by an international project to deflect the comet. Bulfin (2015) contains detailed information on these and other Victorian explorations of the ways humanity could be destroyed. There was also non-impact-related concern in 1910 when it was suggested that the tail of Halley's comet might contain gases that could poison our atmosphere (Bartholomew & Radford, 2011, ch. 16).

　　The threat from asteroids was first recognized in 1941 (Watson, 1941). In 1959 Isaac Asimov urged the eventual creation of a space program for detecting and eliminating such threats (Asimov, 1959).

10　Media interest was fueled by the 1980 Alvarez hypothesis, the 1989 near miss with the asteroid 4581 Asclepius and the 1994 collision of the comet Shoemaker-Levy 9, which left a visible mark on Jupiter comparable in size to the entire Earth.

11　This goal was achieved in 2011, for a total cost of less than $70 million (Mainzer et al., 2011; US House of Representatives, 2013).

12　It is often reported that asteroids are a hundred times as common as comets, suggesting that they make up the overwhelming bulk of the risk. At one level this is true. At the time of writing, 176 near-Earth comets had been identified, compared with 20,000 asteroids (JPL, 2019b). But while comets are 100 times less frequent, they are often larger, so of the 1–10 km NEOs (near-Earth Objects), comets are only 20 times less frequent. Of the NEOs greater than 10 km, four are asteroids and four are comets. Thus for the purposes of existential risk, the background risk from comets may not be that different from that of asteroids.

13   Note that the mass, and thus the destructive energy, of an asteroid is proportional to the cube of the diameter, such that a 1 km asteroid has only a thousandth the energy of a 10 km asteroid. They can also vary in terms of their density and their speed relative to the Earth—for a given size, a denser or faster asteroid has more kinetic energy and is thus more dangerous.

14   Longrich, Scriberas & Wills (2016).

15   When I wrote the first draft of this chapter, most of the risk from the tracked asteroids was in the 2 km asteroid "2010 GZ_{60}," At the time of writing, the chance of a collision over the next century was put at the low but non-negligible level of one in 200,000. Happily, we now know this will miss the Earth. The most risky tracked asteroid is now the 1.3 km asteroid "2010 GD_{37}," whose impact probability in the next century is a mere one in 120,000,000 (JPL, 2019b).

16   The main uncertainty about whether we have found them all stems from those asteroids with orbits close to 1 AU (the distance between the Earth and the Sun) and a period of close to one year, making them undetectable for many years at a time. Fortunately, it is very unlikely that there is such an asteroid. And if there were, it would become visible years before a potential impact (Alan Harris, personal communication).

17   The risk from asteroids between 1 and 10 km in size is even lower than this probability suggests, as the 5% of these remaining untracked are disproportionately at the small end of the scale (the vast majority were near the small end of this range to begin with, and our detection methods have been better at finding the bigger ones).

18   Hazard descriptions are from Alan Harris. Estimates of impact probabilities are from Stokes et al. (2017, p. 25).
    The total number of 1–10 km near-Earth asteroids has most recently been estimated at 921 ± 20 (Tate, 2017). As of April 2019,

895 have been discovered: 95–99% of the total (JPL, 2019a). In order to be conservative, I take the lower bound.

Four near-Earth asteroids over 10 km have been identified (JPL, 2019a): 433 Eros (1898 DQ); 1036 Ganymed (1924 TD); 3552 Don Quixote (1983 SA); 4954 Eric (1990 SQ). NASA (2011) believes this is all of them.

19 The International Asteroid Warning Network was established in 2014 on the recommendation of the UN. The international Spaceguard Foundation was founded in 1996 (UNOOSA, 2018).

20 In 2010 annual funding was $4 million. This was increased to $50 million in 2016, and is understood have remained at similar levels since (Keeter, 2017).

21 Unfortunately comets can be much more difficult to characterize and to divert. Short-period comets (those with orbits of less than 200 years) present some novel problems: they are subject to forces other than gravity, making their trajectories harder to predict, and it is more difficult to rendezvous with them. Things get substantially worse with long-period comets since they are so far from the Earth. We understand neither their overall population, nor the detailed trajectories of those that might threaten us (if they pose a threat next century, it would be on their very first observed approach toward us). Moreover, they would be extremely difficult to deflect as we would have less than a year from first detection (at around the orbit of Jupiter) to the time of impact (Stokes et al., 2017, p. 14).

22 Asteroids are about twenty times as frequent in the 1–10 km size category, but tracking those asteroids has reduced the risk by that same multiple. And comets and asteroids are about equally frequent in the 10 km+ size category (JPL, 2019b).

23 Deflection would be very expensive, but the costs would only need to be paid if a large asteroid on a collision course for Earth were discovered. In such a situation, the people of the Earth would be willing to pay extremely high costs, so it would be more a question of what we can achieve in the time available than one of price. In contrast, the costs of detection and tracking need to be paid whether or not there really is a dangerous asteroid, so even though they are much lower in dollar terms, they may be the greater part of the expected cost, and the part that is harder to get funded.

24 National Research Council (2010), p. 4.

25 See Sagan & Ostro (1994) for an early discussion, and Drmola & Mareš (2015) for a recent survey.

26 One reason it is unlikely is that several of the deflection methods (such as nuclear explosions) are powerful enough to knock the asteroid off course, but not refined enough to target a particular country with it. For this reason, these might be the best methods to pursue.

27 Eruptions are measured using two scales. The volcanic explosivity index (VEI) is an ordinal scale classifying eruptions in terms of their ejecta volume. The magnitude scale is a logarithmic scale of eruption mass, given by $M = \log_{10}$ [erupted mass in kg] − 7. The magnitude scale is generally preferred by scientists, due to practical problems estimating eruption volumes, and the usefulness of a continuous scale in analyzing relationships between magnitude and other parameters. All VEI 8 eruptions with a deposit density of greater than around 1,000 kg/m^3 (most of them) will have magnitudes of 8 or more.

There is no sharp line between supervolcanic eruptions and regular eruptions. Supervolcanic eruptions are those with VEI 8—ejecta volume greater than 1,000 km^3. It is not clear whether flood basalts should count as supervolcanoes, and they have generally been considered separately. See Mason, Pyle & Oppenheimer (2004) for a discussion of the scales.

28 Not all calderas are the result of supereruptions, however. For example, Kilauea in Hawaii has a caldera that was produced by lava flows, rather than from an explosive eruption.

29 This was its last supervolcanic eruption. It had a lesser eruption 176,000 years ago (Crosweller et al., 2012).

30 There is significant uncertainty about the magnitude of global cooling, with estimates ranging from 0.8°C to 18°C. The key driver of climatic effects is the amount of sulfate injected into the upper atmosphere, estimates of which vary by several orders of magnitude. This is usually expressed as a multiple of the Pinatubo eruption in 1991, for which we have accurate measurements.

Early research (Rampino & Self, 1992) found cooling of 3–5°C, with sulfate levels of 38x Pinatubo. More recently, Robock et al. (2009) use a central estimate of 300x Pinatubo, and find cooling of up to 14°C. Recent work by Chesner & Luhr (2010) suggests a sulfate yield of 2–23x Pinatubo—considerably less than early numbers. Yost et al. (2018) offer an extensive review of estimates and methodology, arguing that estimates from Chesner & Luhr (2010) are more robust, and calculating an implied global cooling of 1–2°C. More research is needed to better constrain these estimates.

31 Raible et al., 2016. This inspired Byron to write his poem "Darkness," which begins: "I had a dream, which was not all a dream. / The bright sun was extinguish'd, and the stars / Did wander darkling in the eternal space, / Rayless, and pathless, and the icy earth / Swung blind and blackening in the moonless air; / Morn came and went — and came, and brought no day . . ."

The year without summer also inspired Mary Shelley to write *Frankenstein*, while traveling with Byron and Percy Shelley. In her introduction to the 1831 edition she describes how, forced indoors by the "wet, ungenial summer and incessant rain," the group entertained themselves by telling ghost stories, one of which became *Frankenstein* (Shelley, 2009).

32 This is known as the "Toba catastrophe hypothesis" and was popularized by Ambrose (1998). Williams (2012) argues that imprecision in our current archeological, genetic and paleoclimatological techniques makes it difficult to establish or falsify the hypothesis. See Yost et al. (2018) for a critical review of the evidence. One key uncertainty is that genetic bottlenecks could be caused by founder effects related to population dispersal, as opposed to dramatic population declines.

33 Direct extinction, that is. Such an event would certainly be a major stressor, creating risk of subsequent war. See Chapter 6 on risk factors.

The Toba eruption had a magnitude of 9.1, and is the largest eruption in the geological record (Crosweller et al., 2012). On a uniform prior, it is unlikely (4%) that the largest eruption for 2 million years would have occurred so recently. This raises the possibility that the record is incomplete, or that the estimate of Toba's magnitude is inflated.

34 Rougier et al. (2018). Estimating the return period for Toba-sized eruptions (magnitude 9 or more) is difficult, particularly with only

one data point. Rougier's model suggests between 60,000 and 6 million years, with a central estimate of 800,000 years (personal communication). This estimate is highly sensitive to the upper limit for eruptions, which Rougier places at 9.3. I've rounded all these numbers to one significant figure to reflect our level of confidence.

35 Wilcox et al. (2017); Denkenberger & Blair (2018).

36 Barnosky et al. (2011). Though note that *many* things have been suggested as possible causes of the end-Permian mass extinction. See Erwin, Bowring & Yugan (2002) for a survey of proposed causes.

37 This could involve both climate modeling and analysis of the fossil record to see whether past eruptions caused any global or local extinctions. This latter angle might be easier than with asteroids due to the higher frequency of supervolcanic eruptions.

38 When one of the forces would increase or decrease, the star's size changes in response until they are balanced again. The rapid collapsing and exploding can be seen as failed attempts to rebalance these forces.

39 This can happen when the nuclear fuel of a large star runs low, reducing the pressure, or when a tiny white dwarf star drains off too much mass from a close companion star, increasing the gravitational squeezing. The former is more common and is known as a core-collapse supernova. The latter is known as a thermonuclear supernova (or Type Ia supernova).

40 Baade & Zwicky (1934); Schindewolf (1954); Krasovsky & Shklovsky (1957).

41 Bonnell & Klebesadel (1996).

42 This same effect massively increases the range at which they could be deadly to the Earth, which is sometimes interpreted as a reason to be more concerned about gamma ray bursts relative to supernovae. However, it also makes it possible that the explosion will miss us, due to being pointed in the wrong direction. In a large enough galaxy, these effects would exactly cancel out, with the narrowness of the cone having no effect on the average number of stars that a stellar explosion exposes to dangerous radiation levels. In our own galaxy, the narrowness of the cone actually *reduces* the typical number of stars affected by each blast, since it increases the

chance that much of it is wasted, shooting out beyond the edges of our galaxy.

43   This gamma ray burst (GRB 080319B) occurred about 7.5 billion years ago at a point in space that is now more than 10 billion light years away (due to cosmic expansion—author's calculation). This is 3,000 times further away than the Triangulum Galaxy, which is usually the most distant object visible with the naked eye (Naeye, 2008).

44   When these cosmic rays interact with our atmosphere, they also cause showers of high-energy particles to reach the Earth's surface, including dangerous levels of muon radiation.

An event of this type may have played a role in initiating the Ordovician mass extinction approximately 440 million years ago (Melott et al., 2004).

45   We can eliminate the risk from core collapse supernovae as nearby candidates would be very obvious and are not present. However, about a tenth of the risk is from thermonuclear supernovae (type Ia) which are harder to detect and thus it is harder to be sure they are absent (The et al., 2006). Similarly, it is very hard to find binary neutron stars that might collide in order to rule out the risk from this type of gamma ray burst. Given the difficulties and our more limited of understanding of gamma ray bursts, I have declined to give a numerical estimate of how much lower the risk over the next century is compared to the baseline risk.

46   Melott & Thomas (2011) estimate the frequency of extinction-level supernovae events at one in every 5 million centuries. This uses a distance threshold of 10 parsecs. Wilman & Newman (2018) reach a similar estimate, of one in every 10 million centuries.

Melott & Thomas (2011) estimate the total rate of extinction-level GRB (gamma ray burst) events at one in every 2.5 million centuries. This includes both long and short GRBs. Piran & Jimenez (2014) give probabilistic estimates of extinction-level GRB events having happened in the past. They find a probability of over 90% for such a long GRB having occurred in the last 5 billion years, and 50% of one having occurred in the last 500 million years. For short GRBs, they find much lower probabilities—14% in the last 5 billion years, and 2% in the last 500 million years.

These probability estimates (and particularly those of GRBs) are much rougher than those for asteroids and comets, due to the field being at an earlier stage. For example, the estimates for the energy released by supernovae and gamma ray bursts (and the cone angle for GRBs) are based on individual examples that are thought to be representative, rather than on detailed empirical distributions of known energy levels and cone angles for these events. In addition, while we have a reasonable understanding of which events could cause a 30% depletion of global ozone, more work is needed to determine whether this is the right threshold for catastrophe.

47 Some more detailed examples include: determining if there is a level of fluence that is a plausible extinction event, based on the predicted effects of ozone depletion on humans and crops; incorporating the observed distribution of supernova and gamma ray burst energy levels (and cone angles) into the model instead of relying on a paradigm example for each; taking into account the geometrical issues around cone angles from note 42 to this chapter; and doing a sensitivity analysis on the model to see if there are any plausible combinations of values that could make this risk competitive with asteroid risk (then attempting to rule those out).

I'd also encourage blue-sky thinking to see if there are any possible ways existing models could be underestimating the risk by an order of magnitude or more.

48 This is addressed in detail in Chapter 8.

49 Masson-Delmotte et al. (2013) say it is "virtually certain" (over 99%) that orbital forcing—slow changes in the Earth's position relative to the Sun—cannot trigger widespread glaciation in the next thousand years. They note that climate models simulate no glaciation in the next 50,000 years, provided atmospheric carbon dioxide concentrations stay above 300 ppm. We also know that glacial periods are common enough that if they posed a high risk of extinction, we should see it in the fossil record (indeed most of *Homo sapiens'* history has been during glacial periods).

However, since we are considering many other risks that are known to have low probabilities, it would be good if we could improve our understanding of just how low the probability of entering a glacial period is, and just how much risk of global civilization collapse it might pose. Notably, the Agricultural Revolution happened just as the last glacial period was ending, suggesting that even if they pose very little extinction risk, they may make agricultural civilization substantially harder.

50 Adams & Laughlin (1999). Disruption by a passing black hole is less likely still, since stars vastly outnumber black holes.

51 This probability is difficult to estimate from observation as it would destroy any observers, censoring out any positive examples from our data set. However, Tegmark & Bostrom (2005) present an ingenious argument that rules out vacuum collapse being more likely than one in a billion per year with 99.9% confidence. Buttazzo et al. (2013) suggest that the true chance is less than one in 10^{600} per year, while many others think that our vacuum actually is the true vacuum so the chance of collapse is exactly zero.

It might also be possible to trigger a vacuum collapse through our own actions, such as through high-energy physics experiments. Risks from such experiments are discussed on pp. 160–161.

52 The geological record suggests a chance of roughly one in 2,000 per century. It is still debated whether the process is random or periodic. See Buffett, Ziegler & Constable (2013) for a summary of recent developments.

53 Lingam (2019).

54 The idea that our species' longevity is evidence that natural risk is low is briefly mentioned by Leslie (1996, p. 141) and Bostrom (2002b). To my knowledge, the first attempt to quantify evidence from the fossil record is Ord & Beckstead (2014). My colleagues and I have further developed this line of reasoning in Snyder-Beattie, Ord & Bonsall (2019).

55 All these techniques give estimates that are based on averages. If we know we are not in an average time, they might no longer apply. It is extremely unlikely that we will detect a 10 km asteroid on a collision course for Earth. But if we did, we would no longer be able to help ourselves to laws of averages. I do not know of any natural threats where our current knowledge suggests that our risk of extinction is significantly elevated (and we should be surprised to find ourselves in such a situation, since they must be rare). Indeed, it is much more common for the knowledge we acquire to show that the near-term risk from a threat—such as asteroids or supernovae—is actually lower than the longterm average.

56 There are some indirect applications to unrecoverable collapse. The major hazards that have been identified appear to pose a broadly similar level of risk of unrecoverable collapse and extinction (say, within a factor of ten), so there is some reason to think that finding the extinction risk is very small would also have bearing on the collapse risk. What would be needed to break this is a natural hazard that is especially good at posing collapse risk relative to extinction risk. This is harder to find than one might think, especially when you consider that a lot of the fossil evidence we use is for species that are much less robust to extinction than we are, due to smaller geographical ranges and dependence on a small number of food sources—it would have to be able to permanently destroy civilization across the globe without causing such species to go extinct.

Another approach would be to run the first of my methods using the lifetime of civilization instead of the lifetime of *Homo sapiens*. As this is about 100 centuries, we'd get a best-guess estimate between 0% and 1% per century. Which is something, but definitely not as comforting. More research on how to strengthen these estimates and bounds for irrevocable civilization collapse would be very valuable.

57 There is considerable uncertainty about the 200,000-year estimate for the origin of *Homo sapiens* and for many related dates we will consider later. My 200,000 estimate refers to the "Omo" fossil remains, which are widely regarded as being *Homo sapiens*. More recently discovered fossils from Jebel Irhoud in Morocco are dated to roughly 300,000 years ago, but it is still debated whether they should be considered *Homo sapiens* (see note 2 to Chapter 1). But all these dates are known to be correct to within a factor of two and that is sufficient accuracy to draw the qualitative conclusions later on. Feel free to substitute them with any other estimates you prefer, and see how the quantitative estimates change.

58 This is not strictly true, as in some mathematical contexts probability zero events can happen. But they are infinitely unlikely, such as flipping a coin forever and never getting tails. Of course, we also don't have enough evidence to suggest that human extinction is infinitely unlikely in this sense.

59 This area of research is ongoing and clearly very important for the study of existential risk, which is all about unprecedented events.

One way to state the question is: what probability should we assign to failure if something has succeeded on each of the n trials so far? This is sometimes known as the problem of zero-failure data. Estimators that have been suggested include:

0	Maximum likelihood estimator.
$\frac{1}{3n}$	"One-third" estimator (Bailey, 1997).
$\sim\frac{1}{2.5n}$	Approximation of method from Quigley & Revie (2011).
$\frac{1}{2n+2}$	Bayesian updating with a maximum entropy prior.
$\sim\frac{1}{1.5n}$	50% confidence level (Bailey, 1997).
$\frac{1}{n+2}$	Bayesian updating with a uniform prior.
$\frac{1}{n}$	"Upper bound" estimator.

Note that the widespread "rule of three" (Hanley, 1983) is not attempting to answer the same question: it suggests using $3/n$, but as an upper bound (at 95% confidence) rather than as a best guess. We will use a more direct approach to estimate such bounds and ask for a higher confidence level.

I think the arguments are strongest for the Bayesian updating with a maximum entropy prior, which ends up giving an estimate right in the middle of the reasonable range (after a lot of trials, or when the possibility of failure is spread continuously through time).

60   The general formula for the upper bound is $1-(1-c)^{100/t}$, where c is the level of confidence (e.g., 0.999) and t is the age of humanity in years (e.g., 200,000).

61   This is not quite the same as saying that there is a 99.9% chance that the risk is below 0.34%. It just means that if the risk were higher than 0.34%, a 1 in 1,000 event must have occurred. This should be enough to make us very skeptical of such an estimate of the risk without substantial independent reason to think it so high. For example, if all other observed species had natural-cause extinction rates of 1% per century, we might think it is more likely that we do too—and that we got very lucky, rather than that we are exceptional. However, we shall soon see that related species have lower extinction risk than this, so this does not offer a way out.

62   On the basis of fossil evidence, we are confident that divergence occurred at least 430,000 years ago (Arsuaga et al., 2014). See White, Gowlett & Grove (2014) for a survey of estimates

from genomic evidence, which range from around 400,000 to 800,000 years ago.

63 All species' age estimates in this chapter are from the fossil evidence. It is difficult to get the complete data for all species in the genus *Homo* as new species are still being discovered, and there are several species which have only been found in a few sites. Therefore, using the dates between the earliest and latest known fossils for each species will probably greatly underestimate their lifespan. One response is to restrict our attention to the species found in more than a few sites and this is what I've done. Unfortunately, this increases a type of bias in the data where we are less likely to know about short-lived species as there will typically be fewer fossilized remains (causing this to underestimate natural risk). However, since *Homo sapiens* is known to have a longevity greater than 200,000 years there is evidence that its extinction chance is not very similar to those of any extremely short-lived species that may have been missed out.

64 One might wonder whether a constant hazard rate is a reasonable model of how species go extinct. For example, it assumes that their objective chance of going extinct in the next century is independent of how long they have lived so far, but perhaps species are more like organisms, in that older species are less fit and at increased risk. Such a systematic change in extinction risk over time would affect my analysis. However, it appears that species lifespans within each family are indeed fairly well approximated by a constant hazard rate (Van Valen, 1973; Alroy, 1996; Foote & Raup, 1996).

65 This could also be said of the previous method, as *Homo sapiens* is arguably a successful continuation of the species before it.

66 This special form of survivorship bias is sometimes known as anthropic bias or an observation selection effect.

67 My colleagues and I have shown how we can address these possibilities when it comes to estimating natural existential risk via how long humanity has survived so far (Snyder-Beattie, Ord & Bonsall, 2019). We found that the most biologically plausible models for how anthropic bias could affect the situation would cause only a small change to the estimated probabilities of natural risk.

68 All dates given are for when the event ended. Extinction rates are from Barnosky et al. (2011).

It has recently been suggested that the Devonian and Triassic events may have reduced species numbers more from lowering the origination rate of new species than raising the extinction rate of existing species (Bambach, 2006). If so, this would only strengthen the arguments herein, by reducing the frequency of the type of extinction events relevant to us to a "Big Three."

Note also that there is a lot of scientific uncertainty around what caused most of these, including the biggest. But for our purposes this doesn't matter too much, since we still know that these events are extremely rare and that is all we use in the argument.

69 Even in the case of an asteroid impact, where technology and geographical distribution are very helpful, we could be at increased risk due to our reliance on technology and the farming of very few types of crop. It is conceivable that a smaller society of hunter-gatherers would be more resilient to this, since they would have skills that are rare now but which might become essential (Hanson, 2008). However, I very much doubt that this risk has increased overall, especially considering the fact that our world still contains people who are relatively isolated and live in relatively untouched tribal groups.

4 ANTHROPOGENIC RISKS

1 Toynbee (1963).
2 The contribution of fusion to an atomic bomb goes far beyond this higher efficiency. A fission bomb has a natural size limit set by the critical mass of its fuel (some tricks allow this to be exceeded, but only by a small multiple). In contrast, the fusion fuel has no such constraints and much larger bombs could be built. Moreover, the neutrons emitted by the fusion can cause fission in the bomb's massive uranium tamper. This is known as a fission-fusion-fission bomb and this final stage of fission can produce most of the energy.
3 Compton (1956), pp. 127–8.
4 Albert Speer, the German minister of armaments, gave a chilling account (Speer, 1970, p. 227): "Professor Heisenberg had not given any final answer to my question whether a successful nuclear fission could be kept under control with absolute certainty or might continue as a chain reaction. Hitler was plainly not delighted with the possibility that the earth under his rule might be transformed into a

glowing star. Occasionally, however, he joked that the scientists in their unworldly urge to lay bare all the secrets under heaven might some day set the globe on fire. But undoubtedly a good deal of time would pass before that came about, Hitler said; he would certainly not live to see it."

One cannot be sure from this whether it was exactly the same concern (a thermonuclear reaction spreading through the atmosphere) or a related kind of uncontrolled explosion.

5   Teller had made very "optimistic" assumptions about the parameters involved in getting the fusion reaction going, and had not taken account of the rate at which the heat of the explosion would radiate away, cooling it faster than the new fusion heated it up (Rhodes, 1986, p. 419).

6   This report has subsequently been declassified and is available as Konopinski, Marvin & Teller (1946).

7   The report ends: "One may conclude that the arguments of this paper make it unreasonable to expect that the N + N reaction could propagate. An unlimited propagation is even less likely. However, the complexity of the argument and the absence of satisfactory experimental foundation makes further work on the subject highly desirable" (Konopinski, Marvin & Teller, 1946).

In contemporary discussion, the probability of "three in a million" is often given, either as the estimate of the chance of ignition or as a safety threshold that the chance needed to be below. This number does not occur in the report and appears to have entered the public sphere through an article by Pearl S. Buck (1959). While intriguing, there is no convincing evidence that such a probability was used by the atomic scientists in either manner.

8   David Hawkins, the official historian of the Manhattan Project, has said that the possibility kept being rediscovered by younger scientists and that the leadership at Los Alamos had to keep "batting it down," telling them that it had been taken care of. In the end, Hawkins did "more interviews with the participants on this particular subject, both before and after the Trinity test, than on any other subject" (Ellsberg, 2017, pp. 279–80).

9   Peter Goodchild (2004, pp. 103–4): "In the final weeks leading up to the test Teller's group were drawn into the immediate preparations when the possibility of atmospheric ignition was revived by Enrico

Fermi. His team went to work on the calculation, but, as with all such projects before the introduction of computers, these involved simplifying assumptions. Time after time they came up with negative results, but Fermi remained unhappy about their assumptions. He also worried whether there were undiscovered phenomena that, under the novel conditions of extreme heat, might lead to an unexpected disaster."

10 From his private notes written the next day (Hershberg, 1995, p. 759). The full quotation is: "Then came a burst of white light that seemed to fill the sky and seemed to last for seconds. I had expected a relatively quick and light flash. The enormity of the light quite stunned me. My instantaneous reaction was that something had gone wrong and that the thermal nuclear [sic] transformation of the atmosphere, once discussed as a possibility and jokingly referred to a few minutes earlier, had actually occurred."

Perhaps from staring into this abyss, Conant was one of the first people to take the destruction of civilization due to nuclear war seriously. When the war ended, he returned to Harvard and summoned its chief librarian, Keyes Metcalf, for a private meeting. Metcalf later recalled his shock at Conant's request (Hershberg, 1995, pp. 241–2): "We are living in a very different world since the explosion of the A-bomb. We have no way of knowing what the results will be, but there is the danger that much of our present civilization will come to an end . . . It might be advisable to select the printed material that would preserve the record of our civilization for the one we can hope will follow, microfilming it and making perhaps 10 copies and burying those in different places throughout the country. In that way we could ensure against the destruction that resulted from the fall of the Roman Empire."

Metcalf looked into what this would require, and prepared a rough plan for microfilming the most important 500,000 volumes, or a total of 250 million pages. But in the end they did not pursue this, reasoning both that its becoming public would cause significant panic, and that written records would probably survive in the libraries of university towns that would not suffer direct hits from atomic weapons. However, when Metcalf resigned from Harvard, he began a project of ensuring vast holdings of important works in major universities in the southern hemisphere, perhaps inspired by the conversation with Conant and fear of nuclear catastrophe (Hershberg & Kelly, 2017).

11 Weaver & Wood (1979).

12 If a group cares deeply about the accuracy of their own internal work, they can set up a "red team" of researchers tasked with proving the work wrong. This team should be given ample time, until they overcome their initial loyalties to the work so far, beginning to hope it is wrong rather than right. They also should be given ample resources, praise and incentives for finding flaws.

13 Part of any proper risk analysis is a measure of the stakes and a comparison with the benefits. These benefits became *much* smaller once Hitler was defeated, necessitating a much lower probability threshold for the disaster, but it seems that the risk wasn't re-evaluated.

14 At least a few people in government do appear to have found out about it. Serber (1992, p. xxxi): "Compton didn't have enough sense to shut up about it. It somehow got into a document that went to Washington. So every once in a while after that, someone happened to notice it, and then back down the ladder came the question, and the thing never was laid to rest."

15 One of the best methods for eliciting someone's subjective probability for an event is to offer a series of small bets and see how extreme the odds need to be before they take them. As it happened, Fermi did exactly this, the evening before the Trinity test, taking bets on whether the test would destroy the world. However, since it was obvious that no one could collect on their bets if the atmosphere *had* ignited, this must have been at least partly in jest. History does not relate who took him up on this nor what odds they took.

16 The fuel was a compound of lithium with deuterium (an isotope of hydrogen that is conducive to fusion reactions). The purpose of the lithium was to react with a neutron, producing the extremely rare hydrogen isotope, tritium. This tritium would then fuse with the deuterium, releasing a lot of energy.

17 15 Mt fell well outside their uncertainty range of 4 to 8 Mt (Dodson & Rabi, 1954, p. 15).

18 The Japanese were understandably upset at being hit by a US nuclear weapon again, just nine years after Nagasaki, and this caused a diplomatic incident. Even the scientific results were a

disaster: they collected relatively little useful data as the larger blast destroyed much of their test equipment.

19 The lithium-7 was reacting in an unanticipated way, producing both more tritium and more neutrons, which drove the fusion and fission reactions much further than expected. It is difficult to make any precise claims about the relative contributions of the two lithium isotopes as the weapon involved several interacting stages, but I believe it is roughly right to say that the contributions of the two kinds of lithium were similar, for the weapon had an amount of lithium-7 equal to 150% of the amount of lithium-6 and got an additional 150% energy release.

20 One reason is that they appear to have taken more caution with the first of these calculations. For the atmosphere to ignite, they would not only need to be wrong in their calculations, but wrong by an amount in excess of their safety factors.

There is also the fact that their first calculation was a yes/no question, while the second wasn't. So there were more ways the second could go wrong. I've demonstrated that it contained a major mistake, but the fuel they recommended *did* still explode, so I suppose a more coarse-grained assessment might still count that calculation as a success.

And finally, there is a question of priors. Even if their method of answering questions was completely unreliable (e.g., flipping a coin), all that means is that it doesn't provide a useful update to your prior probability estimate for the event. It is hard to say what that should have been in the case of igniting the atmosphere, but it is reasonable for it to have been well below 50%, perhaps below 1%.

21 The report on Soviet bombing targets was delivered on August 30, 1945 (Rhodes, 1995, p. 23).

22 Another key technical development was multiple independently targetable re-entry vehicles (MIRVs). These enabled a single ICBM to split and hit several locations. This shifted the strategic balance toward first strike, as the power that struck first could potentially take out several enemy ICBMs with each of its own. This in turn increased the reliance on hair-trigger alert as the retaliating power would need to launch its missiles while the attacking missiles were still on their way in.

23 Within five months 140,000 people died in Hiroshima from a yield of about 15 kilotons. The world's arsenal is about 200,000 times

this, so the naïve extrapolation would suggest about 30 billion deaths, or about four times the world's population. But such a calculation makes two major mistakes.

First, it ignores the fact that many people do not live in big dense cities: there are nowhere near enough nuclear warheads to hit all towns and villages. And second, it ignores the fact that bigger nuclear weapons become less efficient at killing, per kiloton. This is because the blast energy is spread out in a three-dimensional ball, while the city is in a two-dimensional disc, which occupies a smaller and smaller fraction of the ball as the energy increases. Thus an increasing fraction of the blast energy is wasted as the weapon is scaled up. Mathematically, the blast damage scales as the two-thirds power of the energy.

24 Ball (2006) estimates 250 million direct deaths from an all-out nuclear war.

The Office of Technology Assessment (1979) describes US government estimates of direct death tolls ranging from 20 to 165 million in the US, and 50 to 100 million in the Soviet Union. Note that these estimates should be adjusted for a present-day case—the population of US cities has increased substantially since the 1970s, and the collapse of the Soviet Union has presumably restricted the targets of a US attack to Russia. Ellsberg (2017, pp. 1–3) describes a classified report prepared for President Kennedy by the Joint Chiefs of Staff, which estimated the immediate deaths from a nuclear attack on the Soviet Union and China at 275 million, rising to 325 million after six months, numbers that would also have to be scaled up for present populations.

25 There were often further checks that may have prevented these incidents escalating all the way to nuclear war. For a skeptical take on how close these close calls were, see Tertrais (2017).

26 There are far more close calls and accidents than I could do justice to in this book. For example, NORAD reported that false alarms led to six Threat Assessment Conferences and 956 Missile Display Conferences even just in the five years from January 1978 to May 1983 (Wallace, Crissey & Sennott, 1986).

27 Brezhnev (1979); Gates (2011); Schlosser (2013).

28 Reports differ on whether there were five missiles shown, or just a single missile (with four more appearing in a second event later that night).

29 Lebedev (2004); Schlosser (2013); Chan (2017).

30 Forden, Podvig & Postol (2000); Schlosser (2013).

31 Feld (1976) estimates that a one-megaton warhead can irradiate an area of roughly 2,500 km² with a lethal dose, implying one would need at least 60,000 such weapons to irradiate the Earth's land area. This significantly exceeds current stockpiles of around 9,000 deployed warheads, which have an average yield considerably below one megaton.

32 Such a "doomsday device" was first suggested by Leo Szilard in 1950 and its strategic implications were more fully developed by Herman Kahn (Bethe et al., 1950). A cobalt bomb (or similar salted weapon) plays a major role in the plots of *On the Beach* and *Dr. Strangelove*, taking nuclear war in both cases from a global catastrophe to an extinction threat.

   The greatest obstacle to destroying all of humanity with such a weapon is ensuring that lethal radiation is distributed evenly across the Earth, particularly when taking into account shelters, weather and oceans.

   Russia's *Poseidon* nuclear torpedo—currently being developed— is allegedly equipped with a cobalt warhead. Information about the weapon was ostensibly leaked by accident, but is suspected to have been deliberately released by the Russian government, so should be viewed with some skepticism (BBC, 2015).

33 It is sometimes said that the burning of the oil wells in Kuwait refuted nuclear winter. But this isn't right. Carl Sagan thought the burning of the oil wells would cause detectable global cooling because the soot would reach the stratosphere. But the oil-well fires were too small to loft it high enough. This puts a small amount of pressure on the part of the model about how high soot from firestorms would be lofted, but doesn't affect anything that comes after that. There are examples of forest fires elevating smoke as high as nine kilometers (Toon et al., 2007).

34 Robock, Oman & Stenchikov (2007).

35 Though there wouldn't be enough time for great ice sheets to build up over Europe and North America. The Last Glacial Maximum saw global mean temperatures around 6°C cooler than pre-industrial levels (Schneider von Deimling et al., 2006).

36 Cropper & Harwell (1986); Helfand (2013); Xia et al. (2015).
37 Baum et al. (2015); Denkenberger & Pearce (2016).
38 While Sagan (1983) and Ehrlich et al. (1983), who previously worked on nuclear winter, did suggest extinction was possible, those in the field now do not.

   Luke Oman (Oman & Shulman, 2012): "The probability I would estimate for the global human population of zero resulting from the 150 Tg of black carbon scenario in our 2007 paper would be in the range of one in 10,000 to one in 100,000. I tried to base this estimate on the closest rapid climate change impact analogue that I know of, the Toba supervolcanic eruption approximately 70,000 years ago. There is some suggestion that around the time of Toba there was a population bottleneck in which the global population was severely reduced. Climate anomalies could be similar in magnitude and duration. Biggest population impacts would likely be Northern Hemisphere interior continental regions with relatively smaller impacts possible over Southern Hemisphere island nations like New Zealand . . . I don't know offhand anyone that would estimate higher but I am sure there might be people who would. [I asked two colleagues] who did respond back to me, saying in general terms 'very close to 0' and 'very low probability'.'"

   Richard Turco (Browne, 1990): "my personal opinion is that the human race wouldn't become extinct, but civilization as we know it certainly would."

   Alan Robock (Conn, Toon & Robock, 2016): "Carl [Sagan] used to talk about extinction of the human species, but I think that was an exaggeration. It's hard to think of a scenario that would produce that. If you live in the Southern Hemisphere, it's a nuclear free zone, so there wouldn't be any bombs dropped there presumably. If you lived in New Zealand and there wasn't that much temperature change because you're surrounded by an ocean, there's lots of fish and dead sheep around, then you probably would survive. But you wouldn't have any modern medicine . . . you'd be back to caveman days. You wouldn't have any civilization, so it's a horrible thing to contemplate, but we probably couldn't make ourselves extinct that way."

   Mark Harwell and Christine Harwell (1986): "It seems possible that several hundred millions of humans could die from the direct effects of nuclear war. The indirect effects could result in the loss of one to several billions of humans. How close the latter projection would come to loss of all humans is problematical, but the current best estimation is that this result would not follow from the physical societal perturbations currently projected to occur after a large-scale nuclear war."

39   There would be serious issues with advanced electronic technology as these locations wouldn't always have the factories or knowledge to make replacement parts. But things look a lot better for the thousands of technologies humans invented prior to the last hundred years. For example, I can't see why they would be reduced to a pre-industrial level, nor why they wouldn't be able to eventually recover current technology levels.

40   For example, a recent paper from the US Department of Energy argued that much less soot would reach the upper atmosphere compared with the main nuclear winter models (Reisner et al., 2018).

41   In some cases, additional uncertainty can make things better. In particular, it can increase the amount of regression to the mean (or regression to one's prior). So if the estimated outcome seemed unlikely initially, residual uncertainty provides a reason to fall back toward this initial guess. But in this case I don't see any good reasons to assign substantially greater prior probability to a small amount of cooling rather than a large amount, or to a small famine rather than a large one. Moreover, if you count existential catastrophe as much worse than the deaths alone and think that the median case is very unlikely to cause this, then uncertainty makes things a lot worse.

42   Adapted from Kristensen & Korda (2019d). Total yield from author's calculations, using data from Kristensen & Korda (2018, 2019a–e), Kristensen & Norris (2018), Kristensen, Norris & Diamond (2018).

43   Presumably the risk of accidental war is also substantially lower than during the Cold War—as the probability of deliberate war goes down, the probability of interpreting a false alarm as a deliberate strike should also go down, at least insofar as there are humans in the loop. This fits with the track record of so many serious false alarms occurring during times of extreme tension, such as the Cuban Missile Crisis.

44 Both the 70,000 and 14,000 figures include retired warheads. There are around 9,000 "active" warheads today (Kristensen & Korda, 2019d).

45 Robock et al. (2007). Modeling by Reisner et al. (2018), mentioned in note 40, finds a much smaller effect from a similar exchange.

46 The collapse of the Intermediate-Range Nuclear Forces (INF) treaty, which saw the US and Soviet Union agree to eliminate short- and medium-range land-based missiles, is particularly concerning.

Russian President Vladimir Putin's 2018 speech to the Federal Assembly painted a worrying picture of mistrust between the US and Russia, and the ongoing efforts to modernize and strengthen Russia's nuclear capacity (Putin, 2018).

47 Horowitz (2018).

48 While the greenhouse effect is real, it turned out not to be the reason garden greenhouses work. Most of the warming in a greenhouse is actually due to the fact that the glass physically traps the warm daytime air, preventing it from floating away at night via convection. Greenhouses made of substances that are transparent to both visible and infrared light still work, while those with a small hole at the top to let the warm air out don't.

49 This is why I don't consider climate change to be the first anthropogenic risk. While the mechanism of CO_2 production from burning fossil fuels pre-dates nuclear weapons, emissions have only recently become high enough to start to pose a threat to humanity.

Between 1751 and 1980 cumulative global carbon emissions from fossil fuels were around 160 Gt, compared with over 260 Gt from 1981 to 2017 (Ritchie & Roser, 2019).

50 Pre-industrial figure from Lindsey (2018); 2019 figure from NOAA (2019).

51 Allen et al. (2018), p. 59. This compares the period 1850–1900 with a 30-year period centered on 2017, assuming the recent rate of warming continues.

52 From 1880 to 2015 (CSIRO, 2015, LSA, 2014). The one standard deviation confidence interval is 19 cm to 26 cm.

53 From 1750 to 2011 (IPCC, 2014, p. 4).

54 Also known as a positive feedback. Unfortunately this causes some confusion as positive climate feedbacks are bad and negative feedbacks are good. I shall thus use the clearer terms "amplifying feedbacks" and "stabilizing feedbacks" instead.

55 To see how this is possible, suppose that the background sound starts at a level of 100 W/m^2 and that the contribution from the speaker is 10%. In that case the first amplification adds 10 W/m^2 to the sound level near the microphone. When this additional sound is amplified, it adds 1 W/m^2, then this adds 0.1 W/m^2, and so forth. Even though sound continually creates more sound, the total effect would be modest, summing to 111.11 . . . W/m^2. If the speaker's volume was turned up (or the microphone brought closer) such that the speaker added 100% (or more) to what was there already, the sum would diverge (100 + 100 + 100 + . . .) and the sound would quickly grow louder until it hit the physical limits of what the microphone can register or what the speaker can produce.

56 Gordon et al. (2013) find an amplifying effect of 2.2 W/m^2/K in their observation window of 2002 to 2009, and estimate the longterm feedback strength between 1.9 and 2.8 W/m^2/K.

57 The greenhouse effect makes Venus far hotter than Mercury despite being almost twice as far from the Sun. We will return to the longterm fate of the Earth in Chapter 8.

58 Goldblatt et al. (2013) find no runaway greenhouse effect with atmospheric concentrations of 5,000 ppm CO_2. Tokarska et al. (2016) find that the burning of 5,000 Gt C, a low estimate of the total fossil fuel reserves, results in atmospheric concentrations just under 2,000 ppm CO_2, suggesting that even if we burned all the fossil fuels, we would not trigger a runaway greenhouse effect.

59 Both moist and runaway greenhouse effects can be understood in terms of the equilibrium on Earth, between incoming solar radiation and outgoing radiation in heat and reflected light. In our current stable regime, increases in surface temperature are matched by increases in the radiation escaping Earth, keeping our climate relatively stable. But there are limits to the amount of radiation that can escape the atmosphere, which are determined, in part, by its water vapor content.

In a *runaway greenhouse*, the Earth's temperature exceeds one of these limits, beyond which its surface and atmosphere can warm, but no more thermal radiation can escape. This results in runaway warming, with the Earth's surface warming until it reaches a new equilibrium, hundreds of degrees warmer, by which point the oceans have boiled off entirely. A *moist greenhouse* is a stable intermediate state, much warmer than our own, and with much more water vapor in the atmosphere. Over geological timescales, a *moist greenhouse* will also result in the complete loss of Earth's water, due to vapor loss from the upper atmosphere into space.

60   This required a very large amount of greenhouse gas to trigger: about 1,550 ppm of carbon dioxide. This is higher than the amount of carbon dioxide in the atmosphere by 2100 in the IPCC's most pessimistic scenario (Collins et al., 2013, p. 1096). When the simplifications are accounted for, it may require much more than this, or be completely impossible without additional solar radiation (Popp, Schmidt & Marotzke, 2016). The model did not produce a useful estimate of the time frame for this warming (due to its simplifications), but the author suggests it would probably take many thousands of years, which might provide time for mitigation (Popp, personal communication).

61   The planet was modeled as entirely ocean, this ocean was only 50 meters deep, and there were no seasons. The paper's authors are well aware that these simplifications mean these results may not apply to the actual Earth, and do not claim otherwise.

62   McInerney & Wing (2011).

63   The *permafrost region* occupies 23 million square kilometers—24% of the land area of the Northern Hemisphere—but the extent of actual permafrost is estimated to cover 12 to 17 million square kilometers (Zhang et al., 2000).

64   There is an estimated 1,672 Gt C in Arctic permafrost (Tarnocai et al., 2009). Emissions from 1750 to 2017 are estimated at 660 ± 95 Gt C (Le Quéré et al., 2018).

65   The IPCC says: "Overall, there is *high confidence* that reductions in permafrost extent due to warming will cause thawing of some currently frozen carbon. However, there is *low confidence* on the magnitude of carbon losses through CO_2 and CH_4 emissions to the atmosphere" (Ciais et al., 2013, p. 526).

66   The estimate is 0.29 ± 0.21°C (Schaefer et al., 2014).

67   1,500 to 7,000 Gt C (Ciais et al., 2013, p. 473).

68   The IPCC says it is "very unlikely that methane from clathrates will undergo catastrophic release (high confidence)" (Collins et al., 2013, p. 1,115). This sounds reassuring, but in the official language of the IPCC, "very unlikely" translates into a 1% to 10% chance,

which then sounds extremely alarming. I don't know what to make of this as the context suggests it was meant to reassure.

69 These are cumulative emissions from 2012–2100 on the RCP 6.0 and RCP 8.5 pathways, consistent with "baseline scenarios" without additional efforts to constrain emissions. Emissions compatible with the Paris Agreement, which commits countries to keep warming below 2°C, are much lower. The IPCC (2014, p. 27) estimates that 2018–2100 emissions must be kept below ~340 Gt C for a 66% chance of keeping warming below 2°C.

70 Assuming that the emission rate continues to grow at 3% per year (Pierrehumbert, 2013).

71 The more recent estimates are toward the upper end of this range. This includes fuel which it is not currently economical to recover, as well as undiscovered fuel. Of course it is possible that even more than this could be found, extracted and burned. Over time, more and more types of fossil fuel deposit have become economically viable (witness the rise of fracking). While new types of deposit may become cheaper by historical standards, solar power is also becoming cheaper at a very fast rate and is already competitive on price with fossil fuels in some places. I therefore doubt that new types of deposit will become economically viable, when solar energy is considered as an alternative. Global reserves—known, economically viable deposits—contain ~1,000–2,000 Gt C (Bruckner et al., 2014, p. 525).

72 Tokarska et al. (2016), p. 852. The few existing studies of the consequences of burning all the fossil fuels use the lower bound estimate of 5,000 Gt C. Research into even more extreme scenarios, where we burned 10,000 Gt C or more, would be valuable.

73 It is very difficult to estimate the probability that emissions will exceed a given amount of carbon. The IPCC doesn't attempt to do so at all. It prefers to treat the pathways as a menu of policy options: things you choose from, not things that happen to you. There is value in this approach, but it would also be very useful to have some idea of the likelihood of different pathways—especially as there is no top-level agent who can actually make a choice from this menu.

74 Bar-On, Phillips & Milo (2018). This is overwhelmingly in plants and bacteria, which together contain 96% of biomass carbon.

An estimated further 1,200 Gt C is in dead biomass, usually called necromass (Kondratyev, Krapivin & Varotsos, 2003, p. 88). This is organic matter in soils and can also be emitted, primarily through deforestation and forest fires. Peat (carbon-dense soil used as fuel) is an example of necromass.

75 From a combination of agriculture and industry. It is important to note that not all of this has stayed in the atmosphere.

76 There are actually several measures of climate sensitivity; this one is called the Equilibrium Climate Sensitivity. It is technically a measure of warming resulting from a given amount of "radiative forcing," which includes the effects of greenhouse gases as well as other changes to the Earth that move the balance between how much energy is received in sunlight and how much is radiated back out. The official unit for radiative forcing is watts per square meter, but it is commonly understood in terms of the degrees of warming produced by a doubling of atmospheric carbon dioxide.

77 Beade et al. (2001), p. 93.

78 In the language of IPCC, "likely" means that there is at least a two-thirds chance the true sensitivity lies in this range (IPCC, 2014, p. 16). For uncertainty about cloud feedbacks see Stevens & Bony (2013).

79 Ciais et al. (2013), p. 526.

80 Emissions from 1750 to 2017 are estimated at 660 ± 95 Gt C. Of this, ~430 Gt C is from fossil fuel and industry, and ~235 Gt C is from land-use change (Le Quéré et al., 2018).

81 Their term "likely" officially means 66% to 100% chance, though one would expect them to have used "very likely" if they thought it was greater than 90%. In keeping with the roughness of the confidence level for this interval, the IPCC makes it clear that these probabilities are not based on statistical measures of the scientific uncertainty, but represent expert judgment (Cubasch et al., 2013, pp. 138–42). When looking in more detail, we can see that the literature contains some climate models with very broad probability distributions over the climate sensitivity, allowing non-trivial chance of a sensitivity greater than 6°C or even 10°C. However, the fat right-hand tail of these distributions is very dependent on the choice of prior (Annan & Hargreaves, 2011). This means that the data doesn't rule out high sensitivities, but doesn't support them

either. It is thus hard to say anything precise about the chance that climate sensitivity exceeds 4.5°C, or about it exceeding higher thresholds such as 6°C.

See Weitzman (2009) for one attempt at accounting for some of this uncertainty, and its implications for policy-making. He estimates a 5% chance of "generalized climate sensitivity" (accounting for a wider range of feedback mechanisms) exceeding 10°C warming within two centuries, and a 1% chance of it exceeding 20°C, with one doubling of emissions.

82 On top of this, the usefulness of this logarithmic relationship itself has also been questioned. Some scientists have found that when climate feedbacks and the changing properties of carbon sinks are taken into account, their models produce a nearly linear relationship between cumulative emissions (in Gt C) and warming. This gives similar predictions for medium emissions scenarios, but suggests much more warming if the emissions are high. For example, Tokarska et al., 2006, p. 853.

83 In July 1979—the very month I was born (Charney et al., 1979).

84 Rogelj et al. (2016).

85 Tai, Martin & Heald (2014) find that under the IPCC's most pessimistic scenario, global food production would decrease by 16% by 2050 relative to 2000. But this takes into account neither adaptation nor the impact of carbon dioxide on crop yields, both of which are expected to have significant, albeit uncertain, offsetting effects. A recent meta-analysis found that crop-level adaptations alone could increase yields by 7–15% (Challinor et al., 2014).

Such a reduction in food supply would have disastrous consequences for millions of people, but would pose little risk to civilization.

86 IPCC (2014), pp. 14–15.

87 We don't see such biodiversity loss in the 12°C warmer climate of the early Eocene, nor the rapid global change of the PETM, nor in rapid regional changes of climate. Willis et al. (2010) state: "We argue that although the underlying mechanisms responsible for these past changes in climate were very different (i.e. natural processes rather than anthropogenic), the rates and magnitude of climate change are similar to those predicted for the future and therefore potentially relevant to understanding future

biotic response. What emerges from these past records is evidence for rapid community turnover, migrations, development of novel ecosystems and thresholds from one stable ecosystem state to another, but there is very little evidence for broad-scale extinctions due to a warming world."

There are similar conclusions in Botkin et al. (2007), Dawson et al. (2011), Hof et al. (2011) and Willis & MacDonald (2011). The best evidence of warming causing extinction may be from the end-Permian mass extinction, which may have been associated with large-scale warming (see note 91 to this chapter).

88   The measure is known as the "wet-bulb temperature" and may become lethal at around 95°F (Sherwood & Huber, 2010).

89   Author's calculation based on the information in Sherwood & Huber (2010).

90   Indeed the extinction effects of the PETM seem surprisingly mild. For example, McInerney & Wing (2011) state: "[in the PETM] Terrestrial and marine organisms experienced large shifts in geographic ranges, rapid evolution, and changes in trophic ecology, but few groups suffered major extinctions with the exception of benthic foraminifera [a type of micro-organism]."

91   A recent paper suggests that ocean temperatures may have risen by as much as 8°C during the end-Permian extinction, possibly driven by a huge injection of atmospheric CO_2 (Cui & Kump, 2015). The precise levels of warming and CO_2 concentration remain uncertain, due to relatively sparse geological evidence over this period. While this is just one of many putative causes for the end-Permian extinction, these uncertainties, and our inability to rule out that the biggest mass extinction was caused by rapid warming, are ultimately bad news.

92   Using geoengineering as a last resort could lower overall existential risk even if the technique is *more* risky than climate change itself. This is because we could adopt the strategy of only deploying it in the unlikely case where climate change is much worse than currently expected, giving us a second roll of the dice.

Here is a simplified numerical example. Suppose climate change has a 0.1% chance of being extremely severe, in which case it has a 50% chance of directly causing our extinction, for an overall extinction risk of 0.05%. And suppose that geoengineering fixes the climate, but produces its own 1% risk of extinction. Starting geoengineering now would be a bad idea, since its 1% risk is higher than the overall 0.05% risk. But if we only commence geoengineering if climate change turns out to be extremely severe, then geoengineering will reduce the overall risk: for we only face its 1% risk of extinction in cases where we were otherwise facing a 50% chance. This conditional geoengineering strategy would thus lower overall extinction risk from 0.05% to 0.001%. This can happen in more realistic models too. The key is waiting for a situation when the risk of using geoengineering is appreciably lower than the risk of not using it. A similar strategy may be applicable for other kinds of existential risk too.

93 Ehrlich (1969).

94 From a speech in 1969, quoted in Mann (2018).

95 16.6 million people in the 1960s, 3.4 million in the 1970s, and an average of ~1.5 million per decade since then (Hasell & Roser, 2019). Note that these are only the deaths from identifiable famines and are not complete accounts of all deaths related to food scarcity.

96 These improvements in productivity came with significant environmental costs.

97 He is often credited with saving roughly a billion lives. There are many challenges with making such an estimate, including the fact that it is very hard to estimate how many lives the green revolution actually saved, that many other people were essential to the green revolution, and that if he hadn't produced these varieties someone else may well have done so. Perhaps the best way to think of it is simply that he played a central role in one of the greatest humanitarian success stories of the twentieth century. But I think there is something to the attempts to quantify the impact, even if the result is only very rough, as it helps us better understand the scale of what an individual can achieve for the world. In the case of Borlaug, my rough guess is that the real number is in the tens to hundreds of millions—still a fantastic achievement, and possibly more than anyone else in human history. A great resource on individuals whose work saved millions of lives is *Scientists Greater than Einstein* (Woodward, Shurkin & Gordon, 2009) and its website www.scienceheroes.com, which estimates that Borlaug saved about 260 million lives.

98 UN DESA (2019). Much of the remaining growth is thus from demographic inertia (the disproportionate fraction of people of child-bearing age due to higher past fertility) rather than because people are having many children.

99 Adapted from Roser, Ritchie & Ortiz-Ospina (2019).

100 Wise (2013); Gietel-Basten (2016); Bricker & Ibitson (2019).

101 It is not clear that further increases in power and prosperity will continue to mean more (adverse) impact on the environment. For one thing, humans value a flourishing environment so they use some of their new-found wealth and power to heal it and to switch their consumption to more expensive but less harmful products. This has led to a theory of the *environmental Kuznets curve*, which posits that adverse environmental impacts increase with per capita income during industrialization, but eventually start to fall back down as societies become richer still. There is some evidence to support this, but it is mixed. The theory probably applies to some types of environmental damage but not others, and offers no guarantees when the turning point will come. There is also the issue that the poorer countries are still near the start of their curves, so things might get worse before getting better, regardless. See Stern (2004).

It is often suggested that economic growth will have to stop (or consumption plateau) if we are to avoid destruction of our finite planet. But this is not as obvious as it first seems. The way economists define consumption and growth includes goods and services such as education, software, art, research and medicine, where additional value can be created without concomitant environmental costs. We could also have growth in green technologies that displace damaging consumption. While environmentally costly consumption would need to plateau, there is nothing in theory preventing us from focusing on growth in these other areas, creating a world with beauty, knowledge and health that far surpass what we have today, while *reducing* our environmental impact. This seems to me to be a superior goal to that of limiting all growth.

102 Fossil fuels (Roberts, 2004); phosphorous (Cordell, Drangert & White, 2009); topsoil (Arsenault, 2014); fresh water (Gleick & Palaniappan, 2010); metals (Desjardins, 2014).

103 Accessible fresh water is estimated as ~2% of the world's groundwater (Boberg, 2005).

104 As these will then be in people's narrow self-interest. There was a famous bet between the business professor Julian Simon and Paul Ehrlich about this, operationalized in terms of whether a representative basket of raw materials would increase in price (representing scarcity) or decrease (representing abundance) over time. Simon won the bet, though this was quite dependent on the exact choices of resource and time period, so little should be read into it.

105 Kolbert (2014); Ceballos et al. (2015).

106 Neither set of data is representative of all species: the fossil record is biased toward species that fossilize easily, while the modern statistics are biased toward species of interest and species that we already have reason to think might be under threat. There are also special statistical issues to do with the fact that the modern record samples extinction rates over very short time periods, where we should expect much more natural variability than over the million-year periods of the fossil record (Barnosky et al., 2011, pp. 51–2).

107 Ceballos et al. (2015).

108 Barnosky et al. (2011), p. 54. If all currently threatened species went extinct, the fraction would rise to about 30%. But it is unclear how to interpret this. It shows how we might be able to get roughly halfway to the mass extinction level, but it is not at all clear that such species *will* go extinct or that extinction would climb the rest of the way to 75%.

109 While one can never know for certain everything someone said or did not say, there is no reason to believe he ever made any pronouncements on bees. See O'Toole (2013).

110 Aizen et al. (2009).

5 FUTURE RISKS

1 Churchill (1946).

2 Rutherford's comments were made on September 11, 1933 (Kaempffert, 1933). His prediction was in fact partly self-defeating, as its confident pessimism grated on Szilard, inspiring him to search for a way to achieve what was said to be impossible

(Szilard & Feld, 1972, p. 529). There is some debate over the exact timing of Szilard's discovery and exactly how much of the puzzle he had solved (Wellerstein, 2014). Rutherford remained skeptical of atomic power until his death in 1937. There is a fascinating possibility that he was not wrong, but deliberately obscuring what he saw as a potential weapon of mass destruction (Jenkin, 2011). But the point would still stand that the confident public assertions of the leading authorities were not to be trusted.

This conversation with Fermi was in 1939, just after nuclear fission in uranium had been discovered. Fermi was asked to clarify the "remote possibility" and ventured "ten percent." Isidor Rabi, who was also present, replied, "Ten percent is not a remote possibility if it means that we may die of it. If I have pneumonia and the doctor tells me that there is a remote possibility that I might die, and it's ten percent, I get excited about it" (Rhodes, 1986, p. 280).

Wilbur Wright explained to the Aéro-club de France in 1908: "Scarcely ten years ago, all hope of flying had almost been abandoned; even the most convinced had become doubtful, and I confess that in 1901 I said to my brother Orville that men would not fly for 50 years. Two years later, we ourselves were making flight" (Holmes, 2008, p. 91).

3   It is a shame that scientists ruined their reputation for this. One can imagine a world in which scientists (at least at the very top) were more circumspect and only baldly asserted that something was impossible when it really was. When it would merely require a change of paradigm for the thing to be true—or when it would be the biggest surprise of the decade—they could simply say that. Having such a reputation for well-calibrated forecasts would have been a real asset for the scientific community, as well as being valuable for policymakers and the community at large.

But no matter how high a bar you draw for scientific eminence or credentials particularly related to the very claim in question, there are people who made claims of certainty or ridicule, yet turned out quite wrong.

4   The qualifier "on humans" is necessary. The track record of technological progress and the environment is at best mixed, with many technologies inflicting severe harms. Sometimes cleaner technologies have been able to displace the harmful ones, and I believe

this trend will continue, making continued technological progress ultimately positive for the environment. But the evidence for this is mixed and time may prove me wrong. See Stern (2004) for a discussion of this.

5   As the Swedish mathematician, Olle Häggström, puts it in his excellent treatise on future technology (Häggström, 2016): "the currently dominant attitude towards scientific and technological advances is tantamount to running blindfold and at full speed into a minefield." While we don't know exactly how many mines are in the field, or whether we might survive treading on one, running through without looking is not the optimal policy. One disanalogy is that while there are few upsides to running into a minefield, technological and scientific progress holds enormous potential benefits. Perhaps I would alter the image to humanity running blindfolded through a minefield, in order to reach a safer and more desirable location.

6   Christakos et al. (2005), p. 107.

7   Christakos et al. (2005), pp. 108–9. While there are several diseases that could fit with the symptoms, there is substantial evidence that it was the bacterium *Yersinia pestis*, carried in the fleas of black rats. Most damningly, its DNA has been recovered from the bones of those who died in the Black Death (Haensch et al., 2010).

8   The mortality rate of the plague varied with the region and demographics. This makes it extremely difficult to extrapolate out the death toll from the limited historical data. Considering death tolls in England, Ziegler gives a credible range of 23–45%, and suggests that one-third is a reasonable estimate, which can be extended to Europe as a whole (Ziegler, 1969). More recently, Benedictow (2004) gave an estimate of 60%—much higher than traditional estimates and meeting with skepticism from many of his colleagues. My guess is that such a high toll is unlikely, but cannot yet be ruled out. From an estimated historical population for Europe at the time of 88 million, Ziegler's 23–45% range corresponds to 20–40 million and Benedictow's 60% corresponds to 53 million European deaths.

One often sees much higher death tolls for the Black Death in popular articles, including a startling figure of 200 million—far in excess of the 80 million people living in Europe at the time. Luke

Muehlhauser (2017) heroically tracked down the source of this statistic to a popular 1988 article in *National Geographic* (Duplaix, 1988), which was clearly not referring to the Black Death in particular, but was an attempt at a total figure for pandemics of the plague during the Middle Ages. It wasn't until the sixteenth century that the European population recovered to where it was before the Black Death (Livi-Bacci, 2017, p. 25).

9   This estimate is based largely on Muehlhauser (2017). My lower bound assumes 25% mortality in Europe, on a starting population of 88 million; 25% mortality in the Middle East, on a starting population of 5.4 million in Egypt and Syria, and 2 million elsewhere in the region; and no mortality in Asia, for a total of 24 million deaths. My upper bound assumes 50% mortality in Europe, on a starting population of 88 million; 25% mortality in the Middle East on a higher starting population of 9 million in Egypt and Syria, and 6 million elsewhere in the region; and 15 million deaths in China, for a total of 63 million deaths. World population in 1340 is taken as 442 million in both cases (Livi-Bacci, 2017, p. 25), giving global mortality estimates of 5.4% and 14.2%.

This is considerably more than some of the worst catastrophes in recent history, in terms of proportional death tolls: First World War (0.8%); Second World War (2.9%); 1918 influenza (3–6%). See Muehlhauser (2017) for an extensive discussion.

10 Early suggestions of extinction-level pandemics appear in Mary Shelley's novel *The Last Man* (1826) and H. G. Wells' (non-fiction) essay "The Extinction of Man" (1894). As Wells put it: "for all we know even now we may be quite unwittingly evolving some new and more terrible plague — a plague that will not take ten or twenty or thirty per cent, as plagues have done in the past, but the entire hundred."

Joshua Lederberg's article "Biological Warfare and the Extinction of Man" (1969) is the first I know of to seriously discuss the possibility of human extinction from engineered pathogens.

11 The Plague of Justinian may have altered the course of history by sending the Byzantine Empire into decline and allowing the ascent of Islam in the region.

In the absence of estimates for global death toll in the scholarship, Muehlhauser (2017) consulted an expert who suggested applying the 20% mortality rate in Constantinople (Stathakopoulos, 2004) to the population of the empire of 28 million (Stathakopoulos, 2008), for a total death toll of roughly 5.6 million. World population in 451 CE is estimated at 210 million (Roser, Ritchie & Ortiz-Ospina, 2019).

As with the Black Death, the Plague of Justinian reappeared several times over the following centuries. It took an even greater human toll over such a time frame, but these aggregate numbers don't really represent a single catastrophe and cannot be used to determine the fraction of the world's people who were killed.

12 See Nunn & Qian (2010) for a summary of estimates. Snow & Lanphear (1988) give estimates of mortality for various tribes in the north-eastern US ranging from 67 to 95%.

The island of Hispaniola provides a striking example of the difficulties in determining death toll. While estimates of the local population in the decades *after* colonisation are bounded in the tens of thousands, estimates of the 1492 population range from 60,000 to 8 million (Cook, 1998).

13 For this upper bound, I use the estimate of 60.5 million for the pre-Columbian population of the Americas from Koch et al. (2019), who propose 90% mortality over the next century. I take an estimate of rest-of-world population as 419 million, from Livi-Bacci (2017). Together this gives 54.5 million deaths on a world population of 479.5 million, or 11%, which I round to 10%.

This isn't strictly comparable with the other global mortality estimates in this section as it is a population *reduction*, not a count of deaths. It may undercount the total deaths (since new people were being born) or it may overcount them if it is partly a result of lowered birth rate rather than increased death rate. There is also a large mismatch in timespans. The Columbian exchange figures are estimated over a 100-year period, which is vastly longer than that of the Black Death, Plague of Justinian or 1918 flu.

Even with new immigrants arriving from the rest of the world, it took about three and a half centuries for the population of the Americas to recover to its pre-Columbian levels (1492–1840) (Roser, Ritchie & Ortiz-Ospina, 2019).

14 Such global reach was made possible by the recent increases in travel speed of motorized transport, as well as the increased use of such transport for trade and troop movements. Estimates of the death toll are from Taubenberger & Morens (2006).

15   In addition to this historical evidence, there are some deeper biological observations and theories suggesting that pathogens are unlikely to lead to the extinction of their hosts. These include the empirical anti-correlation between infectiousness and lethality, the extreme rarity of diseases that kill more than 75% of those infected, the observed tendency of pandemics to become less virulent as they progress and the theory of optimal virulence. However, there is no watertight case against pathogens leading to the extinction of their hosts.

16   This is, of course, a near impossible claim to assess. The outbreak is estimated to have killed over 100,000 troops in the final stages of the war, so may have had some influence on the outcome (Wever & van Bergen, 2014). One could also point to the far-reaching impacts of single cases: US President Woodrow Wilson fought an infection in the months leading up to the 1919 Peace Conference, which may have played a role in his failure to secure his vision for peace (Honigsbaum, 2018).

17   At the time of writing, the world population is estimated to be 7.7 billion (UN DESA, 2019).

     Estimates of world population immediately before the Agricultural Revolution are generally in the order of several million. Weeks (2015) gives a figure of 4 million. Coale (1974) and Durand (1977) put it at 5–10 million. Livi-Bacci (2017, p. 26) suggests population before 35,000 BCE was no more than several hundred thousand, growing very slowly to several million around the dawn of agriculture. Altogether, for most of human history, our population was 1,000–10,000 times smaller than it is today.

18   HIV (Keele, 2006); Ebola (Leroy et al., 2005); SARS (Cyranoski, 2017); influenza (Ma, Kahn & Richt, 2008). H5N1 flu, the high-mortality strain known as "bird flu," originated in commercial poultry populations in Asia (Sims et al., 2005).

19   Jones et al. (2008). However, it is hard to be sure, as there are rival explanations for the observed increases, such as our increasing ability to detect and classify pathogens.

20   This may initially seem a profound change, but it probably doesn't weigh too heavily. Much of the history of our species (and related species) did not have the benefit of isolated populations anyway, yet these unified populations still had very low extinction rates.

21 Though of course a few scattered populations surviving the initial
    devastation would not guarantee humanity ultimately survives. We
    would still need a minimal viable population to repopulate our
    species and to successfully restore civilization. We would also be
    exceptionally vulnerable to other risks during our reduced state.

22 CRISPR-Cas9 is a tool enabling researchers to edit genomes by
    removing, adding and changing portions of the DNA sequence. It
    was a significant breakthrough, allowing for much easier, cheaper
    and more accurate gene editing than was previously available.

    A gene drive is a technique for propagating particular genes
    within a population, by increasing the probability that a given
    trait is inherited to over 50%. This is an incredibly powerful
    tool, allowing researchers to pursue genetic modification on a
    population level.

23 Cost per genome was $9 million in early 2007 (Wetterstrand,
    2019). At the time of writing, Dante Labs offers whole genome
    sequencing for €599 (~$670) (Dante Labs, 2019).

    One study finds publications in synthetic biology increasing by
    660% when comparing 2012–2017 to 2000–2006 (Shapira &
    Kwon, 2018). VC funding for biotechnology increased from ~$3
    billion in 2012 to ~$7 billion in 2016 (Lightbown, 2017).

24 Herfst et al. (2012).

25 Taubenberger & Morens (2006) estimate the mortality rate for the
    1918 flu at upward of 2.5%.

26 The experiment by Yoshihiro Kawaoka also involved producing a
    mammal-to-mammal transmissible strain of H5N1 using ferrets,
    though Kawaoka's experiment started with a hybrid of H5N1 and
    H1N1 viruses. He was initially asked to remove some details by
    the US National Science Advisory Board for Biosecurity, but his
    full paper ended up published in *Nature* (Imai et al., 2012; Butler
    & Ledford, 2012).

27 This lack of transparency seems to be driven by fear of embar-
    rassment, which would clearly not be a sufficient reason for stif-
    ling this critical information. Stakeholders require these rates to
    assess whether labs are living up to their claimed standards and
    how much risk they are posing to the public. Getting BSL-3 and
    BSL-4 labs to provide this information (whether by appealing to

their conscience or through regulation) would seem to be a clear win for biosecurity.

28 One BSL-4 lab, the Galveston National Laboratory, must be commended for already voluntarily reporting its incidents (GNL, 2019). Others need to follow this lead: either voluntarily, through self-regulation or through government regulation.

A promising avenue is to follow the Federal Aviation Administration's approach where after each plane crash it looks for lessons from what went wrong and ways that practices could be improved.

29 And there are many other worrying examples too. For instance in 2014, GlaxoSmithKline accidentally released 45 liters of concentrated polio virus into a river in Belgium (ECDC, 2014). In 2004, SARS escaped from the National Institute of Virology in Beijing. They didn't realize some of the workers had been infected until a worker's mother came down with it too. And in 2005 at the University of Medicine and Dentistry in New Jersey, three mice infected with bubonic plague went missing from the lab and were never found (US Department of Homeland Security, 2008).

30 Details from Anderson (2008) and Spratt (2007). The maximum fine for such a breach was £5,000, and it is not clear whether it was even levied. Foot-and-mouth virus is a SAPO Category 4 pathogen, equivalent to BSL-4 but for animal pathogens.

31 The research of both Fouchier and Kawaoka was conducted in enhanced BSL-3 labs. This is the standard level for non-human-transmissible H5N1 (Chosewood & Wilson, 2009). But because the entire point of the experiment was to make it transmissible for a model animal that stands in for human, some of the experts believe that BSL-4 should have been required (Imperiale & Hanna, 2012). Others disagree, saying that enhanced BSL-3 is still appropriate (García-Sastre, 2012).

32 Trevisanato (2007).

33 While Gabriel de Mussis gave a contemporary account of this taking place during the siege of Caffa, it is probably not a first-hand account and could easily have been an embellishment (Kelly, 2006). Even if true, there may well have been other ways for the Black Death to reach Europe (Wheelis, 2002).

34 Shoham & Wolfson (2004); Zelicoff & Bellomo (2005).

35 Janet Parker, a medical photographer working at the hospital, may have been the last ever death from smallpox. Depressingly, just twelve years earlier, there had been an outbreak from the same building, which saw 73 people infected with a milder strain of the virus. The source was a medical photographer working in the same studio in which Janet Parker was subsequently infected (Shooter et al., 1980).

36 Hilts (1994); Alibek (2008). The cause was remarkably mundane, according to Alibek's account of the incident. A technician had removed a clogged air filter for cleaning. He left a note, but it didn't get entered in the main logbook. So they turned the anthrax drying machines on at the start of the next shift and blew anthrax out over the city for several hours before someone noticed.

In a report on the accident, US microbiologist Raymond Zilinskas (1983) remarked: "No nation would be so stupid as to locate a biological warfare facility within an approachable distance from a major population center."

Note that while extremely lethal, anthrax does not spread from human to human, so there was no pandemic risk. Instead, the example is important as an example of catastrophic safety failure with known lethal agents.

37 Mutze, Cooke & Alexander (1998); Fenner & Fantini (1999).

38 Sosin (2015). There were no known infections.

39 The entire episode is extremely well documented, giving an idea of the level of acceptance and motivation behind the attack. Colonel Bouquet, who was to take charge of the fort, responded to Amherst's letter: "I will try to inocculate [sic] the Indians by means of Blankets that may fall in their hands, taking care however not to get the disease myself." Amherst wrote back, "You will Do well to try to Innoculate [sic] the Indians by means of Blankets, as well as to try Every other method that can serve to Extirpate this Execrable Race."

Even before Amherst's first request, Captain William Trent had documented "[We] gave them two Blankets and an Handkerchief out of the Small Pox Hospital. I hope it will have the desired effect." Military records confirm that these were "taken from people in the Hospital to Convey the Smallpox to the Indians." The fort commander reimbursed them for the "sundries got to replace in kind those which were taken from people in the hospital to convey smallpox to the Indians" (D'Errico, 2001).

40 The confirmed cases are Canada (1940–58), Egypt (1960s–?), France (1915–66?), Germany (1915–18), Iraq (1974–91), Israel (1948–?), Italy (1934–40), Japan (1934–45), Poland (?), Rhodesia (1977), South Africa (1981–93), Soviet Union (1928–91), Syria (1970s?–?), United Kingdom (1940–57), United States (1941–71) (Carus, 2017).

41 Leitenberg (2001), Cook & Woolf (2002). A great many details about the program were published by the defector Ken Alibek in his book *Biohazard* (2008). However, it is not clear how reliable his account is, so I have only included details that have been independently substantiated.

42 The CDC (Centers for Disease Control and Prevention) notes 29 deaths and 31 injuries from criminal biological attacks between 1960 and 1999 (Tucker, 1999). During the Second World War 200,000 Chinese civilians are estimated to have been killed through a combination of biological and chemical attacks, perpetrated by the Japanese army. Some of these attacks were primitive, such as the release of thousands of plague-ridden rats, and it remains unclear how many of these deaths are attributable to what we would now consider biological weapons (Harris, 2002). It has also been suggested that the Rhodesian government used biological warfare against its own population in the late 1970s (Wilson et al., 2016).

43 While this must surely be a strike against bioweapons posing a large existential risk, it is unclear how strong the evidence really is. Pandemic deaths are dominated by extremely rare outlier events, which occur less than once a century. So a century of bioweapon development without major catastrophe provides little statistical evidence. To really get all we can out of the raw data, one would want to model the underlying distributions and see whether the biowarfare and bioterror distributions have heavier tails than that of natural pandemics.

44 Technical mastery of the techniques required is not something that can be learned from academic materials alone. Even experienced scientists can find it very difficult to learn new techniques without in-person training. Successfully operating such a large project in complete secrecy is fraught with difficulties, and is perhaps the

greatest operational barrier. See Danzig et al. (2011) for a discussion of this in relation to the case of Aum Shinrikyo.

45 Acemoglu (2013); RAND (n.d.).

46 In a power law, the probability of an event of size x is proportional to x^a, where a is a parameter lower than -1. The closer a is to -1, the more slowly the probability of extreme events drops off, and the more extreme the statistical behavior.

The power laws I mentioned as having especially heavy tails are those with a between -2 and -1. These distributions are so extreme that they don't even have well-defined means: the probability of larger and larger events drops off so slowly that the sum corresponding to their expected size fails to converge. The value of a for war is estimated to be -1.4 (Cederman, 2003) and -1.8 for terrorism with biological or chemical agents (Clauset & Young, 2005).

There is much debate about whether the distributions of various disasters are *really* power laws. For example, log-normal distributions have right-hand tails that approximate a power law, so could be mistaken for them, but have a lower probability of small events than in a true power law. For our purpose, we don't really need to distinguish between different heavy-tailed distributions. We are really just interested in whether the right-hand tail (the distribution of large events) behaves as a power law ($\sim x^a$), what its exponent is, and over what domain the power law relationship actually holds.

Any actual distribution will only be well fitted by a power law up to some level. Beyond some point other limits (such as the total population who could be affected) will kick in and the real probability will usually be less than that given by the power law. This makes the use of power laws to model the chances of events outside the observed domain quite speculative (though this is less problematic if using it as an upper bound to the true probability). This also implies that the actual distributions probably *do* have means, though these could easily be higher than the mean of the historical record, or higher even than the highest observed event so far.

47 The cost to create the first human genome sequence is estimated at \$0.5–1 billion (~\$0.7–1.4 billion when adjusted for inflation)

(NHGRI, 2018). At the time of writing, Dante Labs offers whole genome sequencing for €599 (see note 23 to this chapter).

48   Carlson (2016).

49   The first gene drives were performed in 2015 (DiCarlo et al., 2015), and one team planned on using these techniques in the 2016 competition (iGEM Minnesota Team, 2016). The landmark paper on gene editing using CRISP-Cas9 was published in August 2012 (Jinek et al., 2012), and several teams used this method in the 2013 competition (iGEM, 2013).

50   Danzig et al. (2011). Eight people were killed, and 200 injured, in the group's first sarin attack in 1994, which targeted judges involved in cases against the group. Soon after, they murdered a suspected police informant using VX nerve agent. The following year, they killed 13 people and injured 6,000 in their Tokyo subway attack.

51   In a letter to Einstein regarding the contents of their Manifesto (dated February 11, 1955) Russell wrote: "although the H-bomb at the moment occupies the centre of attention, it does not exhaust the destructive possibilities of science, and it is probable that the dangers of bacteriological warfare may before long become just as great" (Russell, 2012).

52   From Lederberg's article "Biological Warfare and the Extinction of Man" (1969).

53   For example, Pinker writes "Bioterrorism may be another phantom menace. Biological weapons, renounced in a 1972 international convention by virtually every nation, have played no role in modern warfare. The ban was driven by a widespread revulsion at the very idea, but the world's militaries needed little convincing, because tiny living things make lousy weapons" (Pinker, 2018, p. 306).

54   See note 54 to Chapter 2.

55   Tucker (2001). The Nuclear Non-Proliferation Treaty verifies the compliance through the International Atomic Energy Agency, which has 2,500 staff. The Chemical Weapons Convention verifies compliance through the Organisation for the Prohibition of Chemical Weapons, which has 500 staff.

56   The Soviet Union signed the BWC in 1972 and ratified it in 1975 (Davenport, 2018). Their bioweapons program ran from 1928 to at least 1991 (Carus, 2017).

57 South Africa signed the BWC in 1972 and ratified it in 1975 (Davenport, 2018). Their bioweapons program ran from 1981 to 1993 (Gould & Folb, 2002).

58 Iraq signed the BWC in 1972 and ratified it in 1991 (Davenport, 2018). Their bioweapons program ran from circa 1974 to 1991 (Carus, 2017).

59 In 2018, US National Security Advisor John Bolton said "There are . . . states that are parties to the Biological Weapons Convention that we think are violating it" (Bolton & Azar, 2018).

60 Israel is known to have had a bioweapons program in the past (Carus, 2017), and is one of just ten states that have neither signed nor ratified (182 states have signed, including all other developed nations) (Davenport, 2018).

61 Note that there are other hurdles remaining. It is not easy to create a functioning virus from its DNA alone (though it has been achieved by a small team). And it is currently difficult to replace the DNA in a bacterium. In addition, there are limits to how long a sequence can be synthesized, with the DNA of many organisms being currently out of reach.

62 DiEuliis, Carter & Gronvall (2017); IGSC (2018).

63 A common objection to mandatory screening is that it would allow rivals access to the intellectual property of the DNA sequences being ordered. But there look to be cryptographic solutions to this problem (Esvelt, 2018).

There is a strong track record of such locks being broken when they are used in consumer products, but they may still be able to provide some useful security by requiring the malicious actors to include a computer expert as well as a bio expert. They may also help to "keep honest people honest," by removing the temptation for academic researchers to perform experiments on controlled pathogens.

64 The term was coined by Bostrom (2011b). They are also informally known as "infohazards."

65 See Bostrom, Douglas & Sandberg (2016) for an introduction to the idea, including a formal analysis and some solutions. Lewis (2018) applies the idea to biotechnology information hazards.

66 This situation is exacerbated by additional uncertainty in the size of the benefit or risk, for that creates a wider distribution of

estimates of the net benefit, such that the most optimistic outlier is even further from the center of their peers.

I said that it only takes one overly rosy estimate to release the information, but if the scientist requires a journal to publish the information, then it actually requires two—an author and an editor. This hints at a technique for resolving this problem at the level of journal editors, where there are fewer parties to get on board. One approach, suggested by Lewis (2018), is to have the first journal to reject a paper on safety grounds share their decision with others, to avoid the paper's author shopping around until they find one of the journals whose estimate of the danger was especially optimistic.

Esvelt (2018) suggests encouraging pre-registration of potentially dangerous research, so that open and broad discussions about safety can happen before the dangerous information has been generated.

67 In 1999, Ayman al-Zawahiri (now leader of al-Qaeda) wrote of his plan to start researching chemical and biological weapons: "Despite their extreme danger, we only became aware of them when the enemy drew our attention to them by repeatedly expressing concern that they can be produced simply" (Wright, 2002).

68 The treaty was the Geneva Protocol of 1925, which had a section outlawing first use of bacteriological weapons between its signatory states. The Japanese did not sign it until 1970 but gained information from its existence (Harris, 2002, p. 18).

69 Lewis et al. (2019).

70 For example, I have taken care to use only examples which are sufficiently widely known.

71 McCarthy et al. (1955). AI has some foundations going further back than the Dartmouth conference, but that summer of 1956 is usually considered the beginning of AI as a field of inquiry.

72 This is known as Moravec's Paradox, after AI and robotics pioneer Hans Moravec, who wrote in 1988: "But as the number of demonstrations has mounted, it has become clear that it is comparatively easy to make computers exhibit adult-level performance in solving problems on intelligence tests or playing checkers, and difficult or impossible to give them the skills of a one-year-old when it comes to perception and mobility."

73 Major improvements to the structure include convolutional neural networks (CNNs) and recurrent neural networks (RNNs). Major improvements to the training include adaptions to stochastic gradient descent, such as Adam and Nesterov Momentum. Hardware improvements were driven by the switch from CPUs to GPUs, and now to even more specialist hardware such as TPUs. These successes have all built on each other in a virtuous cycle—now that neural networks are so good, it is worth assembling the large datasets to train them and worth making specialist hardware to run them, which makes them all the better, warranting more and more investment.

74 He et al. (2015).

75 Phillips et al. (2011); Ranjan et al. (2018).

76 Translation (Hassan et al., 2018); generating photos (Karras et al., 2017); voice mimicry (Jia et al., 2018); autonomous driving (Kocić, Jovičić & Drndarević, 2019); stacking Lego blocks (Haarnoja et al., 2018).

77 Bernstein & Roberts (1958); IBM (2011). Over the past few decades, chess programs have gained around 50 Elo points per year, roughly half of which came from algorithmic improvements, and half from hardware gains (Grace, 2013).

78 Silver et al. (2018). One needs to be careful with such numbers to also consider the hardware used. AlphaZero was trained using an enormous amount of computing power (5,000 TPUs), meaning that in this four hours it was able to simulate a vast number of games of chess against other versions of itself, using these to work out how best to play. This is an important caveat in comparing AlphaZero's achievement to other breakthroughs as the software improvements are somewhat smaller than they first look. But I think the actual time taken is still the key figure for the relevance to AI risk, showing how quickly in real time an AI system could get out of control.

79 Strogatz (2018).

80 AlphaZero may have even exceeded the level where Go experts had thought perfect play lies. The conventional wisdom was that the best human players would need a three- or four-stone handicap to win if facing perfect play (Wilcox & Wilcox, 1996). After 30 hours, AlphaZero was more than 700 Elo points above the top

professional. While it is difficult to convert between handicap stones and Elo at these extremely high levels of play, this is in the same ballpark as the predictions for perfect play (Labelle, 2017). It would be fascinating to see a version of AlphaZero play against the best humans with increasing handicaps to see how many stones ahead it really is.

81   Technically Ke Jie was referring to the "Master" version of AlphaGo Zero which preceded AlphaZero (*Wall Street Journal*, 2017).

82   The breakthrough result was the DQN algorithm (Mnih et al., 2015) which successfully married deep learning and reinforcement learning. DQN gave human-level performance on 29 out of 49 Atari games. But it was wasn't fully general: like AlphaZero, it needed a different copy of the network to be trained for each game. Subsequent work has trained a single network that can play all games at human level or above, achieving an average score of 60% human level (Espeholt et al., 2018).

83   Attendance at one of the leading conferences, NeurIPS, increased by a factor of 4.8 between 2012 and 2018. AI VC funding increased by a factor of 4.5 between 2013 and 2018 (Shoham et al., 2018).

84   The survey was given to all researchers who published at two of the top machine-learning conferences in 2015 (NeurIPS and ICML). The data comes from the 352 researchers who responded (Grace et al., 2018).

85   Interestingly there was a large and statistically significant difference between the timelines of researchers from different continents. Researchers from North America thought the chance would reach 50% in 74 years' time, while those from Asia thought it would reach 50% in just 30 years (Europeans were about halfway between).

   Note also that this estimate may be quite unstable. A subset of the participants were asked a slightly different question instead (emphasizing the employment consequences by talking of all *occupations* instead of all *tasks*). Their time by which there would be a 50% chance of this standard being met was 2138, with a 10% chance of it happening as early as 2036. I don't know how to interpret this discrepancy, but it suggests we take these estimates cautiously.

86   Adapted from Brundage et al. (2018), Coles (1994) and Shoham et al. (2018). Images from Goodfellow et al. (2014), Radford, Metz & Chintala (2015), Liu & Tuzel (2016) and Karras et al. (2017).

87 Taking anything else as the starting point would require believing you could systematically do better than the relevant technical community at predicting their success. Perhaps one ground for thinking this would be that the experts are biased toward optimism about achieving their goals—but note that the public expect AGI even sooner (Zhang & Dafoe, 2019).

88 This analogy isn't perfect. AI researchers are not trying to build a new species to let loose in the wild, but to create new entities that can solve problems. However a growing number of them are trying to do this via general purpose intelligence, which involves agency and initiative. As we shall see, the current paradigm of AGI would naturally acquire sub-goals of controlling the world to protect itself and secure its ends.

In theory, there could be multiple species each in control of their own destiny, if they had limited ambitions and lacked the power to substantially interfere with each other.

89 It is certainly conceivable that our values ultimately boil down to something simple, such as the classical utilitarian doctrine of increasing the sum of positive experience. But even here there are two major challenges. First, even positive experience is too complex and poorly understood for us to be currently able to specify to the agent. Maybe in the future when we understand the nature of experience there will be a simple formulation, but there isn't yet. Second, the question of whether classical utilitarianism is the best moral principle is (fiercely) disputed. If we implemented that and were wrong—perhaps missing other key features of what is good in life, or about how it should ideally be distributed—we could lock in a greatly inferior world. I'm more sympathetic to classical utilitarianism than most philosophers, but wouldn't want to risk this. I think we should all take such moral uncertainty seriously.

90 My own view on this is that human values actually have a lot in common. For good reasons, we devote most of our attention to the differences, rather than to the facts that we are almost all in favor of longer, healthier, more prosperous lives, control over our life paths, a flourishing environment and so forth. I'd propose something like having the AI systems promote lives agreed

values while being cautious about the disputed or uncertain values—making sure to leave humans in control of resolving these disputes or uncertainties in the future, through our own reflection and discussion.

91 There are technical ways of understanding what is going on here. Stuart Russell (2014) likens it to a common issue in optimization: "A system that is optimizing a function of n variables, where the objective depends on a subset of size $k<n$, will often set the remaining unconstrained variables to extreme values; if one of those unconstrained variables is actually something we care about, the solution found may be highly undesirable."

Alignment researchers liken the situation to *Goodhart's Law* (Goodhart, 1975): "Any observed statistical regularity will tend to collapse once pressure is placed upon it for control purposes." This law was originally proposed to think about the problems of setting targets that correlate with what we really want. While the targets may get met, they often cease to correspond with what we ultimately cared about in the process.

92 This could come up in one of two ways. Model-based systems would plan out the consequences of being turned off and see that it would greatly restrict the space of all future trajectories, typically cutting off many of the best ones. Actions leading to being turned off would therefore be assigned very low values.

Model-free systems could also learn to avoid being turned off. Orseau & Armstrong (2016) show how if the agent is sometimes shut down while learning, this can lead to biases in its learned behavior (they also suggest a potential solution to the problem).

For most of what follows, I'll assume the advanced AI is model-based. Or at least that it is capable of using its background knowledge of the world to succeed at some complex and difficult tasks on the first try, rather than always requiring many thousands of failed attempts before groping its way to success. While this takes us somewhat beyond current systems at the time of writing, it is compatible with the current paradigm and is a prerequisite to being counted as generally intelligent. I won't need to assume that it is better at succeeding on its first attempts than a human.

93 Omohundro (2008); Bostrom (2012). For a detailed explanation of how these instrumental goals could lead to very bad outcomes for humanity, see Nick Bostrom's *Superintelligence* (2014).

94 Learning algorithms rarely deal with the possibility of changes to the reward function at future times. So it is ambiguous whether they would assess future states by the current reward function or the future reward function. Researchers have begun to explore these possibilities (Everitt et al., 2016), and they each come with challenges. Using the future reward function helps with the problem of agents resisting human efforts to bring their reward function into better alignment, but it exacerbates the problem of agents being incentivized to "wire-head"—changing their own reward function into one that is more easily satisfied.

95 Several of these instrumental goals are examples of "distribution shifts"—situations where the agent faces importantly different situations during deployment that lead to it taking actions that were never exhibited during training or testing. In this case, the agent may never have opportunities to become more powerful than its human controllers during testing, and thus never have a need to exhibit its behaviors involving deception or seizing control of resources.

96 For example, in *Enlightenment Now*, Steven Pinker (2018, pp. 299–300) says of AI risk scenarios that they: "depend on the premises that . . . (2) the AI would be so brilliant that it could figure out how to transmute elements and rewire brains, yet so imbecilic that it would wreak havoc based on elementary blunders of misunderstanding."

97 Also, note that an agent may well be able to notice the general issue that its values are likely to be misaligned with ours (warranting an adversarial approach to humanity) even without having a perfect understanding of our values. In that case, even if it was designed to try to replace its existing values with our own, it could still be misaligned, albeit less dangerously so.

There are several promising lines of alignment research related to allowing agents to update their reward functions to better align with ours. One is the broad set of ideas around "corrigibility"—how to make agents that don't resist changes to their goals. Another is the uncertainty-based approach to reward learning, where rather than acting as if it is certain of its current guess as to the human's values, the agent acts as if it is in a state of moral uncertainty, with degrees of belief in various human values based on the evidence it has seen so far (Russell, 2019). That incentivizes the agent to defer to humans (who know more about their values) and to ask for guidance when it needs it. Given my own work on philosophical issues around moral uncertainty, I find this approach particularly promising (MacAskill & Ord, 2018; MacAskill, Bykvist & Ord, forthcoming). And getting it right will require further engagement with this part of philosophy.

98   Indeed, humans are likely to be cheaper and more effective at general-purpose physical action in the world for some time, making robots very much a second-best choice.

99   Even if 99% were erased, it would still have tens of copies remaining, ready to repopulate onto any new computers that were built.

100   There are several known cases in which criminals have taken over more than a million computers. The largest known botnet was Bredolab, which contained more than 30 million computers. It was created by a hacker network and made money by leasing out time on the hijacked computers to other criminal organizations. At its height it was able to send out more than 3 billion infected emails every day.

101   It is interesting to consider just how much power they acquired. In 1942 the Axis powers (excluding Japan) controlled ~\$1.3 trillion in GDP (1990-dollars) (Harrison, 1998), representing ~30% of the world's GDP (Maddison, 2010).

The Soviet Union covered 22.4 million square kilometers, 16% of the world's land area. At its height, during the reign of Genghis Khan's grandson, Kublai Khan, the Mongol Empire had a population of 100 million (Lee, 2009), representing ~25% of world population (Roser et al., 2019).

Given how much their nations were focused on war, their fractions of world military power would probably be even higher than these numbers indicate, but this is harder to objectively measure.

102   One way this could be a good outcome is if the AI system itself was a worthy successor to humanity, creating as good a future as humanity could have hoped to achieve. One sometimes hears this offered as a reason not to worry about the risks of unaligned AI.

While I think there is something to this idea, it is by no means a panacea. Once we take seriously the idea that our best future may involve replacing ourselves, it would seem unlikely that all such replacements are equally good. And effectively licensing any group of programmers to unilaterally trigger such a whole-sale replacement of humanity would be an appalling process for deciding how we should pass on the torch. Furthermore, if we think that the AI system may itself be a subject of moral value, this raises serious possibilities that it could in fact suffer, or otherwise produce a world of negative value—especially if designed by humanity at a time when we know so little about the nature of conscious experience.

103 Metz (2018).

104 Stuart Russell (2015): "As Steve Omohundro, Nick Bostrom, and others have explained, the combination of value misalignment with increasingly capable decision-making systems can lead to problems—perhaps even species-ending problems if the machines are more capable than humans. Some have argued that there is no conceivable risk to humanity for centuries to come, perhaps forgetting that the interval of time between Rutherford's confident assertion that atomic energy would never be feasibly extracted and Szilard's invention of the neutron-induced nuclear chain reaction was less than twenty-four hours."

Russell's Center for Human-Compatible AI is one of the leading research centers for AI alignment. His book, *Human Compatible* (2019), is a ground-breaking and readable introduction to the problem of building safe artificial general intelligence.

105 Shane Legg, co-founder and Chief Scientist of DeepMind, also leads their research on AI safety. When he was asked in an interview about the chance of human extinction within a year of developing AGI, he said (Legg & Kruel, 2011): "I don't know. Maybe 5%, maybe 50%. I don't think anybody has a good estimate of this . . . It's my number 1 risk for this century, with an engineered biological pathogen coming a close second (though I know little about the latter)."

106 Alan Turing (1951), co-inventor of the computer and one of the founders of the field of artificial intelligence: ". . . it seems probable that once the machine thinking method had started, it would

not take long to outstrip our feeble powers. There would be no question of the machines dying, and they would be able to converse with each other to sharpen their wits. At some stage therefore we should have to expect the machines to take control, in the way that is mentioned in Samuel Butler's 'Erewhon.'"

This novel by Samuel Butler (1872) was developed from his 1863 essay "Darwin among the machines" (Butler, 1863), which was arguably the first consideration of existential risk from intelligent machines.

Turing's concerns were echoed by his fellow code-breaker, the eminent statistician and computing pioneer I. J. Good (1959): "Once a machine is designed that is good enough . . . it can be put to work designing an even better machine. At this point an 'explosion' will clearly occur; all the problems of science and technology will be handed over to machines and it will no longer be necessary for people to work. Whether this will lead to a Utopia or to the extermination of the human race will depend on how the problem is handled by the machines. The important thing will be to give them the aim of serving human beings."

The AI pioneer Norbert Wiener discussed the problem of retaining human oversight over advanced AI systems (Wiener, 1960): "Though machines are theoretically subject to human criticism, such criticism may be ineffective until long after it is relevant. To be effective in warding off disastrous consequences, our understanding of our man-made machines should in general develop *pari passu* with the performance of the machine. By the very slowness of our human actions, our effective control of our machines may be nullified."

Marvin Minsky (1984) warned of the risks of creating powerful AI servants who may misunderstand our true goals: "The first risk is that it is always dangerous to try to relieve ourselves of the responsibility of understanding exactly how our wishes will be realized . . . the greater the range of possible methods we leave to those servants, the more we expose ourselves to accidents and incidents. When we delegate those responsibilities, then we may not realize, before it is too late to turn back, that our goals have been misinterpreted, perhaps even maliciously. We see this in such classic tales of fate as *Faust*, the *Sorcerer's Apprentice*, or the *Monkey's Paw* by W.W. Jacobs."

Richard Sutton, a pioneer of reinforcement learning and co-author of the most widely used textbook on the subject, states there is "certainly a significant chance within all of our expected lifetimes" that human-level AI will be created, then goes on to say the AI agents "will not be under our control," "will compete and cooperate with us," and that "if we make superintelligent slaves, then we will have superintelligent adversaries." He concludes that "We need to set up mechanisms (social, legal, political, cultural) to ensure that this works out well" but that "inevitably, conventional humans will be less important" (Sutton, 2015), (Alexander, 2015).

Other top researchers who have spoken publicly about risks from AI include Jeff Clune (2019): ". . . even if there is a small chance that we create dangerous AI or untold suffering, the costs are so great that we should discuss that possibility. As an analogy, if there were a 1% chance that a civilization-ending asteroid could hit Earth in a decade or ten, we would be foolish not to begin discussing how to track it and prevent that catastrophe."

Ian Goodfellow (OSTP, 2016): "Over the very long term, it will be important to build AI systems which understand and are aligned with their users" values ... Researchers are beginning to investigate this challenge; public funding could help the community address the challenge early rather than trying to react to serious problems after they occur."

107 Szilard & Winsor (1968), pp. 107–8.

108 While the open letter spoke mainly in generalities (Future of Life Institute, 2015), its attached research agenda explicitly spoke of the need to investigate risks to humanity of the type discussed in this section (Russell, Dewey & Tegmark, 2015).

109 Future of Life Institute (2017).

110 This was an excerpt from Russell (2014), and is similar to the arguments given here.

111 This is a shockingly high estimate. The only other community of researchers I can imagine who may have estimated such a high probability of their work leading to catastrophically bad outcomes for humanity are the atomic scientists in the lead-up to the bomb. And yet I'm grateful to the researchers for their frank honesty about this.

112 See, for example, Pinker in *Enlightenment Now* (2018, p. 300).

113 Demis Hassabis has addressed these issues explicitly (Bengio et al., 2017): "The coordination problem is one thing we should focus on now. We want to avoid this harmful race to the finish where corner-cutting starts happening and safety gets cut. That's going to be a big issue on global scale."

114 If systems could improve their own intelligence, there is a chance this would lead to a cascade called an "intelligence explosion." This could happen if improvements to a system's intelligence made it all the more capable of making further improvements. This possibility was first noted by I. J. Good (1959) and is a plausible mechanism whereby progress could rapidly spiral out of control. In the survey mentioned earlier (Grace et al., 2018), 29% of respondents thought it likely that the argument for why we should expect an intelligence explosion is broadly correct.

But it is by no means guaranteed. For one thing, it wouldn't just require an AI that is more intellectually capable of AI research than a human—it would need to be more capable than the entire AI research community (at a comparable cost). So there may be time to detect that a system is at a roughly human level before it is capable of an intelligence explosion.

Moreover, it is possible that the difficulty of making successive improvements to a system's intelligence could increase faster than its intelligence does, making the "explosion" quickly peter out. Indeed, there presumably must be *some* point at which it peters out like this, so the real question is whether there is any part near the beginning of the process during which improvements beget greater improvements. For some exploration of this, see Bostrom (2014, p. 66).

115 Metz (2018). Stuart Russell concurs (Flatow, Russell & Koch, 2014): "What I'm finding is that senior people in the field who have never publicly evinced any concern before are privately thinking that we do need to take this issue very seriously, and the sooner we take it seriously the better."

The advice of Hassabis and Russell echoes a prescient warning by I. J. Good (1970): "Even if the chance that the ultraintelligent machine will be available is small, the repercussions would be so enormous, good or bad, that it is not too early to entertain the possibility. In any case by 1980 I hope that the implications and the safeguards will have been thoroughly discussed, and this is my main reason for airing the matter: an association for considering it should be started."

If we had taken Good's advice, we might have been decades ahead of where we are now, facing only a small and well-managed risk.

116 In the worst cases, perhaps even negative value—an outcome worse than extinction.

117 Orwell (1949, p. 121) is explicit on this point: "There are only four ways in which a ruling group can fall from power. Either it is conquered from without, or it governs so inefficiently that the masses are stirred to revolt, or it allows a strong and discontented Middle Group to come into being, or it loses its own self-confidence and willingness to govern. These causes do not operate singly, and as a rule all four of them are present in some degree. A ruling class which could guard against all of them would remain in power permanently."

118 One could even make a case that this was the first major existential risk. On this view, the first wave of anthropogenic existential risk came from these dangerous ideologies that had recently been discovered, which in a globalized world might be able to become unshakable. The technological risks (starting with nuclear weapons) would be the second wave.

In support of this idea, one could point to Nazi Germany's rhetoric of a "thousand-year Reich" as evidence of their ambitions for designing a truly lasting regime. And note that it would not have needed to be a very high probability for it to count—perhaps a one in a thousand chance would be enough (as that is more than a century worth of natural risk).

While a work of fiction, *Nineteen Eighty-Four* shows that Orwell's concerns were about a truly existential catastrophe. He painted a vision of a world that was in perpetual conflict between three totalitarian superpowers, each of which used insidious social and technological means to make rebellion impossible. A key aspect of the vision was that it might represent a *permanent* dystopia: "If you want a picture of the future, imagine a boot stamping on a human face—forever." Foreshadowing the idea of existential risk, he likened the outcome to extinction: "If you are a man, Winston, you are the last man. Your kind is extinct; we are the inheritors. Do you understand that you are *alone*? You are outside history, you are non-existent."

While the book was published in 1949, his letters during the war attest that he was genuinely worried about these possibilities (it wasn't mere speculation) and that many of the ideas pre-dated the development of atomic weapons (Orwell, 2013). In Orwell's example, almost no one—not even the elites—had anything of real value in their lives. That is one possibility, but clearly outcomes short of that could also be dystopian, as the immiseration of the many could easily outweigh the enrichment of the few.

While I think this is a credible case, overall I'm inclined to still treat nuclear weapons (either the threat of igniting the atmosphere or of global nuclear war) as the first major (and anthropogenic) existential risk.

119　Though note that even if they didn't initially have aims of global expansion, things may still have gone in that direction once their ability to do so was assured. And even if they only started with the means to create a regime that lasted decades, that may have bought them enough time to develop the technological and social methods to expand that to centuries, which would buy the time to expand the reach much further again.

120　Scott Alexander's *Meditations on Moloch* (2014) is a powerful exploration of such possibilities.

121　C. S. Lewis (1943) alludes to this possibility when considering the increases in humanity's power over nature, particularly through genetic technologies. He notes that this power may well increase to a point where a single generation (or part of one) can effectively control the subsequent direction of humanity and all successive generations: "The real picture is that of one dominant age—let us suppose the hundredth century AD—which resists all previous ages most successfully and dominates all subsequent ages most irresistibly, and thus is the real master of the human species. But then within this master generation (itself an infinitesimal minority of the species) the power will be exercised by a minority smaller still. Man's conquest of nature, if the dreams of some scientific planners are realized, means the rule of a few hundreds of men over billions upon billions of men."

122 Most normative views have this counterintuitive property because the behaviors the view recommends don't factor in the chance that the view itself could be false. Since there would be little cost to locking in a true view and much to gain, they would often recommend this. Notable exceptions would include views that pay no heed at all to consequences (such that they don't see much concern about an action that would lead to a different view taking over forever) and views that have strong liberal presumptions built in (such that even if concerned about that prospect, the normative theory explicitly allows the freedom to reject it).

While I'm concerned about the possibility of prematurely converging to a normative theory we would all have reason to regret, I don't see the fact a theory recommends locking itself in as a reason to reject it. Rather, I think that the correct solution lies at the level of moral uncertainty, which I've written on extensively elsewhere (MacAskill, Bykvist & Ord, forthcoming). People should retain some uncertainty about which normative theories are true and this gives us strong moral uncertainty-driven reasons to resist locking in a theory, even if we think there is a high chance it is true—we need to hedge against the possibility that we are mistaken.

123 Bostrom (2013) warns against this, while Butler (1863, 1872) flirts with the prospect. It would all but guarantee that humanity's lifespan was limited by the background rate of natural risks (though of course anthropogenic risks could do us in even sooner). And it would ensure we never achieve the possibilities of longevity or settlement beyond the Earth which we would otherwise be capable of, and which may be an important part of our potential.

124 Worlds where we renounce any attempts to leave the Earth (perhaps in order to leave the heavens pristine) may be another plausible example. See Chapter 8 for some thoughts on why most of the value we could achieve may lie beyond the Earth.

125 The text was: "No amendment shall be made to the Constitution which will authorize or give to Congress the power to abolish or interfere, within any State, with the domestic institutions thereof, including that of persons held to labor or service by the laws of said State."

It passed Congress and was even endorsed by Lincoln, but was never ratified. It is unclear whether it would have actually worked, as it may have still been possible to repeal it first, and then abolish slavery. In addition, it wouldn't have *guaranteed* the perpetuation of slavery, as each slave-owning state could still abolish slavery within its own borders (Bryant, 2003).

126 At least not without being precipitated by an early development of advanced AGI. Such a catastrophe may well be better thought of as an AI risk.

127 Note that even on this view options can be instrumentally bad if they would close off many other options. So there would be instrumental value to closing off such options (for example, the option of deliberately causing our own extinction). One might thus conclude that the only thing we should lock in is the minimization of lock-in.

This is an elegant and reasonable principle, but could probably be improved upon by simply delaying our ability to choose such options, or making them require a large supermajority (techniques that are often used when setting up binding multiparty agreements such as constitutions and contracts). That way we help avoid going extinct by accident (a clear failing of wisdom in any society), while still allowing for the unlikely possibility that we later come to realize our extinction would be for the best.

128 The main reason for this disparity in likelihood is that self-replicating machines appear to be a much more difficult technological pathway compared to fabricators, taking much longer to become economically self-sustaining and thus receiving much less development work (Phoenix & Drexler, 2004). However, scientific curiosity and niche applications would eventually tempt us to try it, so safeguards would need to be found.

Atomically precise manufacturing could enable cheap production of nuclear weapons. One might have thought this impossible, since the technology only rearranges atoms, and uranium or plutonium atoms are not part of the feedstock. But uranium is actually present in seawater at a concentration that is just short of being economically viable to extract with existing technology (Schneider & Sachde, 2013). By reducing the costs of making the equipment needed to extract it (and reducing the energy costs of running it by allowing cheap solar power), atomically precise manufacturing may make uranium much more accessible. A bad actor would still need to enrich the concentration of uranium-235 to make weapons-grade material, but this too is likely to become cheaper and easier in the wake of such a powerful general-purpose manufacturing technology.

129   We can see that the chance of back-contamination from Mars causing an existential catastrophe must be very small by considering the hurdles it would have to overcome. There would have to *be* life on the Martian surface, despite its extreme inhospitability and the fact that all prior attempts to find evidence of life there have come up empty. And even if there was, it would need to be able to flourish in the very different environment of Earth, and to be able to produce existential damage. Official studies of this risk have generally concluded that it is very low, but have advised extreme caution nonetheless (Ammann et al., 2012).

Even though the chance looks small, the need for measures to prevent back-contamination from other planets or moons is an agreed part of the 1967 Outer Space Treaty, which is the basic legal framework for international space law. And the existential risk from back-contamination was one of the first risks mentioned in the philosophical literature (Smart, 1973, p. 65): "Similar long-term catastrophic consequences must be envisaged in planning flight to other planets, if there is any probability, even quite a small one, that these planets possess viruses or bacteria, to which terrestrial organisms would have no immunity."

The risk of back-contamination first came up at the time of the Moon landing. It hadn't yet been confirmed that the Moon was sterile, so the US Surgeon General pushed NASA to institute serious protections, saying that it was not outlandish to set aside 1% of the budget to guard against great catastrophe on Earth (Atkinson, 2009). In the end, they spent around $8 million, less than a twentieth of a percent of the cost of the Apollo Program, on its quarantine system (Mangus & Larsen, 2004).

From our increased knowledge of microbiology, we can now see that this system was inadequate (in particular, we didn't yet know about the possibility of ultramicrobacteria or gene transfer agents). This should give us pause about the validity of our current knowledge.

But worse, there was little attempt to get scrutiny of the techniques, and insufficient will to actually use the quarantine system when it conflicted with other mission objectives. For example, after the original plan to lift the command module from the sea was thwarted by the lack of an appropriate crane, it was decided that the astronauts would have to leave the module while it was floating in the sea. This almost certainly let some of the fine moon dust into the ocean, making many of the other aspects of the quarantine system moot (National Research Council, 2002). We thus failed to properly handle this (very small) existential risk.

From what I've seen of the discussion around back-contamination from Mars, these issues are now being taken much more seriously (and won't run into conflict with the needs of a human crew).

130   The chance of an environmental catastrophe from an unprotected sample is widely considered to be small. We can think of these protections as attempting to reduce this chance by a further factor of a million (Ammann et al., 2012).

I am quite skeptical that the probability can really be reduced by this amount, and they don't seem to be taking into account that even BSL-4 facilities have pathogen escapes (as seen earlier in this chapter). But maybe they will be able to reduce the chance of escape to something like one in a thousand, which would be a significant advance on the quarantine from the Apollo Program.

131   Though I would recommend simply waiting a few more decades, at which point we could presumably perform most of the same tests *in situ* on Mars. The risk may be small and well managed, but do we need to run it at all?

132   One reason it is unlikely is that there is no sign that there is any other intelligent life out there. See note 44 to Chapter 2 for an outline of my own thinking on the "Fermi paradox" and whether we are indeed alone.

Another is that there are millions of other centuries in which it could have arrived, so the chance it first arrives now is very low. This would be offset if it was lying in wait, but then it would be vastly more advanced than us, leaving us at its mercy. This fact that it is very unlikely we could do anything meaningful to resist does not alter the total probability of existential risk via a hostile alien civilization, but it does suggest that the risk may be moot, as there may be nothing we can realistically do to substantially increase or decrease it.

133 The dangers from passive SETI are analogous to those of opening email attachments from untrusted third parties. For example, if they have developed superintelligent AI, they could send an algorithm for an advanced hostile AI.

None of this is likely, but since these activities only matter if there really are nearby alien civilizations, the main relevant question is the ratio of peaceful to hostile civilizations. We have very little evidence about whether this is high or low, and there is no scientific consensus. Given the downside could be much bigger than the upside, this doesn't sound to me like a good situation in which to take active steps toward contact.

134 Of course in some sense, almost everything is unprecedented, being different from prior events in the small details. I'm not meaning to suggest that this suffices to produce a risk. Instead I'm only interested in cases where there is a major change to a prima facie important parameter, taking it outside the historical range. The exact kinds of thing that undermine the comfort of having a long track record of events like that with no catastrophes. Sometimes this could involve the conditions being unprecedented in the Universe, on Earth, since *Homo sapiens*, or since civilization began—it depends on whether the concern is that it would collapse civilization, cause our extinction, destroy our planet or do damage on a cosmic scale.

Kurt Vonnegut's 1963 novel *Cat's Cradle* is a powerful early exploration of this kind of existential risk. He imagines an artificial form of ice crystal ("ice-nine") which is solid at room temperature and which causes a chain reaction in liquid water, turning it all into ice-nine. Since this form of ice is not naturally occurring in Earth's history and has such dramatic properties, it would count as an unprecedented condition in my sense. In the book, this causes an existential catastrophe when it comes into contact with the Earth's oceans, turning all water into this strange solid state.

135 Consider that there are millions of scientists, so even if the experiments they try have just a one in a million subjective chance of extinction, that may still be too high. (Especially when there are biases and selection effects leading even conscientious scientists to systematically underestimate the risks.)

136 There are several key governance problems. First, the scientists typically apply their epistemic standard of high confidence that there is no catastrophe *conditional upon their base scientific theories and models being correct*, rather than considering the stakes or the track record of such theories and models (Ord, Hillerbrand & Sandberg, 2010).

Second, the cases tend to be decided solely by scientists. While they are the appropriate experts on much at issue, they lack important expertise on risk analysis or on evaluating the stakes. It also creates various biases and conflicts of interest, where the very people whose jobs (or whose colleagues' jobs) depend on a verdict are responsible for deciding that verdict. And it goes against widely held norms where the people who would be exposed to a (disputed) threat should have some say or representation in determining whether it is allowed to go ahead.

One possible improvement to this situation would be to have an international body that these issues could be brought to (perhaps part of the UN), with individuals responsible for assembling the best arguments for and against, and a scientifically literate judge to make a ruling on whether the experiment should proceed at this time, or whether it should be delayed until a better case can be made for it. I would envisage very few experiments being denied. (This model may work even if the judgments had no formal power.)

137 Nuclear weapons would not have made the list, as fission was only discovered in 1938. Nor would engineered pandemics, as genetic engineering was first demonstrated in the 1960s. The computer hadn't yet been invented, and it wasn't until the 1950s that the idea of artificial intelligence, and its associated risks, received serious discussion from scientists. The possibility of anthropogenic global warming can be traced back to 1896, but the hypothesis only began to receive support in the 1960s, and was only widely recognized as a risk in the 1980s.

A 1937 US government report on the future of technology provides an excellent example of the difficulties in forecasting (Ogburn, 1937; Thomas, 2001). It did not include nuclear energy, antibiotics, jet aircraft, transistors, computers or anything regarding space.

138 Bostrom (2013; 2018).

6 THE RISK LANDSCAPE

1 Einstein & *New York Times* (1946).

2 From an online survey by GitHub user "Zonination" (Zonination, 2017). These results are very similar to those found in a CIA experiment of intelligence officers (Heuer, 1999).

3 This makes it hard to use the phrase "it is highly unlikely that X" as part of an argument that more attention needs to be paid to X. This wouldn't be true if "highly unlikely" corresponded to a probability range such as one in ten to one in 100, as these numbers could easily be used to suggest that the risk needed to be taken seriously. This causes problems for the IPCC, which uses such phrases instead of numerical probabilities in its reports.

4 Pinker (2018), p. 295.

5 A further reason some people avoid giving numbers is that they don't want to be pinned down, preferring the cloak of vagueness that comes with natural language. But I'd love to be pinned down, to lay my cards on the table and let others see if improvements can be made. It is only through such clarity and openness to being refuted that we make intellectual progress.

6 My estimate of one in 10,000 per century is equivalent to a life expectancy of 1 million years. While I think that it is plausible the true extinction rate is given by the mass extinction record, at about one in 100 million years, I also think there is a chance that the typical species lifespans are a better guide, which pulls the average up a lot. Recall that the fossil record only provides a reliable guide to natural *extinction* risks, not to other kinds of existential risk. Here I am assuming that they are roughly the same level as the extinction risks, as this seems about right for the risks we've explored in detail, but this is more uncertain.

7 This corresponds to a Bayesian approach of starting with a prior and updating it in light of the evidence. In these terms, what I'm suggesting is that we start with a weak prior set by base rates and other factors that would go into a best-guess estimate before you saw the hard evidence (if any). I don't see good arguments for starting with a prior probability very close to zero.

8 How do my estimates compare with others? Serious estimates of these risks by scholars who have given them careful attention are rare. But thankfully, several pioneers of existential risk have put

down their own numbers. John Leslie (1996, pp. 146–7) estimated a 30% risk over the next five centuries (after which he thought we'd very likely be on track to achieve our potential). Nick Bostrom (2002b) said about the total existential risk over the long term: "My subjective opinion is that setting this probability lower than 25% would be misguided, and the best estimate may be considerably higher." Martin Rees (2003) estimated a 50% chance of a global (though perhaps temporary) collapse of civilization within the twenty-first century (the text of the book is unclear as to what scale of disaster is being estimated, but he has since clarified that it is the collapse of civilization). My estimates are in line with theirs.

In addition, Carl Sagan provided an illustrative estimate of 60% chance of extinction over the next 100 years (Sagan, 1980, p. 314; Sagan et al., 1980). Interestingly, this was in 1980, prior to the discovery of nuclear winter and his seminal writing about the badness of human extinction. However, it is not clear if the estimate represents his considered view. For it was simply stated without further comment among a set of vital statistics for Earth as they might appear in a hypothetical "Encyclopedia Galactica."

9 Another problem with business-as-usual estimates is that it can be hard to define what it even means: what kind of response by humanity are we to use as the default? While the all-things-considered risk can be hard to estimate, it is quite well defined—it is simply one's credence that a catastrophe will occur.

10 Cotton-Barratt, Daniel & Sandberg (forthcoming).

11 The more precise rule is to imagine more fine-grained decrements, such as the factor that is easiest to reduce by 1% of its current level. Then apply this rule many times, working on one factor until another becomes easier to reduce by a percent and switching to that. If there are sufficient diminishing marginal returns to working on each factor and a large enough budget, one may end up working on all three factors.

12 The CSER team proposes three classifications in all: *critical systems*, *global spread mechanism* (which corresponds closely to "Scaling"), and *prevention and mitigation failure* (which is related to the human elements of "Prevention" and "Response"). Their scheme was designed to classify the broader class of global catastrophic risks (which need not be existential). See Avin et al. (2018) for further detail.

13 One might think that this risk is in fact a certainty; that humanity will
    come to an end *eventually*. But recall that existential catastrophes
    are defined relative to the best we could achieve—catastrophes
    that destroy humanity's longterm potential. If humanity (or our
    descendants) go extinct after fulfilling our longterm potential, that
    is existential success, not failure. So the total existential risk is
    roughly the same as the chance that we fail to fulfill our longterm
    potential. The roughness comes from the possibility that we fail to
    fulfill our potential for some other reason, such as very gradually
    degrading our potential, or keeping our potential intact but never
    acting to fulfill it. These may still be serious threats to our longterm
    future, warranting detailed study and action. But they are not ways
    that our generation could destroy humanity's future and are thus
    not the subject of this book.

14 There are two main ways this assumption could fail: hellish
    catastrophes, and correlations between the objective probabilities
    of risks and the value of realizing our potential.

    Regarding the former, consider that a precise reckoning would
    have us compare the expected value of each risk—the product of
    their probability and their stakes. But if their stakes are very similar
    (say within 1% of each other), then we only lose a tiny amount of
    accuracy if we compare them by probability alone. And in many
    cases there is a strong argument for the stakes being within a per-
    cent or so of each other.

    This is because the difference in value between a world where
    humanity fulfills its potential and one where we destroy our poten-
    tial is typically much greater in absolute terms than the difference
    between the various outcomes in which our potential has been
    destroyed. For instance, extinction and a permanent collapse of
    civilization are two ways that our future could be very small and
    contain very little value. The difference between these is therefore
    much smaller than the difference between either one and an expan-
    sive future where we have a thousand millennia of breathtaking
    achievement.

    However, there are also existential risks where the value of the
    future would not come crashing down to something near zero,
    but would be very large and negative. These are cases where we
    achieve nearly the maximum in scale (time, space, technological
    capability), but fill this future with something of negative value.

The difference in value between such a hellish outcome and extinction could rival the difference between extinction and the best achievable future. For such risks one needs to modify the total risk approach. For example, if the risk involved a future as negative as the best future is positive, then you would want to weight this risk twice as much (or even abandon the total risk approach entirely, switching to the more cumbersome approach of expected value). As I think such risks are very low (even adjusting for this increased weighting) I won't explore the details.

The second issue concerns a subtle form of correlation—not between two risks, but between risks and the value of the future. There might be risks that are much more likely to occur in worlds with high potential. For example, if it is possible to create artificial intelligence that far surpasses humanity in every domain, this would increase the risk from misaligned AGI, but would also increase the value we could achieve using AGI that was aligned with human values. By ignoring this correlation, the total risk approach underweights the value of work on this risk.

This can be usefully understood in terms of there being a common cause for the risk and the benefit, producing the correlation. A high ceiling on technological capability might be another common cause between a variety of risks and extremely positive futures. I will set this possibility aside in the rest of the book, but it is an important issue for future work to explore.

15 Note that if several risks are very highly correlated, it may be best to think of them as a single risk: the risk that any of these related catastrophes happen. It could be named for the common cause of the catastrophes, rather than for the proximate causes.

16 Though it is possible for risks to become anticorrelated when they lie on divergent paths the future could take. For example, risks from lack of global coordination and risks from global totalitarianism.

17 In general, I caution very heavily against assuming statistical independence. Such an assumption often leads one to underestimate the chance of extreme events where all variables move the same way. A version of this assumption is at play when people assume variables are normally distributed (since a normal distribution arises from the sum of many independent variables via the central limit theorem). A famous example of this going wrong is in the Black–Scholes option pricing model, which assumes normal

NOTES

distributions and thus grossly underestimates the chance of large correlated price movements.

However, the case of aggregating existential risks may be a rare situation where it is not too bad to assume independence as we are *less* worried about cases when many events happen together.

18 Today that would include the United States, Russia, China and Europe. By the end of the coming century the list could be quite different.

19 I was not involved in the original Global Burden of Disease study (World Bank, 1993; Jamison et al., 2006), but I played a very minor role in advising on the normative foundation of its more recent reports (GBD, 2012), making the case that the discount rate on health should be set to zero—one of the main changes from the earlier versions.

I was even more inspired by its companion project, *Disease Control Priorities in Developing Countries* (Jamison et al., 1993; Jamison et al., 2006). Rather than looking at how much ill-health was produced by each cause, it assessed how effective different health interventions were at preventing ill-health for each dollar spent. This opened my eyes to the startling differences in cost-effectiveness between different ways of improving health and how donating to the right charity can have hundreds or thousands of times as much impact (Ord, 2013). I went on to be an adviser to the third edition (Jamison, Gelband et al., 2018; Jamison, Alwan et al., 2018).

20 When I say "increases" I mean to imply that the risk factor causes the increase in existential risk, not just that they are correlated. In particular, it needs to be the case that action on the risk factor will produce a corresponding change in the level of existential risk. This could be reflected in the mathematics by using Judea Pearl's *do operator* (e.g., $\Pr(X|\text{do}(f = f_{min}))$) (Pearl, 2000).

21 It is possible that there will be no minimum or maximum achievable value (either because the domain is infinite, or because it is an open interval). I've ignored this possibility in the main text for ease of presentation, but it presents no special obstacle. Since the probability of existential risk is bounded above and below, we can replace the expression $\Pr(X|f = f_{max})$ with a supremum (the smallest probability higher than $\Pr(X|f = f')$ for all achievable f') and replace $\Pr(X|f = f_{min})$ with a corresponding infimum.

22 One could also consider the *range* of F. That is, the difference between $\Pr(X|f = f_{min})$ and $\Pr(X|f = f_{max})$. This corresponds to the sum of F's contribution and its potential, and is a property that doesn't depend on the status quo level.

23 One could also consider the elasticity of existential risk with respect to f near f_{sq}. That is, the proportional change in $\Pr(X)$ with respect to a small proportional change in f. This is a unitless measure of sensitivity to the risk factor, allowing it to be compared between different risk factors.

24 Economic risk factors could arise from a change in the absolute level of prosperity (poverty), the direction of change from the status quo (decline), or the rate of change (stagnation).

25 Even if they had only direct effects, we could still count them as risk factors (since the strict definition I'm using specifies only that they increase risk, not that they do so indirectly).

26 We could also think of artificial intelligence as a risk factor. An effect such as AI-related unemployment would not be an existential risk, but since it may threaten massive political upheaval it could still be a risk factor. And one could even approach unaligned AGI as a risk factor rather than as an existential risk. For it isn't a stand-alone mechanism for destroying our potential, but rather a new source of agency; one that may be motivated to use whatever means are required to permanently wrest control of our future. If an artificially intelligent system does cause our downfall, it won't be by killing us with the sheer force of its intellect, but with engineered plagues or some other existential threat.

27 This also raises the question of variables that both increase and decrease existential risk over different parts of their domains (i.e., where existential risk is non-monotonic in that variable). I suggest that so long as the effect on existential risk is monotonic within the domain of plausible levels of f, we think of it as a risk factor or security factor. But if it is non-monotonic within even this range, we need to think of it as a more complex kind of factor instead.

For example, if using degrees of warming above pre-industrial levels as a measure of climate change, it is possible that driving the temperature all the way back to pre-industrial levels (or beyond) would eventually become counterproductive to existential risk. However, so long as there is little practical danger of this kind of over-response, it makes sense to treat warming as a risk factor.

28 We can define measurements of a security factor that mirror those of risk factors. We can speak of its current contribution to our safety (to the chance that we *don't* suffer existential catastrophe), and of its potential for further lowering existential risk, were the factor to be increased as much as possible. Finally, we could consider the effect of marginal improvements in the security factor upon the total amount of existential risk.

29 We might generally suspect it to be easier to lower a risk by a percentage point if it starts off at 20% than if it starts at 5%. I used to think a good heuristic was that it should be equally easy to halve the probability of a risk, regardless of its starting point. But things might look different if the risk were extremely high, such as 99.9%. Then the catastrophe might seem over-determined to happen (for otherwise the risk would be lower). So a more subtle heuristic might be that it is equally easy to reduce the odds ratio of the risk by a factor of two. This would mean that risks with a middling probability (say 30% to 70%) would be in a sweet spot for ease of reducing by a percentage point.

But note that not all such risks are equal. In some cases the middling chances we assign to risks like AI might really represent our uncertainty between worlds where it is very hard and worlds where it is easy, so even though the average is middling, it may not be easy to move the probability with our work. (As a toy example, there could be one risk with a genuine 50% chance of occurring, and another that is either extremely unlikely [0.1%] or extremely likely [99.9%] but where we don't know which. This latter risk would be less tractable than its subjective level of risk [50%] would lead us to think.)

30 MacAskill (2015), pp. 180–5.

31 Sometimes it is the short-term neglectedness that counts: how many resources are being spent on it right now. But more often it is the longterm neglectedness: how many resources will be spent on it in total, before it is too late. When the allocation may soon change dramatically (such as when a field is taking off) these can be very different.

32 The way to define the terms is to note that cost-effectiveness is the rate of change of value with respect to the resources spent: d value

/ d resources. Owen Cotton-Barratt has shown that we can then break this into three factors (Wiblin, 2017):

$$\underbrace{\frac{d\ value}{d\ resources}}_{cost\text{-}effectiveness} = \underbrace{\frac{d\ value}{d\%\ solved}}_{importance} \times \underbrace{\frac{d\%\ solved}{d\%\ resources}}_{tractability} \times \underbrace{\frac{d\%\ resources}{d\ resources}}_{neglectedness}$$

33 I owe this point to Owen Cotton-Barratt.

34 Some risks may have a long time between the last moment when action could be usefully taken and the moment of catastrophe. When prioritizing based on which risk comes first, we date them by the last moment action could be usefully taken.

   If our work becomes gradually less effective as time goes on, a more complex appraisal is needed. This is the case with climate change, where even though the catastrophic damages would be felt a long time from now, lowering emissions or developing alternative energy sources makes more difference the sooner we do it.

35 The diameter of NEOs fits a power-law distribution with exponent –3.35 (Chapman, 2004). The size of measles epidemics in isolated communities fits a power law with exponent –1.2 (Rhodes & Anderson, 1996). Fatalities from many other natural disasters—tsunamis, volcanoes, floods, hurricanes, tornadoes—also fit power-law distributions. This fit usually fails beyond some large size, where the actual probabilities of extremely large events are typically lower than a power law would predict (e.g., measles outbreaks are eventually limited by the size of the population). However, the warning-shot analysis still works so long as the power law provides an upper bound for the real probability.

36 I owe this point to Andrew Snyder-Beattie.

37 He makes this point in his dissertation on existential risk and longtermism (Beckstead, 2013), which is one of the best texts on existential risk.

38 The "Collingridge dilemma" is a special case of this leverage/near-sightedness trade-off as it relates to the regulation of new technologies. Collingridge (1982) notes that the further away one is from the deployment of some technology, the more power one has to control its trajectory, but the less one knows about its impacts.

39 World governments spend 4.8% of GDP on education (World Bank, 2019b)—around $4 trillion per year. Targeted spending

on existential risk reduction is on the order of $100 million. See note 56 to Chapter 2 for more details on estimating spending on existential risk.

40 This is for money directed specifically at lowering existential risk, rather than more general money dedicated to areas associated with existential risk (such as climate change and biosecurity). Also, I'm imagining a world that looks like ours today. If an existential risk were to pose a clear emergency (such as a large asteroid bearing down on us), the amount of direct work warranted may be much higher.

7 SAFEGUARDING HUMANITY

1 Asimov (1979), p. 362. I have capitalised the initial "t."
2 We could also characterize these as:

1. Avoid failing immediately & make it impossible to fail
2. Determine how to succeed
3. Succeed

3 Protecting our potential (and thus existential security more generally) involves locking in a commitment to avoid existential catastrophe. Seen in this light, there is an interesting tension with the idea of minimizing lock-in (p. 158). What is happening is that we can best minimize overall lock-in (coming from existential risks) by locking in a small amount of other constraints.

But we should still be extremely careful locking anything in, as we might risk cutting off what would have turned out to be the best option. One option would be to not strictly lock in our commitment to avoid existential risk (e.g., by keeping total risk to a strict budget across all future centuries), but instead to make a slightly softer commitment that is merely very difficult to overturn. Constitutions are a good example, typically allowing for changes at later dates, but setting a very high bar to achieving this.

4 There are many ways one could do this: by avoiding new fires being started, by making sure the buildings are not fire dangers, or by employing a well-resourced fire department. There are analogous options for protecting our potential.

5 A numerical example may help explain this. First, suppose we succeeded in reducing existential risk down to 1% per century and kept it there. This would be an excellent start, but it would have

to be supplemented by a commitment to further reduce the risk. Because at 1% per century, we would only have another 100 centuries on average before succumbing to existential catastrophe. This may sound like a long time, but it is just 5% of what we've survived so far and a tiny fraction of what we should be able to achieve.

In contrast, if we could continually reduce the risk in each century, we needn't inevitably face existential catastrophe. For example, if we were to reduce the chance of extinction by a tenth each successive century (1%, 0.9%, 0.81% . . .), there would be a better than 90% chance that we would never suffer an existential catastrophe, no matter how many centuries passed. For the chance we survive all periods is:

$$(100\% - 1\%) \times (100\% - 0.9\%) \times (100\% - 0.81\%) \times \ldots$$
$$\approx 90.4598\%$$

This means there would be a better than 90% chance we survive until we reach some external insurmountable limit—perhaps the death of the last stars, the decay of all matter into energy, or having achieved everything possible with the resources available to us.

Such a continued reduction in risk may be easier than one would think. If the risks of each century were completely separate from those of the next, this would seem to require striving harder and harder to reduce them as time goes on. But there are actions we can take now that reduce risks across many time periods. For example, building understanding of existential risk and the best strategies for dealing with it; or fostering civilizational prudence and patience; or building institutions to investigate and manage existential risk. Because these actions address risks in subsequent time periods as well, they could lead to a diminishing risk per century, even with a constant amount of effort over time. In addition, there may just be a limited stock of novel anthropogenic risks, such that successive centuries don't keep bringing in new risks to manage. For example, we may reach a technological ceiling, such that we are no longer introducing new technological risks.

6 How we prioritize between these parts is a balancing act between getting sustainable longterm protections in place and fighting fires to make sure we last long enough to enjoy those sustainable protections. And this depends on how we think the risk is distributed over time. It is even possible to have situations where

we might be best off with actions that pose their own immediate risk if they make up for it in how much they lower longterm risk. Potential examples include developing advanced artificial intelligence or centralizing control of global security.

7 The name was suggested by William MacAskill, who has also explored the need for such a process and how it might work.

Nick Bostrom (2013, p. 24) expressed a closely related idea: "Our present understanding of axiology might well be confused. We may not now know—at least not in concrete detail—what outcomes would count as a big win for humanity; we might not even yet be able to imagine the best ends of our journey. If we are indeed profoundly uncertain about our ultimate aims, then we should recognize that there is a great option value in preserving—and ideally improving—our ability to recognize value and to steer the future accordingly. Ensuring that there will be a future version of humanity with great powers and a propensity to use them wisely is plausibly the best way available to us to increase the probability that the future will contain a lot of value. To do this, we must prevent any existential catastrophe."

It is unclear how exactly how long such a period of reflection would need to be. My guess is that it would be worth spending centuries (or more) before embarking on major irreversible changes to our future—committing ourselves to one vision or another. This may sound like a long time from our perspective, but life and progress in most areas would not be put on hold. Something like the Renaissance may be a useful example to bear in mind, with intellectual projects spanning several centuries and many fields of endeavor. If one is thinking about extremely longterm projects, such as whether and how we should settle other galaxies (which would take millions of years to reach), then I think we could stand to spend even longer making sure we are reaching the right decision.

8 I think that some of the best serious reflection about ideal futures has been within science fiction, especially as it has license to consider worlds that go far beyond the narrow technological limits of our own generation. "Hard" science fiction has explored societies and achievements whose ambitions are limited only by the most fundamental physical limits. "Soft" science fiction has explored

what might go wrong if various ideals of our time were taken to extremes or what new ethical issues would come up if new technologies gave us radically new personal or societal options. A good example combining both aspects is *Diaspora* by Greg Egan (1997), in which almost all beings are digital, greatly changing the space of possible utopias.

However, such thought has also been limited by being fiction. This forces a tension between exploring worlds that could genuinely be utopias and making those worlds sufficiently entertaining for the reader, typically by allowing the possibility of fundamental threats to human wellbeing. And it means that the criticism they receive is mainly directed at writing style, characterization and so forth, rather than as constructive attempts to refine and develop their visions of the future.

9 The difficulty of anticipating the results may actually make it easier to start the process—for it acts as a veil of ignorance. If we were fairly sure of which future the Long Reflection would ultimately endorse, we'd be tempted to judge this by the lights of our current ethical understanding. Those whose current views are far from where we would end up may then be tempted to obstruct the process. But from a position where we are uncertain of the destination, we can all see the benefits in choosing a future based on further reflection, rather than simply having a struggle between our current views. And this veil of ignorance may even overcome the problems of people having irrationally high confidence in their current views. For if different camps think their view is uniquely well supported by argument, they will also think it has a higher than average chance of being the outcome of a careful process of reflection.

10 If compromise futures were considered even less attractive than either of the "pure views" we started with, then we could ultimately just choose randomly from among the undefeated pure views— perhaps with probabilities related to their degree of support.

But I'm generally optimistic that there are win-win compromises. For example, moral theories can be divided into those whose judgment of the value of outcomes increases roughly in line with the amount of resources, and those where there are steeply diminishing returns. Classical utilitarianism is an example of the former, where two galaxies could support twice as much happiness as one and would thus be twice as good. Common-sense morality is an example of the latter, where most people's untutored intuitions show little interest in creating flourishing beyond the scale of a planet or galaxy. Such differences give rise to opportunities for deals that both views see as highly favorable. I call this phenomenon *moral trade* (Ord, 2015).

In particular, there is room for a "grand deal" between moral theories where the views with diminishing marginal utility of resources get to decide the entire future of our galaxy, while the views that highly value additional resources get to decide the future of all the other galaxies in the universe (so long as they won't use these for things which are actively disapproved of by the former theories). This should avoid conflict, by giving both groups an outcome they think of as more than 99% as good as is possible—much better than the expected gains of fighting to control the future or flipping a coin for the right to do so.

11 It is possible that a successful Long Reflection would require the improvements to our abilities stemming from one of these radical changes. If so, we would be in a tricky situation and would have to consider the relative risks of making the change without understanding its consequences versus continuing with our unimproved abilities and potentially missing something important.

12 A useful comparison is to the Renaissance. Most people in Europe were not actively involved in this rebirth of culture and learning, yet it is this grand project for which Europe in the fourteenth to seventeenth centuries is best remembered. Notable differences include that the Long Reflection would be a global project and that it should be more open to everyone to participate.

13 Schell (1982), p. 229.

14 The Long Reflection may overlap with the final phase of achieving our potential, perhaps substantially. For it is only irreversible actions that must await our reflection. There may be domains of irreversible action that get resolved and can then be acted on, while others are still under debate.

15 I sometimes hear colleagues suggest that one thing that could be more important than existential risk is the consideration of how to think about infinite value (Bostrom, 2011a; Askell, 2018). This has two parts: one is a challenge to theories like utilitarianism that are difficult to apply in an infinite universe (such as cosmologists believe our universe to be), and the other is a question of whether there

might be prospects of creating something of infinite value (which would seem to trump the large but finite value of safeguarding humanity).

I'm not sure whether these questions are crazy or profound. But either way, they can be left until after we achieve existential security. The case for avoiding existential catastrophe doesn't rely on theories like utilitarianism, and if infinite value really can be created, then existential security will increase the chances we achieve it. So even questions like these with potentially game-changing effects on how we think of the best options for humanity in the future seem to be best left to the Long Reflection.

There may yet be ethical questions about our longterm future which demand even more urgency than existential security, so that they can't be left until later. These would be important to find and should be explored concurrently with achieving existential security.

16 Stephen Hawking (Highfield, 2001): "I don't think the human race will survive the next thousand years, unless we spread into space. There are too many accidents that can befall life on a single planet. But I'm an optimist. We will reach out to the stars."

Isaac Asimov (1979, p. 362): "And if we do that over the next century, we can spread into space and lose our vulnerabilities. We will no longer be dependent on one planet or one star. And then humanity, or its intelligent descendants and allies, can live on past the end of the Earth, past the end of the sun, past (who knows?) even the end of the universe."

Michael Griffin, NASA Administrator (2008): "The history of life on Earth is the history of extinction events, and human expansion into the Solar System is, in the end, fundamentally about the survival of the species."

Derek Parfit (2017b, p. 436): "What now matters most is how we respond to various risks to the survival of humanity. We are creating some of these risks, and we are discovering how we could respond to these and other risks. If we reduce these risks, and humanity survives the next few centuries, our descendants or successors could end these risks by spreading through this galaxy."

Elon Musk (2018): ". . . it's important to get a self-sustaining base. Ideally on Mars because Mars is far enough away from Earth that a war on Earth, the Mars base might survive, is more likely to survive than a moon base."

Carl Sagan (1994, p. 371) implicitly suggested it when saying: "In the littered field of discredited self-congratulatory chauvinisms, there is only one that seems to hold up, one sense in which we are special: Due to our own actions or inactions, and the misuse of our technology, we live at an extraordinary moment, for the Earth at least—the first time that a species has become able to wipe itself out. But this is also, we may note, the first time that a species has become able to journey to the planets and the stars. The two times, brought about by the same technology, coincide—a few centuries in the history of a 4.5 billion-year-old planet. If you were somehow dropped down on the Earth randomly at any moment in the past (or future), the chance of arriving at this critical moment would be less than 1 in 10 million. Our leverage on the future is high just now."

But he goes on to suggest something more like the existential security I am proposing (1994, p. 371): "In a flash, they create world-altering contrivances. Some planetary civilizations see their way through, place limits on what may and what must not be done, and safely pass through the time of perils. Others, not so lucky or so prudent, perish."

17 My colleagues Anders Sandberg and Stuart Armstrong spell out the logic and mathematics in more detail (Armstrong & Sandberg, 2013). They show that the number of redundant copies only needs to increase logarithmically in order to have a non-zero chance that at least one copy exists at all times.

18 The spread of these risks *is* limited by the speed of light, so cosmic expansion would limit their spread to a finite region (see Chapter 8). This isn't very helpful for us though, as the region of desolation right now would include everywhere we could ever reach. In the distant future, things are a little better: all the galactic groups will be causally isolated, so we may be spread over millions of independent realms. However, these locations cannot repopulate each other, so a 1% risk would on average permanently wipe out 1% of them. On some views about what matters, this would be just as bad as a 1% chance of losing all of them. Even if we only care about having at least one bastion of humanity survive, this isn't very helpful. For without the ability to repopulate, if there were a sustained one in a thousand chance of extinction of each realm per century, they would all be gone within 5 million years. This might seem like a long time, but since we would have to survive a

hundred billion years to reach the point in time when the universe is divided up like this, it doesn't appear to offer any useful protection. The real protection comes not from redundancy, but from taking the risks seriously and working to prevent them.

19 How much it helps is an open question. Firstly, the extent it helps depends on how much of the existential risk is uncorrelated between planets and how best to model the risk. One model is to think of some fraction of the aggregate risk being uncorrelated and to say that spreading to other planets removes that part. Eliminating this part of our aggregate risk may thus make a major change to our chance of achieving our potential. But we could also model our situation with some fraction of the risk *each century* being uncorrelated (e.g., 5 percentage points out of a total of 10). In this example, eliminating uncorrelated risk (without solving the correlated risk) would just double the expected length of time before an existential catastrophe from ten centuries to 20, increasing humanity's lifespan by just a small fraction. I'm not sure which of these models is the better way of looking at it.

There is also a question of cost-effectiveness. Space settlement does not look to me to be one of the most cost-effective ways to reduce risk over this century. As a simple example, building similar sustainable colonies in remote parts of the Earth (Antarctica, under the sea . . .) would be much cheaper and would protect against many of the same risks. But perhaps it is a mistake here to think of the money for space settlement as coming from the same fixed budget as other risk reduction. It is such an inspiring project that the money may well be found from other sources, and the inspiration it produces (along with the knowledge that humanity really is destined for the stars) may ultimately *increase* the total resources forthcoming for existential security.

20 Depending on the details of how we define existential catastrophes, it may be possible to suffer two of them. For example, suppose that we lost 99% of our potential in an existential catastrophe. As I don't require complete destruction of our potential in order to count as an existential risk, this would count. In the years that follow, it may still make sense to preserve the remaining 1% of our potential from further catastrophes. If our potential were truly vast to begin with, this 1% remaining may also be vast compared to the issues of the day

that usually concern us, and the case for focusing on preserving our remaining potential may still be very strong. In this case, it makes sense for people after the time of the first existential catastrophe to adopt all the thinking surrounding existential risk.

We could define existential risk relative to our remaining potential, such that humanity could suffer several successive existential catastrophes, or relative to our initial potential, such that only the first one counts. I'm not sure which definition is best, so I leave this open. But note that it doesn't really change the arguments of this section. Even though these people would have the ability to learn from the first existential catastrophe, it only helps them preserve the scraps of value that remain possible—the first catastrophe was overwhelmingly more important and it had to be faced by people with no precedent.

21 This is explored by Groenewold (1970) and Bostrom (2002b).

22 These actions may be aimed at any stage of a catastrophe— preventing its initiation, responding to its spread, or creating resilience to its effects—but securing the resources, gathering the information and planning the actions still needs to be pre-emptive.

23 I owe this point to Bostrom (2013, p. 27).

24 This situation is sometimes called "Knightian uncertainty," or just "uncertainty," which is then distinguished from situations of "risk," where we have access to the probabilities (Knight, 1921). There are several slightly different ways of making this distinction, such as reserving the term "uncertainty" for situations where we have absolutely no quantifiable information about whether the event will occur.

I won't adopt this terminology here, and will carry on using "risk" for existential risks. Note that almost all uses of "risk" in this book denote these situations where we don't know the objective probabilities, but where we do have at least a small amount of quantifiable knowledge about whether the catastrophe will occur (e.g., that the chance of nuclear war in the next minute is less than 50%).

25 See Rowe and Beard (2018) for an overview of attempts and methodologies for estimating existential risk.

26 Lepore (2017).

27 A fault tree is a schematic representation of the logical relationships between events, particularly those leading up to failure. This allows the user to identify possible sources of failure in terms of the

sequences and combinations of events that must occur, and estimate their likelihood.

28 The issue of anthropic selection effects when estimating the risk of extinction was raised by Leslie (1996, pp. 77, 139–41) and explored in Bostrom (2002a). See Ćirković, Sandberg & Bostrom (2010) for a detailed analysis of "anthropic shadow": the censoring of the historical record for various events related to extinction risk.

29 This is outlined, with reference to the Large Hadron Collider, in Ord, Hillerbrand & Sandberg (2010). The situation can be easily understood in a Bayesian framework. We have a prior credence over what the objective probability is, as well as a piece of evidence that it is what the scientists have calculated. Our posterior estimate is therefore somewhere between our prior and the scientists' estimate. When the scientists' estimate is extremely low, this posterior estimate will tend to be higher than it.

This issue concerns all low-probability risks, but only really needs to be addressed in those with high enough stakes to warrant the extra analysis.

30 This is because for low-probability high-stakes risks there is more room for the true probability to be higher than the estimate, than to be lower. For example, if the estimate is one in a million and there is an equal chance of it being ten times higher or a tenth as high, the former exerts a larger effect on the expected size of the true probability, pulling it up. In other words, if you haven't already adjusted for this effect, then your point estimate of the underlying probability is often lower than your expectation of the underlying probability, and it is this latter number that is the decision-relevant probability.

31 One interesting starting point might be to create a body modeled on the IPCC, but aimed at assessing existential risk as a whole. This would be a new international advisory body under the auspices of the United Nations, focused on finding and explaining the current scientific consensus on existential risk.

32 Beck (2009), p. 57.

33 H. G. Wells was an enthusiastic advocate for world government for much of his career (Wells, 1940, pp. 17–18): "It is the system of nationalist individualism and uncoordinated enterprise that is the world's disease, and it is the whole system that has to go

. . . The first thing, therefore that has to be done in thinking out the primary problems of world peace is to realise this, that we are living in the end of a definite period of history, the period of the sovereign states. As we used to say in the eighties with ever-increasing truth: 'We are in an age of transition.' Now we get some measure of the acuteness of the transition. It is a phase of human life which may lead, as I am trying to show, either to a new way of living for our species or else to a longer or briefer dégringolade of violence, misery, destruction, death and the extinction of mankind."

Bertrand Russell (1951) wrote: "Before the end of the present century, unless something quite unforeseeable occurs, one of three possibilities will have been realized. These three are:

1. The end of human life, perhaps of all life on our planet.
2. A reversion to barbarism after a catastrophic diminution of the population of the globe.
3. A unification of the world under a single government, possessing a monopoly of all the major weapons of war."

And more recently Nick Bostrom has advocated for humanity forming what he calls a "Singleton" (2006). This could be a form of world government, but it doesn't have to be. As I understand his concept, humanity is a singleton if it is in a situation where it behaves roughly like a coherent agent. This involves humanity avoiding outcomes that are Pareto-inferior by the lights of the people of the world (i.e., negative-sum conflicts such as war). But it needn't involve a single political point of control.

34 Einstein (1948), p. 37. Einstein was motivated by extinction risk, but from a somewhat different dynamic from that which worries me most. Where I've stressed the problem of bad actors or defection from moratoria within individual nations, Einstein was chiefly focused on the need to remove the ability for one nation to wage war on another once the methods of waging war posed a risk of extinction.

35 Somewhat inaccurately, as it is neither red nor a telephone. Nor does it sit on the president's desk. In reality it is a secure teletype link (then fax, and now email), located at the Pentagon.

36 The Soviet ambassador Anatoly Dobrynin (1995, p. 100) gives a memorable recollection: "Nowadays one can hardly imagine just

how primitive were our embassy's communications with Moscow in the dreadful days of the Cuban crisis, when every hour, not just every day, counted for so much. When I wanted to send an urgent cable to Moscow about my important conversation with Robert Kennedy, it was coded at once into columns of numbers (initially this was done by hand and only later by machine). Then we called Western Union. The telegraph agency would send a messenger to collect the cable . . . who came to the embassy on a bicycle. But after he pedaled away with my urgent cable, we at the embassy could only pray that he would take it to the Western Union office without delay and not stop to chat on the way with some girl!"

37 One could think of this in terms of the modern military concept of an OODA loop (the time needed to Observe, Orient, Decide and Act). The OODA loop of diplomacy was far too slow to appropriately manage the unfolding events on the ground.

They did have some faster options, such as immediate radio and television announcements, but these required conducting the diplomacy in front of the entire world, making it much harder for the parties to back down or agree to domestically or internationally unpopular terms.

38 The OPCW's 2019 budget is €70 million, or $79 million (OPCW, 2018). Staff numbers from OPCW (2017).

39 These commendable efforts have been led by the International Gene Synthesis Consortium (IGSC, 2018).

40 US Department of State (n.d.). By most accounts, the treaty was a significant step toward disarmament, successfully eliminating a large class of weapons from the arsenals of the two great nuclear powers and putting in place robust verification procedures (Kühn & Péczeli, 2017).

41 I've suggested extinction risk rather than the broader idea of existential risk because the latter would involve an additional difficulty of assessing which other outcomes count as existential catastrophes.

Catriona McKinnon (2017) has made some helpful suggestions for how a crime of deliberate or reckless imposition of extinction risk could be created in international criminal law.

42 For example, while many states have laws against imposing risks on others (such as drunk driving), international criminal law has no precedent for this (McKinnon, 2017, p. 406). And while it may seem that nothing could be more fitting of the title "a crime against

humanity," the use of the word "humanity" is ambiguous and is sometimes interpreted here in the sense of "essential human dignity," rather than as the totality of all humans. For example, in relation to the crimes of the Holocaust, Altman & Wellman (2004) describe an understanding of the term as "Harm was done to the humanity of the Jewish victims, but that is not to say that harm was done to humanity itself."

The issue of finding thresholds for what counts as increasing a risk unnecessarily (and for adjudicating it) is a serious one. For example, we would not want to include trivial increases, such as releasing carbon dioxide with a short car journey, but we don't have access to precise probabilities with which to set a higher threshold. And if the proposal would make heads of state fear that their everyday actions, such as reducing a gasoline levy, may open them up to prosecution, then it would be very hard to get their consent to establish the law.

43 For example, to pose a 1% existential risk. It would of course be illegal to actually kill everyone or cause the collapse of civilization, but since there would be no punishment after the fact, that is not especially relevant. So the law would need to punish the imposition of risk or the development of the systems that may lead to the catastrophe.

Ellsberg (2017, p. 347) eloquently captures the insanity of the current state of affairs: "Omnicide—threatened, prepared, or carried out—is flatly illegitimate, unacceptable, as an instrument of national policy; indeed, it cannot be regarded as anything less than criminal, immoral, evil. In the light of recent scientific findings, of which the publics of the world and even their leaders are still almost entirely unaware, that risk is implicit in the nuclear planning, posture, readiness, and threats of the two superpowers. That is intolerable. It must be changed, and that change can't come too soon."

44 UNESCO (1997).

45 These include Finland (1993–), Canada (1995–), Israel (2001–6), Germany (2004–), Scotland (2005–), Hungary (2008–12), Singapore (2009–), Sweden (2011–), Malta (2012–) and Wales (2016–). There are a lot of lessons to be learned from their mixed record of success and failure, with several being weakened or

abolished, especially after changes of political control at the national level. See Nesbit & Illés (2015) and Jones, O'Brien & Ryan (2018).

46 An early critique was that of Hans Jonas (1984, p. 22): "One other aspect of the required new ethics of responsibility for the distant future is worth mentioning: the doubt it casts on the capacity of representative government, operating by its normal principles and procedures, to meet the new demands . . . the future is not represented . . . the nonexistent has no lobby, and the unborn are powerless."

47 And even more problematically, the policy may affect who comes to exist at that future time and whether there are any future people at all.

48 Such an institution could also represent children, as they too have interests that predictably diverge from those of adults, but are denied a vote.

49 Smart (1984), p. 140. Bostrom (2014) expands on this and other aspects of what going slow does and doesn't achieve.

50 Slow progress (as opposed to merely shifting all dates back by some number of years) may also give us more time to identify threats before they strike, and more time to deal with them. This is because it would effectively speed up our reaction time.

51 They also come with a more well-known shadow cost on the environment. The arguments there are similar and I also endorse using some fraction of the gains from technology to counteract these costs.

52 We could also think of this as technological progress in our current time not making *humanity* more prosperous at all. Even thought of narrowly in terms of money, it may be merely making our own generation more prosperous at the expense of large reductions in the expected prosperity of a vast number of future generations.

The same can be said in the narrow terms of technology itself. Creating technology at a breakneck pace is a greedy strategy. It optimizes the level of technology next year, but reduces the expected technology level across the longterm future.

53 It is hard to find such time, when the academic incentives are set up to push people toward publishing more papers and rewarding

producers of technical papers, not papers on ethics or governance. But academics are ultimately in charge of their own incentive structure and should push to change it, if it is letting them (and humanity) down.

54 Indeed, a good choice for a young scientist or technologist would be to go to work in government. The lack of scientific literacy and expertise in government is most often lamented by precisely the people who have those skills and could be applying them in government. Put another way, it is unreasonable to blame people working on policy for not being great at science, but more reasonable to blame people who are great at science for not working on policy.

55 UN (n.d.).

56 See Grace (2015). There is some debate over how successful the Asilomar Conference was. In the decades after the guidelines were created, some of the risks envisioned by the scientists turned out not to be as great as feared, and many of the regulations were gradually unwound. Some critics of Asilomar have also argued that the model of self-regulation was inadequate, and that there should have been more input from civil society (Wright, 2001).

57 See Bostrom (2002b).

58 This distinction is from Bostrom (2014), and the analysis owes a great deal to his work on the topic.

59 The precise half-life is the natural logarithm of 2 (≈ 0.69) divided by the annual risk, whereas the mean survival time is simply 1 divided by the annual risk.

But note that it is just the objective probability of survival that is characterized by a decaying exponential. Since we don't know the half-life, our subjective probability of survival is the weighted average of these exponentials and is typically not itself an exponential. In particular, it will typically have a fatter tail. (This same effect comes up when we are uncertain of the discount rate; see pp. 257–8.)

60 There may also be risks that fit neither of these categories.

61 The distinction between state and transition risks is not sharp. In particular, for risks with a changing character, it can depend upon the timescale we are looking at. Take the risk of nuclear winter. At some scales, it acted as a state risk. In the years from 1960 to

1990 this was a reasonable model. But if we zoom in, we see a set of transitions that needed to be managed. If we zoom out to include the time up to the present, then it feels like two regimes (during and post–Cold War) with very different hazard rates. If we zoom out to include the entire time humanity remains vulnerable to nuclear weapons, it may look like a state risk again on a scale of centuries, with the ebb and flow of geopolitics on a decadal level being washed out. And if we zoom out even further, such that there is only a small region of nuclear war risk sandwiched between the pre-nuclear and post-nuclear eras, then it may again be best thought of in terms of a transition risk: how should humanity best navigate the transition to a regime in which we harness nuclear energy.

A similar issue may arise with the risk from AGI. Once it is developed, we would enter a state where humanity is vulnerable to AGI accident or misuse by any of the actors who gain access to it. This state will only end when actions are taken to end it. This period (which may be short) will be an AGI state risk, while when zoomed out it is a transition risk.

Despite mixed cases like these, it remains a useful distinction. Indeed, even in these very cases, it is a useful lens through which to understand the changing nature of the risks.

62   This idea was introduced by Bostrom (2013, pp. 24–6).

63   It is, of course, a cliché for a researcher to suggest that more research is needed. I hope the reader will be able to see why more research on existential risk will indeed be especially valuable to humanity. Here, research isn't needed merely for a more definitive answer to an arbitrary academic question. It is required in order to be able to answer a fundamentally important question (which actions would best safeguard the longterm potential of humanity?) that has had hardly any study thus far.

64   For example, at the time of writing there have only been two published studies on the climate effects of full-scale nuclear war since the Cold War ended in 1991 (Robock, Oman & Stenchikov, 2007; and Coupe et al., 2019), and no detailed study of its agricultural effects since 1986 (Harwell & Hutchinson, 1986).

65   For example, the research fellowship which has given me the time needed to write this book was funded by an individual donor.

66 They have also made a large grant supporting the Future of Humanity Institute at Oxford, where I work.

67 Their focus on the research that is actually most helpful (guided by a passion for the cause) is especially valuable, for a general increase in research funding for existential risk might be expected to flow mainly toward established research (perhaps after suitable rebranding), leaving little for more foundational or daring work. We might also expect general funding to go to more well-understood risks (such as asteroids) at the expense of bigger, but less well-understood risks (such as those from advanced artificial intelligence); or to risks that are catastrophic, but not really existential. If mainstream granting bodies were to start funding calls for existential risk, they would need to take care not to distort the priorities of the field. See also Bostrom (2013, p. 26).

68 Other academic institutes include the Future of Life Institute (FLI) and the Global Catastrophic Risk Institute (GCRI).

69 Environmentalism is a useful example. It was much less of a partisan political issue in the early days, when it had many great successes. It was Richard Nixon who established the US Environmental Protection Agency, and Reagan (1984) who stated "Preservation of our environment is not a liberal or conservative challenge, it's common sense." I think it may have had even more success if this non-partisan spirit had been kept alive.

70 Consider environmentalism. The chief issues facing early environmentalists were pollution, biodiversity loss, extinction and resource scarcity. But they didn't call themselves "extinctionists" or "pollutionists." They found their identity not in the problems they were fighting, but in the positive value they were fighting to protect.

71 At the time of writing, DeepMind and OpenAI are the most prominent examples. They are in need of great researchers in AI safety, and also great software engineers—especially those who take existential risk seriously.

72 Organizations focused on reducing existential risk include:

The Future of Humanity Institute (FHI)

The Centre for the Study of Existential Risk (CSER)

The Future of Life Institute (FLI)

The Global Catastrophic Risk Institute (GCRI)

The Berkeley Existential Risk Initiative (BERI)

The Open Philanthropy Project (OpenPhil)

The Nuclear Threat Initiative (NTI)

The Bulletin of the Atomic Scientists

The Global Challenges Foundation

The Law and Governance of Existential Risk group (LGER)

Alliance to Feed the Earth in Disasters (ALLFED)

The high-impact careers site 80,000 Hours maintains an up-to-date job board, including such positions:

80000hours.org/job-board

and explanations of the kinds of careers that can really help:

80000hours.org/career-reviews

73   In keeping with this, I have signed over the entire advance and royalties from this book to charities helping protect the longterm future of humanity.

74   Eig (2014). McCormick should share the credit with the birth-control activist, Margaret Sanger (who first secured McCormick's donations), and the scientists Gregory Pincus and John Rock, whose research she funded.

75   Fleishman, Kohler & Schindler (2009), pp. 51–8. See note 97 to Chapter 4.

8   OUR POTENTIAL

1   Wells (1913), p. 60.

2   I use the term "civilization"—as I have done throughout this book—to refer to humanity since the Agricultural Revolution (which I round to 10,000 years, reflecting our imprecise knowledge of its beginning). This is a broader definition than the more commonly used 5,000 years since the time of the first city states. I use this longer time as I believe the Agricultural Revolution was the more important transition and that many of the things we associate with civilization will have been gradually accumulating during this time of villages and towns preceding the first cities.

3   Using the fossil record, estimates of median species lifetime for mammals range from 0.6 million years (Barnosky et al., 2011) to 1.7 million years (Foote & Raup, 1996). I set aside estimates using

molecular phylogeny, which generally give longer estimates, as that methodology is less widely accepted.

For all species in the fossil record estimates range from 1 million years (Pimm et al., 1995) to 10 million years (De Vos et al., 2015). May (1997, p. 42) concludes: "if one is to speak of an average, it might be better to offer a range like 1–10 million years."

4 Most atmospheric carbon has a lifetime of around 300 years, but there is a long tail of carbon that survives many times longer than this. Archer (2005) finds that within 100,000 years, 7% of fossil fuel carbon will remain.

5 After the end-Permian extinction, which saw 96% of species go extinct around 250 million years ago, a full recovery took around 8–9 million years for marine species, and slightly longer for land species (Chen & Benton, 2012).

6 Forey (1990); Zhu et al. (2012); Shu et al. (1999).

7 The oldest cyanobacteria fossils are somewhere between 1.8 and 2.5 billion years old (Schirrmeister, Antonelli & Bagheri, 2011).

Simple life is generally accepted as having emerged at least 3 billion years ago (Brasier et al., 2006).

"Complex life" is not a precisely defined term. I take it as referring to the level of the Cambrian explosion (541 million years ago), or the appearance of Ediacaran biota (about 600 million years ago). The exact boundary makes little difference in what follows.

8 This scenario is from Christopher Scotese (Barry, 2000). It should be understood as speculative.

9 Indeed, this will happen within just 100,000 years. When our early human ancestors gazed at the stars, they too saw shapes unknown to us.

10 The first set of plants to die are those that use C_3 carbon fixation for photosynthesis, which requires a higher level of carbon dioxide. Roughly 3% of plants use C_4 carbon fixation for photosynthesis, which works at carbon dioxide levels far below the critical limits for C_3 (Kellogg, 2013).

There is significant uncertainty in all of these estimates. We can be reasonably confident that the runaway and moist greenhouse effects pose an upper bound on how long life can continue to exist on Earth, but we remain uncertain about when they will occur, due to the familiar limitations of our climate models. Wolf & Toon (2015) find a moist greenhouse will occur at around 2 billion years, whereas Leconte et al. (2013) place a lower bound at 1 billion years.

The open question is whether carbon dioxide depletion or temperature increases will render Earth uninhabitable before the runaway or moist greenhouse limits are reached. Rushby et al. (2018) estimate carbon dioxide depletion will occur in around 800 million years for C_3 photosynthesis, and around 500 million years later for C_4 photosynthesis.

Over such long timespans, we cannot ignore the possibility that evolution may lead to new species able to exist in climates inhospitable to presently existing life forms. Indeed, the first C_4 plants only appeared around 32 million years ago (Kellog, 2013).

11 The Sun is getting brighter at a rate of about 10% per billion years, and will continue to do so for around 5 billion years, when it enters its red giant phase. It is this surprisingly small relative change that would spell the end of complex life absent our intervention. By about 6 billion years' time, we'd need to absorb or deflect about half the incoming light.

12 Schröder & Connon Smith (2008).

13 Conventional star formation will cease in about one to 100 trillion years, but there are many proto-stars (called brown dwarfs) that are too small to ignite on their own. Over these cosmological timescales, their collisions will create a small but steady stream of new stars that will keep going for at least a million times as long as conventional star formation (Adams & Laughlin, 1997; Adams & Laughlin, 1999).

14 The patterns of the stars are reflected in some of the earliest post-agricultural artifacts, and knowledge of the stars is culturally and practically important today for many indigenous peoples who have retained their forager lifestyle. There is even a tantalizing possibility that oral traditions have preserved some ancestral mythology about the stars for more than 50,000 years: there are indigenous groups in North America, Siberia and Australia who all call the same constellation "The Seven Sisters" in their own languages. The constellation is the Pleiades, which was also known as "The Seven Sisters" to the ancient Greeks (Wilson, 2001).

15 We don't know precisely how many. Extrapolating the count of galaxies visible in the Hubble Ultra Deep Field image shows there are at least 150 billion galaxies visible with present technologies. But

this will undercount since we can't detect them all, and overcount because there were more galaxies in the early universe, many of which have since merged (the Hubble image shows these distant regions as they were long ago when the light left them). Using a recent estimate of 0.0009 galaxies per cubic megalight-year at the present moment (Conselice et al., 2016), I calculate 400 billion galaxies in the observable universe right now.

Galaxies come in a vast range of sizes, from more than a trillion stars down to perhaps just thousands. Most are much smaller than the Milky Way. This wide variety of scales for the galaxies adds to the uncertainty. We may find that there are many more small and faint galaxies than we had anticipated, greatly increasing the number of galaxies in the observable universe, but simultaneously making the average galaxy less impressive.

16 The ratio is a little better if we compare this just to the *land* area of the Earth, but even our ocean (surface or floor) is much easier to settle than are the distant planets and moons.

17 The hourly energy from the Sun is $\sim 3.2 \times 10^{20}$ J (Tsao, Lewis & Crabtree, 2006), compared with our annual energy consumption of $\sim 6 \times 10^{20}$ J (IEA, 2019).

18 When such a feat of astronomical engineering is discussed, people often jump straight to its ultimate realization: a Dyson sphere, entirely encapsulating the Sun. But such an extreme version introduces other challenges and downsides. Instead, it is best thought of as a scalable approach.

19 One approach is to make individual solar collectors and put them in orbit around the Sun. Arguably we've already started this, with some of our existing spacecraft and satellites. While there are complexities to do with getting rid of the waste heat and sending the captured energy somewhere useful, this approach is relatively simple at first. However, it becomes more complicated once there are enough collectors to capture a significant fraction of the Sun's energy (as then one needs to orchestrate their orbits to avoid collisions).

Another promising approach is to use not satellites, but "statites." These are objects that are not in orbit, but which avoid falling into the Sun by having their gravitational pull toward the Sun exactly canceled by the pressure of light pushing them away. Balancing these forces requires the collectors to be very light per unit area, but it does look achievable. While there are substantial challenges in engineering each collector, they would require very little building material and scaling the project up is simply a matter of making more of them and dropping them in place. My colleagues Eric Drexler and Anders Sandberg have done feasibility calculations, estimating the mass needed for enough statites to absorb all sunlight to be around 2×10^{20} kg. This is around the mass of Pallas, the third largest asteroid in our Solar System (Sandberg, n.d.).

20   Even if fossil fuels were to remain useful in vehicles (which need to carry their own energy sources), their carbon emissions could be easily reversed by carbon dioxide scrubbers, powered by the abundant solar energy.

21   There may also be limits to the directions spacecraft can be sent with this method, so we may not be able to use it to send craft directly *to* our nearest stars.

Since the spacecraft we have already sent beyond our Solar System are not aimed at the nearest stars, they will proceed past them. Since they weren't launched with enough speed to escape the Milky Way, they are destined to wander through our galaxy for an extremely long time, perhaps swinging past many stars before eventually being destroyed.

22   Overbye (2016).

23   It is typically imagined that such a settlement would be on a planet, but it could instead be on a moon or in a space station constructed from material in asteroids. The latter might make a superior early base of operations as the initial craft wouldn't need to survive a descent onto a planet, or to construct a massive rocket in order to get back into space.

24   See note 44 to Chapter 2 for an outline of my own thinking on the "Fermi paradox" and whether we are alone.

25   If the life were less advanced than us, it may pose a test to our morality; if it were more advanced, it may pose a threat to our survival. Or if the ceiling on technological ability lies not too many centuries into the future, then there is a good chance we would meet any other intelligent beings after we had all reached the same level: as technological equals.

26 One can understand this by imagining lines connecting each pair of stars in our galaxy that are closer than some distance d to each other. For small values of d, only a small proportion of stars get connected. But there is a critical level for d at which point a giant connected component appears, which connects almost all stars in the galaxy. My colleague, Anders Sandberg, has calculated this to be at about six light years.

The critical distance would be even less if we took advantage of the fact that stars drift past each other. If we waited for these close approaches, we wouldn't have to travel so far in each step.

There is also a complicating factor that perhaps not every star system is sufficiently settleable to enable new journeys from there. This seems less likely now that we know rocky planets are so common, but may still be true. This would effectively thin out the set of stars and increase the critical distance.

27 This is not the fastest or most efficient way to settle the galaxy, especially if we can travel further in each step. I focus on it because it is the *easiest* way—the one that requires the least technology, the least planning and the fewest resources from our own Solar System.

28 Adams & Laughlin (1997).

29 Large groups are known as "clusters," but occupy the same position in the scale hierarchy.

30 These intersections are sometimes known as "superclusters," though that term is also sometimes used to refer to a wider region around the intersection, such that each galaxy is considered part of some supercluster. Either way, superclusters are a useful concept in mapping our environment, but not especially relevant to our potential.

31 The discovery that the universe is expanding is generally credited to Edward Hubble and Georges Lemaître, who reached the conclusion independently in 1927 and 1929 respectively (Gibney, 2018). The accelerating expansion of the universe was discovered only in the late 1990s (Riess et al., 1998)—work that won the 2011 Nobel Prize in Physics.

In the paragraphs that follow, I'm describing the limits as they would be under the simplest known account of accelerating expansion, where it is due to a cosmological constant. This is known as the "concordance cosmology" or ΛCDM. Other explanations of accelerating expansion (including that it is illusory) may produce quite different limits, or even no limits at all.

32 The light from these galaxies has only had 13.8 billion years (the age of our universe) to reach us, but they are currently 46 billion light years away, as the space in between has been expanding in the meantime.

33 The 63 billion light year limit is the sum of the distance we can currently observe (46.4 billion light years) and the distance we can currently affect (16.5 billion light years).

If someone traveled away from the Earth, they could see a bit further in that direction. In the extreme case, if they traveled at the speed of light, they could eventually reach a point currently about 16 billion light years away from Earth and then see an entire eventually observable universe centered on that distant point. They wouldn't see *more* than someone here, but would see different parts including some that will never be visible from here. But according to our current best theories, anything more than 79 billion light years from here (the sum of these distances) is absolutely impossible to observe.

34 Surprisingly this affectable region extends slightly beyond the "Hubble sphere"—the region containing all galaxies that are receding from us at less than the speed of light (currently with a radius of 14.4 billion light years). This is because it is still possible to reach some of the closest galaxies that are receding faster than the speed of light. This may appear impossible as nothing can travel through space faster than the speed of light, but we can use the same trick that those distant galaxies themselves are using. They recede so quickly not because they are traveling quickly through space, but because the space between us is expanding. If you shine a torch into the sky, the very light you emit will also recede from you faster than the speed of light, since the intervening space itself expands. Some of the photons you release will eventually reach about 2 billion light years beyond the Hubble sphere. Indeed, since almost everything you do affects the pattern of photons reflected off the Earth into deep space, it is almost impossible to avoid affecting things 16 billion light years away as you go about your daily life.

Thus, while people often use the term "Hubble sphere" or "Hubble volume" as a stand-in for everything we can hope to affect, they should really use "affectable universe," which is both more descriptive and more accurate.

35 Author's calculation based on a density of 0.009 galaxies per cubic megalight-year, from Conselice et al. (2016). These numbers for how many more galaxies become visible or cease to be affectable each year depend sensitively on the unresolved question of how many galaxies there are (see note 15 to this chapter).

36 A key challenge is very small particles of dust strewn through the intergalactic void. If a spacecraft collides with these at a substantial fraction of the speed of light, then the collision would be devastating. The chance of a spacecraft not meeting any such dust grains on its journey decreases exponentially with distance traveled, so longer distances traveled in a single step could present a big challenge. Some form of shielding is probably required. My colleague, Eric Drexler, has calculated that sending several layers of shielding material in advance of the spacecraft could protect the payload, but of course this is still speculative.

The distances could probably be reduced (perhaps markedly so) by taking advantage of the sparse scattering of stars that lie between the galaxies.

37 The expected value of our future is something like the product of its duration, scale, quality and the chance we achieve it. Because these terms are multiplied together, increasing any of them by a given factor has the same effect on the expected value. Thus our marginal efforts are best spent on the one that is easiest to improve in relative terms.

38 This argument, about how safety beats haste, was first put forward by Nick Bostrom (2003), though with different empirical assumptions. He measured the annual cost of delay by the energy in the starlight of the settleable region of our universe that we are failing to harness. However, I don't think starlight will be the majority of the resources we could harness (less than a thousandth of a star's mass is turned to energy via starlight), and I think the shrinking size of this settleable region is crucial.

My own guess is that the annual proportional loss is roughly equal to the proportion of galaxies that become unreachable due to cosmic expansion. It is entirely possible that this too will soon come to look like the wrong answer: for example, if it was technologically impossible to ever travel between galaxies, or if the evidence for accelerating expansion was overturned. But I think it is likely that the general point will remain: that the annual proportional loss is very small—likely less than one part in a billion. This is because most of the relevant timescales that would set this proportion are themselves measured in billions of years (the age of the universe, the lifespans of most stars, the time for which galaxies will continue to form stars, the age of the Earth and the duration of life on Earth so far).

39 This is from a speech he gave to the Cambridge Apostles in 1925 when he was twenty-one (Mellor, 1995). This is the same Ramsey who developed the economic theory of discounting and argued against discounting based on the mere passage of time alone (see Appendix A).

40 Some of these thoughts were directly inspired by Bostrom (2005, 2008).

APPENDICES

1 I probably got my dollar in enjoyment of seeing my whimsical thirty-year-long plan come to fruition, but let's set that aside . . .

2 It is not *exactly* the same effect—my income has increased not only due to economic growth, but also due to being further along in my life.

3 Some economists, such as Dasgupta (2008), also incorporate social preferences for equality in the parameter η. This could increase its size beyond what is implied by individual diminishing marginal utility.

4 It derives from the arguments given in Ramsey (1928).

An alternative model involves computing the net present value of a future monetary benefit by considering that an earlier monetary benefit could (usually) be increased in size by investing it until that later date. So the net present value of a later benefit could be thought of as the amount of money that we would need to invest today in order for it to compound to the given size by the given future date. This line of argument suggests a discount rate that depends on the interest rate rather than the growth rate.

However, this justification for discounting doesn't apply when the option of such investment is not available. This is the case here—for existential catastrophes would presumably cut off such investments or make it impossible for future generations to be benefited by them. This is clearly the case for extinction and seems likely in other cases too.

5 This point has been made well by Ng (2016) and (2005).

6 Indeed, while many great philosophers have argued against pure time preference—see Sidgwick (1907), Parfit (1984) and Broome (2005)—I know of no philosophers who support its inclusion in the social discount rate, so it may be completely unanimous. For those who know philosophy, this is truly remarkable since philosophers disagree about almost every topic, including whether they are the only person in the world and whether there are any true moral claims (Bourget & Chalmers, 2014).

Note that there is a certain amount of talking past each other in the debate between philosophers and economists over discounting. Philosophers often say they are in favor of a zero discount rate, when that isn't the right term for what they mean (i.e., they have no quarrel with monetary benefits to people mattering less if those people are richer in the future). The philosophers are usually talking about a zero rate of pure time preference, or that the ηg term is inapplicable for the topic they are considering (such as for health benefits).

7 A recent survey of 180 economists who publish on the social discount rate found that their most common estimate for the pure rate of time preference was 0%, with a median of 0.5% (Drupp et al., 2018, p. 120).

8 Ramsey (1928), p. 543; Harrod (1948), p. 40. Arthur Pigou (1920, p. 25) suggested that non-zero pure time preference "implies . . . our telescopic faculty is defective."

9 I doubt that this is the job of the economist either. Not only does it give an impoverished conception of economics, yielding all the ground on normative matters, but it yields that ground to what amounts to an opinion poll.

Even if economics does not want to be concerned with normative matters, there are others who are so concerned, reflecting deeply on these matters and arriving at novel conclusions backed by strong arguments. Some of these people work in the economics department, some in the philosophy department, and some scattered across other areas within academia or without. They have certainly not reached agreement on all moral problems, but they do have some hard-won knowledge of normative matters. A decision to replace their insight with a broad survey (or with the opinions of the current government) is itself a normative choice, and seems to me a poor one.

10 While an early paper on this topic (Cropper, Aydede & Portney, 1994) showed participants had a strong preference for saving fewer lives sooner rather than more lives later, this didn't provide any real evidence for pure time preference. For in follow-up questions, many of them said they made their choice because the future is uncertain and because it would likely have technology for saving lives—rather than due to pure time preference (see Menzel (2011) for more details).

A follow-up study by Frederick (2003) was better able to isolate time preference from these confounding explanations. For example, he asked people to compare one person dying next year in the United States from exposure to pollutants to one person dying 100 years from now in the same circumstances: 64% said these were "equally bad," 28% said the earlier deaths were worse, and 8% said the later deaths were worse. Of the 28% who appeared to exhibit pure time preference, they thought a death now was equal to about three deaths in 100 years. So the average time preference across all the participants was less than a quarter of a percent per annum over the next century (and presumably would decrease further in future centuries in line with other experiments).

11 This could be due to the remaining existential risks, to the possibility that even a successful future doesn't last that long, or to failures to achieve a flourishing future which don't qualify as existential risks (for example a gradual slide toward ruin that we could have prevented at any point, but simply failed to).

12 Stern, 2006. Stern's choice of a catastrophe rate of about 10% per century was fairly arbitrary, and was not an attempt to quantify the best evidence about future risks. However, I think it is in the right ballpark for the risk over the next century.

While most of the discussion about his approach to discounting centered on his very small value for δ, he did effectively include the ηg term. But as the trajectories of growth rates were generated within his model, it is harder to explicitly see how it affected his results (see Dasgupta (2007) for a deep analysis and comparison to the earlier work of Nordhaus).

13 There are good arguments for why the pure rate of time preference should be a constant over time (thus giving an exponential curve). This is because it is the only way to avoid "time inconsistency" where as time passes you predictably change your mind about which of two benefits is superior. But this argument doesn't apply for the growth rate or the catastrophe rate, which are empirical parameters and should be set according to our best empirical estimates.

14 We saw in Chapter 3 that the natural risk rate is probably lower than one in 200,000 per year (to account for us surviving 200,000 years so far and for related species surviving much longer than this on average). A 50% chance of getting to a period with a catastrophe rate of at most one in 200,000 has a discounted value in excess of 100,000 years.

15 The argument is based on that given by Martin Weitzman (1998), though he doesn't address discounting based on the catastrophe rate. The main trick is to see that we are discounting for the chance that a catastrophe has occurred before the given time, so the effective discount factor at a given time is the probability-weighted average of the discount factors in the worlds we find credible. It is then fairly simple to see that this is not equivalent to discounting at the average rate (or any fixed rate), and that in the long run it tends toward discounting at the lowest rate in which we have nonzero credence. Thus even if you know there is a constant hazard rate, your uncertainty over what this rate is can produce non-exponential discounting.

16 This depends on whether the action just reduces the risk in the near term, or whether it has sustained effects on risk.

17 For example, if you think there is at least a 10% chance we survive more than a million years, this is equivalent to saying that the certainty-equivalent discount rate declines to a value small enough that the discounted value of the future is at least 10% × 1,000,000 = 100,000 times as much as this year.

18 Parfit (1984); Ng (1989); Arrhenius (2000).

19 This is due to a phenomenon that arises when multiple averages are combined. The comedian Will Rogers is said to have quipped: "When the Okies left Oklahoma and moved to California, they raised the average intelligence level in both states." This intitially sounds impossible, but further thought reveals it could happen if the people who moved state were below average for Oklahoma (so their leaving increased its average) but above the average of California (so their arriving increased its average). This is now known as the Will Rogers Phenomenon and has important implications in medical statistics (Feinstein, Sosin & Wells, 1985).

It arises here if it is possible for someone to be born in either of two different generations. If their wellbeing would be below the average of the first generation and above the average of the second, moving them would raise both averages (and thus the sum of generational averages) without affecting any individual's wellbeing nor changing who exists. Since the sum of the averages has gone up by some amount it is possible to modify the example, lowering everyone's utility by a smaller amount such that everyone is slightly worse off but the sum of the generational averages has still gone up. A theory that can prefer an alternative with the same population which is worse for everyone is generally regarded as fatally flawed (especially if there is no gain in some other dimension such as equality).

But is it possible for someone to be born in either of two different generations? It seems that it is. For example, present-day medical technology freezes embryos such that couples can choose when to have them implanted. If the embryo could be implanted immediately, or alternatively 30 years later, then it could be born in two different generations. If it were to have the same wellbeing in each case and this was between the average wellbeing levels of each of the generations, we get the Will Rogers Phenomenon. Similar versions of this apply even if you date the person to conception rather than birth, as existing medical technology can be used to have the same sperm fertilize the same ovum now, or in 30 years. The worry here is not that *in vitro* fertilization will cause practical problems for conducting longterm analysis, but that the principle of the sum of generational averages is theoretically unsound since it can go up even if all individuals' wellbeing goes down.

More generally, many rating systems based on multiple averages have this flaw. For example, it is possible to make the GDP per capita of all countries go up just by moving individuals between countries. We should always be skeptical of such measures.

20 This would lead to a large, but not vast, value of the future. Depending on one's assumptions, the entire future might be worth something like ten times as much as the present generation.

21 Narveson (1973).

22 See Narveson (1967, 1973), Parfit (1984, 2017a) and Frick (2014).

23 Though if each outcome had completely different people, then the world with low wellbeing levels wouldn't be worse either, so this still doesn't completely capture our intuitions on the case.

24 See Narveson (1973) and Heyd (1988).

25 Examples of problems that occur include:
- being morally indifferent between a future where everyone has low wellbeing and a future (comprised of a different set of people) where everyone has high wellbeing;
- having moral rankings change when "irrelvant alternatives" are introduced (such as preferring A to B when they are the only choices, but then B over A, when an inferior option C is also available);
- creating cyclical preferences across choice situations (leading you to prefer A to B, B to C and C to A);
- having cyclical orderings of value (saying that A is better than B, B is better than C and C is better than A);
- saying that all outcomes that differ even slightly in how many people exist are incomparable with each other.

26 There is some recent work trying to justify the asymmetry through appeal to something more fundamental, such as that of Frick (2014).

27 At least if considered on their own. Many proponents of person-affecting accounts of the value of the wellbeing of future generations combine this with other moral principles that would recognize the badness of extinction. If so, their overall moral views don't suffer from this kind of counterintuitiveness, but nor do they pose any threat to the claim I am trying to defend: that human extinction would be extremely bad.

28 Beckstead (2013, p. 63) makes this point particularly well. Similarly, someone who found the Total View most plausible should be very cautious about following its advice in a choice like that of the repugnant conclusion.

29 DoD (1981).

30 DoD (1981), p. 8.

31 DoD (1981), p. 12.

32 Oxnard Press-Courier (1958); DoD (1981), p. 8.

33 DoD (1981), p. 20.

34 DoD (1981), p. 21. Most alarmingly, a critical mechanism that prevented one of the bombs from detonating appears to have failed on the other bomb (Burr, 2014). McNamara is quoted in US Department of State (1963).

35 DoD (1981), p. 22.

36 DoD (1981), p. 28; Broder (1989).

37 DoD (1981), p. 29.

38 Accidental nuclear detonation was more likely then than it would be today, as the B-52's weapons did not yet satisfy the "one-point safety" standard. See Philips (1998).

39 SAC (1969); Risø (1970); DoD (1981), p. 30; Philips (1998); Taagholt, Hansen & Lufkin (2001), pp. 35–43. The early-warning system had three lines of communication to the US: radio relayed by the B-52 bomber on airborne alert, direct radio and a bomb alarm. The plane crash cut the first of these. If a nuclear bomb had detonated, this would have cut the direct radio link too and triggered the bomb alarm, making the accident impossible to distinguish from a Soviet nuclear strike.

40 DoD (1981), p. 31.

41 Bordne first revealed his story to a Japanese newspaper in 2015, and it was subsequently published in the *Bulletin of the Atomic Scientists* (Tovish, 2015). The account has been disputed by other former missileers (Tritten, 2015).

42 So risk 1 is $(p_1/p_2) \times ((1-p_2)/(1-p_1))$ times as important as risk 2. We could rewrite this as $(p_1/(1-p_1)) / (p_2/(1-p_2))$ which is the ratio of their odds ratios. So if you want a single number to express the counterfactual importance of each risk (which doesn't need to be adjusted depending on the risk you are comparing it to) the odds ratio works perfectly.

43   You might wonder whether this brings up a question about how to individuate risks. For example, what makes something a 90% risk rather than two overlapping 50% risks? It turns out that there is no real dependence on how we individuate risks. Instead, it depends what we are asking. If you are considering lowering a set of risks that would constitute a 90% total existential risk were there no other risks at play, then this is just like lowering an individual risk with a probability of 90%.

    The fact that the "big risk" could be a collection of smaller risks that move together opens up some intriguing possibilities. For example, suppose that risk this century is 10% and eliminating it would leave all future risk as 90%. If you were in a position to either reduce all near-term risk by some amount or all later risk, this effect would come up, suggesting that acting on the later risk gets the nine-fold boost. (That said, acting on future risk would also typically get a penalty, which may exceed this, since we should expect additional people to also be in a position to help with it.)

44   The former reduces the total 91% existential risk by 0.9 percentage points, to 90.1%. The latter reduces it by 0.1 percentage points to 90.9%. The effect is surprising because the reduction of the 90% risk to 89% is also a smaller fractional change to that risk. The key to understanding this intuitively is that it is the fractional change to the chance of *not* having the catastrophe that matters.

45   It also happens regardless of whether there are several large risks or a multitude of smaller risks: for example, the same effects happen if there are 100 independent risks of 2% each.

46   This doesn't require us to assume that the centuries after the catastrophe have zero value, just that they have the same amount of value as each other and that this is less than those before the catastrophe.

47   Another way to see this is that the expected value of our future without risk reduction is some number V. Eliminating the probability of existential catastrophe in the first century is equivalent to getting a safe century for free, followed by the original value of the future from that point on. So the value we add is the value of a century for humanity. Or we could ask how many years it would take to build up the amount of risk you eliminated. In this basic model, the value of eliminating the risk is the value of that many years.

Note also that when I say the value of a century of humanity, I am referring to its *intrinsic* value. Since humanity's actions now can greatly affect the intrinsic value of future centuries, much of the all-things-considered value of a century is in its *instrumental value*. For example, the amount by which we improve the stock of knowledge, technology, institutions and environmental resources that we pass on to future generations. And of course, the amount by which we increase or decrease the total existential risk (though in this basic model, the instrumental value of our existential risk reduction is at most as high as the intrinsic value of the century).

48 The rate of increase of value doesn't have to stay higher than the hazard rate forever, in order to have a big impact. This is good, as the evidence we have suggests that the extremely long-run hazard rate will be roughly constant (due to a small amount of uneliminable risk), which would require value to grow exponentially over the extremely long run to offset it. But it seems likely that value we can create with a given amount of raw resources will eventually reach a limit, and the rate at which we acquire new resources is limited by the speed of light to be cubic, or less.

49 One might object to this based on counterfactuals: these insights are useful, but other people in the future would develop them anyway, so there is no counterfactual impact on the future. There is some important truth to this. While there would still be some counterfactual impact of this book's insights, this would be in terms of advancing the conversation such that future people are in a position to make advances that build on these ones. But those further advances may have diminishing marginal value. So on this counterfactual basis, the value of work now upon future risk will be less than it appears, and may diminish over time.

But this doesn't really affect the case I'm making. For if we are assuming that other people in the future will be doing important cumulative work on existential risk, then that suggests the risk won't be constant over future centuries, but will be decreasing. Either way, there is a similar effect, as we are just about to see.

50 Yew-Kwang Ng (2016) also noticed this counterintuitive effect.

51 The term comes from Bostrom (2013). David Deutsch (2011) has an admirable defense of the contrary view.

We may also reach a form of social or political maturity, where we are no longer flirting with radical new systems such as the totalitarian and communist experiments of the twentieth century, and have developed a stable society that could never again descend into tyranny.

52 The boost to the value depends roughly on the ratio between the risk over the next century and the longer term risk per century. For example, if there is a one in ten chance of existential catastrophe this century, but this declined rapidly to a background natural risk rate of less than one in 200,000 per century, then the value of eliminating risk this century would be boosted by a factor of 20,000 compared to the basic model.

53 We could think about this mathematically as having an asymmetric probability distribution for the value of the future (one that is perhaps symmetric in log-space). The expected value of the future corresponds to the mean of this distribution and this may be substantially higher than the median.

54 Others have tried extending and interpolating the scale, but have done so in ways that involved arbitrary or problematic elements. Several people have tried to add a K4 level for "the universe" but applied this to the entire universe or the observable universe, neither of which is the right concept. Carl Sagan had an early form of continuous Kardashev scale, but it forced all levels to be exactly 10 orders of magnitude apart. Since they are actually about 9 and 11, this broke the connection between the Kardashev levels and the structure of the cosmos, which was a very big loss. I think it better to just interpolate between the two integer Kardashev levels, so that each order of magnitude takes you roughly a ninth of the way from K0 to K1, but an eleventh of the way from K2 to K3. Sagan also added a K0 level, but his was just an arbitrary location 10 orders of magnitude before K1, such that the fraction of the way we've traveled from K0 to K1 did not bear any real meaning.

55 This is an order of magnitude estimate, with about 1 million people in ancient Mesopotamia at the time writing was discovered, consuming about 100 W in energy from food and expending about 100 W in work/heat. The truth may be a small factor higher than this due to inaccuracies in those numbers or if their livestock consumed substantially more food than the human population.

BIBLIOGRAPHY

Acemoglu, D. (2013). "The World Our Grandchildren Will Inherit," in I. Palacios-Huerta (ed.), *In 100 Years: Leading Economists Predict the Future* (pp. 1–36). MIT Press.

Adams, F. C., and Laughlin, G. (1997). "A Dying Universe: The Long-Term Fate and Evolution of Astrophysical Objects." *Reviews of Modern Physics*, 69(2), 337–72.

—(1999). *The Five Ages of the Universe: Inside the Physics of Eternity.* Free Press.

Aizen, M. A., Garibaldi, L. A., Cunningham, S. A., and Klein, A. M. (2009). "How Much Does Agriculture Depend on Pollinators? Lessons from Long-Term Trends in Crop Production." *Annals of Botany*, 103(9), 1,579–88.

Alexander, S. (2014). Meditations on Moloch. https://slatestarcodex.com/2014/07/30/meditations-on-moloch/.

—(2015). AI Researchers on AI Risk. https://slatestarcodex.com/2015/05/22/ai-researchers-on-ai-risk/.

Alibek, K. (2008). *Biohazard.* Random House.

Allen, M., et al. (2018). "Framing and Context," in V. Masson-Delmotte, et al. (eds.), *Global Warming of 1.5°C.* An IPCC Special Report on the impacts of global warming of 1.5°C above pre-industrial levels and related global greenhouse gas emission pathways, in the context of strengthening the global response to the threat of climate change (pp. 49–91), in press.

Alroy, J. (1996). "Constant Extinction, Constrained Diversification, and Uncoordinated Stasis in North American Mammals." *Palaeogeography, Palaeoclimatology, Palaeoecology*, 127(1), 285–311.

Altman, A., and Wellman, C. H. (2004). "A Defense of International Criminal Law." *Ethics*, 115(1), 35–67.

Alvarez, L. W., Alvarez, W., Asaro, F., and Michel, H. V. (1980). "Extraterrestrial Cause for the Cretaceous-Tertiary Extinction." *Science*, 208(4448), 1,095–108.

Ambrose, S. H. (1998). "Late Pleistocene Human Population Bottlenecks, Volcanic Winter, and Differentiation of Modern Humans." *Journal of Human Evolution*, 34(6), 623–51.

Ammann, W., et al. (2012). "Mars Sample Return Backward Contamination—Strategic Advice and Requirements." *National Aeronautics and Space Administration*.

Anderson, I. (2008). "Foot and Mouth Disease 2007: A Review and Lessons Learned—Report to the UK Prime Minister and the Secretary of State for Environment Food and Rural Affairs." London: The Stationery Office.

Annan, J. D., and Hargreaves, J. C. (2011). "On the Generation and Interpretation of Probabilistic Estimates of Climate Sensitivity." *Climatic Change*, 104(3–4), 423–36.

Antón, S. C., Potts, R., and Aiello, L. C. (2014). "Evolution of Early Homo: An Integrated Biological Perspective." *Science*, 345 (6192), 1236828.

Archer, D. (2005). "Fate of Fossil Fuel CO_2 in Geologic Time." *Journal of Geophysical Research*, 110(C9).

Armstrong, S., and Sandberg, A. (2013). "Eternity in Six Hours: Intergalactic Spreading of Intelligent Life and Sharpening the Fermi Paradox." *Acta Astronautica*, 89, 1–13.

Arnett, R. L. (1979). "Soviet attitudes towards nuclear war survival (1962–1977): has there been a change?" [PhD thesis]. The Ohio State University.

Arrhenius, G. (2000). "An Impossibility Theorem for Welfarist Axiologies." *Economics and Philosophy*, 16, 247–66.

Arsenault, C. (December 5, 2014). "Only 60 Years of Farming Left If Soil Degradation Continues." *Scientific American*.

Arsuaga, J. L., et al. (2014). "Neandertal Roots: Cranial and Chronological Evidence from Sima de los Huesos." *Science*, 344(6190), 1,358–63.

Asimov, Isaac (August 1959). "Big Game Hunting in Space." *Space Age*.

—(1979). *A Choice of Catastrophes: The Disasters that Threaten Our World*. Simon and Schuster.

Askell, A. (2018). "Pareto Principles in Infinite Ethics" [PhD Thesis]. Department of Philosophy, New York University.

Atkinson, N. (2009). How to Handle Moon Rocks and Lunar Bugs: A Personal History of Apollo's Lunar Receiving Lab. https://www.universetoday.com/35229/how-to-handle-moon

-rocks-and-lunar-bugs-a-personal-history-of-apollos-lunar-receiving
-lab/.

Avin, S., et al. (2018). "Classifying Global Catastrophic Risks." *Futures*, 102, 20–6.

Baade, W., and Zwicky, F. (1934). "On Super-Novae." *Proceedings of the National Academy of Sciences*, 20(5), 254–9.

Bacon, F. (2004). "Novum Organum," in G. Rees and M. Wakely (eds.), *The Oxford Francis Bacon*, vol. 11: *The Instauratio magna Part II: Novum organum and Associated Texts* (pp. 48–586). Oxford University Press (original work published in 1620).

Baier, A. (1981). "The Rights of Past and Future Persons," in E. Partridge (ed.), *Responsibilities to Future Generations: Environmental Ethics* (pp. 171–83). Prometheus Books.

Bailey, R. T. (1997). "Estimation from Zero-Failure Data." *Risk Analysis*, 17(3), 375–80.

Ball, D. (2006). "The Probabilities of 'On the Beach': Assessing 'Armageddon Scenarios' in the 21st Century" (Working Studies Paper No . 401), in Strategic and Defence Studies Centre.

Bambach, R. K. (2006). "Phanerozoic Biodiversity Mass Extinctions." *Annual Review of Earth and Planetary Sciences*, 34(1), 127–55.

Bar-On, Y. M., Phillips, R., and Milo, R. (2018). "The Biomass Distribution on Earth." *Proceedings of the National Academy of Sciences*, 115(25), 6,506–11.

Barnosky, A. D., et al. (2011). "Has the Earth's Sixth Mass Extinction Already Arrived?" *Nature*, 471 (7336), 51–7.

Barry, P. L. (2000). Continents in Collision: Pangea Ultima. https://science.nasa.gov/science-news/science-at-nasa/2000/ast06oct_1.

Bartholomew, R. E., and Radford, B. (2011). *The Martians have Landed! A History of Media-Driven Panics and Hoaxes.* McFarland.

Baum, S. D., Denkenberger, D. C., Pearce, J. M., Robock, A., and Winkler, R. (2015). "Resilience to Global Food Supply Catastrophes." *Environment Systems and Decisions*, 35(2), 301–13.

BBC (November 12, 2015). "Russia Reveals Giant Nuclear Torpedo in State TV 'leak.'" BBC News.

Beade, A. P. M., Ahlonsou, E., Ding, Y., and Schimel, D. (2001). "The Climate System: An Overview," in J. T. Houghton, et al. (eds.), *Climate Change 2001: The Scientific Basis. Contribution of Working Group I to the Third Assessment Report of the Intergovernmental Panel on Climate Change.* Cambridge University Press.

Beck, U. (2009). *World at Risk* (trans. C. Cronin). Polity Press.

Beckstead, N. (2013). "On the Overwhelming Importance of Shaping the Far Future" [PhD Thesis]. Department of Philosophy, Rutgers University.

Benedictow, O. J. (2004). *The Black Death, 1346–1353: The Complete History*. Boydell Press.

Bengio, Y., et al. (2017). Creating Human-level AI: How and When? (Panel from The Beneficial AI 2017 Conference) [Video]. https://www.youtube.com/watch?v=V0aXMTpZTfc.

Bernstein, A., and Roberts, M. de V. (1958). "Computer v Chess-Player." *Scientific American*, 198(6), 96–105.

Bethe, H., Brown, H., Seitz, F., and Szilard, L. (1950). "The Facts About the Hydrogen Bomb." *Bulletin of the Atomic Scientists*, 6(4), 106–9.

Blanton, T., Burr, W., and Savranskaya, S. (2012). *The Underwater Cuban Missile Crisis: Soviet Submarines and the Risk of Nuclear War*. National Security Archive, Electronic Briefing Book No. 399. National Security Archive.

Boberg, J. (2005). "Freshwater Availability," in J. Boberg (ed.), *How Demographic Changes and Water Management Policies Affect Freshwater Resources* (pp. 15–28). RAND Corporation.

Bolton, J., and Azar, A. (2018). Press Briefing on the National Biodefense Strategy. https://www.whitehouse.gov/briefings-statements/press-briefing-national-biodefense-strategy-091818/.

Bonnell, J. T., and Klebesadel, R. W. (1996). "A Brief History of the Discovery of Cosmic Gamma-Ray Bursts." *AIP Conference Proceedings*, 384, 977–80.

Bostrom, N. (2002a). *Anthropic Bias: Observation Selection Effects in Science and Philosophy*. Routledge.

—(2002b). "Existential Risks: Analyzing Human Extinction Scenarios and Related Hazards." *Journal of Evolution and Technology*, 9.

—(2003). "Astronomical Waste: The Opportunity Cost of Delayed Technological Development." *Utilitas*, 15(3), 308–14.

—(2005). A Philosophical Quest for our Biggest Problems (talk at TEDGlobal). https://www.ted.com/talks/nick_bostrom_on_our_biggest_problems.

—(2006). "What Is a Singleton." *Linguistic and Philosophical Investigations*, 5(2), 48–54.

—(2008). "Letter from Utopia." *Studies in Ethics, Law, and Technology*, 2(1).

—(2009). "Pascal's Mugging." *Analysis*, 69(3), 443–5.

—(2011a). "Infinite Ethics." *Analysis and Metaphysics*, 10, 9–59.

—(2011b). "Information Hazards: A Typology of Potential Harms from Knowledge." *Review of Contemporary Philosophy*, (10), 44–79.

—(2012). "The Superintelligent Will: Motivation and Instrumental Rationality in Advanced Artificial Agents." *Minds and Machines*, 22(2), 71–85.

—(2013). "Existential Risk Prevention as Global Priority." *Global Policy*, 4(1), 15–31.

—(2014). *Superintelligence: Paths, Dangers, Strategies.* Oxford University Press.

—(2018). "The Vulnerable World Hypothesis" (Working Paper, v. 3.45).

Bostrom, N., and Ćirković, M. M. (2008). "Introduction," in N. Bostrom and M. Ćirković (eds.), *Global Catastrophic Risks* (pp. 1–30). Oxford University Press.

Bostrom, N., Douglas, T., and Sandberg, A. (2016). "The Unilateralist's Curse and the Case for a Principle of Conformity." *Social Epistemology*, 30(4), 350–71.

Botkin, D. B., et al. (2007). "Forecasting the Effects of Global Warming on Biodiversity." *BioScience*, 57(3), 227–36.

Bourget, D., and Chalmers, D. J. (2014). "What Do Philosophers Believe?" *Philosophical Studies*, 170(3), 465–500.

Brand, S. (April 2000). "Taking the Long View." *Time*.

Brasier, M., McLoughlin, N., Green, O., and Wacey, D. (2006). "A Fresh Look at the Fossil Evidence for Early Archaean Cellular Life." *Philosophical Transactions of the Royal Society B: Biological Sciences*, 361(1470), 887–902.

Brezhnev, L. (1979). Brezhnev Message to President on Nuclear False Alarm, Diplomatic Cable (No. 1979STATE295771) from Sec State (D.C.) to Moscow American Embassy. National Security Archive. United States Department of State.

Bricker, D., and Ibitson, J. (2019). *Empty Planet: The Shock of Global Population Decline.* Crown.

Broder, J. (May 9, 1989). "H-Bomb Lost at Sea in '65 off Okinawa, U.S. Admits." *Los Angeles Times*.

Broome, J. (2005). "Should We Value Population?" *Journal of Political Philosophy*, 13(4), 399–413.

Browne, M. W. (January 23, 1990). "Nuclear Winter Theorists Pull Back." *The New York Times*.

Bruckner T., et al. (2014). "2014: Energy Systems," in O. Edenhofer, et al. (eds.), *Climate Change 2014: Mitigation of Climate Change. Contribution of Working Group III to the Fifth Assessment Report of the Intergovernmental Panel on Climate Change* (p. 1,465). Cambridge University Press.

Brundage, M., et al. (2018). The Malicious Use of Artificial Intelligence: Forecasting, Prevention, and Mitigation. ArXiv, https://arxiv.org/pdf/1802.07228.

Bryant, C. (2003). "Stopping Time: The Pro-Slavery and 'Irrevocable' Thirteenth Amendment." *Harvard Journal of Law and Public Policy*, 26(2), 501–49.

Buchner, B. K., et al. (2017). *Global Landscape of Climate Finance 2017.* Climate Policy Initiative.

Buck, P. S. (March 1959). "The Bomb—The End of the World?" *The American Weekly.*

Buffett, B. A., Ziegler, L., and Constable, C. G. (2013). "A Stochastic Model for Palaeomagnetic Field Variations." *Geophysical Journal International*, 195(1), 86–97.

Bulfin, A. (2015). "'To Arms!' Invasion Narratives and Late-Victorian Literature." *Literature Compass*, 12(9), 482–96.

Burke, E. (1790). *Reflections on the French Revolution.* James Dodsley.

Burr, W. (2014). "New Details on the 1961 Goldsboro Nuclear Accident." National Security Archive, Electronic Briefing Book No. 475. National Security Archive.

Butler, D., and Ledford, H. (2012). "US Biosecurity Board Revises Stance on Mutant-Flu Studies." *Nature.*

Butler, S. (June 13, 1863). *Darwin Among the Machines.* The Press.

—(1872). *Erewhon.* Ballantyne and Co.

Buttazzo, D., et al. (2013). "Investigating the Near-Criticality of the Higgs Boson." *Journal of High Energy Physics*, 2013(12), 89.

BWC ISU (2019). Biological Weapons Convention—Budgetary and Financial Matters (January 21, 2019, Letter from BWC Implementation Support Unit to BWC Representatives). https://www.unog.ch/80256E DD006B8954/(httpAssets)/1FE92995054B8108C1258394004233A D/$file/2019-0131+2018+MSP+Chair+letter+on+financial+measures .pdf.

Carlson, R. (2016). On DNA and Transistors. http://www.synthesis.cc /synthesis/2016/03/on_dna_and_transistors.

Carus, W. S. (2017). "A Century of Biological-Weapons Programs (1915–2015): Reviewing the Evidence." *The Nonproliferation Review*, 24(1–2), 129–53.

Ceballos, G., et al. (2015). "Accelerated Modern Human-Induced Species Losses: Entering the Sixth Mass Extinction." *Science Advances*, 1(5), e1400253.

Cederman, L.-E. (2003). "Modeling the Size of Wars: From Billiard Balls to Sandpiles." *The American Political Science Review*, 97(1), 135–50.

Challinor, A. J., et al. (2014). "A Meta-Analysis of Crop Yield under Climate Change and Adaptation." *Nature Climate Change*, 4(4), 287–91.

Chan, S. (September 18, 2017). "Stanislav Petrov, Soviet Officer Who Helped Avert Nuclear War, Is Dead at 77." *The New York Times*.

Chapman, C. R. (2004). "The Hazard of Near-Earth Asteroid Impacts on Earth." *Earth And Planetary Science Letters*, 222(1), 1–15.

Charney, J. G., et al. (1979). "Carbon Dioxide and Climate: A Scientific Assessment." *National Academy of Sciences*.

Chen, Z.-Q., and Benton, M. J. (2012). "The Timing and Pattern of Biotic Recovery Following the End-Permian Mass Extinction." *Nature Geoscience*, 5(6), 375–83.

Chesner, C. A., and Luhr, J. F. (2010). "A Melt Inclusion Study of the Toba Tuffs, Sumatra, Indonesia." *Journal of Volcanology and Geothermal Research*, 197(1), 259–78.

Chosewood, L. C., and Wilson, D. E. (eds.) (2009). "Biosafety in Microbiological and Biomedical Laboratories." HHS Publication No. (CDC) 21–1112 (5th ed.). Centers for Disease Control and Prevention.

Christakos, G., et al. (eds.) (2005). "Black Death: The Background," in *Interdisciplinary Public Health Reasoning and Epidemic Modelling: The Case of Black Death* (pp. 103–52). Springer.

Christian, D. (2004). *Maps of Time*. University of California Press.

Churchill, W. (1946). Speech, "The Sinews of Peace," March 5, 1946, at Westminster College, Fulton, Missouri, US [Radio Broadcast]. BBC Archives.

Ciais, P., et al. (2013). "Carbon and Other Biogeochemical Cycles," in T. F. Stocker, et al. (eds.), *Climate Change 2013: The Physical Science Basis. Contribution of Working Group I to the Fifth Assessment Report of the Intergovernmental Panel on Climate Change* (pp. 465–570). Cambridge University Press.

Ćirković, M. M., Sandberg, A., and Bostrom, N. (2010). "Anthropic Shadow: Observation Selection Effects and Human Extinction Risks." *Risk Analysis*, 30(10), 1,495–506.

Clauset, A., and Young, M. (2005). Scale Invariance in Global Terrorism. ArXiv, https://arxiv.org/abs/physics/0502014.

Clune, J. (2019). AI-GAs: AI-Generating Algorithms, an Alternate Paradigm for Producing General Artificial Intelligence. ArXiv, http://arxiv.org/abs/1905.10985.

Coale, A. J. (1974). "The History of the Human Population." *Scientific American*, 231(3), 40–51.

Cohen, G. A. (2011). "Rescuing Conservatism: A Defense of Existing Value," in *Reasons and Recognition: Essays on the Philosophy of T. M. Scanlon* (pp. 203–26). Oxford University Press.

Cohen, M. N. (1989). *Health and the Rise of Civilization*. Yale University Press.

Coles, L. S. (1994). "Computer Chess: The Drosophila of AI." *AI Expert*, 9(4).

Collingridge, D. (1982). *The Social Control of Technology*. St. Martin's Press.

Collins, G. S., Melosh, H. J., and Marcus, R. A. (2005). "Earth Impact Effects Program: A Web-Based Computer Program for Calculating the Regional Environmental Consequences of a Meteoroid Impact on Earth." *Meteoritics and Planetary Science*, 40(6), 817–40.

Collins, M., et al. (2013). "Long-Term Climate Change: Projections, Commitments and Irreversibility," in T. F. Stocker, D., et al. (eds.), *Climate Change 2013: The Physical Science Basis. Contribution of Working Group I to the Fifth Assessment Report of the Intergovernmental Panel on Climate Change* (pp. 1,029–136). Cambridge University Press.

Compton, A. H. (1956). *Atomic Quest*. Oxford University Press.

Conn, A., Toon, B., and Robock, A. (2016). Transcript: Nuclear Winter Podcast with Alan Robock and Brian Toon. https://futureoflife.org/2016/10/31/transcript-nuclear-winter-podcast-alan-robock-brian-toon/.

Conselice, C. J., Wilkinson, A., Duncan, K., and Mortlock, A. (2016). "The Evolution of Galaxy Number Density at z<8 and its Implications." *The Astrophysical Journal*, 830(2), 83.

Cook, M., and Woolf, A. (2002). "Preventing Proliferation of Biological Weapons: U.S. Assistance to the Former Soviet States" (CRS Report for Congress) [Report RL31368]. US Homeland Security Digital Library.

Cook, N. D. (1998). *Born to Die: Disease and New World Conquest, 1492–1650* (vol. 1). Cambridge University Press.

Cordell, D., Drangert, J.-O., and White, S. (2009). "The Story of Phosphorus: Global Food Security and Food for Thought." *Global Environmental Change*, 19(2), 292–305.

Cotton-Barratt, O., Daniel, M., and Sandberg, A. (n.d.). "Defence in Depth against Human Extinction: Prevention, Response, Resilience, and Why they all Matter" [manuscript in preparation].

Coupe, J., Bardeen, C. G., Robock, A., and Toon, O. B. (2019). "Nuclear Winter Responses to Nuclear War Between the United States and Russia in the Whole Atmosphere Community Climate Model Version 4 and the Goddard Institute for Space Studies ModelE." *Journal of Geophysical Research: Atmospheres*, 8,522–43.

Cropper, M. L., Aydede, S. K., and Portney, P. R. (1994). "Preferences for Life-Saving Programs: How the Public Discounts Time and Age." *Journal of Risk and Uncertainty*, 8(3), 243–65.

Cropper, W. P., and Harwell, M. A. (1986). "Food Availability after Nuclear War," in M. A. Harwell and T. C. Hutchinson (eds.), *The Environmental Consequences of Nuclear War (SCOPE 28)*, vol. 2: *Ecological, Agricultural, and Human Effects*. John Wiley and Sons.

Crosweller, H. S., et al. (2012). "Global Database on Large Magnitude Explosive Volcanic Eruptions (LaMEVE)." *Journal of Applied Volcanology*, 1(1), 4.

CSIRO (2015). Sea Level Data—Update of Reconstructed GMSL from 1880 to 2013. http://www.cmar.csiro.au/sealevel/sl_data_cmar.htm.

Cubasch, U., et al. (2013). "Introduction," in T. F. Stocker (eds.), *Climate Change 2013: The Physical Science Basis. Contribution of Working Group I to the Fifth Assessment Report of the Intergovernmental Panel on Climate Change*. Cambridge University Press.

Cui, Y., and Kump, L. R. (2015). "Global Warming and the End-Permian Extinction Event: Proxy and Modeling Perspectives." *Earth-Science Reviews*, 149, 5–22.

Cyranoski, D. (2017). "Bat Cave Solves Mystery of Deadly SARS Virus—and Suggests New Outbreak Could Occur." *Nature*, 552(7683), 15–16.

D'Errico, P. (2001). Jeffery Amherst and Smallpox Blankets. https://people.umass.edu/derrico/amherst/lord_jeff.html.

Dante Labs (2019). Dante Labs Tests. https://us.dantelabs.com /collections/our-tests.

Danzig, R., et al. (2011). "Aum Shinrikyo: Insights Into How Terrorists Develop Biological and Chemical Weapons." Center for a New American Security.

Dasgupta, P. (2007). "Commentary: The Stern Review's Economics of Climate Change." *National Institute Economic Review*, 199(1), 4–7.

—(2008). "Discounting Climate Change." *Journal of Risk and Uncertainty*, 37(2–3), 141–69.

Davenport, K. (2018). Biological Weapons Convention Signatories and States-Parties. https://www.armscontrol.org/factsheets/bwcsig.

Dawson, T. P., Jackson, S. T., House, J. I., Prentice, I. C., and Mace, G. M. (2011). "Beyond Predictions: Biodiversity Conservation in a Changing Climate." *Science*, 332(6025), 53–8.

De Vos, J. M., Joppa, L. N., Gittleman, J. L., Stephens, P. R., and Pimm, S. L. (2015). "Estimating the Normal Background Rate of Species Extinction." *Conservation Biology*, 29(2), 452–62.

Deevey, E. S. (1960). "The Human Population." *Scientific American*, 203(3), 194–204.

Denkenberger, D. C., and Blair, R. W. (2018). "Interventions that may Prevent or Mollify Supervolcanic Eruptions." *Futures*, 102, 51–62.

Denkenberger, D. C., and Pearce, J. M. (2016). "Cost-Effectiveness of Interventions for Alternate Food to Address Agricultural Catastrophes Globally." *International Journal of Disaster Risk Science*, 7(3), 205–15.

Desjardins, J. (2014). A Forecast of When We'll Run Out of Each Metal. https://www.visualcapitalist.com/forecast-when-well-run-out -of-each-metal/.

Deutsch, D. (2011). *The Beginning of Infinity: Explanations that Transform the World*. Viking.

DiCarlo, J. E., Chavez, A., Dietz, S. L., Esvelt, K. M., and Church, G. M. (2015). "Safeguarding CRISPR-Cas9 Gene Drives in Yeast." *Nature Biotechnology*, 33(12), 1,250–5.

Diderot, D. (1755). "Encyclopedia," in P. Stewart (trans.), *Encyclopédie ou Dictionnaire raisonné des sciences, des arts et des métiers*, vol. 5 (pp. 635–648A). Michigan Publishing.

DiEuliis, D., Carter, S. R., and Gronvall, G. K. (2017). "Options for Synthetic DNA Order Screening, Revisited." *MSphere*, 2(4).

Dobrynin, A. (1995). *In Confidence: Moscow's Ambassador to Six Cold War Presidents*. Random House.

DoD (1981). "Narrative Summaries of Accidents Involving US Nuclear Weapons (1950–1980)." Homeland Security Digital Library. US Department of Defense.

Dodson, R. W., and Rabi, I. I. (1954). *Meeting Minutes of the Forty-First Meeting of the General Advisory Committee to the U.S. Atomic Energy Commission*. United States Atomic Energy Commission.

Downes, L. (2009). *The Laws of Disruption: Harnessing the New Forces that Govern Business and Life in the Digital Age*. Basic Books.

Drmola, J., and Mareš, M. (2015). "Revisiting the deflection dilemma." *Astronomy and Geophysics*, 56(5), 5.15–5.18.

Drupp, M. A., Freeman, M. C., Groom, B., and Nesje, F. (2018). "Discounting Disentangled." *American Economic Journal: Economic Policy*, 10(4), 109–34.

Duplaix, N. (1988). "Fleas: The Lethal Leapers." *National Geographic*, 173(5), 672–94.

Durand, J. D. (1960). "The Population Statistics of China, A.D. 2–1953." *Population Studies*, 13(3), 209–56.

—(1977). "Historical Estimates of World Population: An Evaluation." *Population and Development Review*, 3(3), 253.

Dylan, B. (1963). "Let me die in my footsteps" [Lyrics]. *The Freewheelin' Bob Dylan*. Columbia Records.

ECDC (2014). "Communicable Disease Threats Report, Week 37, 7–13 September 2014." European Centre for Disease Prevention and Control.

Egan, G. (1997). *Diaspora*. Millennium.

Ehrlich, P., et al. (1983). "Long-Term Biological Consequences of Nuclear War." *Science*, 222(4630), 1,293–300.

Ehrlich, P. R. (September 1969). "Eco-Catastrophe." *Ramparts*.

EIA (2019). "Electric Power Monthly with Data for April 2014." US Energy Information Administration.

Eig, J. (2014). *The Birth of the Pill: How Four Crusaders Reinvented Sex and Launched a Revolution*. W. W. Norton.

Einstein, A. (1948). "A Reply to the Soviet Scientists." *Bulletin of the Atomic Scientists*, 4(2), 35–8.

Einstein, A., and *The New York Times* (May 25, 1946). "Atomic Education Urged by Einstein Scientist in Plea for $200,000 to Promote New Type of Thinking." *The New York Times*.

Eisenhower, D. (1956). Letter, DDE to Richard L. Simon, Simon and Schuster, Inc. DDE's Papers as President, DDE Diaries Series, Box 14, April 1956 Miscellaneous (5).

Ellsberg, D. (2017). *The Doomsday Machine: Confessions of a Nuclear War Planner*. Bloomsbury Publishing.

Engels, F. (1892). *The Condition of the Working Class in England in 1844* (trans. F. K. Wischnewetzky). Swan Sonnenschein and Co.

Erwin, D. H., Bowring, S. A., and Yugan, J. (2002). "End-Permian Mass Extinctions: A Review," in C. Koeberl and K. G. MacLeod (eds.), *Special Paper 356: Catastrophic Events and Mass Extinctions: Impacts and Beyond* (pp. 363–83). Geological Society of America.

Espeholt, L., et al. (2018). "{IMPALA}: Scalable Distributed Deep-{RL} with Importance Weighted Actor-Learner Architectures," in J. Dy and A. Krause (eds.), *Proceedings of the 35th International Conference on Machine Learning* (pp. 1,407–16). PMLR.

Esvelt, K. M. (2018). "Inoculating Science against Potential Pandemics and Information Hazards." *PLOS Pathogens*, 14(10), e1007286.

Everitt, T., Filan, D., Daswani, M., and Hutter, M. (2016). "Self-Modification of Policy and Utility Function in Rational Agents." *Artificial General Intelligence*, LNAI 9782, 1–11.

Farquhar, S. (2017). Changes in Funding in the AI Safety Field. https://www.centreforeffectivealtruism.org/blog/changes-in-funding-in-the-ai-safety-field/.

Feinstein, A. R., Sosin, D. M., and Wells, C. K. (1985). "The Will Rogers Phenomenon. Stage Migration and New Diagnostic Techniques as a Source of Misleading Statistics for Survival in Cancer." *The New England Journal of Medicine*, 312(25), 1,604–8.

Feld, B. T. (1976). "The Consequences of Nuclear War." *Bulletin of the Atomic Scientists*, 32(6), 10–3.

Fenner, F., and Fantini, B. (1999). "The Use of Rabbit Haemorrhagic Disease Virus for Rabbit Control," in *Biological Control of Vertebrate Pests: The History of Myxomatosis—an Experiment in Evolution*. CABI Publishing.

Flatow, I., Russell, S., and Koch, C. (2014). "Science Goes to the Movies: 'Transcendence'" (I. Flatow, interviewer) [Audio file from 24:33]. *Science Friday*.

Fleishman, J. L., Kohler, J. S., and Schindler, S. (2009). *Casebook for The Foundation: A Great American Secret*. PublicAffairs.

Foote, M., and Raup, D. M. (1996). "Fossil Preservation and the Stratigraphic Ranges of Taxa." *Paleobiology*, 22(2), 121–40.

Forden, G., Podvig, P., and Postol, T. A. (2000). "False Alarm, Nuclear Danger." *IEEE Spectrum*, 37(3), 31–9.

Forey, P. L. (1990). "The Coelacanth Fish: Progress and Prospects." *Science Progress* (1933–), 74(1), 53–67.

Frederick, S. (2003). "Measuring Intergenerational Time Preference: Are Future Lives Valued Less?" *Journal of Risk and Uncertainty*, 26(1), 39–53.

Frick, J. (2017). "On the Survival of Humanity." *Canadian Journal of Philosophy*, 47(2–3), 344–67.

Frick, J. D. (2014). "'Making People Happy, Not Making Happy People': A Defense of the Asymmetry Intuition in Population Ethics" [PhD Thesis]. Department of Philosophy, Harvard University.

Future of Life Institute (2015). Research Priorities for Robust and Beneficial Artificial Intelligence: An Open Letter. https://futureoflife .org/ai-open-letter/.

—(2017). Asilomar AI Principles. https://futureoflife.org/ai-principles/.

Galway-Witham, J., and Stringer, C. (2018). "How Did *Homo sapiens* Evolve?" *Science*, 360(6395), 1,296–8.

Gapminder. (2019). Life Expectancy (years). https://www.gapminder .org/data/.

García-Sastre, A. (2012). "Working Safely with H5N1 Viruses." *MBio*, 3(2).

Gates, R. M. (2011). *From the Shadows: The Ultimate Insider's Story of Five Presidents and How They Won the Cold War.* Simon and Schuster.

GBD (2012). "The Global Burden of Disease Study 2010." *The Lancet*, 380(9859), 2,053–260.

Gibney, E. (2018). "Belgian Priest Recognized in Hubble-Law Name Change." *Nature.*

Gietel-Basten, S. (2016). "Japan is Not the Only Country Worrying About Population Decline—Get Used to a Two-Speed World." *The Conversation.*

GiveWell (2019). 2019 GiveWell Cost-effectiveness Analysis—Version 3. https://docs.google.com/spreadsheets/d/1McptF0GVGv-QBlhWx _IoNVstWvt1z-RwVSu16ciypgs/.

Giving What We Can (2019). https://www.givingwhatwecan.org/.

Gleick, P. H., and Palaniappan, M. (2010). "Peak Water Limits to Freshwater Withdrawal and Use." *Proceedings of the National Academy of Sciences*, 107(25), 11,155–62.

GNL. (2019). Laboratory Safety at UTMB. Galveston National Laboratory, University of Texas Medical Branch. https://www.utmb.edu/gnl/about/lab-safety.

Goldberg, S. (1983). "How Many People Have Ever Lived?" in S. Goldberg (ed.), *Probability in Social Science* (pp. 19–31). Birkhäuser.

Goldblatt, C., Robinson, T. D., Zahnle, K. J., and Crisp, D. (2013). "Low Simulated Radiation Limit for Runaway Greenhouse Climates." *Nature Geoscience*, 6(8), 661–7.

Good, I. J. (1959). "Speculations on Perceptrons and Other Automata." Research Lecture, RC-115. IBM, Yorktown Heights, New York, June 2.

—(1970). "Some Future Social Repercussions of Computers." *International Journal of Environmental Studies*, 1(1–4), 67–79.

Goodchild, P. (2004). *Edward Teller, the Real Dr. Strangelove*. Harvard University Press.

Goodfellow, I. J., et al. (2014). Generative Adversarial Networks. ArXiv, https://arxiv.org/abs/1406.2661.

Goodhart, C. (1975). "Problems of Monetary Management: The U.K. Experience," in *Papers in Monetary Economics*. Reserve Bank of Australia.

Gorbachev, M., and Hertsgaard, M. (September 24, 2000). "Mikhail Gorbachev Explains What's Rotten in Russia." *Salon*.

Gordon, N. D., Jonko, A. K., Forster, P. M., and Shell, K. M. (2013). "An Observationally Based Constraint on the Water-Vapor Feedback." *Journal of Geophysical Research: Atmospheres*, 118(22), 12,435–43.

Gould, C., and Folb, P. (2002). *Project Coast: Apartheid's Chemical and Biological Warfare Programme* (R. Berold, ed.). United Nations Publications UNIDIR.

Grace, K. (2013). "Algorithmic Progress in Six Domains" [Technical report 2013-3]. Machine Intelligence Research Institute.

—(2015). "The Asilomar Conference: A Case Study in Risk Mitigation" [Technical report 2015-9]. Machine Intelligence Research Institute.

Grace, K., Salvatier, J., Dafoe, A., Zhang, B., and Evans, O. (2018). "Viewpoint: When Will AI Exceed Human Performance? Evidence from AI Experts." *Journal of Artificial Intelligence Research*, 62, 729–54.

Greaves, H., and Ord, T. (2017). "Moral Uncertainty About Population Axiology." *Journal of Ethics and Social Philosophy*, 12(2), 135–67.

Griffin, M. (2008). "NASA's Direction, Remarks at the Mars Society Convention," August 3, 2006, in *Leadership in Space: Selected Speeches of NASA Administrator Michael Griffin, May 2005–October 2008* (pp. 133–8). National Aeronautics and Space Administration.

Griffith, G. (November 1897). "The Great Crellin Comet." *Pearsons Weekly's Christmas.*

Groenewold, H. J. (1970). "Modern Science and Social Responsibility," in P. Weingartner and G. Zecha (eds.), *Induction, Physics and Ethics.* Synthese Library (Monographs on Epistemology, Logic, Methodology, Philosophy of Science, Sociology of Science and of Knowledge, and on the Mathematical Methods of Social and Behavioral Sciences), vol. 31 (pp. 359–78). Springer.

Haarnoja, T., et al. (2018). "Composable Deep Reinforcement Learning for Robotic Manipulation." 2018 IEEE International Conference on Robotics and Automation (ICRA), 6,244–51. IEEE.

Haensch, S., et al. (2010). "Distinct Clones of Yersinia Pestis Caused the Black Death." *PLOS Pathogens*, 6(10), e1001134.

Häggström, O. (2016). "Here Be Dragons: Science, Technology and the Future of Humanity," in *Here Be Dragons.* Oxford University Press.

Hanley, J. A. (1983). "If Nothing Goes Wrong, Is Everything All Right?" *JAMA*, 249(13), 1743.

Hanson, R. (2008). "Catastrophe, Social Collapse, and Human Extinction," in N. Bostrom and M. Ćirković (eds.), *Global Catastrophic Risk.* Oxford University Press.

Harari, Y. N. (2014). *Sapiens: A Brief History of Humankind.* Random House.

Harris, S. H. (2002). *Factories of Death: Japanese Biological Warfare, 1932–45, and the American Cover-Up.* Psychology Press.

Harrison, M. (1998). "The Economics of World War II: An Overview," in M. Harrison (ed.), *The Economics of World War II: Six Great Powers in International Comparison* (pp. 1–42). Cambridge University Press.

Harrod, R. F. (1948). *Towards a Dynamic Economics: Some Recent Developments of Economic Theory and Their Application to Policy.* Macmillan and Co.

Harwell, M. A., and Harwell, C. C. (1986). "Integration of Effects on Human Populations," in M. A. Harwell and T. C. Hutchinson (eds.), *The Environmental Consequences of Nuclear War (SCOPE 28)*, vol.

2: *Ecological, Agricultural, and Human Effects* (pp. 469–92). John Wiley and Sons.

Harwell, M. A., and Hutchinson, T. C. (1986). *The Environmental Consequences of Nuclear War (SCOPE 28)*, vol. 2: *Ecological, Agricultural, and Human Effects*. John Wiley and Sons.

Hasell, J., and Roser, M. (2019). Famines. Our World in Data. https://ourworldindata.org/famines.

Hassan, H., et al. (2018). Achieving Human Parity on Automatic Chinese to English News Translation. ArXiv, http://arxiv.org/abs/1803.05567.

Haub, C., and Kaneda, T. (2018). How Many People Have Ever Lived on Earth? https://www.prb.org/howmanypeoplehaveeverlivedon earth/.

He, K., Zhang, X., Ren, S., and Sun, J. (2015). "Delving Deep into Rectifiers: Surpassing Human-Level Performance on ImageNet Classification." *2015 IEEE International Conference on Computer Vision (ICCV)*, 1,026–34. IEEE.

Helfand, I. (2013). "Nuclear Famine: Two Billion People at Risk?" *Physicians for Social Responsibility*.

Henrich, J. (2015). *The Secret of Our Success: How Culture Is Driving Human Evolution, Domesticating Our Species, and Making Us Smarter*. Princeton University Press.

Herfst, S., et al. (2012). "Airborne Transmission of Influenza A/H5N1 Virus Between Ferrets." *Science*, 336(6088), 1,534–41.

Hershberg, J. G. (1995). *James B. Conant: Harvard to Hiroshima and the Making of the Nuclear Age*. Stanford University Press.

Hershberg, J., and Kelly, C. (2017). James Hershberg's Interview. https://www.manhattanprojectvoices.org/oral-histories/james-hershbergs-interview.

Heuer, R. J. (1999). "Chapter 12: Biases in Estimating Probabilities," in *Psychology of Intelligence Analysis*. Center for the Study of Intelligence.

Heyd, D. (1988). "Procreation and Value: Can Ethics Deal with Futurity Problems?" *Philosophia*, 18(2–3).

Highfield, R. (October 16, 2001). "Colonies in Space May Be Only Hope, Says Hawking." *Daily Telegraph*.

Hilts, P. J. (November 18, 1994). "Deaths in 1979 Tied to Soviet Military." *The New York Times*.

Hof, C., Levinsky, I., Araújo, M. B., and Rahbek, C. (2011). "Rethinking Species' Ability to Cope with Rapid Climate Change." *Global Change Biology*, 17(9), 2,987–90.

Holmes, D. B. (2008). *Wilbur's Story*. Lulu.com.

Honigsbaum, M. (2018). "Spanish Influenza Redux: Revisiting the Mother of all Pandemics." *The Lancet*, 391(10139), 2,492–5.

Horowitz, M. C. (2018). "Artificial Intelligence, International Competition, and the Balance of Power." *Texas National Security Review*, 1(3), 37–57.

IBM (2011). Deep Blue. https://www.ibm.com/ibm/history/ibm100/us /en/icons/deepblue/.

IDC (2019). Worldwide Spending on Artificial Intelligence Systems Will Grow to Nearly \$35.8 Billion in 2019, According to New IDC Spending Guide. https://www.idc.com/getdoc.jsp?containerId=prUS 44911419.

IEA (2018). "Costs and Benefits of Emergency Stockholding," *Insights Series 2018*, International Energy Agency.

—(2019). "Global Energy and CO2 Status Report: The Latest Trends in Energy and Emissions in 2018—Data Tables," International Energy Agency.

iGEM (2013). Jamboree/Team Abstracts. http://2013.igem.org/Jamboree /Team_Abstracts.

iGEM Minnesota Team (2016). Shifting Gene Drives Into Reverse: Now Mosquitoes Are the Yeast of Our Worries. http://2016.igem.org /Team:Minnesota.

IGSC (2018). International Gene Synthesis Consortium Updates Screening Protocols for Synthetic DNA Products and Services. https:// www.prnewswire.com/news-releases/international-gene-synthesis -consortium-updates-screening-protocols-for-synthetic-dna -products-and-services-300576867.html?tc=eml_cleartime.

Imai, M., et al. (2012). "Experimental Adaptation of an Influenza H5 HA Confers Respiratory Droplet Transmission to a Reassortant H5 HA/H1N1 Virus in Ferrets." *Nature*, 486(7403), 420–8.

IMARC Group (2019). "Ice Cream Market: Global Industry Trends, Share, Size, Growth, Opportunity and Forecast 2019–2024." *IMARC*.

Imperiale, M. J., and Hanna, M. G. (2012). "Biosafety Considerations of Mammalian-Transmissible H5N1 Influenza." *MBio*, 3(2).

IPCC (2014). "Summary for Policymakers," in C. B. Field, et al. (eds.), *Climate Change 2014: Impacts, Adaptation, and Vulnerability. Part A: Global and Sectoral Aspects. Contribution of Working Group II to the Fifth Assessment Report of the Intergovernmental Panel on Climate Change* (pp. 1–32). Cambridge University Press.

Jamison, D. T., et al. (2018). "Universal Health Coverage and Intersectoral Action for Health: Key Messages from Disease Control Priorities," 3rd ed. *The Lancet*, 391(10125), 1,108–20.

Jamison, D. T., et al. (eds.) (2006). *Disease Control Priorities in Developing Countries*, 2nd ed. Oxford University Press.

Jamison, D. T., et al. (eds.) (2018). *Disease Control Priorities: Improving Health and Reducing Poverty*, vol. 9: *Disease Control Priorities*, 3rd ed. Washington, D.C.: World Bank.

Jamison, D. T., et al. (eds.) (2006). *Global Burden of Disease and Risk Factors*. World Bank and Oxford University Press.

Jamison, D. T., Mosley, W. H., Measham, A. R., and Bobadilla, J. L. (eds.) (1993). *Disease Control Priorities in Developing Countries*. Oxford University Press.

Jenkin, J. G. (2011). "Atomic Energy is 'Moonshine': What Did Rutherford Really Mean?" *Physics in Perspective*, 13(2), 128–45.

Jia, Y., et al. (2018). "Transfer Learning from Speaker Verification to Multispeaker Text-to-Speech Synthesis." *Advances in Neural Information Processing Systems*, 4,480–90.

Jinek, M., et al. (2012). "A Programmable Dual-RNA-Guided DNA Endonuclease in Adaptive Bacterial Immunity." *Science*, 337(6096), 816–21.

Jonas, H. (1984 [1979]). *The Imperative of Responsibility*. University of Chicago Press.

Jones, K. E., et al. (2008). "Global Trends in Emerging Infectious Diseases." *Nature*, 451(7181), 990–3.

Jones, N., O'Brien, M., and Ryan, T. (2018). "Representation of Future Generations in United Kingdom Policy-Making." *Futures*, 102, 153–63.

JPL (2019a). Discovery Statistics—Cumulative Totals. https://cneos.jp l.nasa.gov/stats/totals.html.

—(2019b). Small-Body Database. https://ssd.jpl.nasa.gov/sbdb.cgi.

Kaempffert, W. (September 12, 1933). "Rutherford Cools Atom Energy Hope." *The New York Times*.

Kahneman, D. (2011). *Thinking, Fast and Slow*. Macmillan.

Kaplan, J. O., Pfeiffer, M., Kolen, J. C. A., and Davis, B. A. S. (2016). "Large-Scale Anthropogenic Reduction of Forest Cover in Last Glacial Maximum Europe." *PLOS ONE*, 11(11), e0166726.

Karras, T., Aila, T., Laine, S., and Lehtinen, J. (2017). Progressive Growing of GANs for Improved Quality, Stability, and Variation. ArXiv, http://arxiv.org/abs/1710.10196.

Keele, B. F. (2006). "Chimpanzee Reservoirs of Pandemic and Nonpandemic HIV-1." *Science*, 313(5786), 523–6.

Keeter, B. (2017). NASA Office to Coordinate Asteroid Detection, Hazard Mitigation. https://www.nasa.gov/feature/nasa-office-to -coordinate-asteroid-detection-hazard-mitigation.

Kellogg, E. A. (2013). "C4 photosynthesis." *Current Biology*, 23(14), R594–9.

Kelly, J. (2006). *The Great Mortality: An Intimate History of the Black Death, the Most Devastating Plague of All Time*. HarperCollins.

Kennedy, J. F. (1961). JFK Address at UN General Assembly, September 25, 1961. JFK Library Foundation.

—(1962). "Message from the President John F. Kennedy to the Bulletin of the Atomic Scientists." *Bulletin of the Atomic Scientists*, 18(10), 2.

—(1963). American University Address, June 10, 1963. Washington, D.C. John F. Kennedy Library.

King, D., et al. (2015). *Climate Change: A Risk Assessment*. Centre for Science and Policy.

Knight, F. H. (1921). *Risk, Uncertainty and Profit*. Houghton Mifflin.

Koch, A., Brierley, C., Maslin, M. M., and Lewis, S. L. (2019). "Earth System Impacts of the European Arrival and Great Dying in the Americas after 1492." *Quaternary Science Reviews*, 207, 13–36.

Kocić, J., Jovičić, N., and Drndarević, V. (2019). "An End-to-End Deep Neural Network for Autonomous Driving Designed for Embedded Automotive Platforms." *Sensors*, 19(9), 2,064.

Kolbert, E. (2014). *The Sixth Extinction: An Unnatural History*. Henry Holt and Company.

Kondratyev, K. Y., Krapivin, V. F., and Varotsos, C. A. (2003). *Global Carbon Cycle and Climate Change*. Springer.

Konopinski, E. J., Marvin, C., and Teller, E. (1946). Ignition of the Atmosphere with Nuclear Bombs [Report LA-602]. Los Alamos National Laboratory.

Krasovsky, V., and Shklovsky, I. (1957). "Supernova Explosions and their Possible Effect on the Evolution of Life on the Earth." *Proceedings of the USSR Academy of Sciences*, 116, 197–9.

Kristensen, H. M., and Korda, M. (2018). "Indian Nuclear Forces, 2018." *Bulletin of the Atomic Scientists*, 74(6), 361–6.

—(2019a). "Chinese Nuclear Forces, 2019." *Bulletin of the Atomic Scientists*, 75(4), 171–8.

—(2019b). "French Nuclear Forces, 2019." *Bulletin of the Atomic Scientists*, 75(1), 51–5.

—(2019c). "Russian Nuclear Forces, 2019." *Bulletin of the Atomic Scientists*, 75(2), 73–84.

—(2019d). Status of World Nuclear Forces. https://fas.org/issues /nuclear-weapons/status-world-nuclear-forces/.

—(2019e). "United States Nuclear Forces, 2019." *Bulletin of the Atomic Scientists*, 75(3), 122–34.

Kristensen, H. M., and Norris, R. S. (2018). "North Korean Nuclear Capabilities, 2018." *Bulletin of the Atomic Scientists*, 74(1), 41–51.

Kristensen, H. M., Norris, R. S., and Diamond, J. (2018). "Pakistani Nuclear Forces, 2018." *Bulletin of the Atomic Scientists*, 74(5), 348–58.

Kühn, U., and Péczeli, A. (2017). "Russia, NATO, and the INF Treaty." *Strategic Studies Quarterly*, 11(1), 66–99.

Labelle, F. (2017). Elo Win Probability Calculator. https://wismuth.com /elo/calculator.html#system=goratings.

Le Quéré, C., et al. (2018). "Global Carbon Budget 2018." *Earth System Science Data*, 10(4), 2,141–94.

Lebedev, A. (May 21, 2004). "The Man Who Saved the World Finally Recognized." MosNews.

Leconte, J., Forget, F., Charnay, B., Wordsworth, R., and Pottier, A. (2013). "Increased Insolation Threshold for Runaway Greenhouse Processes on Earth-Like Planets." *Nature*, 504(7479), 268–71.

Lederberg, J. (1969). "Biological Warfare and the Extinction of Man." Stanford M.D., 8(4), 15–17.

Lee, C. (2009). "Who Were the Mongols (1100–1400 CE)? An Examination of their Population History," in J. Bemmann, H. Parzinger, E. Pohl, and D. Tseveendorzh (eds.), *Current Archaeological Research in Mongolia* (pp. 579–92). Rheinische Friedrich-Wilhelms-Universität Bonn.

Legg, S., and Kruel, A. (2011). Q & A with Shane Legg on Risks from AI. https://www.lesswrong.com/posts/No5JpRCHzBrWA4jmS/q-and-a -with-shane-legg-on-risks-from-ai.

Leitenberg, M. (2001). "Biological Weapons in the Twentieth Century: A Review and Analysis." *Critical Reviews in Microbiology*, 27(4), 267–320.

Lepore, J. (January 30, 2017). "The Atomic Origins of Climate Science." *The New Yorker.*

Leroy, E. M., et al. (2005). "Fruit Bats as Reservoirs of Ebola Virus." *Nature,* 438(7068), 575–6.

Leslie, J. (1996). *The End of the World: The Science and Ethics of Human Extinction.* Routledge.

Lewis, C. S. (1943). *The Abolition of Man.* Oxford University Press.

Lewis, G. (2018). Horsepox Synthesis: A Case of the Unilateralist's Curse? https://thebulletin.org/2018/02/horsepox-synthesis-a-case-of-the -unilateralists-curse/.

Lewis, G., Millett, P., Sandberg, A., Snyder-Beattie, A., and Gronvall, G. (2019), "Information Hazards in Biotechnology." *Risk Analysis,* 39(5), 975–81.

Lightbown, S. (2017). VC Investment in Biotech Blasts through $10B Barrier in 2017. https://pitchbook.com/news/articles /vc-investment-in-biotech-blasts-through-10b-barrier-in-2017.

Lindsey, R. (2018). Climate Change: Atmospheric Carbon Dioxide. https://www.climate.gov/news-features/understanding-climate /climate-change-atmospheric-carbon-dioxide.

Lingam, M. (2019). "Revisiting the Biological Ramifications of Variations in Earth's Magnetic Field." *The Astrophysical Journal,* 874(2), L28.

Liu, M.-Y., and Tuzel, O. (2016). Coupled Generative Adversarial Networks. ArXiv, https://arxiv.org/pdf/1606.07536.

Livi-Bacci, M. (2017). *A Concise History of World Population* (6th ed.). John Wiley and Sons.

Longrich, N. R., Scriberas, J., and Wills, M. A. (2016). "Severe Extinction and Rapid Recovery of Mammals across the Cretaceous-Palaeogene Boundary, and the Effects of Rarity on Patterns of Extinction and Recovery." *Journal of Evolutionary Biology,* 29(8), 1,495–512.

Lordkipanidze, D., et al. (2006). "A Fourth Hominin Skull from Dmanisi, Georgia." *The Anatomical Record* Part A: Discoveries in Molecular, Cellular, and Evolutionary Biology, 288A(11), 1146–57.

Lovelock, J. (2019). *Novacene: The Coming Age of Hyperintelligence.* Penguin.

LSA (2014). Global sea level time series. Laboratory for Satellite Altimetry, NOAA/NESDIS/STAR.

Ma, W., Kahn, R. E., and Richt, J. A. (2008). "The Pig as a Mixing Vessel for Influenza Viruses: Human and Veterinary Implications." *Journal* of *Molecular and Genetic Medicine: An International Journal of Biomedical Research*, 3(1), 158–66.

MacAskill, W., Bykvist, K., and Ord, T. (n.d.). *Moral Uncertainty* (in press). Oxford University Press.

MacAskill, W. (2014). "Normative Uncertainty" [PhD Thesis]. Faculty of Philosophy, University of Oxford.

—(2015). *Doing Good Better: Effective Altruism and a Radical New Way to Make a Difference*. Guardian Faber Publishing.

MacAskill, W., and Ord, T. (2018). "Why Maximize Expected Choice-Worthiness?" *Noûs*, 1–27.

Macaulay, T. B. (1900). *The Complete Works of Thomas Babington Macaulay*, vol. 6. Houghton Mifflin.

Maddison, A. (2010). Historical Statistics of the World Economy: 1–2008 AD. https://datasource.kapsarc.org/explore/dataset/historical-statistics-of-the-world-economy-1-2008-ad/.

Mainzer, A., et al. (2011). "NEOWISE Observations of Near-earth Objects: Preliminary Results." *The Astrophysical Journal*, 743(2), 156.

Mangus, S., and Larsen, W. (2004). "Lunar Receiving Laboratory Project History" [Report S-924]. NASA.

Mann, C. C. (January 2018). "The Book that Incited a Worldwide Fear of Overpopulation." *Smithsonian Magazine*.

Marin, F., and Beluffi, C. (2018). Computing the Minimal Crew for a Multi-Generational Space Travel towards Proxima Centauri b. ArXiv, http://arxiv.org/abs/1806.03856.

Mason, B., Pyle, D., and Oppenheimer, C. (2004). "The Size and Frequency of the Largest Explosive Eruptions on Earth." *Bulletin of Volcanology*, 66(8), 735–48.

Masson-Delmotte, V., et al. (2013). "Information from Paleoclimate Archives," in T. F. Stocker, et al. (eds.), *Climate Change 2013: The Physical Science Basis. Contribution of Working Group I to the Fifth Assessment Report of the Intergovernmental Panel on Climate Change* (pp. 383–464). Cambridge University Press.

Mastrandrea, M., et al. (2010). "Guidance Note for Lead Authors of the IPCC Fifth Assessment Report on Consistent Treatment of Uncertainties." IPCC.

May, R. M. (1997). "The Dimensions of Life on Earth," in P. H. Raven (ed.), *Nature and Human Society: The Quest for a Sustainable World*. National Academies Press.

McCarthy, J., Minsky, M. L., Rochester, N., and Shannon, C. E. (1955). "A Proposal for the Dartmouth Summer Research Project on Artificial Intelligence." Unpublished.

McDonald's Corporation (2018). Form 10-K, "Annual Report Pursuant to Section 13 or 15(D) of the Securities Exchange Act of 1934 for the Fiscal Year ended December 31, 2017" (McDonald's Corporation 2017 Annual Report). McDonald's Corporation.

McEvedy, C., and Jones, R. (1978). *Atlas of World Population History*. Penguin.

McGuire, B. (1965). "Eve of Destruction" [Lyrics]. Dunhill.

McInerney, F. A., and Wing, S. L. (2011). "The Paleocene-Eocene Thermal Maximum: A Perturbation of Carbon Cycle, Climate, and Biosphere with Implications for the Future." *Annual Review of Earth and Planetary Sciences*, 39(1), 489–516.

McKinnon, C. (2017). "Endangering Humanity: An International Crime?" *Canadian Journal of Philosophy*, 47(2–3), 395–415.

McNamara, R. S. (October 14, 1992). "One Minute to Doomsday." *The New York Times*.

Mecklin, J. (2018). "It is 5 Minutes to Midnight." *Bulletin of the Atomic Scientists*, 63(1), 66–71.

Medwin, T. (1824). *Conversations of Lord Byron*. H. Colburn.

Mellor, D. H. (1995). "Cambridge Philosophers I: F. P. Ramsey." *Philosophy*, 70(272), 243–62.

Melott, A. L., et al. (2004). "Did a Gamma-Ray Burst Initiate the Late Ordovician Mass Extinction?" *International Journal of Astrobiology*, 3(1), 55–61.

Melott, A. L., and Thomas, B. C. (2011). "Astrophysical Ionizing Radiation and Earth: A Brief Review and Census of Intermittent Intense Sources." *Astrobiology*, 11(4), 343–61.

Menzel, P. T. (2011). "Should the Value of Future Health Benefits Be Time-Discounted?" in *Prevention vs. Treatment: What's the Right Balance?* (pp. 246–73). Oxford University Press.

Metz, C. (June 9, 2018). "Mark Zuckerberg, Elon Musk and the Feud Over Killer Robots." *The New York Times*.

Milanovic, B. (2016). *Global Inequality: A New Approach for the Age of Globalization*. Harvard University Press.

Minsky, M. (1984). Afterword, in *True Names*. Bluejay Books.

Mnih, V., et al. (2015). "Human-Level Control through Deep Reinforcement Learning." *Nature*, 518(7540), 529–33.

Montgomery, P. (June 13, 1982). "Throngs Fill Manhattan to Protest Nuclear Weapons." *The New York Times*.

Moore, G. E. (1903). *Principia Ethica*. Cambridge University Press.

Moravec, H. (1988). *Mind Children: The Future of Robot and Human Intelligence*. Harvard University Press.

Morris, E. (2003). *The Fog of War*. Sony.

Muehlhauser, L. (2017). How Big a Deal Was the Industrial Revolution? http://lukemuehlhauser.com/industrial-revolution/.

Mummert, A., Esche, E., Robinson, J., and Armelagos, G. J. (2011). "Stature and Robusticity during the Agricultural Transition: Evidence from the Bioarchaeological Record." *Economics and Human Biology*, 9(3), 284–301.

Musk, E. (2018). Q & A at South by Southwest 2018 Conference [Video]. https://youtu.be/kzlUyrccbos?t=2458.

Mutze, G., Cooke, B., and Alexander, P. (1998). "The Initial Impact of Rabbit Hemorrhagic Disease on European Rabbit Populations in South Australia." *Journal of Wildlife Diseases*, 34(2), 221–7.

Naeye, R. (2008). A Stellar Explosion You Could See on Earth! https://www.nasa.gov/mission_pages/swift/bursts/brightest_grb.html.

Narveson, J. (1973). "Moral Problems of Population." *Monist*, 57(1), 62–86.

NASA (2011). NASA Space Telescope Finds Fewer Asteroids Near Earth (NASA Content Administrator, ed.). https://www.nasa.gov/mission_pages/WISE/news/wise20110929.html%0A.

National Research Council (2002). "Appendix B: A History of the Lunar Receiving Laboratory," in *The Quarantine and Certification of Martian Samples*. National Academies Press.

—(2010). *Defending Planet Earth: Near-Earth-Object Surveys and Hazard Mitigation Strategies*. Washington, D.C.: National Academies Press.

Nesbit, M., and Illés, A. (2015). "Establishing an EU 'Guardian for Future Generations'"—Report and Recommendations for the World Future Council, Institute for European Environmental Policy.

Newton, I., and McGuire, J. E. (1970). "Newton's 'Principles of Philosophy': An Intended Preface for the 1704 'Opticks' and a

Related Draft Fragment." *The British Journal for the History of Science*, 5(2), 178–86.

Ng, Y.-K. (1989). "What Should We Do About Future Generations?: Impossibility of Parfit's Theory X." *Economics and Philosophy*, 5(2), 235–53.

—(2005), "Intergenerational Impartiality: Replacing Discounting by Probability Weighting." *Journal of Agricultural and Environmental Ethics*, 18(3), 237–57.

—(2016). "The Importance of Global Extinction in Climate Change Policy." *Global Policy*, 7(3), 315–22.

NHGRI (2018). Human Genome Project FAQ. https://www.genome .gov/human-genome-project/Completion-FAQ.

NOAA (2019). Global Monthly Mean CO2. https://www.esrl.noaa .gov/gmd/ccgg/trends/.

Norris, R. S., and Kristensen, H. M. (2012). "The Cuban Missile Crisis: A Nuclear Order of Battle, October and November 1962." *Bulletin of the Atomic Scientists*, 68(6), 85–91.

Nunn, N., and Qian, N. (2010). "The Columbian Exchange: A History of Disease, Food, and Ideas." *Journal of Economic Perspectives*, 24(2), 163–88.

O'Toole, G. (2013). If the Bee Disappeared Off the Face of the Earth, Man Would Only Have Four Years Left to Live. https://quoteinvestigator .com/2013/08/27/einstein-bees/.

Obama, B. (2016). Remarks by President Obama and Prime Minister Abe of Japan at Hiroshima Peace Memorial. Obama White House.

Office for Technology Assessment (1979). *The Effects of Nuclear War.*

Ogburn, W. F. (1937). *Technological Trends and National Policy, including the Social Implications of New Inventions.* HathiTrust.

Oman, L., and Shulman, C. (2012). Nuclear Winter and Human Extinction: Q & A with Luke Oman. http://www.overcomingbias .com/2012/11/nuclear-winter-and-human-extinction-qa-with-luke -oman.html.

Omohundro, S. M. (2008). "The Basic AI Drives." *Proceedings of the 2008 Conference on Artificial General Intelligence*, 483–92. IOS Press.

OPCW (2017). "The Structure of the OPCW" [Fact Sheet]. Organisation for the Prohibition of Chemical Weapons.

—(2018). Decision—Programme and Budget of the OPCW for 2019. https://www.opcw.org/sites/default/files/documents/2018/11/c23dec10%28e%29.pdf.

Ord, T. (2013). *The Moral Imperative toward Cost-Effectiveness in Global Health.* The Center for Global Development.

—(2015). "Moral Trade." *Ethics*, 126(1), 118–38.

Ord, T., and Beckstead, N. (2014). Chapter 10, in M. Walport and C. Craig (eds.), *Innovation: Managing Risk, Not Avoiding It.* The Government Chief Scientific Adviser's annual report.

Ord, T., Hillerbrand, R., and Sandberg, A. (2010). "Probing the Improbable: Methodological Challenges for Risks with Low Probabilities and High Stakes." *Journal of Risk Research*, 13(2), 191–205.

Orseau, L., and Armstrong, S. (2016). "Safely Interruptible Agents." *Proceedings of the Thirty-Second Conference on Uncertainty in Artificial Intelligence*, 557–66. AUAI Press.

Orwell, G. (1949). *Nineteen Eighty-Four.* Secker and Warburg.

—(2013). "To Noel Willmett/18 May 1944," in P. Davison (ed.), *George Orwell: A Life in Letters.* Liveright Publishing.

OSTP (2016). "Request for Information on the Future of Artificial Intelligence: Public Responses." White House Office of Science and Technology Policy.

Overbye, D. (April 12, 2016). "Reaching for the Stars, Across 4.37 Light-Years." *The New York Times.*

Oxnard Press-Courier (March 12, 1958). "Accidents Stir Concern Here and in Britain." *Oxnard Press-Courier.*

Parfit, D. (1984). *Reasons and Persons.* Oxford University Press.

—(2017a). "Future People, the Non-Identity Problem, and Person-Affecting Principles." *Philosophy and Public Affairs*, 45(2), 118–57.

—(2017b). *On What Matters*, vol. 3. Oxford University Press.

Pauling, L. (1962). "Linus Pauling Nobel Lecture: Science and Peace." The Nobel Peace Prize 1962. Nobel Media.

Peabody Energy (2018). "2018 Annual Report." Peabody Energy Corp.

Pearl, J. (2000). *Causality: Models, Reasoning and Inference.* Cambridge University Press.

Pearson, G. (1999). *The UNSCOM Saga: Chemical and Biological Weapons Non-Proliferation.* St. Martin's Press.

Philips, A. F. (1998). 20 Mishaps That Might Have Started Accidental Nuclear War. http://nuclearfiles.org/menu/key-issues/nuclear-weapons/issues/accidents/20-mishaps-maybe-caused-nuclear-war.htm.

Phillips, P. J., et al. (2011). "Distinguishing Identical Twins by Face Recognition." *Face and Gesture*, 185–92. IEEE.

Phoenix, C., and Drexler, E. (2004). "Safe Exponential Manufacturing." *Nanotechnology*, 15(8), 869–72.

Pierrehumbert, R. T. (2013). "Hot Climates, High Sensitivity." *Proceedings of the National Academy of Sciences*, 110(35), 14,118–19.

Pigou, A. C. (1920). *The Economics of Welfare* (1st ed.). Macmillan and Co.

Pimm, S. L., Russell, G. J., Gittleman, J. L., and Brooks, T. M. (1995). "The Future of Biodiversity." *Science*, 269(5222), 347–50.

Pinker, S. (2012). *The Better Angels of Our Nature: Why Violence has Declined*. Penguin.

—(2018). *Enlightenment Now: The Case for Reason, Science, Humanism, and Progress*. Penguin.

Piran, T., and Jimenez, R. (2014). "Possible Role of Gamma Ray Bursts on Life Extinction in the Universe." *Physical Review Letters*, 113(23), 231102-1–231102-6.

Pope, K. O., Baines, K. H., Ocampo, A. C., and Ivanov, B. A. (1997). "Energy, Volatile Production, and Climatic Effects of the Chicxulub Cretaceous/Tertiary Impact." *Journal of Geophysical Research: Planets*, 102(E9), 21,645–64.

Popp, M., Schmidt, H., and Marotzke, J. (2016). "Transition to a Moist Greenhouse with CO_2 and Solar Forcing." *Nature Communications*, 7(1), 10,627.

Putin, V. (2018). Presidential Address to the Federal Assembly. http://en.kremlin.ru/events/president/news/56957.

Quigley, J., and Revie, M. (2011). "Estimating the Probability of Rare Events: Addressing Zero Failure Data." *Risk Analysis*, 31(7), 1,120–32.

Radford, A., Metz, L., and Chintala, S. (2015). Unsupervised Representation Learning with Deep Convolutional Generative Adversarial Networks. ArXiv, https://arxiv.org/pdf/1511.06434.

Raible, C. C., et al. (2016). "Tambora 1815 as a Test Case for High Impact Volcanic Eruptions: Earth System Effects." *Wiley Interdisciplinary Reviews: Climate Change*, 7(4), 569–89.

Rampino, M. R., and Self, S. (1992). "Volcanic Winter and Accelerated Glaciation Following the Toba Super-Eruption." *Nature*, 359(6390), 50–2.

Ramsey, F. P. (1928). "A Mathematical Theory of Saving." *The Economic Journal*, 38(152), 543.

RAND (n.d.). RAND Database of Worldwide Terrorism Incidents. https://www.rand.org/nsrd/projects/terrorism-incidents.html.

Ranjan, R., et al. (2018). "Deep Learning for Understanding Faces: Machines May Be Just as Good, or Better, than Humans." *IEEE Signal Processing Magazine*, 35(1), 66–83.

Rawls, J. (1971). *A Theory of Justice*. Belknap.

Reagan, R., and Weinraub, B. (February 12, 1985). "Transcript of Interview with President Reagan on a Range of Issues." *The New York Times*.

Rees, M. (2003). *Our Final Century*. Random House.

Reisner, J., et al. (2018). "Climate Impact of a Regional Nuclear Weapons Exchange: An Improved Assessment Based on Detailed Source Calculations." *Journal of Geophysical Research: Atmospheres*, 123(5), 2,752–72.

Rhodes, C. J., and Anderson, R. M. (1996). "Power Laws Governing Epidemics in Isolated Populations." *Nature*, 381(6583), 600–2.

Rhodes, R. (1986). *The Making of the Atomic Bomb*. Simon and Schuster.

—(1995). *Dark Sun: The Making of the Hydrogen Bomb*. Simon and Schuster.

Riess, A. G., et al. (1998). "Observational Evidence from Supernovae for an Accelerating Universe and a Cosmological Constant." *The Astronomical Journal*, 116(3), 1,009–38.

Risø (1970). *Project Crested Ice. A Joint Danish-American Report on the Crash near Thule Air Base on 21 January 1968 of a B-52 Bomber Carrying Nuclear Weapons* (Report No. 213). Forskningscenter Risø, Atomenergikommissionen.

Ritchie, H., and Roser, M. (2019). CO_2 and Other Greenhouse Gas Emissions. Our World in Data. https://ourworldindata.org /co2-and-other-greenhouse-gas-emissions.

Roberts, Paul. (2004). *The End of Oil*. Bloomsbury.

Roberts, Priscilla. (2012). *Cuban Missile Crisis: The Essential Reference Guide*. Abc-clio.

Robock, A., et al. (2009). "Did the Toba Volcanic Eruption of ~74 ka B.P. Produce Widespread Glaciation?" *Journal of Geophysical Research: Atmospheres*, 114(D10).

Robock, A., Oman, L., and Stenchikov, G. L. (2007). "Nuclear Winter Revisited with a Modern Climate Model and Current Nuclear Arsenals: Still Catastrophic Consequences." *Journal of Geophysical Research: Atmospheres*, 112(D13).

Robock, A., et al. (2007). "Climatic Consequences of Regional Nuclear Conflicts." *Atmospheric Chemistry and Physics*, 7(8), 2,003–12.

Rogelj, J., et al. (2016). "Differences between Carbon Budget Estimates Unravelled." *Nature Climate Change*, 6(3), 245–52.

Roser, M. (2015). The Short History of Global Living Conditions and Why it Matters that we Know it. https://ourworldindata .org/a-history-of-global-living-conditions-in-5-charts.

Roser, M., and Ortiz-Ospina, E. (2019a). Global Extreme Poverty: Our World in Data. https://ourworldindata.org/extreme-poverty.

—(2019b). Literacy: Our World in Data. https://ourworldindata.org /literacy.

—(2019). World Population Growth: Our World in Data. https:// ourworldindata.org/world-population-growth.

Rougier, J., Sparks, R. S. J., Cashman, K. V., and Brown, S. K. (2018). "The Global Magnitude–Frequency Relationship for Large Explosive Volcanic Eruptions." *Earth and Planetary Science Letters*, 482, 621–9.

Rowe, T., and Beard, S. (2018). "Probabilities, Methodologies and the Evidence Base in Existential Risk Assessments" [working paper].

Rushby, A. J., et al. (2018). "Long-Term Planetary Habitability and the Carbonate-Silicate Cycle." *Astrobiology*, 18(5), 469–80.

Russell, B. (August 18, 1945). "The Bomb and Civilisation." *Forward*.

—(March 1951). "The Future of Man." *The Atlantic*.

—(2002). "1955 address to the world's press assembled in London: The Russell-Einstein Manifesto," in K. Coates, J. Rotblat, and N. Chomsky (eds.), *The Russell-Einstein Manifesto: Fifty Years On* (Albert Einstein, Bertrand Russell, Manifesto 50). Spokesman Books.

—(2009). *Autobiography*. Taylor and Francis.

—(2012). "Letter to Einstein, 11 February 1955," in K. Coates, J. Rotblat, and N. Chomsky (eds.), *The Russell-Einstein Manifesto: Fifty Years On* (Albert Einstein, Bertrand Russell, Manifesto 50) (pp. 29–30). Spokesman Books.

Russell, S. (2014). Of Myths And Moonshine. https://www.edge.org /conversation/the-myth-of-ai#26015.

—(2015). Will They Make Us Better People? https://www.edge.org /response-detail/26157.

—(2019). *Human Compatible: AI and the Problem of Control*. Allen Lane.

Russell, S., Dewey, D., and Tegmark, M. (2015). "Research Priorities for Robust and Beneficial Artificial Intelligence." *AI Magazine*, 36(4).

SAC (1969). "Project CRESTED ICE: The Thule Nuclear Accident (U)," SAC Historical Study #113. Strategic Air Command.

Sagan, C. (1980). *Cosmos* (1st ed.). Random House.

—(1983). "Nuclear War and Climatic Catastrophe: Some Policy Implications." *Foreign Affairs*, 62(2).

—(1994). *Pale Blue Dot: A Vision of the Human Future in Space.* Random House.

Sagan, C., et al. (December 14, 1980). *Cosmos: A Personal Voyage—Episode 12: Encyclopaedia Galactica* [TV Series]. PBS.

Sagan, C., and Ostro, S. J. (1994). "Dangers of Asteroid Deflection." *Nature*, 368(6471), 501.

Sandberg, A. (n.d.). Dyson Sphere FAQ. https://www.aleph.se/Nada /dysonFAQ.html.

Sandberg, A., Drexler, E., and Ord, T. (2018). Dissolving the Fermi Paradox. ArXiv, http://arxiv.org/abs/1806.02404.

Schaefer, K., et al. (2014). "The Impact of the Permafrost Carbon Feedback on Global Climate." *Environmental Research Letters*, 9(8), 085003, pp. 1–9.

Scheffler, S. (2009). "Immigration and the Significance of Culture," in N. Holtug, K. Lippert-Rasmussen, and S. Lægaard (eds.), *Nationalism and Multiculturalism in a World of Immigration* (pp. 119–50). Palgrave Macmillan UK.

—(2018). *Why Worry About Future Generations?* in Uehiro Series in Practical Ethics. Oxford University Press.

Schell, J. (1982). *The Fate of the Earth.* Avon.

—(June 14, 2007). "The Spirit of June 12." *The Nation.*

Schindewolf, O. H. (1954). "Über die möglichen Ursachen der grossen erdgeschichtlichen Faunenschnitte." *Neues Jahrbuch für Geologie und Paläontologie, Monatshefte*, 1954, 457–65.

Schirrmeister, B. E., Antonelli, A., and Bagheri, H. C. (2011). "The Origin of Multicellularity in Cyanobacteria." *BMC Evolutionary Biology*, 11(1), 45.

Schlosser, E. (2013). *Command and Control: Nuclear Weapons, the Damascus Accident, and the Illusion of Safety.* Penguin.

Schneider, E., and Sachde, D. (2013). "The Cost of Recovering Uranium from Seawater by a Braided Polymer Adsorbent System." *Science and Global Security*, 21(2), 134–63.

Schneider von Deimling, T., Ganopolski, A., Held, H., and Rahmstorf, S. (2006). "How Cold Was the Last Glacial Maximum?" *Geophysical Research Letters*, 33(14).

Schröder, K.-P., and Connon Smith, R. (2008). "Distant Future of the Sun and Earth Revisited." *Monthly Notices of the Royal Astronomical Society*, 386(1), 155–63.

Schulte, P., et al. (2010). "The Chicxulub Asteroid Impact and Mass Extinction at the Cretaceous-Paleogene Boundary." *Science*, 327(5970), 1,214–8.

Seneca, L. A. (1972). *Natural Questions*, vol. II (trans. T. H. Corcoran). Harvard University Press.

Serber, R. (1992). *The Los Alamos Primer: The First Lectures on How to Build an Atomic Bomb*. University of California Press.

Shapira, P., and Kwon, S. (2018). "Synthetic Biology Research and Innovation Profile 2018: Publications and Patents." *BioRxiv*, 485805.

Shelley, M. W. (1826). *The Last Man* (1st ed.). Henry Colburn.

—(2009). "Introduction," in S. Curran (ed.), *Frankenstein* (vol. 1). University of Colorado, Boulder (original work published in 1831).

Sherwood, S. C., and Huber, M. (2010). "An Adaptability Limit to Climate Change due to Heat Stress." *Proceedings of the National Academy of Sciences*, 107(21), 9,552–5.

Shoham, D., and Wolfson, Z. (2004). "The Russian Biological Weapons Program: Vanished or Disappeared?" *Critical Reviews in Microbiology*, 30(4), 241–61.

Shoham, Y., et al. (2018). "The AI Index 2018 Annual Report." AI Index Steering Committee, Human-Centered AI Initiative.

Shooter, R. A., et al. (1980). "Report of the Investigation into the Cause of the 1978 Birmingham Smallpox Occurrence." Her Majesty's Stationery Office.

Shu, D.-G., et al. (1999). "Lower Cambrian Vertebrates from South China." *Nature*, 402(6757), 42–6.

Siddiqi, A. A. (2010). *The Red Rockets' Glare: Spaceflight and the Russian Imagination, 1857–1957*. Cambridge University Press.

Sidgwick, H. (1907). Book III, Chapter IX, in *The Methods of Ethics* (2nd ed., pp. 327–31). Macmillan (original work published 1874).

Silver, D., et al. (2018). "A General Reinforcement Learning Algorithm that Masters Chess, Shogi, and Go through Self-Play." *Science*, 362(6419), 1,140 LP – 1,144.

Sims, L. D., et al. (2005). "Origin and Evolution of Highly Pathogenic H5N1 Avian Influenza in Asia." *Veterinary Record*, 157(6), 159–64.

Sivin, N. (1982). "Why the Scientific Revolution Did Not Take Place in China—or Didn't It?" *Chinese Science*, 5, 45–66.

Slovic, P. (2007). "'If I look at the mass I will never act': Psychic Numbing and Genocide," in *Judgment and Decision Making* (vol. 2).

Smart, J. J. C. (1973). "An Outline of a System of Utilitarian Ethics," in J. J. C. Smart and B. Williams (eds.), *Utilitarianism: For and Against* (pp. 1–74). Cambridge University Press.

—(1984). *Ethics, Persuasion, and Truth*. Routledge and Kegan Paul.

Smith, C. M. (2014). "Estimation of a Genetically Viable Population for Multigenerational Interstellar Voyaging: Review and Data for Project Hyperion." *Acta Astronautica*, 97, 16–29.

Snow, D. R., and Lanphear, K. M. (1988). "European Contact and Indian Depopulation in the Northeast: The Timing of the First Epidemics." *Ethnohistory*, 35(1), 15.

Snyder-Beattie, A. E., Ord, T., and Bonsall, M. B. (2019). "An Upper Bound for the Background Rate of Human Extinction," *Scientific Reports*, 9(1), 11,054.

Sorenson, T. C. (1965). *Kennedy*. Harper and Row.

Sosin, D. M. (2015). "Review of Department of Defense Anthrax Shipments." House Energy and Commerce Subcommittee on Oversight and Investigations.

Speer, A. (1970). *Inside the Third Reich*. Simon and Schuster.

Spratt, B. G. (2007). "Independent Review of the Safety of UK Facilities Handling Foot-and-Mouth Disease Virus." UK Department for Environment, Food and Rural Affairs Archives.

Stathakopoulos, D. C. (2004). *Famine and Pestilence in the Late Roman and Early Byzantine Empire* (1st ed.). Routledge.

—(2008). "Population, Demography, and Disease," in R. Cormack, J. F. Haldon, and E. Jeffreys (eds.), *The Oxford Handbook of Byzantine Studies*. Oxford University Press.

Stern, D. I. (2004). "The Rise and Fall of the Environmental Kuznets Curve." *World Development*, 32(8), 1,419–39.

Stern, N. H. (2006). *The Economics of Climate Change: The Stern Review*. Cambridge University Press.

Stevens, B., and Bony, S. (2013). "What Are Climate Models Missing?" *Science*, 340(6136), 1,053–4.

Stokes, G. H., et al. (2017). "Update to Determine the Feasibility of Enhancing the Search and Characterization of NEOs." Near-Earth Object Science Definition Team.

Strogatz, S. (December 26, 2018). "One Giant Step for a Chess-Playing Machine." *The New York Times*.

Subramanian, M. (2019). 'Anthropocene Now: Influential Panel Votes to Recognize Earth's New Epoch'. *Nature*.

Sutton, R. (2015). "Creating Human-level AI: How and When?" [Slides]. Future of Life Institute.

Sverdrup, H. U., and Olafsdottir, A. H. (2019). "Assessing the Long-Term Global Sustainability of the Production and Supply for Stainless Steel." *BioPhysical Economics and Resource Quality*, 4(2), 8.

Szilard, G. W., and Winsor, K. R. (1968). "Reminiscences," by Leo Szilard, in *Perspectives in American History* (vol. 2). Charles Warren Center for Studies in American History.

Szilard, L., and Feld, B. T. (1972). *The Collected Works of Leo Szilard: Scientific Papers*. MIT Press.

Taagholt, J., Hansen, J., and Lufkin, D. (2001). "Greenland: Security Perspectives" (trans. D. Lufkin). Arctic Research Consortium of the United States.

Tai, A. P. K., Martin, M. V., and Heald, C. L. (2014). "Threat to Future Global Food Security from Climate Change and Ozone Air Pollution." *Nature Climate Change*, 4(9), 817–21.

Tarnocai, C., et al. (2009). "Soil Organic Carbon Pools in the Northern Circumpolar Permafrost Region." *Global Biogeochemical Cycles*, 23(2), 1–11.

Tate, J. (2017). Number of Undiscovered Near-Earth Asteroids Revised Downward. https://spaceguardcentre.com/number-of-undiscovered-near-earth-asteroids-revised-downward/.

Taubenberger, J. K., and Morens, D. M. (2006). "1918 Influenza: The Mother of all Pandemics." *Emerging Infectious Diseases*, 12(1), 15–22.

Tegmark, M. (2014). *Our Mathematical Universe: My Quest for the Ultimate Nature of Reality*. Knopf Doubleday Publishing Group.

Tegmark, Max, and Bostrom, N. (2005). "Is a Doomsday Catastrophe Likely?" *Nature*, 438(7069), 754.

Tertrais, B. (2017). "'On The Brink'—Really? Revisiting Nuclear Close Calls Since 1945." *The Washington Quarterly*, 40(2), 51–66.

The, L.-S., et al. (2006). "Are 44Ti-producing Supernovae Exceptional?" *Astronomy and Astrophysics*, 450(3), 1,037–50.

The Wall Street Journal. (January 6, 2017). "Humans Mourn Loss After Google Is Unmasked As China's Go Master." *The Wall Street Journal.*

Thomas, J. M. (2001). "Predictions." *IUBMB Life* (International Union of Biochemistry and Molecular Biology: Life), 51(3), 135–8.

Tokarska, K. B., et al. (2016). "The Climate Response to Five Trillion Tonnes of Carbon." *Nature Climate Change*, 6(9), 851–5.

Toon, O. B., et al. (2007). "Atmospheric Effects and Societal Consequences of Regional Scale Nuclear Conflicts and Acts of Individual Nuclear Terrorism." *Atmospheric Chemistry and Physics*, 7, 1,973–2,002.

Tovish, A. (2015). The Okinawa missiles of October. https://thebulletin .org/2015/10/the-okinawa-missiles-of-october/.

Toynbee, A. (1963). "Man and Hunger: The Perspectives of History," in FAO (ed.), *Report of the World Food Congress, Washington, D.C., 4 to 18 June 1963*, vol. 2: *Major Addresses and Speeches*. Her Majesty's Stationery Office.

Trevisanato, S. I. (2007). "The 'Hittite Plague,' an Epidemic of Tularemia and the First Record of Biological Warfare." *Medical Hypotheses*, 69(6), 1,371–4.

Tritten, T. J. (December 23, 2015). "Cold War Missileers Refute Okinawa Near-Launch." *Stars and Stripes.*

Tsao, J., Lewis, N., and Crabtree, G. (2006). "Solar FAQs" [Working Draft Version April 20, 2006]. Sandia National Laboratories.

Tucker, J. B. (1999). "Historical Trends Related to Bioterrorism: An Empirical Analysis." *Emerging Infectious Diseases*, 5(4), 498–504.

—(2001). Biological Weapons Convention (BWC) Compliance Protocol. https://www.nti.org/analysis/articles/biological-weapons-convention-bwc/.

Turing, A. (1951). "Intelligent Machinery, A Heretical Theory." Lecture given to "51 Society" in Manchester.

US Department of Homeland Security (2008). "Appendix B: A Review of Biocontainment Lapses and Laboratory-Acquired Infections," in *NBAF Final Environmental Impact Statement*. United States Department of Homeland Security.

US Department of State (n.d.). Treaty Between The United States Of America And The Union of Soviet Socialist Republics on The Elimination of Their Intermediate-Range and Shorter-Range Missiles (INF Treaty). https://2009–2017.state.gov/t/avc/trty/102360.htm.

—(1963). "State-Defense Meeting on Group I, II and IV Papers [Extract]. Gr. 59," Department of State, PM Dep. Ass. Sec. Records, 1961–1963, Box 2, Memoranda. National Archives.

US House of Representatives (2013). *Threats from Space: A Review of U.S. Government Efforts to Track and Mitigate Asteroids and Meteors (Part I and Part II)* [Hearing]. US Goverment Printing Office.

UCS (n.d.). What is Hair-Trigger Alert? https://www.ucsusa.org /nuclear-weapons/hair-trigger-alert.

UN (n.d.). International Day for the Preservation of the Ozone Layer, 16 September. https://www.un.org/en/events/ozoneday/background .shtml.

UN DESA (2019). World Population Prospects 2019, Online Edition.

UNESCO (1997). Declaration on the Responsibilities of the Present Generations Towards Future Generations. http://portal.unesco.org /en/ev.php-URL_ID=13178andURL_DO=DO_TOPICandURL _SECTION=201.html.

UNOOSA (2018). *Near-Earth Objects and Planetary Defence* (Brochure ST/SPACE/73). United Nations Office of Outer Space Affairs.

Van Valen, L. (1973). "Body Size and Numbers of Plants and Animals." *Evolution*, 27(1), 27–35.

Van Zanden, J. L., et al. (2014). "Global Well-Being since 1820," in *How Was Life?* (pp. 23–36). OECD.

Vellekoop, J., et al. (2014). "Rapid Short-Term Cooling Following the Chicxulub Impact at the Cretaceous-Paleogene Boundary." *Proceedings of the National Academy of Sciences*, 111(21), 7,537–41.

Vonnegut, K. (1963). *Cat's Cradle*. Holt, Rinehart and Winston.

Wallace, M. D., Crissey, B. L., and Sennott, L. I. (1986). "Accidental Nuclear War: A Risk Assessment." *Journal of Peace Research*, 23(1), 9–27.

Watson, C., Watson, M., Gastfriend, D., and Sell, T. K. (2018). "Federal Funding for Health Security in FY2019." *Health Security*, 16(5), 281–303.

Watson, F. G. (1941). *Between the Planets*. The Blakiston Company.

Weaver, T. A., and Wood, L. (1979). "Necessary Conditions for the Initiation and Propagation of Nuclear-Detonation Waves in Plane Atmospheres." *Physical Review A*, 20(1), 316–28.

Weeks, J. R. (2015). "History and Future of Population Growth," in *Population: An Introduction to Concepts and Issues* (12th ed.). Wadsworth Publishing.

Weitzman, M. L. (1998). "Why the Far-Distant Future Should Be Discounted at its Lowest Possible Rate." *Journal of Environmental Economics and Management*, 36(3), 201–8.

—(2009). "On Modeling and Interpreting the Economics of Catastrophic Climate Change." *Review of Economics and Statistics*, 91(1), 1–19.

Wellerstein, A. (2014). Szilard's Chain Reaction: Visionary or Crank? http://blog.nuclearsecrecy.com/2014/05/16/szilards-chain-reaction/.

Wells, H. G. (1894). *The Extinction of Man*. Pall Mall Budget.

—(1897). *The Star*. The Graphic.

—(1913). *The Discovery of the Future*. B. W. Huebsch.

—(1940). *The New World Order*. Secker and Warburg.

Wetterstrand, K. A. (2019). DNA Sequencing Costs: Data from the NHGRI Genome Sequencing Program (GSP). www.genome.gov /sequencingcostsdata.

Wever, P. C., and van Bergen, L. (2014). "Death from 1918 Pandemic Influenza during the First World War: A Perspective from Personal and Anecdotal Evidence." *Influenza and Other Respiratory Viruses*, 8(5), 538–46.

Wheelis, M. (2002). "Biological Warfare at the 1346 Siege of Caffa." *Emerging Infectious Diseases*, 8(9), 971–5.

White, S., Gowlett, J. A. J., and Grove, M. (2014). "The Place of the Neanderthals in Hominin Phylogeny." *Journal of Anthropological Archaeology*, 35, 32–50.

WHO (2016). *World Health Statistics 2016: Monitoring Health for the SDGs, Sustainable Development Goals*. World Health Organization.

Wiblin, R. (2017). How to Compare Different Global Problems in Terms of Impact. https://80000hours.org/articles/problem-framework/.

Wiener, J. B. (2016). "The Tragedy of the Uncommons: On the Politics of Apocalypse." *Global Policy*, 7, 67–80.

Wiener, N. (1960). "Some Moral and Technical Consequences of Automation." *Science*, 131(3410), 1,355–8.

Wilcox, B. H., Mitchell, K. L., Schwandner, F. M., and Lopes, R. M. (2017). "Defending Human Civilization from Supervolcanic Eruptions." Jet Propulsion Laboratory/NASA.

Wilcox, B., and Wilcox, S. (1996). *EZ-GO: Oriental Strategy in a Nutshell*. Ki Press.

Williams, E. G. (2015). "The Possibility of an Ongoing Moral Catastrophe." *Ethical Theory and Moral Practice*, 18(5), 971–82.

Williams, M. (2012). "Did the 73 ka Toba Super-Eruption have an Enduring Effect? Insights from Genetics, Prehistoric Archaeology, Pollen Analysis, Stable Isotope Geochemistry, Geomorphology, Ice Cores, and Climate Models." *Quaternary International*, 269, 87–93.

Willis, K. J., Bennett, K. D., Bhagwat, S. A., and Birks, H. J. B. (2010). "4 °C and Beyond: What Did This Mean for Biodiversity in the Past?" *Systematics and Biodiversity*, 8(1), 3–9.

Willis, K. J., and MacDonald, G. M. (2011). "Long-Term Ecological Records and Their Relevance to Climate Change Predictions for a Warmer World." *Annual Review of Ecology, Evolution, and Systematics*, 42(1), 267–87.

Wilman, R., and Newman, C. (eds.) (2018). *Frontiers of Space Risk: Natural Cosmic Hazards and Societal Challenges.* Taylor and Francis.

Wilson, I. (2001). *Past Lives: Unlocking the Secrets of our Ancestors.* Cassell.

Wilson, J. M., Brediger, W., Albright, T. P., and Smith-Gagen, J. (2016). "Reanalysis of the Anthrax Epidemic in Rhodesia, 1978–1984." *PeerJ*, 4, e2686.

Wise, J. (January 9, 2013). "About That Overpopulation Problem." *Slate*.

Wolf, E. T., and Toon, O. B. (2015). "The Evolution of Habitable Climates under the Brightening Sun." *Journal of Geophysical Research: Atmospheres*, 120(12), 5,775–94.

Woodward, B., Shurkin, J. N., and Gordon, D. L. (2009). *Scientists Greater Than Einstein: The Biggest Lifesavers of the Twentieth Century.* Quill Driver Books.

World Bank (1993). *World Bank Report: Investing in Health.* Oxford University Press.

—(2019a). GDP (current US$). https://data.worldbank.org/indicator/ny.gdp.mktp.cd.

—(2019b). Government Expenditure on Education, Total (%of GDP). https://data.worldbank.org/indicator/SE.XPD.TOTL.GD.ZS.

Wright, L. (September 16, 2002). "The Man Behind Bin Laden." *The New Yorker*.

Wright, S. (2001). "Legitimating Genetic Engineering." *Perspectives in Biology and Medicine*, 44(2), 235–247.

Xia, L., Robock, A., Mills, M., Stenke, A., and Helfand, I. (2015). "Decadal Reduction of Chinese Agriculture after a Regional Nuclear War." *Earth's Future*, 3(2), 37–48.

Yokoyama, Y., Falguères, C., Sémah, F., Jacob, T., and Grün, R. (2008). "Gamma-Ray Spectrometric Dating of Late Homo Erectus Skulls from Ngandong and Sambungmacan, Central Java, Indonesia." *Journal of Human Evolution*, 55(2), 274–7.

Yost, C. L., Jackson, L. J., Stone, J. R., and Cohen, A. S. (2018). "Subdecadal Phytolith and Charcoal Records from Lake Malawi, East Africa, Imply Minimal Effects on Human Evolution from the ~74 ka Toba Supereruption." *Journal of Human Evolution*, 116, 75–94.

Zalasiewicz, J., et al. (2017). "The Working Group on the Anthropocene: Summary of Evidence and Interim Recommendations." *Anthropocene*, 19, 55–60.

Zelicoff, A. P., and Bellomo, M. (2005). *Microbe: Are We Ready for the Next Plague?* AMACOM.

Zhang, B., and Dafoe, A. (2019). *Artificial Intelligence: American Attitudes and Trends.* Center for the Governance of AI, Future of Humanity Institute, University of Oxford.

Zhang, T., Heginbottom, J. A., Barry, R. G., and Brown, J. (2000). "Further Statistics on the Distribution of Permafrost and Ground Ice in the Northern Hemisphere." *Polar Geography*, 24(2), 126–31.

Zhu, M., et al. (2012). "Earliest Known Coelacanth Skull Extends the Range of Anatomically Modern Coelacanths to the Early Devonian." *Nature Communications*, 3(1), 772.

Ziegler, P. (1969). *The Black Death.* Collins.

Zilinskas, R. A. (1983). "Anthrax in Sverdlovsk?" *Bulletin of the Atomic Scientists*, 39(6), 24–7.

Zonination (2017). Perceptions of Probability and Numbers. https://github.com/zonination/perceptions.

INDEX

NOTE ON THE AUTHOR

Toby Ord is a Senior Research Fellow in Philosophy at Oxford University. His work focuses on the big-picture questions facing humanity. What are the most important issues of our time? How can we best address them?

His earlier work explored the ethics of global poverty, leading him to make a lifelong pledge to donate 10% of his income to the most effective charities helping improve the world. He created a society, Giving What We Can, for people to join this mission, and together its members have pledged over £1 billion. He then broadened these ideas by co-founding the effective altruism movement in which thousands of people are using reason and evidence to help the lives of others as much as possible.

His current research is on risks that threaten human extinction or the permanent collapse of civilization, and on how to safeguard humanity through these dangers, which he considers to be among the most pressing and neglected issues we face. Toby has advised the World Health Organization, the World Bank, the World Economic Forum, the US National Intelligence Council and the UK Prime Minister's Office.

NOTE ON THE TYPE

The text of this book is set in Linotype Sabon, a typeface named after the type founder, Jacques Sabon. It was designed by Jan Tschichold and jointly developed by Linotype, Monotype and Stempel in response to a need for a typeface to be available in identical form for mechanical hot metal composition and hand composition using foundry type.

Tschichold based his design for Sabon roman on a font engraved by Garamond, and Sabon italic on a font by Granjon. It was first used in 1966 and has proved an enduring modern classic.